AVIAN MYOLOGY

AVIAN MYOLOGY

J. C. GEORGE

DEPARTMENT OF ZOOLOGY
THE MAHARAJA SAYAJIRAO UNIVERSITY OF BARODA
BARODA, INDIA

A. J. BERGER

DEPARTMENT OF ZOOLOGY
UNIVERSITY OF HAWAII
HONOLULU, HAWAII

1966

ACADEMIC PRESS   New York and London

To our teachers
C. J. George and Alfred H. Stockard,
with respect, admiration, and affection

ACADEMIC PRESS INC.
111 Fifth Avenue, New York, New York 10003

United Kingdom Edition published by
ACADEMIC PRESS INC. (LONDON) LTD.
Berkeley Square House, London W.1

LIBRARY OF CONGRESS CATALOG CARD NUMBER: 65–26038

PRINTED IN THE UNITED STATES OF AMERICA

Preface

For the past fifteen years we have been engaged in research on the avian muscular system. During this time we have been constantly aware of how little is actually known about bird muscles and of how much remains to be learned. While our aim in preparing this monograph has been to present an over-all summary of current information on the avian muscular system, we realize that in any synthesis such as this gaps will inevitably remain to be filled.

Gross descriptions of all bird muscles are presented for the first time since the publication of Hans Gadow's and Emil Selenka's chapter in Bronn's "Klassen und Ordnungen des Thier-Reichs" (1891).

Since a universally acceptable classification of birds has not yet appeared, we have used Ripley's "A Synopsis of the Birds of India and Pakistan" (1961), "Check-List of North American Birds" (American Ornithologist's Union, 1957), and Peter's "Check List of Birds of the World," with changes and revisions for our taxonomic sources.

We express our appreciation to all authors and publishers who granted permission to use previously published material; specific acknowledgments appear in the text. Special mention should be made of our indebtedness to the following people from the Maharaja Sayajirao University of Baroda: C. S. Patel, the progressive scientist Vice-Chancellor; S. Sethna, the eminent chemist and Dean; and C. P. Shukla, the distinguished Librarian. We thank all our colleagues at Baroda: R. V. Shah, R. M. Naik, D. A. Chandra-Bose, N. Chinoy, F. Bokdawala, and R. Nene. We are particularly grateful to N. V. Vallyathan for his valuable help in the preparation of illustrations and the manuscript. We should also like to thank S. M. Waghela for making some of the line drawings and R. M. Patel for the final typing of part of the manuscript.

Finally, we wish to record our deep appreciation to our wives who allowed us ungrudgingly to take so much of the time that rightly belonged to them.

November, 1965
                                                        J. C. GEORGE
                                                   ANDREW J. BERGER

Contents

vii

Chapter V

The Pectoralis: Biochemical Aspects

Chapter VI

The Supracoracoideus: Histophysiological Aspects

Chapter VII

Certain Other Wing and Abdominal Muscles: Some Histophysiological Aspects

Chapter VIII

The Energy Problem in Bird Migration

Chapter IX

The Musculature

Chapter X

The Origin of Birds and the Evolution of Sustained Flight

CHAPTER I

Introduction

The most characteristic features of birds are their possession of feathered wings and their ability to fly. It was this unique combination that bestowed upon ancient birds not only the ability to conquer the air but also the right of survival over the ruling reptiles of the Mesozoic age and amidst the rising mammals. In the process of transformation from clumsy reptilian body into the compact and elegant flying machine, there were several fundamental changes in the structure and physiology of the various organ systems. Among them, those embracing the musculoskeletal system are most striking.

The specialized skeletal system of the bird provides a light framework of stability and strength. The appendicular parts of the skeleton are especially adapted to act as springboards for muscular action. A general account of the avian skeleton (Chapter II), therefore, is considered necessary in order to present an accurate picture of the origin, insertion, and disposition of the various muscles described in Chapter IX. No attempt, however, is made to provide detailed descriptions of the various skeletal singularities met with in different birds. For such information the reader may profitably consult the account given by Bellairs and Jenkin (1960).

The advent of the atomic age has had its repercussions on biology, which has been by and large a descriptive science in the past. The development of the electron microscope and the various techniques for the study of the cell at the subcellular levels has brought about a revolution in biology; this has led to the possibility of explaining the so-called mysteries of life processes in terms of physicochemical principles. We have now come to regard function as the complement of structure at the molecular level. In the study of avian myology, too, such an approach is obviously inevitable. For a proper understanding of the mechanism of bird flight, a knowledge of the machinery of the avian muscle cell at the molecular level is essential. The purpose of this book, therefore, is to present this new approach to avian myology together with the older approach of the morphologist.

The two principal flight muscles, the pectoralis and the supracoracoi-

1

deus, which have been studied in considerable detail using histological, histochemical, and biochemical techniques, are dealt with in Chapters III to VI. The hitherto available data on certain other muscles are summarized in Chapter VII.

The problem of energy for migration has been one of the many poorly understood aspects of bird migration. Although it was known for many years that birds accumulate enormous amounts of fat prior to migration and that this fat reserve is exhausted during migratory flight, we had no knowledge as to whether fat is directly used as the fuel or whether it is first converted to carbohydrates. It is now more or less well established that fat is the chief fuel in prolonged muscular activity and that it is utilized directly after conversion to fatty acids. This problem is discussed in Chapter VIII in the light of recent advances.

To the reader we owe an explanation as to why we have dealt with the new approach to avian myology first and the older approach later. It should be emphasized that it is not because we consider that the former is more important than the latter. It is because we believe that the new approach from the cellular and molecular levels is essential for a proper understanding of muscle action itself. On the other hand, the reader will appreciate that gross morphology of muscles showing the complexities in origin, insertion, and disposition in different birds exhibiting different modes of flight is basic knowledge. The gulf between the two approaches is at present a wide one and it is hoped that our present integrated treatment of the subject will stimulate further research in bridging this gulf.

The importance of homology in myological studies at any level cannot be overemphasized. For example, M. supracoracoideus is referred to as M. pectoralis minor and M. subclavius in older literature. In biochemical studies the muscle material used is usually referred to as "breast muscle." In these cases one is at a loss to know whether the term breast muscle means only M. pectoralis or M. supracoracoideus as well. This is unfortunate because, as the reader will see, the two muscles are distinctly different in cellular organization and biochemical properties. The reader will realize, of course, that the metabolism of the muscle is dependent upon its cellular components. For instance, the pigeon pectoralis muscle consists of two distinct types of fibers, red and white. The red fibers metabolize fat and the white ones metabolize glycogen. It will be of fundamental importance to know whether these fiber types in homologous muscles of different vertebrates are also homologous at the cellular and biochemical levels. Such information should have far reaching implications.

Human muscular dystrophy is a worldwide problem. That avian muscle can profitably be used as experimental material is now being increasingly realized. It has been shown that the white fibers in the pigeon pectoralis are more susceptible to atrophy than the red ones when the muscle is subjected to disuse (George and Naik, 1959). This observation has led to further studies in that direction (George and Vallyathan, 1962; Vallyathan *et al.*, 1964, 1965; Cherian *et al.*, 1965). In this context, the report of muscular dystrophy in the domestic chicken by Asmundson and Julian in 1956 and their subsequent studies (Julian and Asmundson, 1963) carried out on a strain of dystrophic chicken deserve special mention. Similarly, Berger (1956) called attention to the presence of M. expansor secundariorum in all birds studied carefully, and pointed up the potential of this muscle for pharmacological investigations. This nonstriated muscle may be 10 cm in length in a large bird and 2 cm in the domestic pigeon. The subcutaneous position of this relatively enormous mass of smooth muscle makes it easily accessible for experimental work, and at least one drug company is known to have used this muscle in testing the reaction of drugs on smooth muscle and the autonomic nervous system. Our ignorance is still greater than our knowledge about M. expansor secundariorum, however. In presenting this book, therefore, we also put forward a case for greater attention to avian myology than it has hitherto received.

On the basis of cellular organization and biochemical properties, the pectoralis and supracoracoideus muscles in various birds have been characterized and classified into different groups (George, 1965). No one is more conscious of the deficiencies and shortcomings in these generalizations than George himself. They are tentative and subject to modification with the emergence of more information. We have also thought it desirable and necessary to conclude with a brief discussion of the little understood subject of the origin of birds and the evolution of sustained flight (Chapter X).

REFERENCES

Bellairs, A.d'A., and Jenkin, C. R. (1960). The skeleton of birds. *In* "Biology and Comparative Physiology of Birds" (A. J. Marshall, ed.), Vol. 1, pp. 241–300. Academic Press, New York.

Berger, A. J. (1956). The expansor secundariorum muscle, with special reference to passerine birds. *J. Morphol.* 99: 137–168.

Cherian, K. M., Vallyathan, N. V., and George, J. C. (1965). Succinic dehydrogenase in the pigeon pectoralis during disuse atrophy. *J. Histochem. Cytochem.* 13: 265–269.

George, J. C. (1965). Evolution of the bird and bat pectoral muscles. *Pavo* 3: (in press).

George, J. C., and Naik, R. M. (1959). Studies on the structure and physiology of the flight muscles of birds. 7. Structure of the pectoralis major muscle of the pigeon in disuse atrophy. *J. Animal Morphol. Physiol.* 6: 95–102.

George, J. C., and Vallyathan, N. V. (1962). Effect of disuse atrophy on pectoralis muscle and blood in the pigeon. *Am. J. Physiol.* **202:** 268–272.

Julian, L. M., and Asmundson, V. S. (1963). Muscular dystrophy of the chicken. *In* "Muscular Dystrophy in Man and Animals" (G. H. Bourne and M. N. Golarz, eds.), pp. 458–498. Hafner, New York.

Vallyathan, N. V., Cherian, K. M., and George, J. C. (1964). Histochemical and quantitative changes in glycogen and phosphorylase during disuse atrophy of the pigeon pectoralis. *J. Histochem. Cytochem.* **12:** 721–728.

Vallyathan, N. V., Cherian, K. M., and George, J. C. (1965). Effect of disuse atrophy on fat metabolism in the pigeon breast muscle. *J. Animal Morphol. Physiol.* **12:** (in press).

CHAPTER II

The Avian Skeleton

The bird skeletal system is a suitable subject for an entire book. It is desirable, however, to review basic features here because the bones of the appendages are the levers upon which skeletal muscles operate and because striated muscles are responsible for tubercles, ridges, and fossae on the skull as well as on other skeletal elements.

There is a vast literature on the avian skeleton, most of which was published during the 19th century. Recent summaries of both the literature and the peculiarities of the avian skeletal system are those of Portmann (1950), Waddington (1952), Van Tyne and Berger (1959), Bellairs and Jenkin (1960), and Storer (1960). Detailed studies of specific groups of birds are those of Barnikol (1952, 1953), Beecher (1962), Bock (1960a,b, 1962), Bock and Miller (1959), Fisher (1955a,b), Harrison (1957), Hofer (1954), Holman (1961), Holmgren (1955), King (1957), Kuroda (1954), Lang (1955, 1956), Pycraft (1900, 1903, 1905, 1907), Simpson (1946), Starck (1955,) Tordoff (1954), Webb (1957), and Woolfenden (1961).

Despite these more recent studies, most current textbooks continue to perpetuate errors, presumably because authors persist in accepting uncritically statements made in such "standard" references as Beddard (1898). At the same time, the more scholarly work of Gadow (Newton and Gadow, 1893–1896) and Coues (1903) seems to be ignored. It should be underscored that "the apparent similarity of structure among all recent birds" has been greatly overemphasized (King, 1957; Bellairs and Jenkin, 1960; Berger, 1960).

Birds have been defined as "glorified reptiles," and zoologists commonly combine birds and reptiles in a single class, the Sauropsida. Birds and reptiles share the following skeletal characters:

1. The skull articulates with the atlas by means of a single occipital condyle.

2. The lower jaw is composed of several elements (usually five: dentary, splenial, angular, surangular, and prearticular) and is hinged on a movable quadrate bone (birds, snakes, some extinct reptiles).

3. Both groups have a single ear ossicle, the columella (or stapes).

4. Most birds have uncinate (epipleural) processes on the ribs—a character found elsewhere only in the Reptilia (e.g., *Sphenodon*, and the fossil pseudopsuchian *Euparkeria*).

5. The "ankle" joint is an intertarsal joint, i.e., it lies between two rows of tarsal bones instead of between the tibia and the proximal tarsals.

6. The backward slant of the pubic bone in birds is similar to the relationship found in some dinosaurs.

It may be pointed out that virtually all paleontologists and comparative anatomists agree that *Archaeopteryx* would have been considered a reptile had it not been for the distinct feather impressions found related to the fossil bones.

The skeleton of flying birds is specialized for lightness and for strength. Reduction in the bone marrow and its replacement by extensions of the air sac system from the lungs decrease the weight of vertebrae, the pelvis, and certain of the long bones in most bird families. Strength is attained by structure of the bones and by the fusion of the main bones of the skull and pelvis. Fusion of several dorsal (back) vertebrae also occurs in some birds. There is a fusion and a consequent reduction in numbers of carpal, metacarpal, tarsal, and metatarsal bones. Despite this fusion, however, the bird skeleton is not a rigid framework. Implied or explicit statements in the literature that the wing bones of hummingbirds, for example, are "fused" are completely erroneous.

I. The Skull

The bones forming the brain case of the adult bird skull typically are completely fused, and all traces of sutures may be obliterated. Some bones of the nasal regions become pneumatized by epithelial outgrowths from the nasolacrimal duct and from the middle meatus of the nasal cavity: others (e.g., otic capsule, occipital, parietal, frontal, quadrate bones, and the interorbital septum) become excavated and pneumatized by extensions of the epithelial lining of the tympanic cavity.

The very large orbits are notable in the bird skull, and the two eyes may equal or exceed the brain weight. A midline interorbital septum separates the two orbits in nearly all birds. According to Bellairs and Jenkin (1960), however, the kiwi (*Apteryx*) lacks such a septum: "The enlarged nasal capsules intervene between the orbits, paralleling the condition in most mammals." It may be noted here that the eyes of most birds are characterized by limited mobility and that those of owls are essentially immovably fixed in large, tubular sclerotic rings (Fig.

II.1). Nevertheless, the extraocular eye muscles are well developed in all birds that have been examined.

The nostrils (external nares) are bounded by two or three bones in most birds: premaxillae, nasals, and, in some birds, the maxillae. In these, the nostrils are said to be *pervious* (i.e., completely open to the exterior). In adult pelicans, boobies (variable), gannets, cormorants, anhingas, and frigatebirds, however, the nostrils are *impervious* or *obsolete* (i.e., there is no external opening to the nasal cavity). Such birds presumably breathe through the mouth.

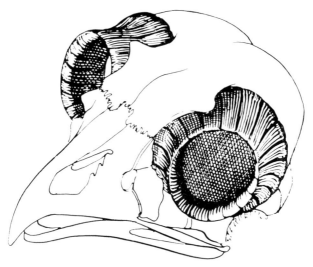

Fig. II.1. Skull of Snowy Owl (*Nyctea scandiaca*) to show the tubular sclerotic rings. (By permission from Berger, 1961.)

The nostrils open into horny tubes in albatrosses, petrels, and their relatives; they open into soft, flexible tubes in some members of the nightjar or nighthawk family (Caprimulgidae).

The temporal region of the skull may be smoothly convex or it may contain a well developed temporal fossa, which serves as an area of origin for certain jaw muscles (e.g., adductor mandibulae, pseudotemporalis superficialis). Similarly, the supraoccipital region may be convex or it may contain well developed, bilateral fossae, often bounded superiorly by prominent bony ridges. These fossae occur especially in birds possessing hypertrophied Mm. depressor mandibulae.

Suture lines and nonfunctional foramina often persist in the adult mandible (referred to as the "lower mandible" by ornithologists). The relative development of the *processus retroarticularis* is correlated with the development of M. depressor mandibulae.

In the majority of birds, the maxillae ("upper mandibles" of ornithologists) undergo some movement (*kinesis*) at a transverse *craniofacial* or *nasofrontal hinge* (the articulation with the cephalic edge of the frontal bones). Among ratite birds (e.g., ostrich, emu, kiwi) and the Hawfinch (*Coccothraustes*), however, there is virtually no movement of the maxillae; in these birds the maxillae are said to be *akinetic* (see Hofer, 1954; Fisher, 1955a,b; Jenkin, 1957; Simonetta, 1957; Webb, 1957; Zusi, 1959, 1962).

II. Vertebral Column and Ribs

The several regions of the vertebral column were designated by Gadow (Newton and Gadow, 1893) as *cervical, dorsal, synsacral, free caudal,* and the *pygostyle* (also called the urostyle).

1. The most frequent number of *cervical vertebrae* is 14 or 15, but among the different bird families the number ranges from 13 (e.g., *Coccyzus, Clamator,* some passerines) to 25 (some swans). A *perforated atlas* is one that has a bony canal for the articulation of the dens of the axis; a *notched atlas* is one that contains an open notch for the dens.

One or several of the posteriormost cervical vertebrae bear short ribs (*cervical* or *cervicodorsal ribs*) that end freely in the neck musculature; these ribs have no ventral bony articulation (Fig. II.2). These rib-bearing cervical vertebrae sometimes are referred to as *cervicodorsal vertebrae*. They should always be included in counts of cervical vertebrae for taxonomic purposes.

2. The *dorsal* (back) *vertebrae* (commonly 4 to 6 in number) are those that do not fuse with the synsacrum and which bear ribs which articulate ventrally with the sternum. These *true ribs* consist of a dorsal segment (*vertebral rib*) that has two articulations with the corresponding dorsal vertebra, and a ventral segment (*sternal rib*) which articulates with the sternocostal process of the sternum. Many authors do not use the term dorsal vertebrae but call them thoracic vertebrae (following mammalian terminology). Van Tyne and Berger (1959) and Berger (1961) preferred to follow the classic work of Gadow in adopting the term dorsal vertebrae.

Two or more (commonly 3 to 5) dorsal vertebrae fuse to form a single *os dorsale* (*notarium*) in a few families of birds (e.g., Podicipedidae, some Falconidae, Cracidae, Gruidae, Pteroclidae, Columbidae). One or more free dorsal vertebrae always are interposed between the notarium and the synsacrum.

3. The *synsacrum* is formed by the fusion of a series (10 to 23) of thoracic, lumbar, sacral, and urosacral vertebrae. Gadow's *thoracic verte-brae* are the anteriormost fused vertebrae in the synsacrum; they may or may not bear *thoracic ribs*. Bellairs and Jenkin (1960) refer to these anterior synsacral vertebrae as *posterior thoracic vertebrae. Thoracic ribs,* when present, articulate dorsally with the anterior synsacral vertebrae;

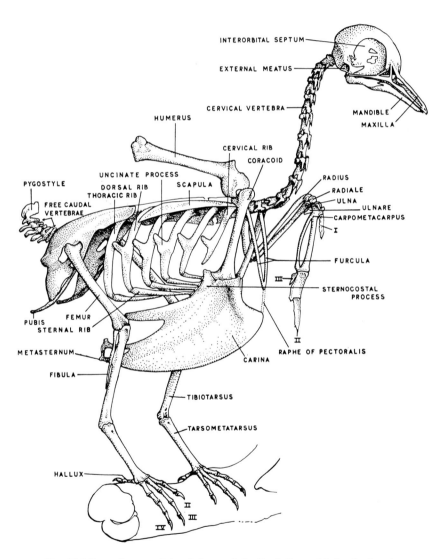

FIG. II.2 Lateral view of the skeleton of the Rock Dove (*Columba livia*).

a sternal segment may be present or absent. Thoracic ribs may articulate with the sternum, fuse with the sternal part of the last true rib (or the preceding thoracic rib), or end freely in the abdominal musculature. There is much individual variation in the number of ribs (both true ribs and thoracic ribs) that articulate with the sternum, and this variation even occurs between the right and left sides of the same specimen.

The lumbar, sacral, and urosacral (fused caudal) vertebrae are poorly defined, partly on their relations to the nerves of the lumbar and sacral plexuses and partly on the configuration of transverse projections and their relationship to the ilia. Bellairs and Jenkin (1960) have discussed the uncertainties in identifying many of the synsacral vertebrae, and point up the need for a thorough modern study of the subject. Most authors identify two true sacral vertebrae, but a few birds (e.g., *Struthio*, *Apteryx*, the Pelecanidae) are said to have three. Thomas Huxley, in 1867, apparently first defined the urosacral vertebrae as "those caudal vertebrae which unite with one another and with antecedent vertebrae to form the 'sacrum' of a bird."

4. From 4 to 9 *free caudal vertebrae* may be found posterior to the synsacrum. There is considerable variation in numbers of free caudal vertebrae within a species. By contrast, the numbers of cervical and dorsal vertebrae are relatively constant within a species.

5. The *pygostyle* (plowshare bone) is said to be formed by the fusion of 4 to 7 embryonic vertebrae (Van Tyne and Berger, 1959: p. 23), or of as many as 10 (Bellairs and Jenkin, 1960: p. 251), but the entire subject is in need of a thorough reinvestigation. The pygostyle serves as an attachment for several of the caudal muscles, for M. piriformis pars caudofemoralis in most birds, and for the dense fascia which anchors the rectrices or tail feathers. A true pygostyle is absent in most ratite birds (present or absent in the ostrich) and in some tinamous.

III. The Sternum

The sternum of most birds (carinates) has a ventrally directed bony *keel* or *carina* (*carina sterni*), which serves as an area of origin for the major flight muscles. The relative development of the keel is directly related to the degree of development of Mm. pectoralis and supracoracoideus. In general, a large keel is related to strong flying ability, but the tinamous are an exception. The keel and the pectoral muscles are hypertrophied in swifts and hummingbirds. The keel is greatly reduced or absent in certain flightless "carinate" birds: for example, a New Zealand ground parrot (*Strigops*) and a rail (*Notornis*).

A group of mostly large, unrelated flightless birds (ostrich, rhea, cassowaries, emu, kiwi) lack a keel on the sternum, and are referred to as ratite birds (i.e., flat-sternumed birds).

The posterior margin of the sternum exhibits great variation among the different families of birds: *notched, fenestrate, entire.*

Bilateral *posterolateral processes* bound open spaces on either side of the posterior *median metasternum* to form a *single-notched sternum* (i.e., a single notch on either side of the midline). A pair of *oblique processes* (arising from the base of the posterolateral processes), or a pair of *intermediate processes* (interposed between the metasternum and the posterolateral process), produce a *double-notched sternum.* Membranes extend between the several processes and serve as areas of origin for the deep posterior and lateral portions of M. pectoralis.

The depth and width of the notches vary considerably in both the single-notched and double-notched condition, and some evidence suggests that the notches decrease in size (owing to continued ossification) with advancing age in some birds. A posterior bar of bone may convert a notch into a foramen (e.g., in some hawks, parrots), thus producing a *fenestrate sternum.* Infrequently, one finds a sternum with a large lateral notch and a posteromedial fenestra (e.g., *Columba livia*). An *entire sternum* lacks notches and fenestrae; the entire horizontal portion of the sternum consists of a solid plate of bone, as in most ratite birds, limpkins, etc.

A peculiar feature of the sternum in swans and cranes is that the carina is excavated and houses one or more loops of the trachea (Fig. II.3).

IV. The Pectoral Girdle

The bony arch for the support of the wing typically consists of three bones: scapula, coracoid, and clavicle. The long, thin, usually flat, scapula extends posteriorly dorsal to the rib cage and parallel to the vertebral column; the bone is very broad and heavy in penguins. The scapula articulates anteriorly with the coracoid, and may be bound by ligaments to the superior end of the clavicle. The remainder of the scapula is anchored in position by the attachment of back and arm muscles (e.g., rhomboid and serratus complex, dorsalis scapulae, proscapulohumeralis). Both the scapula and the coracoid participate in the formation of the *glenoid fossa* (cavity), the articular fossa for the head of the humerus.

The coracoids are robust bones that articulate with the scapulae and clavicles superiorly in most birds; the coracoids and scapulae are fused in ratites and in *Fregata.* Inferiorly, the coracoids articulate with the anterior edge of the sternum. The coracoids, especially, serve as struts to hold the humerus away from the body and the sternum.

In most birds (exceptions: some parrots, touracos, owls, barbets, toucans), the two clavicles fuse inferiorly to form the *furcula* (also, *furculum;* wishbone); the region of fusion may be expanded to form a *hypocleidium*. In some birds (e.g., pelicans; Whale-billed Stork, *Balaeniceps rex*), the hypocleidium is fused to the carina sterni. The furcula

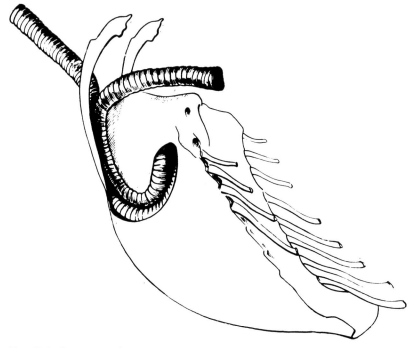

Fɪɢ. II.3. Sternum and trachea of the Sandhill Crane (*Grus canadensis tabida*). (By permission from Berger, 1961.)

is fused to both the sternum and the coracoids in the Hoatzin (*Opisthocomus*). The clavicles are rudimentary or absent in ratites, mesites, *Atrichornis,* and in some parrots, pigeons, and barbets (see Van Tyne and Berger, 1959: p. 24).

Dorsally, the scapula, coracoid, and clavicle bound a *foramen triosseum* in most birds. Only the coracoid and the scapula bound this foramen in touracos, however (Berger, 1960). The tendon of M. supracoracoideus passes dorsally through the foramen triosseum to its insertion on the dorsal surface of the head of the humerus.

V. The Wing Bones

The bones of the forelimb in flying birds are: humerus, radius, ulna, two carpals, carpometacarpus, and three digits (Fig. II.4).

The head of the humerus articulates in the shallow glenoid fossa, formed by the scapula and coracoid. This scapulocoracohumeral articulation is a ball-and-socket joint, which permits free rotation of the humerus. Distally, the humerus articulates with the ulna in a hinge joint (see also the discussion of the hummingbird ulna under M. extensor metacarpi ulnaris). The head of the radius is included in a common

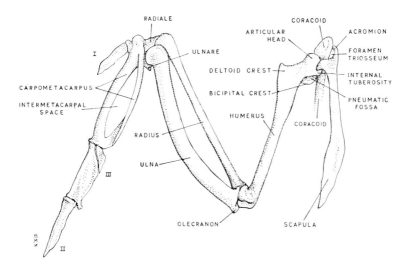

Fig. II.4. Dorsal view of the left wing bones of *Columba livia*.

articular capsule with the olecranon of the ulna, but the radius merely slides back and forth against the distal articular surface of the humerus.

The major flight muscles (Mm. pectoralis and supracoracoideus) insert on the proximal end of the humerus, and much of the major extensor of the forearm (M. humerotriceps) arises from the shaft of the bone throughout nearly its entire length. M. biceps brachii, the major flexor of the forearm, has a tendinous origin from the proximal end of the humerus.

The humerus apparently is pneumatic in nearly all birds. The bone contains an air chamber that is an outgrowth of the interclavicular air sac. The marrow cavity is limited to the ends of the bones, whereas the air chamber occupies most of the interior of the shaft. The *pneumatic foramen,* the entrance to the air chamber, lies in a depressed area (*pneumatic fossa*) on the palmar (ventral) surface near the proximal end of the humerus. There may be either a single or a double pneumatic fossa; the occurrence of each type has been discussed by Berger (1957) and Bock (1962).

Of the two forearm bones, the ulna is always longer and stouter than the radius. The bases (*calami*) of the secondary flight feathers have a ligamentous attachment to the dorsal surface of the ulna. The sites of attachment typically are indicated on the dry bone by a series of bony tubercles.

The degree of rotation of the radius around the ulna, to produce pronation and supination of the hand, apparently has not been determined with any degree of accuracy.

Only two carpal bones are interposed between the forearm and the hand in birds: *os radiale* (*scapholunar*) and *os ulnare* (*cuneiform*). The primary area of insertion of M. flexor carpi ulnaris is on the proximal face of the os ulnare. The long tendon of M. tensor patagii longus often has part of its insertion on the os radiale.

The avian hand or *manus* consists of three metacarpal bones and three digits. The metacarpals are fused at both proximal and distal ends and form the *carpometacarpus.* An *intermetacarpal space* is found between metacarpals II and III.

Montagna (1945), Holmgren (1955), and Fisher and Goodman (1955) believe that only metacarpals II, III, and IV persist in the post-hatching carpometacarpus, and, consequently, that the corresponding digits are numbers II, III, and IV. We believe that available data are inadequate for reaching this conclusion. Therefore, we retain the traditional numbering of the metacarpals and the digits: I, II, and III.

Digit I (the pollex or thumb) has one phalanx in most birds; rarely there are two phalanges. Digit II usually has two phalanges, but there are three in a few birds (e.g., *Gavia, Chen*). Digit III apparently always consists of a single phalanx.

The bird manus is very important for flight in that the primary remiges (flight feathers) are attached to it. *Digital primaries* are attached to the phalanges of digit II; *metacarpal primaries* are attached to the dorsal surface of the carpometacarpus. The number of primary remiges varies only from 9 to 12 in flying birds, but the number of secondary remiges varies from 6 (some hummingbirds) to 32 (Wandering Albatross).

From 2 (hummingbirds) to at least 7 (some touracos) feathers are attached to the pollex to form the *alula* or *bastard wing.* The alula functions as a wing slot in flight.

The relative lengths of the wing segments (arm, forearm, manus) vary widely among birds, and are correlated, in general, with type of flight (Engels, 1941; Fisher, 1946; Berger, 1952, 1953, 1954; Van Tyne and Berger, 1959; Brown, 1961). These differences are demonstrated most strikingly when contrasting the wing skeleton of birds that use a rapid wing beat in flapping flight (e.g., swifts, hummingbirds) and those that are specialized for soaring flight (albatross, pelican, some vultures).

VI. The Pelvic Girdle

The pelvic girdle is formed by the fusion of the synsacrum with three paired bones: ilium, ischium, and pubis (Fig. II.5).

The pubic bones are directed caudally, are fused with the ischia anteriorly, and articulate (usually) with the ischia near their caudal ends. A long, narrow *ischiopubic foramen or fenestra* (closed by a membrane) separates the pubis and ischium between the two areas of contact. A *pubic symphysis* is found only in the ostrich; an *ischiatic symphysis*, only in the rhea. A *pectineal (iliopectineal) process*, located anterior and ventral to the acetabulum, is well developed in most birds that possess the ambiens muscle (see, also, Lebedinsky, 1913).

An *ilioischiatic foramen* exists between the ilium and ischium. A smaller *obturator foramen*, which transmits the tendon of M. obturator internus, lies anterior and ventral to the *ilioischiatic* foramen and anterior to the ischiopubic foramen.

Dorsally, the two ilia may curve dorsomediad toward the neural spines of the anterior synsacral vertebrae, thus bounding *ilioneural canals* on either side of the spines. In most genera, however, there is a deep groove between the neural spines and the dorsomedial edges of the two ilia. Fascicles of M. spinalis thoracis (longissimus dorsi) arise from the bones forming the boundaries of the ilioneural groove or canal.

VII. The Hind Limb

The bony framework of the hind limb consists of the femur, tibiotarsus, fibula, tarsometatarsus, and two to four digits. As in the forelimb, there has been some fusion of bones, with the result that the ankle joint is an intertarsal joint. The proximal tarsal bones fuse with the tibia to form a tibiotarsus. The distal tarsals fuse with three metatarsals to form a single tarsometatarsus (often referred to simply as the tarsus). An independent *first metatarsal* articulates with the medial border of the tarsometatarsus.

The majority of birds have four toes; some have three (e.g., rhea,

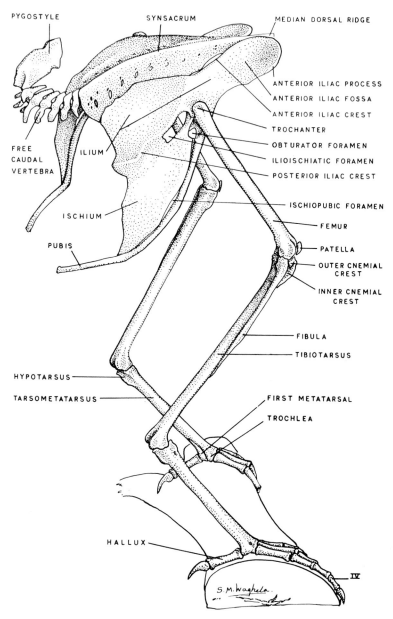

FIG. II.5. An oblique view of the pelvic girdle and hind limbs of *Columba livia*.

cassowary, emu, auks, guillemots, most American plovers, Sanderling, hemipode-quails, bustards, some kingfishers, Black-backed and Northern Three-toed woodpeckers); only the ostrich has but two toes. The most common arrangement in four-toed birds (those with *anisodactyl feet*) has the hallux pointing backward and toes II to IV pointing forward. This pattern produces the so-called "perching foot." In general, the hallux contains two phalanges, digit II has three, digit III has four, and digit IV has five phalanges. The hallux is elevated in certain terrestrial birds (e.g., Cranes).

Colies (hallux reversible) and swifts have *pamprodactyl feet:* all four toes are turned forward. Cuckoos, parrots, puffbirds, barbets, honeyguides, toucans, most woodpeckers, and wrynecks have *zygodactyl feet:* toes I and IV are turned backward, whereas toes II and III are turned forward. Trogons possess *heterodactyl feet:* toes I and II are turned backward and toes III and IV are turned forward. Kingfishers, todies, motmots, bee-eaters, rollers, and hornbills have *syndactyl feet* or *toes:* two or more of the toes are coalescent for a variable length. Other specializations of birds' feet are described by Van Tyne and Berger (1959).

The femur is pneumatized by an extension from the abdominal air sac. All of the bones of the lower limb, including the phalanges of the toes, are said to be pneumatized in a few birds (e.g., screamers, hornbills). Except for its articular surfaces, nearly all of the femur is embedded in muscles, and the bird's thigh is completely covered by contour feathers, being almost completely hidden by the skin of the body. As a result, the thigh and knee usually are not apparent in the living bird. The feathered crus (leg) is the first obvious segment of the hind limb; the bird's ankle joint often is confused with the knee joint. The patella is discussed with M. iliotibialis.

The fibula has a well developed head that articulates with the distal end of the femur and the proximal end of the tibiotarsus. In general, however, the fibula is weakly developed in birds, usually extending distad only about two-thirds the length of the tibiotarsus. A ligament commonly extends from the distal free end of the fibula to the lateral supracondylar ridge near the distal end of the tibiotarsus. In a few birds (e.g., penguins, anhingas), the fibula reaches the distal supracondylar area of the tibiotarsus and may be fused with it.

The proportions of the femur, tibiotarsus, and tarsometatarsus to total length of the limb in several groups of birds have been discussed by Richardson (1942), Fisher (1946), Berger (1952), Holman (1961), and Woolfenden (1961); Storer (1960) has presented an excellent survey of the many adaptations of the hind limb for various habitats and kinds of locomotion.

REFERENCES

Barnikol, A. (1952). Korrelationen in der Ausgestaltung der Schädelform bei Vögeln. *Morphol. Jahrb.* **92:** 373–414.

Barnikol, A. (1953). Vergleichend anatomische und taxonomischphylogenetische Studien am Kopf der Opisthocomiformes, Musophagidae, Galli, Columbae und Cuculi. *Zool. Jahrb.* **81:** 487–526.

Beddard, F. E. (1898). "The Structure and Classification of Birds." Longmans, Green, New York.

Beecher, W. J. (1962). The bio-mechanics of the bird skull. *Bull. Chicago Acad. Sci.* **11:** 10–33.

Bellairs, A. d'A., and Jenkin, C. R. (1960). The skeleton of birds. *In* "Biology and Comparative Physiology of Birds" (A. J. Marshall, ed.), Vol. 1, pp. 241–300. Academic Press, New York.

Berger, A. J. (1952). The comparative functional morphology of the pelvic appendage in three genera of Cuculidae. *Am. Midland Naturalist* **47:** 513–605.

Berger, A. J. (1953). On the locomotor anatomy of the Blue Coua, *Coua caerulea. Auk* **70:** 49–83.

Berger, A. J. (1954). The myology of the pectoral appendage of three genera of American cuckoos. *Misc. Publ. Museum Zool., Univ. Mich.* **85.**

Berger, A. J. (1956). Anatomical variation and avian anatomy. *Condor* **58:** 433–441.

Berger, A. J. (1957). On the anatomy and relationships of *Fregilupus varius,* an extinct starling from the Mascarene Islands. *Bull. Am. Museum Nat. Hist.* **113:** 225–272.

Berger, A. J. (1960). Some anatomical characters of the Cuculidae and the Musophagidae. *Wilson Bull.* **72:** 60–104.

Berger, A. J. (1961). "Bird Study." Wiley, New York.

Bock, W. J. (1960a). Secondary articulation of the avian mandible. *Auk* **77:** 19–55.

Bock, W. J. (1960b). The palatine process of the premaxilla in the passeres. *Bull. Museum Comp. Zool. Harvard Coll.* **122:** 361–488.

Bock, W. J. (1962). The pneumatic fossa of the humerus in the passeres. *Auk* **79:** 425–443.

Bock, W. J., and Miller, W. DeW. (1959). The scansorial foot of the woodpeckers, with comments on the evolution of perching and climbing feet in birds. *Am. Museum Novitates* No. **1931,** 45 pp.

Brown, R. H. J. (1961). Flight. *In* "Biology and Comparative Physiology of Birds" (A. J. Marshall, ed.), Vol. 2, pp. 289–305. Academic Press, New York.

Burt, W. H. (1930). Adaptive modifications in the woodpeckers. *Univ. Calif. (Berkeley) Publ. Zool.* **32:** 455–524.

Cottam, P. A. (1957). The pelicaniform characters of the skeleton of the shoe-bill stork, *Balaeniceps rex. Bull. Brit. Museum Zool.* **5:** 49–72.

Coues, E. (1903). "Key to North American Birds," 5th ed. Dana Estes, Boston, Massachusetts.

Engels, W. L. (1940). Structural adaptations in thrashers (Mimidae: Genus *Toxostoma*) with comments on interspecific relationships. *Univ. Calif. (Berkeley) Publ. Zool.* **42:** 341–400.

Engels, W. L. (1941). Wing skeleton and flight of hawks. *Auk* **58:** 61–69.

Enlow, D. H., and Brown, S. O. (1958). A comparative histological study of fossil and recent bone tissues. Part III. *Texas J. Sci.* **10:** 187–230.

Fell, H. B. (1939). The origin and developmental mechanics of the avian sternum. *Phil. Trans. Roy. Soc.* **B229**: 407–464.

Fell, H. B. (1956). Skeletal development in tissue culture. *In* "The Biochemistry and Physiology of Bone." (G. H. Bourne, ed.), pp. 401–441. Academic Press, New York.

Fisher, H. I. (1945). Flying ability and the anterior intermuscular line on the coracoid. *Auk* **62**: 125–129.

Fisher, H. I. (1946). Adaptations and comparative anatomy of the locomotor apparatus of New World vultures. *Am. Midland Naturalist* **35**: 545–727.

Fisher, H. I. (1955a). An apparatus for measuring kinetics in avian skulls. *Wilson Bull.* **67**: 18–24.

Fisher, H. I. (1955b). Some aspects of the kinetics in the jaws of birds. *Wilson Bull.* **67**: 175–188.

Fisher, H. I. (1955c). Avian anatomy, 1925–1950, and some suggested problems. *In* "Recent Studies in Avian Biology" (A. Wolfson, ed.), pp. 57–104. Univ. Illinois Press, Urbana, Illinois.

Fisher, H. I. (1957). Bony mechanism of automatic flexion and extension in the pigeon's wing. *Science* **126**: 446.

Fisher, H. I., and Ellarson, R. S. (1958). An abnormal sternal apparatus in a Ruffed Grouse, *Bonasa umbellus. Trans. Illinois State Acad. Sci.* **51**: 34–36.

Fisher, H. I., and Goodman, D. C. (1955). The myology of the Whooping Crane, *Grus americana. Illinois Biol. Monographs* **24**, No. 2: 127 pp.

Gladkov, N. A. (1937). The importance of length of wing for the bird's flight. *Arch. Musee Zool. Univ. Moscou* **4**: 35–47.

Gregory, W. K., and Camp, C. L. (1918). Studies in comparative myology and osteology. No. III. *Bull. Am. Museum Nat. Hist.* **38**: 447–563.

Harrison, J. G. (1957). The development of skull pneumatisation in the wood pigeon. *Bull. Brit. Ornithol. Club* **77**: 18–23.

Hofer, H. (1954). Neure Untersuchungen zur Kopfmorphologie der Vögel. *Acta XI Congr. Intern. Ornithol., 1954* pp. 104–137. Birkhäuser, Basel.

Holman, J. A. (1961). Osteology of living and fossil New World quails (Aves, Galliformes). *Bull. Florida State Museum Biol. Sci.* 6, No. 2: 131–233.

Holmgren, N. (1955). Studies on the phylogeny of birds. *Acta Zool. (Stockholm)* **36**: 243–328.

Howard, H. (1929). The avifauna of Emeryville Shellmound. *Univ. Calif. (Berkeley) Publ. Zool.* **32**: 301–394.

Jenkin, P. M. (1957). The filter feeding and food of flamingoes (Phoenicopteri). *Phil. Trans. Roy. Soc.* **B240**: 401–493.

Jollie, M. T. (1957). The head skeleton of the chicken and remarks on the anatomy of this region in other birds. *J. Morphol.* **100**:389–436.

Jollie, M. T. (1958). Comments on the phylogeny and skull of Passeriformes. *Auk* **75**: 26–35.

King, A. S. (1957). The aerated bones of *Gallus domesticus. Acta Anat.* **31**: 220–230.

Kuroda, N. (1954). On some osteological and anatomical characters of Japanese Alcidae (Aves). *Japan. J. Zool.* **11**: 311–327.

Lang, C. (1955). Beiträge zur Entwicklungsgeschichte des Kopfskelettes von *Melopsittacus undulatus. Morphol. Jahrb.* **94**: 335–390.

Lang, C. (1956). Das Cranium der Ratiten mit besondere Berücksichtigung von *Struthio camelus. Z. Wiss. Zool.* **159**: 165–224.

Lebedinsky, N. G. (1913). Beiträge zur Morphologie und Entwicklungsgeschichte des Vogelbeckens. *Jena. Z. Naturw.* **50:** 647–774.

Lowe, P. R. (1928). Studies and observations bearing on the phylogeny of the ostrich and its allies. *Proc. Zool. Soc. London* **1928:** 185–247.

Lowe, P. R. (1939). On the systematic position of the swifts (Suborder Cypseli) and humming-birds (Suborder Trochili), with special reference to their relation to the Order Passeriformes. *Trans. Zool. Soc. London* **24:** 307–348.

Milne-Edwards, A. (1867–1871). "Recherches Anatomiques et Paleontologiques pour servir a l'Histoire des Oiseaux Fossiles," Vol. 1, 1867–1868; Vol. 2, 1869–1871. Masson, Paris.

Mitchell, P. C. (1901a). On the anatomy of the kingfishers, with special reference to the conditions in the wing known as eutaxy and diastataxy. *Ibis* **1901:** 97–123.

Mitchell, P. C. (1901b). On the anatomy of gruiform birds, with special reference to the correlation of modifications. *Proc. Zool. Soc. London* **1901:** 629–655.

Mollier, G. (1937). Beziehungen zwischen Form und Funktion der Sehnen im Muskel-Sehnen-Knochen-System. *Morphol. Jahrb.* **79:** 161–199.

Montagna, W. (1945). A re-investigation of the development of the wing of the fowl. *J. Morphol.* **76:** 87–113.

Nelson, O. E. (1953). "Comparative Embryology of the Vertebrates." McGraw-Hill (Blakiston), New York.

Nero, R. W. (1951). Pattern and rate of cranial 'ossification' in the House Sparrow. *Wilson Bull.* **63:** 84–88.

Newton, A., and Gadow, H. (1893–1896). "A Dictionary of Birds." Adam & Charles Black, London.

Parker, W. K. (1875a). On the morphology of the skull in the woodpeckers (Picidae) and wrynecks (Yungidae). *Trans. Linnean Soc. London, Zool.* **1:** 1–22.

Parker, W. K. (1875b). On aegithognathous birds (Part I). *Trans. Zool. Soc. London* **9:** 289–352.

Portmann, A. (1950). Squelette. *In* "Traité de Zoologie" (P. P. Grassé, ed.), Vol. 15. Masson, Paris.

Pycraft, W. P. (1900). On the morphology and phylogeny of the Palaeognathae (*Ratitae* and *Crypturi*) and Neognathae (*Carinatae*). *Trans. Zool. Soc. London* **15:** 149–290.

Pycraft, W. P. (1903). A contribution towards our knowledge of the morphology of the owls. Part II. Osteology. *Trans. Linnean Soc. London, Zool.* **9:** 1–46.

Pycraft, W. P. (1905). Contributions to the osteology of birds. Part VII. *Eurylaemidae:* with remarks on the systematic position of the group. *Proc. Zool. Soc. London* **1905:** 30–56.

Pycraft, W. P. (1907). Contributions to the osteology of birds. Part IX. *Tyranni; Hirundines; Muscicapi; Lanii;* and *Gymnorhines. Proc. Zool. Soc. London* **1907:** 352–379.

Richardson, F. (1942). Adaptive modifications for tree-trunk foraging in birds. *Univ. Calif. (Berkeley) Publ. Zool.* **46:** 317–368.

Shufeldt, R. W. (1885). Concerning some of the forms assumed by the patella in birds. *Proc. U.S. Natl. Museum* **7:** 324–331.

Shufeldt, R. W. (1888). On the skeleton in the genus *Sturnella,* with osteological notes upon other North-American Icteridae, and the Corvidae. *J. Anat. Physiol.* **22:** 309–348.

Shufeldt, R. W. (1909). Osteology of birds. *N.Y. State Museum, Bull.* **130.**

Simonetta, A. (1957). Osservazioni sulla meccanica del cranio degli uccelli drome-ognati. *Atti Soc. Toscana Sci. Nat. Pisa, Mem.* **B64**: 140–167.

Simpson, G. G. (1946). Fossil penguins. *Bull. Am. Museum Nat. Hist.* **87**: 1–99.

Sims, R. W. (1955). The morphology of the head of the Hawfinch (Coccothraustes coccothraustes). *Bull. Brit. Museum Zool.* **2**, No. 13.

Starck, D. (1955). Die endokraniale Morphology der Ratiten, besonders der Apterygidae und Dinornithidae. *Morphol. Jahrb.* **96**: 14–72.

Steinbacher, G. (1935). Funktionell-anatomische Untersuchungen an Vogelfüssen mit Wendzehen und Ruckzehen. *J. Ornithol.* **83**: 214–282.

Stolpe, M. (1932). Physiologisch-anatomische Untersuchungen über die hintere Extremität der Vögel. *J. Ornithol.* **80**: 161–247.

Storer, R. W. (1945). Structural modifications in the hind limb in the Alcidae. *Ibis* **87**: 433–456.

Storer, R. W. (1960). Adaptive radiation in birds. *In* "Biology and Comparative Physiology of Birds" (A. J. Marshall, ed.), Vol. 1, pp. 15–93. Academic Press, New York.

Sullivan, G. E. (1962). Anatomy and embryology of the wing musculature of the domestic fowl (*Gallus*). *Australian J. Zool.* **10**: 458–518.

Suschkin, P. P. (1899). Zur Morphologie des Vogelskeletts. I. Schädel von Tinnun-culus. *Nouveaux Mem. Soc. Imp. Nat. Moscou* **16**: 1–163.

Suschkin, P. P. (1905). "Zur Morphologie des Vogelskeletts. Vergleichende Osteologie der normalen Tagraubvögel (Accipitres) und die Fragen der Classification." Moscow.

Sy, M. (1936). Funktionell-anatomische Untersuchungen am Vogelflügel. *J. Ornithol.* **84**: 199–296.

Tiemeier, O. W. (1950). The os opticus of birds. *J. Morphol.* **86**: 25–46.

Tordoff, H. B. 1954. A systematic study of the avian family Fringillidae based on the structure of the skull. *Misc. Publ. Museum Zool., Univ. Mich.* **81**.

Van Tyne, J., and Berger, A. J. (1959). "Fundamentals of Ornithology." Wiley, New York.

Verheyen, R. (1953). Contribution à l'étude de la structure pneumatique du crâne chez les oiseaux. *Inst. Roy. Sci. Nat. Belg., Bull.* **29**: 1–24.

Verheyen, R. (1956). Note systématique sur Opisthocomus Hoazin (St.-Müller). *Inst. Roy. Sci. Nat. Belg., Bull.* **32**: 1–8.

Waddington, C. H. (1952). "The Epigenetics of Birds." Cambridge Univ. Press, London and New York.

Watson, M. (1883). Report on the anatomy of the Spheniscidae collected during the voyage of H. M. S. Challenger, during the years 1873–1876. *In* "Zoology of the Voyage of the Challenger," Vol. 7.

Webb, M. (1957). The ontogeny of the cranial bones, cranial peripheral and cranial parasympathetic nerves, together with a study of the visceral muscles of *Struthio. Acta Zool.* (*Stockholm*) **38**: 81–203.

Woolfenden, G. E. (1961). Postcranial osteology of the waterfowl. *Bull. Florida State Museum, Biol. Sci.* **6**, No. 1: 1–129.

Zusi, R. L. (1959). The function of the depressor mandibulae muscle in certain passerine birds. *Auk* **76**: 537–539.

Zusi, R. L. (1962). Structural adaptations of the head and neck in the Black Skim-mer, *Rynchops nigra Linnaeus. Publ. Nuttall Ornithol. Club* (*Cambridge, Mass.*) **3**.

CHAPTER III

The Chief Flight Muscles: Pectoralis and Supracoracoideus

Some fifty different striated muscles and muscle slips have an action on the feathers and bones of the wing. Of these, Mm. pectoralis and supracoracoideus play the major role in elevating and depressing the humerus, and thus the wing as a whole. Both of these muscles arise from the ventral surface of the sternum; thus, the center of gravity remains low. The detailed origins of Mm. pectoralis and supracoracoideus among different genera of birds are given in Chapter IX.

The bulky belly of M. pectoralis converges and inserts by fleshy fibers, typically surrounded by a dense tendinous envelope, on the ventral surface of the deltoid crest (pectoral crest; crista lateralis humeri) of the humerus. The pectoralis muscle, therefore, depresses the humerus.

The fleshy fibers of M. supracoracoideus pass upward and converge on one or more large tendons, which pass dorsad through the triosseal canal (Chapter II). The tendon (rarely, tendons) turns outward to insert on the dorsal surface of the humerus, usually just distal to its articular head. The bony margin of the triosseal canal functions as a pulley, so that the contraction of the ventrally situated belly of M. supracoracoideus elevates the humerus and the wing (Fig. III.1).

M. pectoralis is much larger than M. supracoracoideus in most birds that have been studied. M. pectoralis is said to be 15 times as large as M. supracoracoideus in the Black-backed Gull and, according to Nair (1954), 22 times in the Pariah Kite. In some hummingbirds, however, M. pectoralis is only 1.7 times as large as the supracoracoideus (Stolpe and Zimmer, 1939). Greenewalt (1960) stated that M. pectoralis "has ten times the weight of the small pectoral [M. supracoracoideus]. The scatter from the mean is considerable due of course to the variability in relative weight of the small pectoral muscle." Hartman (1961) compiled a mass of new data on the weights of bird muscles, and concluded that M. supracoracoideus is "largest in those birds that make a quick takeoff. It is especially small in cuculids, tytonids, and strigids." He found that

M. supracoracoideus "ranged from about 0.40 percent of the body in species of the genus *Buteo* to 11.5 percent of the body in trochilids, or 1.8 to 30 percent respectively of the flight muscles."

In summarizing previously published data, Greenewalt (1960) concluded that "for the entire procession of birds, from a tiny kinglet to a mute swan," M. pectoralis "averages 15.5 per cent of the body weight with very little scatter on either side of the mean." Hartman found variation in the ratio of pectoral weight to body weight in the same family: 10 to 17% in herons; 12 to 22% in flycatchers (Tyrannidae); and 14 to 21% in swallows.

Hartman reported that the two pectoral muscles (Mm. pectoralis and supracoracoideus) equaled only 7.8% of the total body weight in *Laterallus albigularis* (Rallidae), and that they equaled 36.7% of the total body weight in *Leptotila rufinucha* (Columbidae). Among many genera of

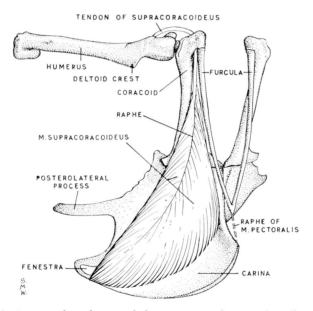

FIG. III.1. An anterolateral view of the sternum and pectoral girdle of *Columba livia* to show the general relationships of the belly and tendon of insertion of M. supracoracoideus. M. pectoralis has been removed, and the humerus has been rotated cephalad to show the site of insertion of M. supracoracoideus on the dorsal surface of the humerus. It may be noted that M. pectoralis arises from all portions of the ventral surface of the sternum not preoccupied by M. supracoracoideus, as well as from the anterolateral surface of most of the clavicle and the adjacent area on the coracoclavicular membrane. In addition, the right and left pectoralis muscles share a common raphe extending between the inferior margin of the furcula and the anterior edge of the carina of the sternum.

hummingbirds he examined, Hartman found that the two pectoral muscles equaled from 21.3 to 34.5% of the total body weight.

Hartman also reported differences in proportions of the two major flight muscles in some species according to sex, latitude, and altitude. The muscles were larger in males than in females in some pelicans, tyrant flycatchers, wrens, tanagers, and many hummingbirds. Specimens of *Florida caerulea* and *Cathartes aura* collected in Panama had heavier muscles than those collected in Florida. Certain cuckoos (*Piaya*, *Crotophaga*) and toucans (*Pteroglossus*) collected at higher elevations had heavier muscles than those taken at lower elevations.

REFERENCES

Greenewalt, C. H. (1960). "Dimensional Relationships for Flying Animals." Greenville, Delaware. (Printed privately.)

Hartman, F. A. (1961). Locomotor mechanisms of birds. *Smithsonian Inst. Misc. Collections* **143:** 1–91.

Nair, K. K. (1954). The bearing of the weight of the pectoral muscles on the flight of some common Indian birds. *J. Animal Morphol. Physiol.* **1:** 71–76.

Stolpe, M., and Zimmer, K. (1939). Der Schwirrflug des Kolibri im Zeitlupenfilm. *J. Ornithol.* **87:** 136–155.

CHAPTER IV

The Pectoralis: Histology and Histochemistry

I. The Red and White Muscle Types

That there are red and white muscles is common knowledge. Everyone from the chef to the sophisticated zoologist, is familiar with the white breast meat and the pale-red leg meat of the chicken. The chicken pectoralis muscle is often referred to as an example of white muscle and the pigeon pectoralis as of the red variety. That the redness of the muscle is due to the hemoglobin present in the cells themselves, and not due to the pervading blood, has long been known.

It should be emphasized that classifying muscles as red or white from a superficial examination is doomed to be an erroneous procedure. What is really important and essential is first of all to know the exact nature of its cell components. Such an approach is judicious for limited histological observations and it becomes all the more necessary as a basis for conducting detailed biochemical investigations requiring considerable precision and accuracy. The pigeon pectoralis muscle and the mammalian diaphragm, for instance, have been, and still are, used as experimental material in several biochemical investigations. The danger involved in not taking into consideration the cellular heterogeneity of the tissue in biochemical investigations has been stressed by George and Susheela (1961) in the case of the mammalian diaphragm. It is one of the purposes of this chapter to elucidate the basic characteristic features responsible for the heterogeneity and thereby the cellular organization of the avian pectoralis muscle.

On a cursory examination, the chicken pectoralis muscle appears to be constituted of only the white type of fibers. Recently this muscle has been shown histochemically to consist of two types of fibers, one containing myoglobin and the other without (Chandra-Bose et al., 1964). The myoglobin-containing fibers are very few in number, whereas those that lack myoglobin predominate (Fig. IV.1). The pigeon pectoralis (Fig. IV.2), on the other hand, has predominantly the myoglobin-

25

containing fibers and considerably fewer myoglobin-lacking fibers (Chinoy, 1963). The diameter of the myoglobin-containing fibers is much less than that of the other type of fibers. In sharp contrast to both the fowl (*Gallus domesticus*) and pigeon (*Columba livia*) pectoralis muscles, that of the sparrow (*Passer domesticus*) has only the narrow myoglobin-containing fibers. However, it should be stated that there are variations in the amount of the myoglobin present in different fibers.

On the basis of the myoglobin content, it is possible to distinguish two types of fibers in the pectoralis muscle of birds: (1) myoglobin-

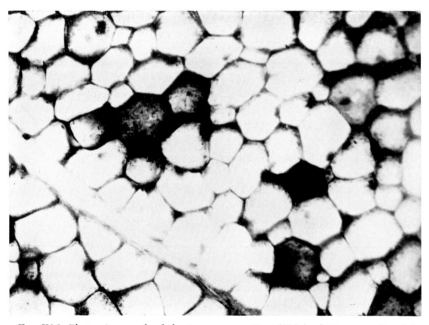

FIG. IV.1. Photomicrograph of the transverse section (T.S.) of M. pectoralis of the domestic fowl showing greater concentration of myoglobin in the narrow red fibers. × 255. (By kind permission, Chandra-Bose *et al.*, 1964.)

containing fibers, and (2) myoglobin-lacking fibers. It is possible to characterize the avian pectoralis also on the same basis: (1) white-mixed, e.g. domestic fowl; (2) red-mixed, e.g. pigeon; and (3) red-unmixed, e.g. hummingbird and sparrow. There is, however, no record of a white-unmixed pectoralis in any bird. It should be of considerable interest to know whether such a pectoralis exists at all in any vertebrate higher than fishes.

The pectoralis muscle is a bipinnate muscle. The outer connective tissue covering is the epimysium; from its inner surface some septa penetrate into the muscle, dividing the muscle irregularly into compartments called fasciculi. These septa forming the outer boundary of the fasciculi constitute the perimysium. Each fasciculus holds together a bundle of muscle fibers. The loose network of connective tissue extensions from the perimysium that envelop each muscle fiber is called the endomysium.

The muscle fiber has a thin outer covering called the sarcolemma. The

Fig. IV.2. Photomicrograph of a transverse section of M. pectoralis of the pigeon. Note the higher concentration of myoglobin in the narrow fibers. × 450. (By kind permission, Chinoy, 1963.)

contractile structure of the fiber consists of muscle columns, myofibrils, and myofilaments. A myofibril is seen to consist of transverse bands which differ in optical density and birefringence. The alternating array of thick, dense and anisotropic filaments are called A (also Q) bands, while the thin less dense, less birefringent and isotropic filaments in the intervening areas are called the I (J) bands. These I bands are

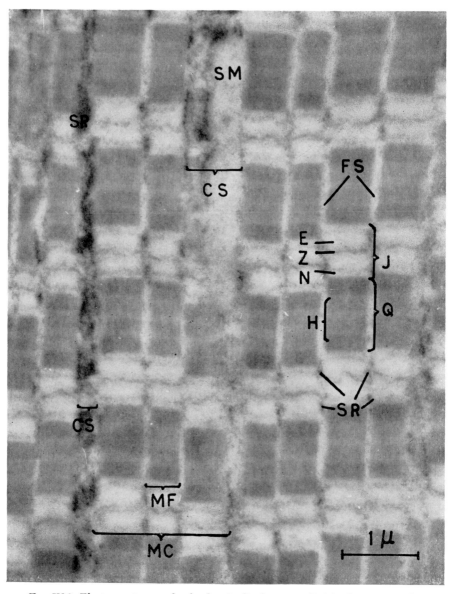

Fig. IV.3. Electron micrograph of a longitudinal section (L.S.) of M. pectoralis of the domestic fowl showing the various components of the muscle fiber. (By kind permission, Bennett and Porter, 1953.)

CS, Intercolumnar sarcoplasm	MF, Myofibril
E, E band	N, N band
FS, Interfibrillar sarcoplasm	Q, Anisotropic band
H, Hensen's stripe	S, Sarcosome or mitochondrion
J, Isotropic band	SR, Sarcoplasmic reticulum
M, M band	SM, Sarcoplasmic matrix
MC, Muscle column	Z, Z band

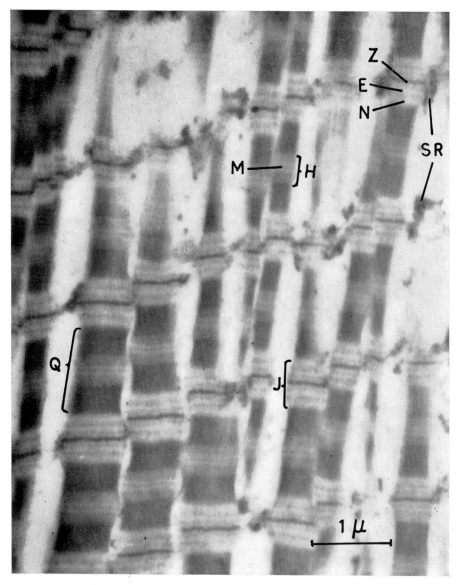

Fig. IV.4. Electron micrograph of L.S. of M. pectoralis of the domestic fowl show-ing clearly myofibrils and myofilaments. Abbreviations same as in Fig. IV.3. (By kind permission, Bennett and Porter, 1953.)

bisected by Z membranes. In the middle of the A band only thick fila-ments are present. This region is called the H zone. On either side of the H zone, the thick and thin filaments interdigitate and the optical den-sity in this region is greatest (Figs. IV.3 and IV.4).

Immediately below the sarcolemma are found the nuclei. They may be found deeper in the fiber among the myofibrils. In the sarcoplasm, which may be defined as the contents of the sarcolemmal bag excluding the nuclei and the fibrillar contractile material, there are five main components: sarcoplasmic matrix, mitochondria or sarcosomes, sarcoplasmic reticulum, sarcoplasmic lipid bodies, and the Golgi apparatus. For detailed descriptions of the structure of the striated muscle in general at the cellular and subcellular levels the recent works of Bennett (1960) and Huxley and Hanson (1960) should be consulted. We shall therefore limit our discourse to some of the basic structural aspects of the pectoralis of the domestic fowl and of the pigeon as examples of white- and red-mixed muscles.

A. Fowl Pectoralis

Of the relatively few electron microscope studies of the avian striated muscle, the first was of the pectoralis of the domestic fowl by Bennett and Porter (1953). The following account of the fowl pectoralis is based on their observations.

A muscle fiber of the fowl pectoralis is on the average about 64 μ in diameter (George and Naik, 1957). The sarcolemma is a thin membrane of about 150 Å to 250 Å thick. On the outside is a loose mesh of collagenous fibers; on the inside, strands of reticulum are found adhering to it.

Many of the nuclei lie immediately under the sarcolemma but they were also seen more deeply embedded in the sarcoplasm of the fiber, between myofibrils. The nuclei have a distinct membrane. No perforations in the nuclear membrane have been noticed. Nevertheless, "pores" similar to those described in all other nuclei have been noticed in the nuclei of the striated muscle cell. At times some nucleolar masses have been noted. The sarcoplasmic matrix is a continuous homogeneous mass of sarcoplasm corresponding to the ground substance matrix of other cells. In it are embedded the sarcosomes and the sarcoplasmic reticulum (Figs. IV.3 and IV.4).

The sarcoplasmic reticulum has been identified as the endoplasmic reticulum of other cells. This tubular sarcoplasmic system exhibits a continuity with the Z band and less frequently with the M band. It forms slender rings around myofibrils at the level of J or M and connects two Z bands across the sarcoplasmic spaces between adjacent myofibrils, between sarcosomes and Z bands, and between Z bands and sarcolemma (Figs. IV.3 and IV.4).

The myofibrils are of strikingly uniform diameter and consist of a close pack of myofilaments in parallel array. The myofilaments run through all bands in the sarcomere but are best seen in the Q band.

The sarcosomes or mitochondria are large bodies bounded by a membrane and found between myofibrils (Fig. IV.5). Kölliker (1857, 1888) was the first to distinguish mitochondria which he called interstitial

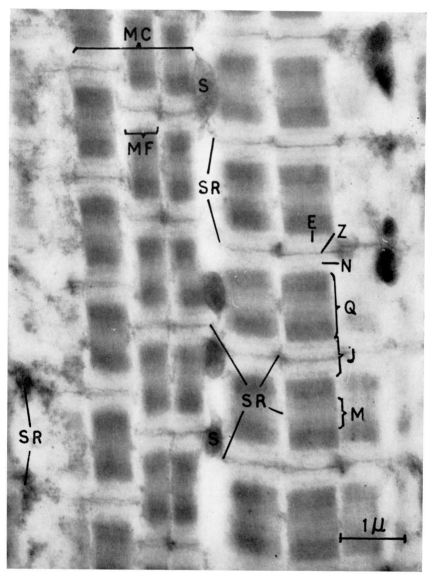

FIG. IV.5. Electron micrograph of L.S. of M. pectoralis of the domestic fowl showing the relation of sarcoplasmic reticulum to Z and M bands and to sarcosomes. Many sarcosomes are seen between the myofibrils. Abbreviations same as in Figs. IV.3 and IV.4. (By kind permission, Bennett and Porter, 1953.)

granules, as distinct from fat droplets, in striated muscle. Their number is clearly less per unit area than in other cells. In number as well as in size, they are conspicuously smaller than those of the pigeon pectoralis. They do not occupy any constant position in relation to the cross bands in the fiber.

No structures similar to fat droplets or Golgi bodies have been found in the fowl pectoralis.

B. Pigeon Pectoralis

The first clear exposition of the histological structure of the pigeon pectoralis was given by Bullard (1912). He described the mitochondria (interstitial granules of Kölliker) and the fat globules as distinct entities and as normal components of the muscle cell. He also recognized the fact that these fat inclusions differed considerably in different muscles as well as in the different fibers of the same muscle. George and Jyoti (1955) studied the histology of the pectoral muscle of the pigeon and some other birds and a bat. They confirmed Bullard's observations on the pigeon breast muscle in its having two types of fibers, a broad white fiber and a narrow red fiber. They concluded however that the fat present as globules in the red fiber is the main source of energy for flight and that Bullard's suggestion of its being reserve food material is only a secondary purpose.

The early electron microscope studies of the pigeon pectoralis were done by Harman (1955). He described the granules mentioned above as cytochondria consisting of two types, the rod-shaped ones, which he called mitochondria, and the spherical ones, sarcosomes (Harman, 1956).

Harman (1955) and Weinreb and Harman (1955) also opposed the generally accepted concept of mitochondrial structure since they could not obtain evidence for the presence of enveloping membranes in the pigeon pectoral muscle mitochondrion.

The pigeon pectoral muscle was reinvestigated by Howatson (1956) and George and Talesara (1961a). The latter authors, on the basis of cytochemical distribution of oxidative enzymes (succinic dehydrogenase and cytochrome oxidase), defined the two types of fibers in the pigeon pectoral muscle (Fig. IV.6) using the light microscope. Mitochondria which are the locale of these enzymes were clearly demonstrated in fresh frozen sections treated for succinic dehydrogenase, as rounded bodies (Figs. IV.10 and IV.11). They found no evidence for believing in the existence of two types of cytochondria (mitochondria and sarcosomes of Harman) and maintained that all are mitochondria (Fig. IV.12). Obviously Harman's so-called sarcosomes are actually the lipid globules. This has also been pointed out by Bennett (1960).

The location of the lipid bodies and mitochondria was shown by Howatson (1956) in an electron microscope study of the pigeon pectoralis muscle (Figs. IV.7, IV.8, and IV.9). The mitochondria are present in between myofibrils as in the fowl pectoral muscle (Bennett and Porter, 1953), but in the pigeon pectoralis they are considerably more numerous and larger in size. The lipid bodies (Figs. IV.7–IV.9) are present, one between two mitochondria, and are frequently associated with the Z band (Howatson, 1956). Contrary to the observation of Har-

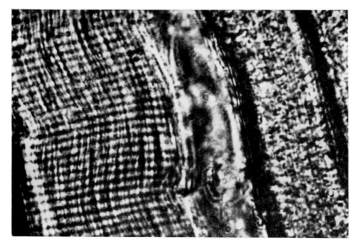

FIG. IV.6. Phase contrast photomicrograph of L.S. of M. pectoralis of pigeon (unstained) showing the two types of fibers. A broad white fiber is on the left and a narrow red is on the right. × 1200. (By kind permission, Naik and George, unpublished work.)

man (1955), this author found that the mitochondrion does possess well defined, double-layered membranes. That the basic nature of the pigeon breast muscle mitochondria is not unlike that of mitochondria from other sources was thus established. Though the lipoid nature of the lipid bodies was also confirmed by him, some doubt was raised for considering them as mere lipid globules because of the presence of a limiting membrane in these bodies. The existence of a limiting membrane is again open to question.

The nuclei of the pigeon pectoralis muscle have not been studied in detail. Observations under the light microscope show that the nuclei of the white fibers occur in the matrix inside the contractile part of the

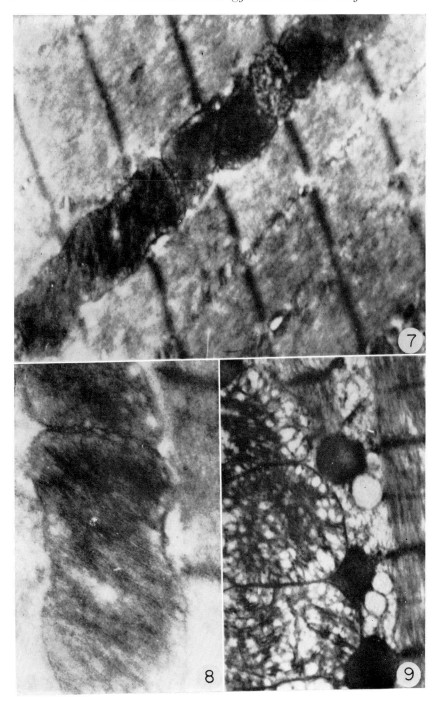

Fig. IV.10. Photomicrograph of the L.S. of M. pectoralis of pigeon showing the distribution and localization of succinic dehydrogenase in the two types of fibers. The narrow red fibers show a markedly greater deposition of diformazan than the broad white fiber in the center. × 810. (By kind permission, George and Talesara, 1961a.)

Fig. IV.7. Electron micrograph of a part of a myofiber from M. pectoralis of pigeon showing large mitochondria (sarcosomes) in between myofibrils. Note the lipid granule in between mitochondria. × 25,000. (By kind permission, Howatson, 1956.)

Fig. IV.8. Part of Fig. IV.7 enlarged to show the mitochondria. × 67,000. (By kind permission, Howatson, 1956.)

Fig. IV.9. M. pectoralis of pigeon, part of poorly preserved muscle fiber showing greatly swollen mitochondria and three lipid granules associated with the Z bands of a myofibril. × 25,000. (By kind permission, Howatson, 1956.)

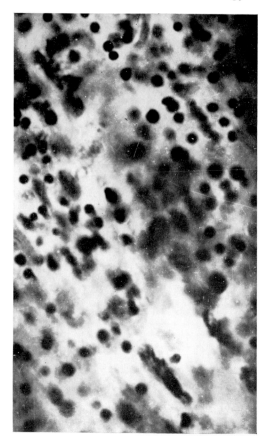

FIG. IV.11. Photomicrograph of L.S. of frozen M. pectoralis of pigeon through the red fibers, showing the localization of succinic dehydrogenase in the mitochondria arranged linearly between myofibrils. × 2000. (By kind permission, George and Talesara, 1961a.)

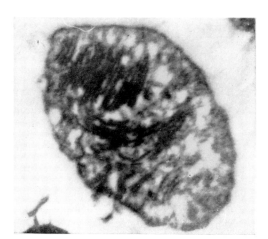

FIG. IV.12. Electron micrograph of the section of an isolated mitochondrion from M. pectoralis of pigeon, showing the enveloping as well as portions of the internal membranes. × 31,000. (By kind permission, Howatson, 1956.)

fiber and are larger than those of the red fiber, in which the nuclei are found in the matrix just beneath the sarcolemma (Fig. IV.39). It is also noticed that there are prominent areas of clear nucleoplasm in the nuclei of the white fiber.

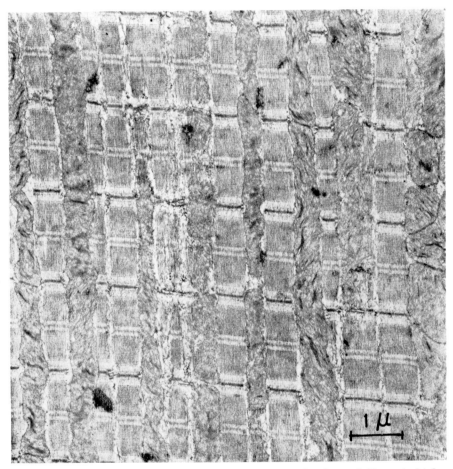

Fɪɢ. IV.13. Electron micrograph of a L.S. of M. pectoralis of Anna's Hummingbird. Note the large mitochondria in close apposition with myofibrils. (By kind permission, Lasiewski *et al.*, 1965.)

The sarcoplasmic reticulum is more prominently seen in the white fibers when subjected to suitable staining techniques under the light microscope (Fig. IV.31).

C. Hummingbird Pectoralis

The pectoralis of the hummingbird like that of the sparrow, is a red, unmixed muscle consisting of only the red, narrow type of fibers. It is profusely supplied with blood through numerous small blood vessels and capillaries (Figs. IV.19 and IV.20). Between myofibrils in each muscle fiber, are numerous large mitochondria linearly arranged (Fig. IV.13). The hummingbird pectoralis is perhaps metabolically the most active vertebrate skeletal muscle known and some of its known physiological features will be dealt with later.

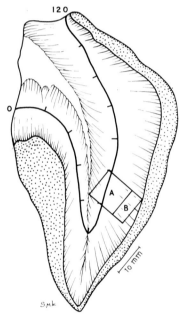

Fig. IV.14. Dorsal view of M. pectoralis of pigeon showing the hypothetical line 0–120 along which the distribution of broad fibers is recorded in Fig. IV.15. The squares A and B indicate the regions of the muscle used for studying the variation in metabolite load and the distribution pattern of the fibers at different depths of the muscle. (By kind permission, George and Naik, 1959a.)

II. Fiber Architecture of Pigeon Pectoralis

A highly active pectoralis muscle, such as that of the pigeon, in which the two distinct types of fibers are sharply differentiated without morphologically distinct intermediate forms but exist side by side (Fig.

IV.2), is undoubtedly of fundamental interest to the physiologist. For a better understanding of muscle function it is important to know the metabolic status and the mode of action of these two types of fibers. Obviously the first step in such an endeavor is to study their relative distribution. This has been done by George and Naik (1959a).

In order to map the distribution of the two types of fibers in the pigeon pectoralis, the authors divided the muscle into twelve regions of 10 mm each in length along a hypothetical line passing midway between the origin of the muscle fasciculi and its centrally placed tendon (Fig. IV.14). This was necessary particularly because of the bipinnate arrangement of the muscle fasciculi. Fresh frozen sections taken at the level of each of these regions and mounted under a microscope were directly exposed onto photographic printing paper. Employing adequate microphotographic techniques, continuous photographic records of the distribution of the broad, white (myoglobin-lacking) fibers were prepared (Fig. IV.15). Such records made for every millimeter depth of the muscle in all the twelve regions provided an excellent picture of the distribution pattern of the fibers. The number of broad fibers per square millimeter was determined by the method of random sampling and when this was done for the entire muscle, a quantitative assessment of the fiber distribution in the different layers of the muscle became possible (Fig. IV.16).

On following the same procedure and counting the number of broad fibers against the number of narrow ones in the sections from different regions of the muscle, George and Naik (1959a) succeeded in establishing a relationship in the distribution pattern of these two types of fibers. Hence, the number of narrow fibers for the corresponding number of broad ones could be readily calculated by using the formula of the regression line obtained (Fig. IV.17).

A typical picture of the distribution of the broad fibers in the pigeon pectoralis is presented in Fig. IV.15. The broad fibers are mainly concentrated at the periphery of each fasciculus throughout the entire muscle. Where there are more broad fibers than the narrow, in any particular region of the muscle, the fasciculi tend to have a smaller cross-sectional area and the broad fibers are closely packed along the border with hardly any intervening narrow fibers. It is also seen (Figs. IV.15 and IV.16) that the superficial part of the muscle has the greatest number of broad fibers and the number gets reduced in the deeper layers. The least number of broad fibers is seen in the central portion in the depth of the muscle. Thereafter, a gradual increase toward the dorsal face of the muscle is seen.

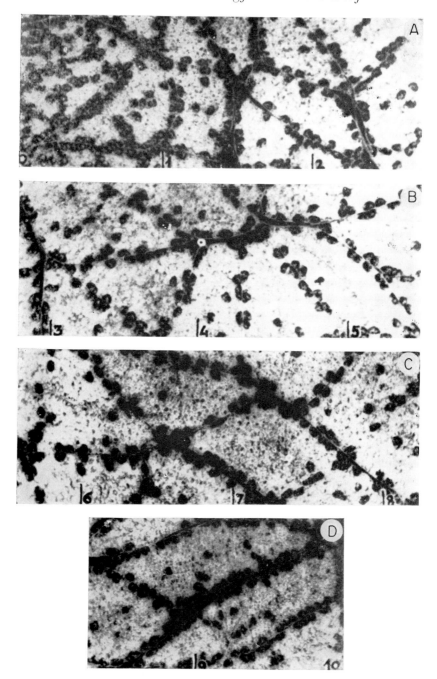

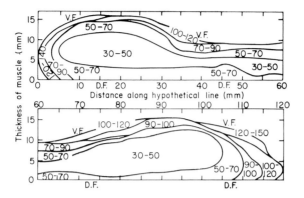

Fɪɢ. IV.16. Cross-sectional view of M. pectoralis along the line 0–120 in Fig. IV.14. The figures in the chart show the number of broad white fibers per square millimeter. D.F., dorsal face of the muscle; V.F., ventral face of the muscle. (By kind permission, George and Naik, 1959a.)

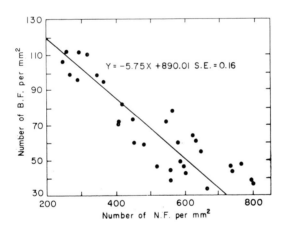

Fɪɢ. IV.17. Relation between the number of broad white fibers and the number of narrow red fibers per square millimeter of a transverse section of the muscle. (By kind permission, George and Naik, 1959a.)

Fɪɢ. IV.15. A,B,C,D. Negative prints of a T.S. of M. pectoralis of pigeon taken from the region A (Fig. IV.14) showing the continuous distribution of broad fibers (darker in color) at different depths of the muscle. The numbers 1–10 indicate the depth in millimeters from the ventral to the dorsal face of the muscle. (By kind permission, George and Naik, 1959a.)

The above observations have shown that the pigeon pectoralis is not a homogeneous mass of one uniform type of cellular elements. There are fundamental differences between the two types of the fibers that constitute it. The relative distribution of these two cell types is not uniform but is different in the different regions of the muscle. There is design and precision in construction. And to believe that this architectural pattern is a mere morphological oddity without any functional significance whatsoever would be against reason. Differences seen at the cellular level could well be based on differences that exist at the molecular level as well. It therefore seems logical to expect different manifestations of function in these fiber types at all levels: organal, cellular, and subcellular.

III. The Red and White Fiber Types of Pigeon Pectoralis

The two types of fibers are easily distinguished even in untreated fresh frozen sections of the pigeon pectoralis. The diameter of the broad fiber is $69.00 \pm 14.00\ \mu$ and that of the narrow $30.11 \pm 6.56\ \mu$ (George and Naik, 1959a). The former shows clear sarcoplasm whereas the latter is studded with granular inclusions, mitochondria, and lipid globules (George and Naik, 1959b).

A. BLOOD SUPPLY

The pigeon pectoralis has a copious blood supply. The distribution of blood capillaries, with respect to the two types of fibers in the muscle, was studied by George and Naik (1960) in specimens injected with India ink. The fibers in the periphery of a fasciculus have a free border without any adjoining capillary. Since the fibers in the periphery are mostly the white ones they lack blood capillaries on their free border. Again, when two broad fibers are side by side in juxtaposition at their apposing sides, a central capillary is conspicuously absent, whereas when a red fiber is in juxtaposition with either another red fiber or a white fiber, a capillary is often seen in the center (Fig. IV.18). But for these differences, the number of capillaries adjoining the white as well as the red fiber is more or less the same. It should be noted, however, that a white fiber has a considerably larger area to be supplied with blood than a red one. So each white fiber per unit area gets considerably less blood than a red fiber. Again, among the white fibers, those that are in juxtaposition with another white fiber and also lacking the central capillary, get still less blood than the other white fibers.

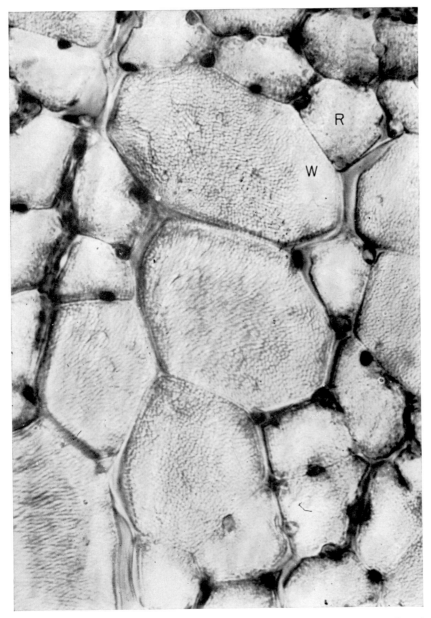

Fɪɢ. IV.18. Photomicrograph of the T.S. of M. pectoralis of pigeon injected with India ink to demonstrate blood capillaries. × 950. (By kind permission, George and Naik, unpublished work.)

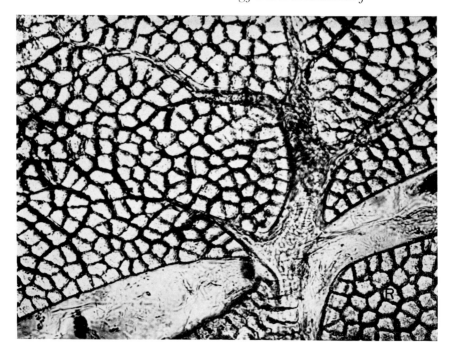

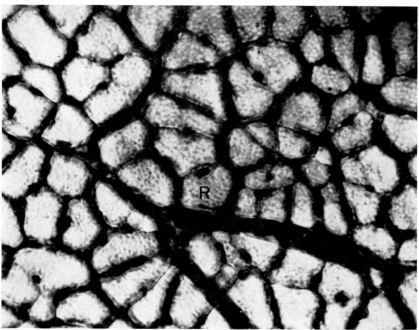

Of all the avian pectoral muscles studied by George and his associates, the most copious blood flow was found in the Rubythroated Humming-bird (Chandra-Bose and George, 1964b). Numerous blood vessels are seen pervading the entire muscle through the large spaces between fibers (Figs. IV.19 and IV.20), the parallel of which is seen only in insects. In the insects, however, there are tracheal tubes in addition to blood vessels (Weis-Fogh, 1964). In the hummingbird pectoralis the capillaries are comparatively very large and one capillary is invariably present between two apposing fibers (Fig. IV.20). In addition the muscle fibers have in them a prominent system of sarcoplasmic reticulum.

B. METABOLITES

It has been mentioned earlier that the broad, white, myoglobin-lacking fibers contain clear sarcoplasm in which lipoid inclusions are conspicuously absent, whereas the narrow, red, myoglobin-containing fibers contain characteristically dense sarcoplasm studded with lipoid inclusions. The chemical nature of the metabolite store in these two diverse cellular systems was investigated by George and Naik (1958a). Using suitable histochemical techniques they established that the broad, white fibers contain a considerably large amount of glycogen but are practically devoid of fat, whereas the narrow, red fibers are loaded with fat but contain very little glycogen (Figs. IV.21 and IV.22). It should be mentioned that in a cross section of the pigeon pectoralis stained for either fat or glycogen, all fibers of the same type do not show the same intensity of staining. What is obtained is a mosaic picture (Fig. IV.23). Nevertheless, the white fibers contain considerably more glycogen and the red fibers more fat. Therefore, they have been called the glycogen-loaded and the fat-loaded fibers, respectively.

C. MITOCHONDRIA

It is well known that mitochondria are the centers of oxidative metabolism. Paul and Sperling (1952) correlated cyclophorase activity with mitochondrial density. Muscles with low cyclophorase activity were found to have low mitochondrial count while those with high cyclo-

---

FIG. IV.19. Photomicrograph of the T.S. of M. pectoralis of the Rubythroated Hummingbird. *Above,* showing the blood supply. × 290. (By kind permission, Chandra-Bose and George, 1964b.) *Below,* stained with hematoxylin. × 810. (By kind permission, Chandra-Bose and George, unpublished work.)

Fig. IV.20. Photomicrograph of the T.S. of M. pectoralis of the Rubythroated Hummingbird treated with Nile blue sulfate showing the distribution of fat, mitochondria, and blood capillaries. The sarcoplasmic reticulum is also stained. × 2610. (By kind permission, Chandra-Bose and George, 1964b.)

Fig. IV.22. Photomicrograph of the T.S. of M. pectoralis of pigeon stained with Sudan black B for fat. The narrow red fibers are more sudanophilic. Mitochondria are deeply stained. × 1600. (By kind permission, Cherian et al., unpublished work.)

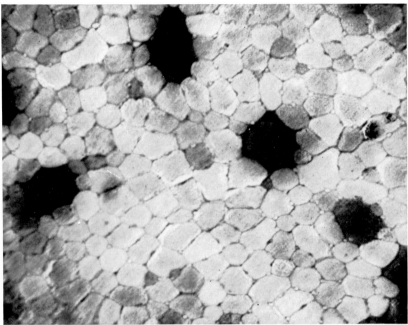

FIG. IV.21. Photomicrograph of the T.S. of M. pectoralis of pigeon stained for the demonstration of glycogen using the PAS technique. Note the higher concentration of glycogen in the broad white fibers. × 400. (By kind permission, Vallyathan *et al.*, 1964.)

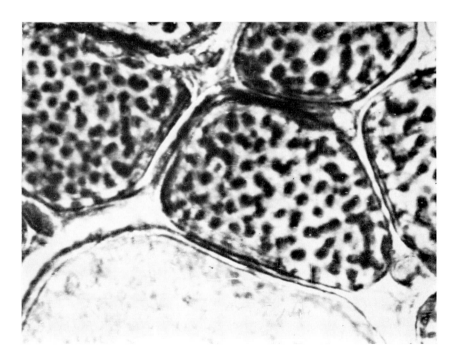

phorase activity had a high mitochondrial count. Chappell and Perry (1953) found that nearly 20% of the total nitrogen of the pigeon breast muscle was derived from mitochondria. In the light of these findings the observation of George and Naik (1958b) that mitochondria are mainly located in the red fibers is of considerable interest. It became clear that the main bulk of mitochondria obtained by Chappell and Perry came from the red fibers. It was also realized that the red and white fiber

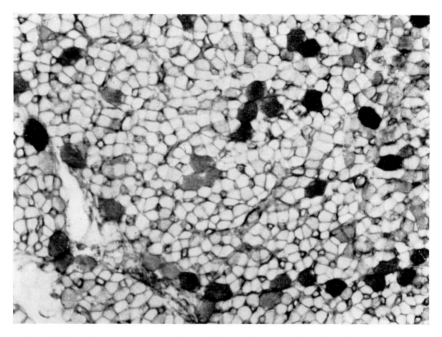

Fig. IV.23. Photomicrograph of the T.S. of M. pectoralis of a 10-day-old pigeon stained for glycogen by the PAS technique. × 525. (By kind permission, Naik, 1961.)

types are two distinctly different metabolic systems and that the existence of such diverse systems is indicative of two different patterns of muscle action.

The exposition of mitochondria in muscle fibers is most readily achieved by histochemically localizing succinic dehydrogenase activity. In doing this, George and Talesara (1961a) clearly showed that mitochondria in the red fibers are considerably more numerous and larger in size than those in the white fibers (Fig. IV.24).

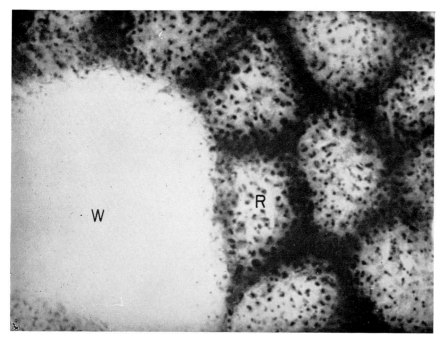

Fɪɢ. IV.24. Photomicrograph of the T.S. of M. pectoralis of pigeon showing the distribution and localization pattern of succinic dehydrogenase in the two types of fibers. The narrow red fibers show a markedly greater deposition of the diformazan granules than the broad white fibers. × 1140. (By kind permission, George and Talesara, 1961a.)

D. Enzymorphology

By virtue of the metabolite store, the white fibers have been called the glycogen-loaded fibers and the red ones the fat-loaded fibers. Obviously the white fibers should metabolize glycogen as a major source of energy and the red ones fat. If this hypothesis is to be proven, it is necessary first to establish that the respective configurations of enzyme systems leading to the two respective metabolic pathways do exist in these cellular systems. It might be expected that each fiber type is also metabolically distinct, where the enzyme systems responsible for one metabolic pathway are predominant while those of the other are insignificant. The purpose of this section is, therefore, to present the available histochemical data on the activity and localization of the different enzyme systems operating in the two types of fibers.

1. *Phosphorylase*

It is known from biochemical studies that phosphorylase exists in two forms: phosphorylase *a* and phosphorylase *b* (Cori, 1956). The former is active without adenosine-5′-phosphate (AMP), whereas the latter becomes active only in the presence of AMP. The muscle enzyme phosphorylase *b* kinase catalyzes the conversion of phosphorylase *b* to

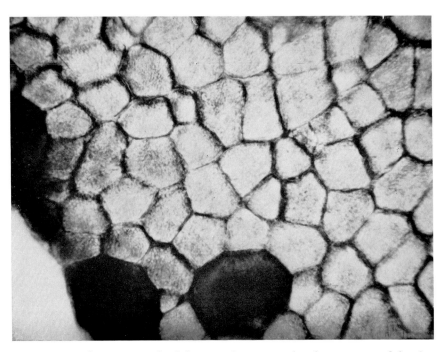

Fig. IV.25. Photomicrograph of the T.S. of M. pectoralis of pigeon stained for the histochemical demonstration of phosphorylase by the method of Eränkö and Palkama. Deeply stained (blue) broad white fibers indicate greater enzyme concentration than the narrow red fibers showing the negative reaction. × 400. (By kind permission, Vallyathan *et al.*, 1964.)

phosphorylase *a*. Phosphorylase activity has been histochemically demonstrated in the pigeon pectoralis (Dubowitz and Pearse, 1960; Vallyathan *et al.*, 1964). The broad, white fibers are stained blue-black and the narrow, red fibers pale purple (Fig. IV.25). This phosphorylase activity probably represents total phosphorylase.

In the histochemical method for demonstration of phosphorylase activity, the polysaccharide (glycogen) synthesized from glucose-1-phosphate has been found to differ from native glycogen. This polysaccharide is formed by amylophosphorylase and stains blue with iodine. On the other hand, that formed by combined activities of amylophosphorylase and branching enzyme stains purple with iodine. The former is digested by both α-amylase and β-amylase while the latter is completely digested by α-amylase but partially by β-amylase (Sasaki and Takeuchi, 1963). Native glycogen stains reddish brown with iodine and is similar to the synthetic polysaccharide resulting from the combined action of amylophosphorylase and the branching enzyme. A similar glycogen has been synthesized histochemically from uridine diphosphate glucose.

2. UDPG-Glycogen Transglucosylase

Biosynthesis of glycogen from uridine diphosphate glucose (UDPG) was shown in muscle using biochemical methods by Leloir and his associates (Leloir *et al.*, 1959). Thus two pathways for the biosynthesis of glycogen, one from glucose-1-phosphate (G1P) catalyzed by amylophosphorylase and branching enzyme and the other from uridine diphosphate glucose catalyzed by the uridine diphosphate glucose-glycogen transglucosylase, have been revealed. Recently this new pathway was histochemically demonstrated by Takeuchi and Glenner (1960). They obtained a red-brown staining of the tissues with iodine, which was digested completely by α-amylase and partially by β-amylase, and similar to that obtained with native glycogen. This means that there is a difference between the mechanism of biosynthesis of glycogen via the G1P and UDPG pathways.

UDPG-Glycogen transglucosylase activity in the rat rectus femoris muscle was histochemically demonstrated by Hess and Pearse (1961). They obtained a considerably higher activity of the enzyme in the red fibers than in the white. On the other hand, these authors found that glycogen synthesis catalyzed by amylophosphorylase from G1P was considerably greater in the white fibers. In the pigeon pectoralis Nene and George (1965a) observed that the activity of the UDPG-glycogen transglucosylase, localized in the sarcoplasmic reticulum, is considerably higher in the white fibers than in the red ones (Fig. IV.26). Among the red fibers again some were more deeply stained than the others, presenting a mosaic picture as is seen in the case of glycogen staining (Fig. IV.23).

According to the present view there are two different pathways for glycogen synthesis and breakdown. The catabolic enzyme is believed to be phosphorylase and the enzyme responsible for synthesis of glycogen *in vivo* to be UDPG-glycogen transglucosylase (Friedman and Larner, 1963). The white fibers of the pigeon pectoralis, therefore, have a higher level of enzymatic activity for the synthesis as well as break down of glycogen than do the red fibers. Evidently these glycogen-loaded fibers are also glycogen-metabolizing fibers.

It has been stated above that Hess and Pearse (1961) obtained a deeper staining in the red than in the white fibers of the rat rectus femoris muscle for UDPG-glycogen transglucosylase. This suggests the

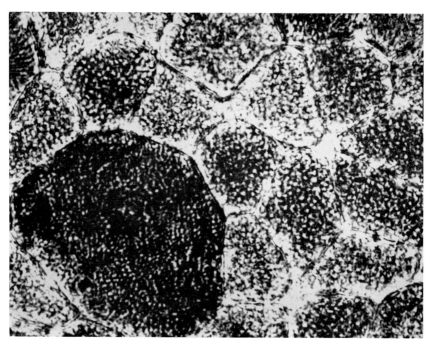

F<small>IG</small>. IV.26. Photomicrograph of a T.S. of M. pectoralis of pigeon showing the histochemical localization of uridine diphosphate glucose glycogen transglucosylase by the method of Takeuchi. Note the greater concentration of the enzyme activity in the broad white fiber. Among the narrow red fibers some are stained darker than others. The enzyme activity appears to be localized in the sarcoplasmic reticulum. The narrow red fibers seem to show higher concentration of the enzyme in the central part of the fibers. × 750. (By kind permission, Nene and George, 1965a.)

possibility of greater glycogen synthesis in the red fibers. In the appendicular muscles other than the pectoralis and supracoracoideus of the pigeon, the red fibers contain more glycogen than the white fibers (Nene and George, 1965b). In this respect, the fibers of the pectoralis and supracoracoideus muscles are unique, and further investigation is necessary to arrive at definite conclusions regarding the metabolism of these fibers.

3. *Aldolase*

The enzyme aldolase, which catalyzes the splitting of 1:6 diphosphate into 3-phosphoglyceraldehyde and α-phosphodihydroxyacetone in the process of glycolysis, has been shown (George and Talesara, 1962a) to have a higher level of activity in the white fibers (Fig. IV.27), thereby indicating higher glycolytic activity in these fibers.

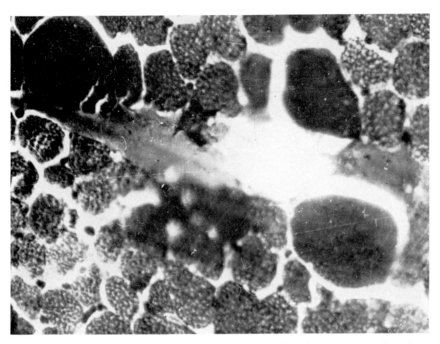

Fig. IV.27. Photomicrograph of a T.S. of M. pectoralis of pigeon treated to show the localization of aldolase. The broad white fibers show greater enzyme activity than the narrow red ones. × 400. (By kind permission, George and Talesara, 1962a.)

4. *Glycolytic Dehydrogenases*

a. *D-Glucose Dehydrogenase.* This enzyme, which catalyzes the conversion of D-glucose to D-gluconic acid, has been located histochemically in the mitochondria of both types of fibers in the pigeon pectoralis (George and Talesara, 1962a).

b. *α-Glycerophosphate Dehydrogenase.* The localization of this enzyme in the pigeon pectoralis (George and Talesara, 1962a) was rather diffuse owing to its high solubility, although mitochondria appeared to be the actual sites of enzyme activity. This enzyme is known to be most active in insect flight muscle, ranging from 6 to 30 times that of the rat leg muscle. At the same time, the insect muscle contains only negligible amounts of lactic dehydrogenase activity, about one-tenth that of the rat leg muscle (Zebe and McShan, 1957). The low lactic dehydrogenase activity in the insect muscle has been attributed to the fact that under anaerobic conditions hexosediphosphate is converted to α-glycerophos-

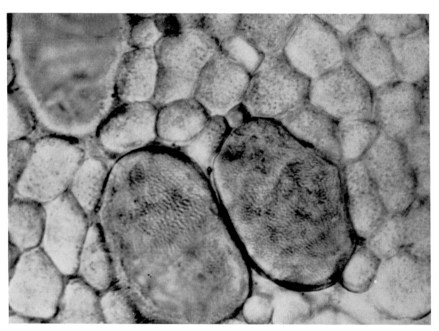

Fig. IV.28. Photomicrograph of a T.S. of M. pectoralis of pigeon treated histochemically to demonstrate the occurrence of cytoplasmic (nonmitochondrial) lactic dehydrogenase. × 640. (By kind permission, George *et al.*, 1963.)

phate and pyruvate and hardly any lactate is formed (Sacktor and Cochran, 1958). Thus α-glycerophosphate is metabolized to oxygen via the cytochrome system. However, a greater role of pyruvate as energy source in insects has been emphasized by Gregg *et al.* (1959).

c. *Lactic Dehydrogenase.* The anaerobic metabolism of carbohydrates in muscle begins with glycogen and ends with lactic acid. The enzyme lactic dehydrogenase catalyzes the reduction of pyruvate to L-lactic acid. Dubowitz and Pearse (1960) observed from histochemical preparations that the red fibers of the pigeon breast muscle have higher lactic dehydrogenase activity than the white fibers and that the enzyme is localized in the mitochondria, which are numerous in these fibers. This was confirmed by George and Talesara by quantitative (1961b) as well as histochemical (1962a) methods. All the same, this is surprising because this enzyme is concerned with carbohydrate metabolism and one would naturally expect the white fibers to have a higher concentration of the enzyme. Blanchaer and Van Wijhe (1962), employing a dif-

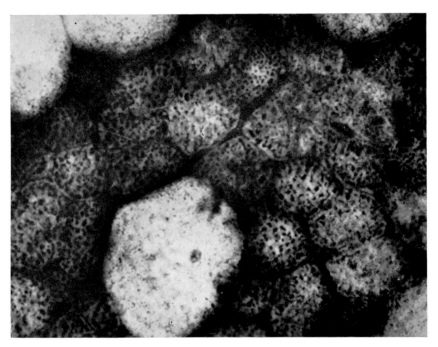

Fig. IV.29. Photomicrograph of a T.S. of M. pectoralis of pigeon showing the lactic dehydrogenase localized in the mitochondria. Note mitochondrial lactic dehydrogenase activity is greater in the narrow red fibers. × 640. (By kind permission, George *et al.*, 1963.)

ferent method of quantitative assay, obtained a higher activity of the enzyme in the white muscle than in the red muscle of the guinea pig.

In the original method of Hess *et al.* (1958), which was followed by Dubowitz and Pearse (1960), the diaphorase was necessary for the demonstration of the enzyme activity. Obviously the red fibers which contain a higher level of diaphorase activity (Dubowitz and Pearse, 1960) should also show a higher level of lactic dehydrogenase activity. George *et al.* (1963), by the addition of phenazine methosulfate to the incubation medium as a direct electron acceptor from Fe^{2+} ions of the iron-flavoprotein, obtained a higher activity of the enzyme in the white fibers. They also found that sections treated with testosterone showed better staining reaction for cytoplasmic lactic dehydrogenase but stained poorly for the mitochondrial lactic dehydrogenase (Figs. IV.28 and IV.29). These authors suggested that testosterone has an inhibitory effect on the diaphorase system as well as on mitochondrial lactic dehydrogenase.

It should be pointed out here that it would not be surprising if all these glycolytic dehydrogenases are also located in the sarcoplasmic reticulum when their histochemical detection via the diaphorase pathway is avoided.

5. *Pentose Cycle Dehydrogenases*

a. Glucose-6-Phosphate Dehydrogenase. This enzyme, which is responsible for the dehydrogenation of glucose-6-phosphate leading to 6-

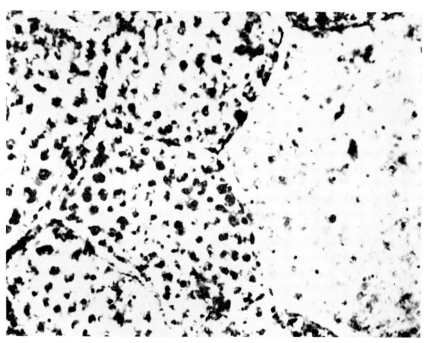

Fig. IV.30. Photomicrograph of a T.S. of M. pectoralis of pigeon treated histochemically to demonstrate glucose-6-phosphate dehydrogenase activity employing the method of Pearse. Note greater concentration of the enzyme in the mitochondria. × 1250. (By kind permission, Nene and George, 1965c.)

phosphogluconate, is the prime mover in diverting the glucose traffic along the pentose phosphate pathway. The most important function of this pathway is now known to be the generation of NADPH$_2$ (reduced nicotinamide-adenine-dinucleotide phosphate) or TPNH (reduced triphosphopyridine nucleotide) for lipogenesis. In a system such as the pigeon pectoralis, where there are two types of fibers (glycogen-loaded and fat-loaded), the detection and localization of this enzyme is of considerable interest.

The activity of this enzyme in the pigeon pectoralis has been histochemically demonstrated in the mitochondria and the sarcoplasmic reticulum (Nene and George, 1965c). Mitochondrial activity of the enzyme is obviously highest in the red fibers. In the white fibers, where the sarcoplasmic reticulum is better developed than in red fibers, the sarcotubular localization of the enzyme is more prominent (Figs. IV.30 and IV.31).

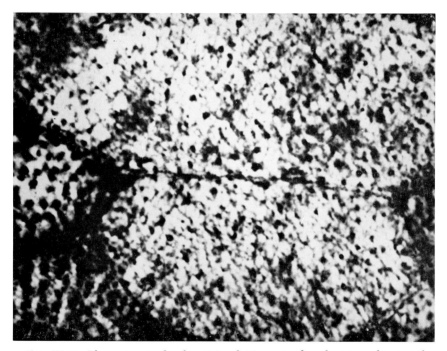

FIG. IV.31. Photomicrograph of a T.S. of M. pectoralis of pigeon showing the localization of glucose-6-phosphate dehydrogenase activity after incorporating phenazine methosulfate in the incubation medium. Note the sarcotubular localization of the enzyme in addition to the mitochondrial. × 1250. (By kind permission, Nene and George, 1965c.)

b. 6-Phosphogluconic Acid Dehydrogenase. 6-Phosphogluconic acid is formed by the oxidation of glucose-6-phosphate, catalyzed by glucose-6-phosphate dehydrogenase. This in turn is converted to D-ribulose-5-phosphate, the key intermediate in the pentose phosphate pathway, by oxidative decarboxylation by 6-phosphogluconic acid dehydrogenase in the presence of NADP. The red fibers of the pigeon pectoralis contain a high concentration of this enzyme.

6. Krebs Cycle Dehydrogenases

Three dehydrogenases of the tricarboxylic acid cycle (isocitric, succinic, and malic dehydrogenase) are mainly localized in the mitochondria. The red fibers of the pigeon pectoralis, which contain numerous mitochondria, obviously have a considerably higher level of the enzyme activities than do the white fibers.

Histochemical techniques described for the demonstration of succinic dehydrogenase, which is the most important member of the Krebs cycle group of oxidative enzymes and other dehydrogenases, are based on the reduction of a tetrazolium salt to a colored compound formazan by the hydrogen removed enzymatically from a substrate, such as sodium succinate in the present case. Using a modified incubation medium, George and Talesara (1961a) demonstrated for the first time the extremely low mitochondrial activity of the enzyme in the white fibers and the high enzyme level in the red fibers of the pigeon pectoralis (Fig. IV.24). The existence of extramitochondrial (cytoplasmic) localization of the enzyme has also been indicated (George *et al.*, 1963).

7. Two Other Dehydrogenases

a. Glutamic Dehydrogenase. Glutamic dehydrogenase, which converts glutamic acid to α-ketoglutarate, an intermediate of the Krebs cycle, has been histochemically demonstrated in the pigeon pectoralis and found to be localized in the mitochondria (George and Talesara, 1962a).

b. β-Hydroxybutyric Dehydrogenase. β-Hydroxybutyric dehydrogenase catalyzes the oxidation of L-β-hydroxybutyric acid to acetoacetic acid. In the pigeon pectoralis, this enzyme also is localized in the mitochondria and therefore the red fibers show considerably higher activity of the enzyme.

8. Cytochrome Oxidase

In the living system the removal of hydrogen from succinate by succinic dehydrogenase results in the reduction of cytochrome *c*. The reduced cytochrome *c* is in turn oxidized by molecular oxygen in the presence of cytochrome oxidase, which is the terminal enzyme in the respiratory chain. Employing the G-Nadi reaction, cytochrome oxidase activity has been demonstrated (Fig. IV.32) in the pigeon pectoralis (George and Talesara, 1961a). The picture obtained was identical with that obtained for succinic dehydrogenase.

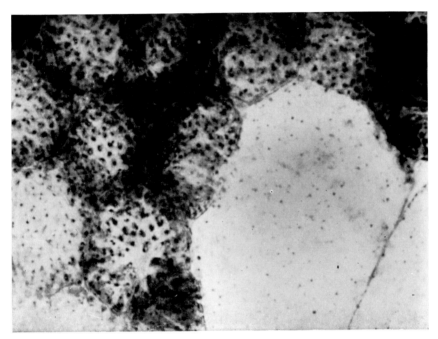

Fig. IV.32. Photomicrograph of a T.S. of M. pectoralis of pigeon showing the localization and distribution pattern of cytochrome oxidase. × 1140. (By kind permission, George and Talesara, 1961a.)

9. *Lipase*

With the introduction of certain improvements in the original Gomori's "Tween 80" method for lipase, a better histochemical localization of lipase activity became possible (George and Iype, 1960). They showed that lipase activity is mainly localized in the red fibers of the pigeon pectoralis. George and Ambadkar (1963) used as substrate a higher "Tween," polyoxyethylene sorbitan trioleate ("Tween 85"), in the histochemical studies on the rat testis. They showed that lipase activity thus demonstrated represented true lipase and not lipase together with some nonspecific esterases, as when "Tween 80" was used. A still further improvement in the histochemical localization of lipase was achieved by using "Tween 85" as substrate and alizarin red S as the stain for coloring the calcium soap formed (Bokdawala and George, 1964). By this method lipase is found to be localized precisely in the numerous mitochondria in the red fibers of the pigeon pectoralis (Fig. IV.33). Mitochondria being considerably smaller in size and fewer in number in

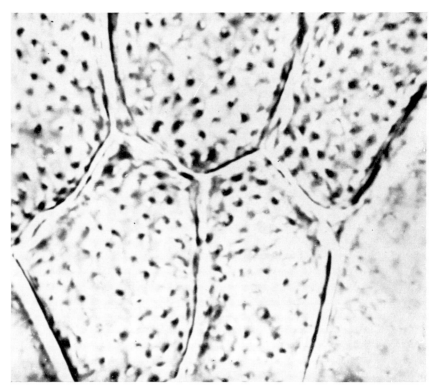

Fig. IV.33. Photomicrograph of a T.S. of M. pectoralis of pigeon showing the localization of lipase activity (substrate: "Tween 85") in the mitochondria. × 1800. (By kind permission, Bokdawala and George, 1964.)

the white fibers, the enzyme activity in these fibers naturally was extremely low. In a recent review on muscle lipase it is suggested that there are two lipases in muscle, one capable of acting on glyceride esters of long-chain fatty acids and localized in the mitochondria, and the other acting on those of short-chain fatty acids but confined mainly to the extramitochondrial regions such as the microsomes (George, 1964).

10. *Esterases*

a. *"Tween 20" Esterase, Indoxyl Acetate Esterase, and α-Naphthyl Acetate Esterase.* Esterases are distinguished from lipase by their inability to readily hydrolyze glyceride esters of long-chain fatty acids. Their action on short-chain fatty acid esters is very rapid but is extremely slow on esters of long-chain fatty acids. It has been stated

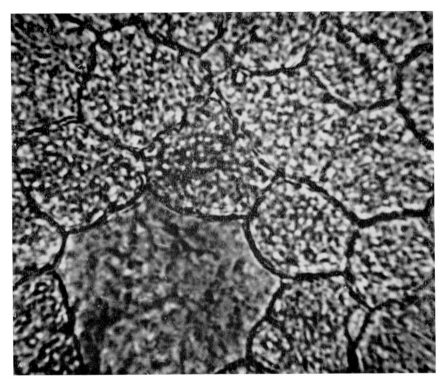

Fɪɢ. IV.34. Photomicrograph of a T.S. of M. pectoralis of pigeon treated to demonstrate esterase activity using "Tween 20." The enzyme activity is uniformly distributed in both types of fibers. Compare with Fig. IV.33 showing the lipase activity localized only in the mitochondria. × 1000. (By kind permission, Cherian *et al.,* unpublished work.)

above that when "Tween 85" is used as substrate, true lipase activity is demonstrated. On the other hand, when a lower "Tween," such as "Tween 80," is used, lipase, as well as some esterase activity, is obtained. The esterase activity is inhibited by sodium taurocholate (George and Ambadkar, 1963). In the pigeon pectoralis, therefore, the enzymatic ac-

tivity seen in the white fibers is mostly esterase activity, whereas that in
the red fibers is mainly lipase. When a low "Tween," "Tween 20"
(polyoxyethylene sorbitan monolaurate) is used, considerably more
esterase activity is demonstrated in both types of fibers, than with higher
"Tweens" (Fig. IV.34). It may, therefore, be concluded that while lipase
activity is confined to mitochondria, esterase activity is extramitochondrial, probably located in the microsomes.

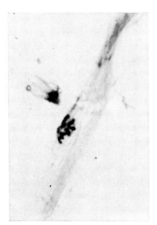

Fig. IV.35. Photomicrograph of an isolated narrow red fiber of M. pectoralis of pigeon showing
the localization of acetylcholinesterase. × 380. (By
kind permission, Chinoy and George, 1965a.)

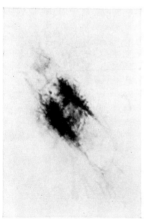

Fig. IV.36. Photomicrograph of an isolated broad
white fiber from M. pectoralis of pigeon showing
the locus of butyrylcholinesterase activity. × 380.
(By kind permission, Chinoy and George, 1965a.)

The same results as with "Tween 20" are obtained in the case of the
other two esterases. Indoxyl acetate esterase activity is denoted by the
blue precipitate of free indoxyl. In the case of the other enzyme reaction, the azo dye gets coupled with the α-naphthyl acetate to give the
colored product.

b. Acetylcholinesterase and Butyrylcholinesterase. Acetylcholinesterase (specific) and butyrylcholinesterase (nonspecific) have been shown to be present at every nerve ending irrespective of the nature of the fiber in the mammalian red and white muscles (Klinar and Župančič, 1962). These cholinesterases have been shown histochemically to be present at the nerve endings (Figs. IV.35 and IV.36) of both the red and the white fibers of the pigeon pectoralis (Chinoy and George, 1965a). According to these authors, the endings in the red as well as

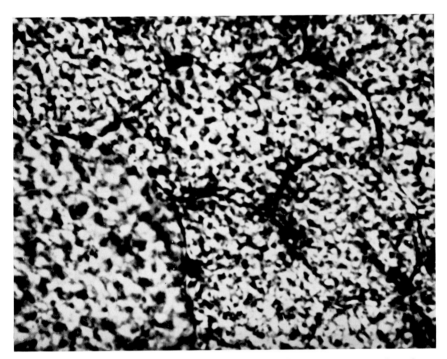

Fig. IV.37. Photomicrograph of a T.S. of M. pectoralis of pigeon treated to show the distribution pattern of alkaline phosphatase. Note the enzyme activity localized in the sarcoplasmic reticulum. × 1600. (By kind permission, Vallyathan and George, 1965.)

in the white fibers of the pigeon pectoralis are morphologically identical in that both are of the "en plaque" type, instead of the red fibers being of the "en grappe" type as is generally believed in the case of red fibers. They have further pointed out that the only point of difference between the endings in the two types of fibers is that in the white fibers butyrylcholinesterase activity is greater and in the red fibers acetylcholinesterase activity is greater. In the case of the pectoralis muscle as a whole, they observed that butyrylcholinesterase activity is greater than that of acetylcholinesterase in the fowl whereas in the pigeon the two enzyme levels are equal. In the sparrow acetylcholinesterase is greater than butyrylcholinesterase.

11. Phosphatases

a. Alkaline Phosphatase and Acid Phosphatase. Histochemical localization of the activity of these enzymes had not been satisfactorily demonstrated in muscle and so they were believed to be absent in muscle tissue

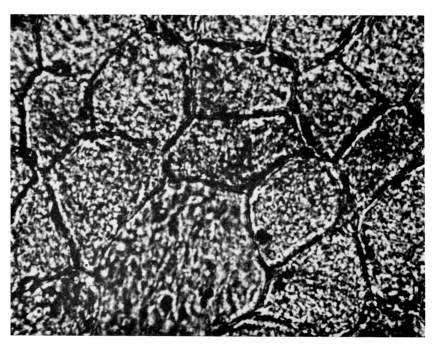

Fig. IV.38. Photomicrograph of a T.S. of M. pectoralis of pigeon showing the histochemical distribution of acid phosphatase activity which is similar to that of alkaline phosphatase. × 1000. (By kind permission, Vallyathan and George, 1965.)

(Beckett and Bourne, 1960). Recently, with the revised Gomori's method (Pearse, 1960) the activity of these enzymes has been histochemically demonstrated (Vallyathan and George, 1965) in the sarcoplasmic reticulum of the red and white fibers of the pigeon pectoralis (Figs. IV.37 and IV.38). A difference in the level of enzyme activity between the two types of fibers was discernible, that of the former enzyme being slightly higher in the red fibers and that of the latter in the white fibers.

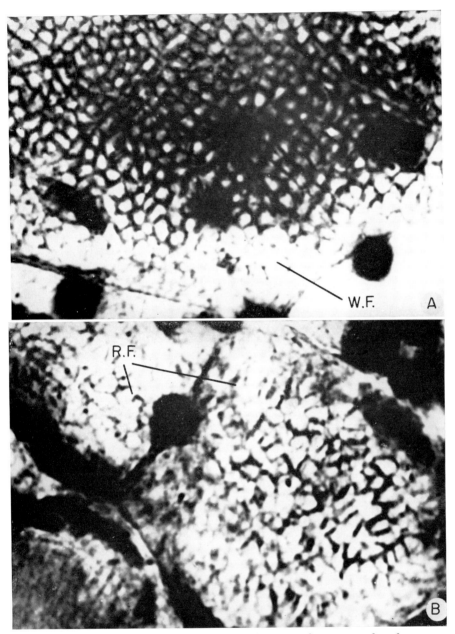

Fig. IV.39. Photomicrographs (A and B) of a T.S. of M. pectoralis of pigeon showing sarcotubular ATPase activity at pH 2.5. The broad white fiber (W.F.) shows greater enzyme activity than the narrow red ones (R.F.). The nuclei in the broad fiber are seen within the substance of the fiber whereas in the narrow fibers they are peripherally placed beneath the sarcolemma. × 2500. (By kind permission, Bokdawala and George, 1965.)

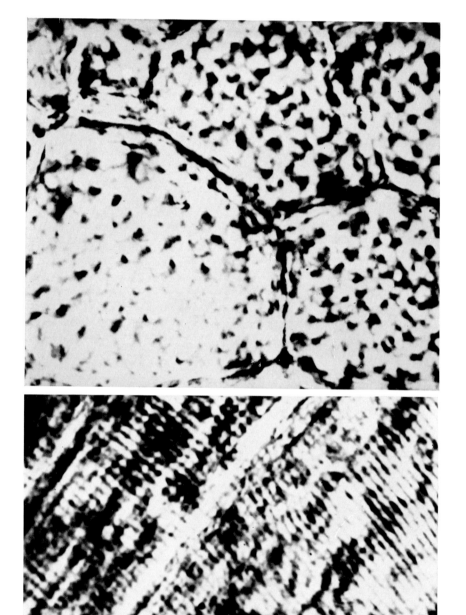

b. Adenosinetriphosphatase (*ATPase*). It is well known that the most important high energy compound in biological systems is adenosinetriphosphate (ATP). The enzyme ATPase, which hydrolyzes the terminal phosphate of ATP releasing free chemical energy, is also universally present. Three different types of ATPase in skeletal muscle have been recognized: mitochondrial, myofibrillar, and sarcotubular. Padykula and Gauthier (1963) demonstrated histochemically the activity of these ATPases in the rat diaphragm. Total ATPase activity with both Ca^{++} and Mg^{++} salts incorporated in the incubation medium, was histochemically demonstrated in the red and white fibers of the pigeon pectoralis (George and Pishawikar, 1959). Greater enzyme activity was found to be in the white fibers.

Quite recently, Bokdawala and George (1965) have shown histochemically that in skeletal muscle both acid and neutral ATPases are present. They obtained intense sarcotubular ATPase activity at pH 2.5 in the white fibers but very low activity at the same pH in the red fibers of the pigeon pectoralis (Fig. IV.39). The higher acid ATPase activity in the white fibers has been attributed to the possibility of a high level of glycolysis and lactic acid formation in these fibers. In contrast these authors obtained with the help of an activator higher mitochondrial activity in the red fibers at a pH of 7.2 (Fig. IV.40). They also demonstrated the sulfhydryl-dependent myofibrillar ATPase at pH 9.4 localized in the A bands of the fiber, a considerably higher enzyme activity being registered in the red fibers (Fig. IV.41). The occurrence of higher acid ATPase activity in the white fibers and the higher neutral ATPase activity in the red fibers could well be a case of functional adaptation at the molecular level.

Fɪɢ. IV.40. Photomicrograph of a T.S. of M. pectoralis of pigeon demonstrating ATPase activity at pH 7.2 using the lead technique of Wachstein and Meisel with dinitrophenol as activator incorporated in the incubation medium. The enhancement of enzyme activity was seen in the mitochondria of the narrow red fibers, and a simultaneous decrease of activity was noted in the broad fibers. × 1800. (By kind permission, Bokdawala and George, 1965.)

Fɪɢ. IV.41. Photomicrograph of a L.S. of M. pectoralis of pigeon showing myofibrillar ATPase activity at pH 9.4 employing the method of Padykula and Herman. The sections were fixed in formalin prior to incubation to prevent contraction of the fibers. The enzyme activity is localized at the cross-striations corresponding to the A band. × 1800. (By kind permission, Bokdawala and George, 1965.)

E. DEVELOPMENT

In early development the paraxial and lateral plate mesoderm differentiates as the myotome, undergoes extensive growth, and eventually gives rise to the skeletal musculature. In the development of the striated muscle fiber four stages have been recognized: (1) the premyoblast, (2) the

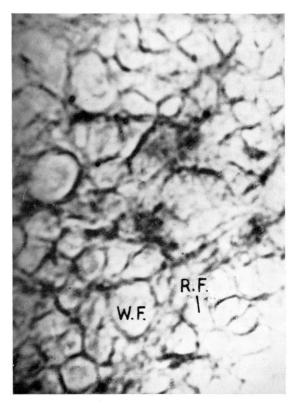

FIG. IV.42. Photomicrograph of a T.S. of M. pectoralis of a 15-day *in ovo* pigeon embryo stained with Sudan black B for the demonstration of fat. The red and white fibers are clearly discernible. R.F., red fiber; W.F., white fiber. × 1500. (By kind permission, Chinoy and George, 1965b.)

myoblast, (3) the myotube, and (4) the muscular fiber. For detailed information regarding the development of the striated muscle, the account given by Boyd (1960) should be consulted. For the present purpose, only certain aspects of the development of the pigeon pectoralis muscle, in the light of some recent studies, will be considered.

The morphological and biochemical differences between the two component types of fibers of the pigeon pectoralis have been enumerated earlier. It should be of interest to know when exactly the differentiation of these fiber types takes place, whether *in ovo* or *ex ovo*. The *in ovo* recognition of these fibers as distinct morphological entities [the broad, white fiber and the narrow, red fiber (Fig. IV.42) having diameters 8.10 μ and 4.05 μ, respectively] was found possible (Chinoy and George, 1965b) 2 days prior to hatching (15 days of incubation). This means

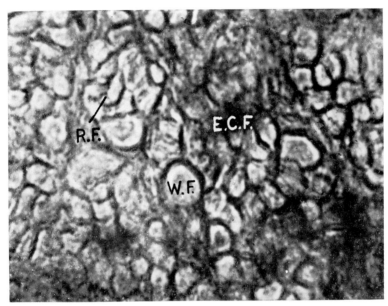

Fig. IV.43. Photomicrograph of T.S. of M. pectoralis of a 1-day *ex ovo* pigeon chick stained for the demonstration of fat. Note the high amount of extracellular (interfiberal) fat. E.C.F., extracellular fat; R.F., red fiber; W.F., white fiber. × 1260. (By kind permission, Chinoy and George, 1965b.)

that the differentiation of the two types of fibers was a genetically determined characteristic of the muscle and that differentiation does not appear as a result of the specialized activity of the muscle after hatching.

On hatching, the muscle was found to have a relatively higher glycogen content than on days immediately after hatching. This reduced glycogen level was maintained for a period of 15 days but again increased about the 24th day. From the second day onward the diameter of the white fibers increased gradually but the red fibers registered a sudden 100% increase in diameter on the third day (13.5 μ and 8.10 μ respectively). Thereafter, the increase in diameter was by and large steady in both types of fibers. With regard to fat, high concentrations of extracellular (interfiberal) fat in the muscle, were noticed at the time of hatching (Fig. IV.43); but during the subsequent days, fat at

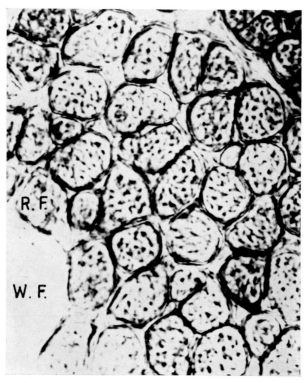

Fig. IV.44. Photomicrograph of a T.S. of M. pectoralis of a 24-day-old pigeon stained with Sudan black B for fat. The narrow red fibers are more sudanophilic than the white ones. R.F., red fiber; W.F., white fiber. × 1500. (By kind permission, Chinoy and George, 1965b.)

this site became reduced, as fat inside the red fibers increased (Fig. IV.44). Simultaneously, increase in mitochondrial density and in the activity of the enzymes succinic dehydrogenase and lipase was also observed (Fig. IV.45). This indicated a shift from glycogen metabolism to fat metabolism in the muscle as a whole (Chinoy and George, 1965b) though the white fibers by themselves become adapted for a glycolytic metabolism.

The action of a muscle is the net result of the collective action of its component fibers. The heterogeneity of the constituent muscle cells as seen in the pigeon pectoralis is both morphological and biochemical. With the increase in our knowledge of the cell, it has become more and more clear that structure and function are complementary to each other

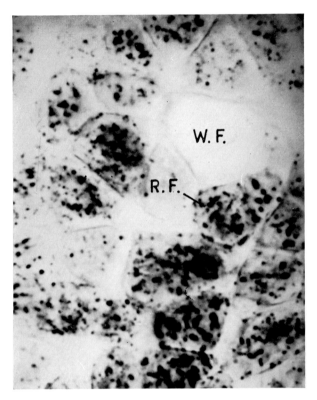

Fig. IV.45. Photomicrograph of the M. pectoralis of a 16-day-old pigeon stained for the demonstration of succinic dehydrogenase. The red fibers contain a higher concentration of the enzyme than the white fibers. Mitochondria appear as clumps. R.F., red fiber; W.F., white fiber. × 1500. (By kind permission, Chinoy and George, 1965b.)

and that the old barriers in our concepts that separated these two aspects are fast disappearing. In this context the *in ovo* origin of the two types of fibers of the pigeon pectoralis as two distinct structural patterns is of special significance. The structural components of a muscle cell (Fig. IV.46) such as the nuclei, the myofibrils with their Z bands,

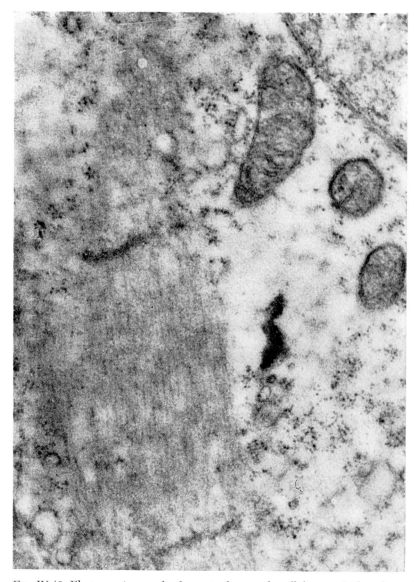

Fig. IV.46. Electron micrograph of a part of a muscle cell from a chick embryo. A portion of the nucleus is seen at the upper right corner. A developing myofibril is seen at the left. Two Z bands with myofilament stretching between them and mitochondria are visible. × 43,500. (By kind permission, Howatson and Ham, 1957.)

and mitochondria, have been shown to exist in immature muscle cell of the chick embryo (Howatson and Ham, 1957).

Recently, the embryonic pigeon pectoralis muscle (from 8- to 12-day incubated eggs) has been studied from *in vitro* cultures (George and Chinoy, 1964). No distinction between the two types of fibers was possible among the myoblasts in culture. These authors, however, observed a considerable amount of neutral lipid inside the nucleus and in the cyto-

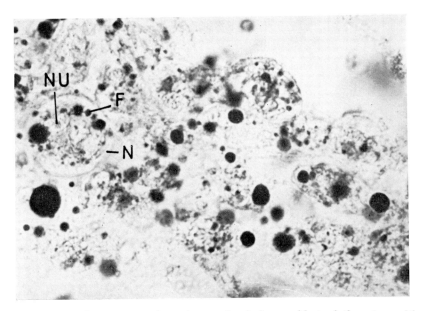

Fig. IV.47. Oil immersion photomicrograph of the myoblast of the pigeon M. pectoralis grown *in vitro*, showing neutral lipid droplets (F) in the nucleus (N). The nucleolus (Nu) is unstained. × 1600. (By kind permission, George and Chinoy, 1964.)

plasm (Fig. IV.47), and phospholipid mostly in the nucleolus (Fig. IV.48). The staining pattern was the same in cultured chicken pectoralis muscle but it differed in that the concentration of lipid was much less. These authors presented evidence to indicate that the lipid in the nucleus is transferred to the cytoplasm. They also postulated that the neutral lipid thus transferred is actually coded lipid, and that the phospholipids form parts of the multienzyme systems and the molecular framework of mitochondria. Obviously lipid specificity and mitochondrial organization thus envisaged should be of paramount importance in systems, such as the avian pectoralis muscle, which are adapted for metabolizing fat as fuel for energy.

It may not be out of place here to mention the role of the avian pectoralis muscle in the process of hatching. This process in birds involves first the "pipping" of the egg shell with the aid of the egg tooth and then the emergence of the chick from the shell. Fisher (1958) described the morphological and histological features of the so-called "hatching muscle" (M. *complexus*) in the chick, and suggested that

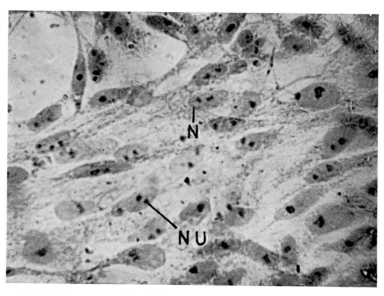

Fig. IV.48. Photomicrograph of the myoblast of pigeon M. pectoralis grown *in vitro* and stained with Luxol Fast Blue B to demonstrate phospholipid and lipoproteins. Note the highest concentration in the nucleolus (Nu). Identical staining for phospholipid was obtained with Elftman's method and acid hematin method. × 1000. (By kind permission, George and Chinoy, 1964.)

power for the rupture of the shell by the egg tooth at hatching is provided by this muscle. Recently George and Iype (1963) studied the glycogen content and lipase activity in the hatching and pectoralis muscles of the chick during the pre-hatching and post-hatching periods. They concluded that the powerful contractions of the hatching muscle bring about the "pipping" of the shell and those of the appendicular muscles, such as the pectoralis, effect the emergence of the chick from the shell.

IV. Characterization of the Fiber Types

In this chapter we have so far considered the various characteristic features of the two types of fibers that constitute the pigeon pectoralis muscle. As we shall see later, even in those birds where the pectoralis muscle is a mixed muscle, the two types of fibers are not as well defined as in the pigeon pectoralis, and variations from these distinct types occur. In characterizing the fibers of the avian pectoralis, therefore, the two types met with in the pigeon pectoralis may be regarded as models representing two divergent lines of structural and functional specialization (Table IV.1).

The distinction between the two types of fibers is achieved most easily and clearly in sections of the muscle treated for the exposition of succinic dehydrogenase activity (Fig. IV.24). Sections of the appendicular muscles of reptiles and mammals similarly treated show three types of fibers, the third being intermediate between the other two types

TABLE IV.1

CHARACTERIZATION OF THE FIBER TYPES

Properties	Type 1	Type 2
Color	Red	White
Diameter	Small	Large
Blood supply	Copious	Little
Myoglobin	High	Low
Sarcoplasm	Granular	Clear
Mitochondria	Numerous	Sparse
Fat	High	Low
Glycogen	Low	High
Lipase	High	Low
Phosphorylase	Low	High
UDPG-Glycogen transglucosylase	Low	High
Aldolase	Low	High
Lactic dehydrogenase		
(Cytoplasmic)	Low	High
(Mitochondrial)	High	Low
Other oxidative enzymes	High	Low
Alkaline phosphatase	Fairly high	Moderate
Acid phosphatase	Moderate	Fairly high
ATPase (acid)	Low	High
ATPase (neutral)	High	Low
Acetylcholinesterase	High	Low
Butyrylcholinesterase	Low	High
Activity	Sustained	Rapid
Contraction	Slow	Fast

(Stein and Padykula, 1962; Ogata and Mori, 1964). The three types may be designated as R (Type 1), W (Type 2), and I (intermediate between R and W). It has already been mentioned that the red mixed pectoralis muscle of the pigeon consists of only the R and W types of fibers. The white mixed pectoralis muscle of the domestic fowl consists of all three types W, I, and R (in the order of predominance) and the red unmixed pectoralis of the House Sparrow of only the R type. The red pectoralis muscle of the Pariah Kite consists of only the I type and that of the starling of the R and I types.

In characterizing the fiber types as above, the question arises whether each of the three types of fibers (W, I, and R, respectively) in the various birds is homologous. If so, it may be said that the I fibers in the pigeon, the W and R in the kite, the W in the starling, and W and I fibers in the sparrow do not exist. In the present state of our knowledge it is not possible to state whether these types are homologous. However, it should be mentioned that these fiber types are differentiated during development in accordance with the nature of contraction designed for a particular mode of flight. The R type of fiber is for sustained flapping flight whereas the W type is for fast and rapid flight. We are not aware of any bird that has only the W type of fibers but there are those with only the R type. In a mixed muscle, the W type fibers should effect a quick take-off and sharp turns while in flight. In those forms in which this quick action becomes more frequent and sustained the W type fibers are replaced by the I type. The starling pectoralis, unlike that of the pigeon, has R and I fibers. In the starling, I fibers have a larger diameter and lesser mitochondrial density and succinic dehydrogenase activity than the R fibers. In characterizing the fiber types the more important criteria are their load of fat, lipase and oxidative enzyme levels, and mitochondrial density. The diameter of the fibers varies in different birds, so much so that the diameter of an R fiber of one species may be greater than that of an I fiber of another species. But, in the same species where two types of fibers are present, the diameter of the R fibers is always less than the other type whether I or W. In birds such as the sparrow, in which there are only R fibers, the differentiation among the fibers might well be biochemical and not morphological. This aspect will be discussed later.

V. Characterization of the Avian Pectoralis

It should be emphasized here that our knowledge of the cellular organization of the avian pectoralis is indeed fragmentary even though much new light has now been thrown by the recent studies of George and his associates (George and Naik, 1957, 1959a,b,c; George and Tale-sara, 1962b; Chandra-Bose and George, 1964a,b, 1965; George, 1965). However, nothing is yet known of the pectoralis in the flightless birds (ratites), the specialized swimmers (penguins), and many flying birds. We should, therefore, feel adequately rewarded if the present discussion would attract more investigators into this practically virgin field and thereby stimulate further research.

The variations in the fiber architecture of the pectoralis muscle in certain birds, with regard to the three basic types of fibers, have been mentioned earlier. In the light of these observations the pectoralis muscles of birds may be classed into the following six groups:

Group 1. Fowl type (*W*, *I*, and *R* fibers)
Group 2. Duck type (*R*, *W*, and *I* fibers)
Group 3. Pigeon type (*R* and *W* fibers)
Group 4. Kite type (*I* fibers)
Group 5. Starling type (*R* and *I* fibers)
Group 6. Sparrow type (*R* fibers)

Group 1

The pectoralis of the domestic fowl (Galliformes) consists predominantly of the *W* and *I* types of fibers and contains very few of the *R* type. Here again it should be pointed out that the concentration of the enzyme succinic dehydrogenase is considerably less than that in the fibers of the pectoralis of other groups (Fig. IV.49).

Group 2

The pectoralis muscle of the domestic duck (Anseriformes) is similar to that of the domestic fowl in that all the three types of fibers are present but it differs in having considerably more *R* fibers (Fig. IV.50). However, the possibility of striking variations existing in the different members of the Order Anseriformes, particularly in the generally long-flying migratory ducks and geese, cannot be ruled out.

Figs. IV.49–91. Photomicrographs of the T.S. of M. pectoralis of various birds, showing mitochondrial localization of succinic dehydrogenase activity.

    W . . . . White fiber type
    I . . . . Intermediate fiber type
    R . . . . Red fiber type

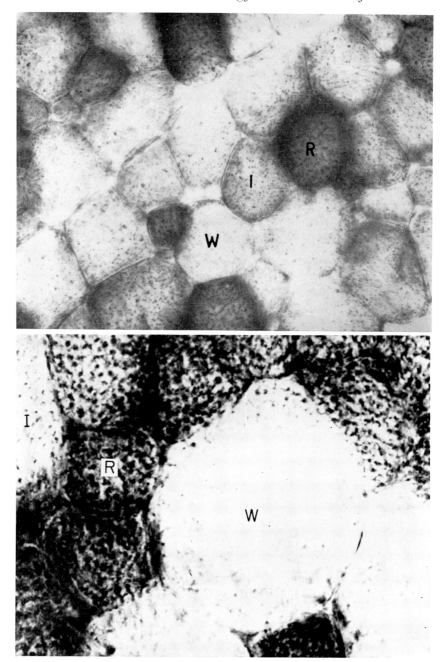

Group 3

The pectoralis of the Blue Rock Pigeon, *Columba livia* (Columbiformes), consisting of two types of fibers (*R* and *W*), has been dealt with in detail earlier (Figs. IV.18 and IV.24). The pectoralis of the Spotted Dove, *Streptopelia chinensis suratensis* (Columbiformes) is very much like the pigeon pectoralis. It is likely that this pattern is characteristic of the pectoralis in Columbiformes. However, it is of considerable interest to mention here that the observations of Bösiger (1950) and of Bösiger-Ensner (1961) on the pectoralis of the quail, *Coturnix c. coturnix*, reveal that the muscle is similar to that of the pigeon, consisting of *R* and *W* fibers. The quail belongs to the Order Galliformes, and the fact that the structure of its pectoralis muscle is similar to that of the columbiform birds suggests that these two orders are closely related phylogenetically (George, 1965).

The following birds belonging to other orders, however, have been found to have their pectoralis similar to that of the pigeon: the Cattle Egret, *Bubulcus ibis coromandus* (Ciconiiformes), the Purple Moorhen, *Porphyrio porphyrio poliocephalus* (Gruiformes), the Koel, *Eudynamys scolopacea* (Cuculiformes), and the Hoopoe, *Upupa epops* (Coraciiformes), also have the *R* and *W* types of fibers (Figs. IV.51, IV.52, IV.53, and IV.54). The mitochondria in the Moorhen pectoralis seem to be strikingly larger than those in any other bird hitherto studied. In the present state of our knowledge it is not possible to say, on the basis of the structure of the pectoralis, how closely these orders of birds are phylogenetically related. Perhaps these structural similarities in the pectoralis muscles are merely a case of convergence in evolution.

FIG. IV.49. Photomicrograph of the transverse section (T.S.) of M. pectoralis of the fowl, showing mitochondrial localization of succinic dehydrogenase activity. *W*, white fiber type; *I*, intermediate fiber type; *R*, red fiber type. × 290. (By kind permission, Chandra-Bose *et al.*, 1964.)

FIG. IV.50. Photomicrograph of the T.S. of M. pectoralis of the domestic duck (Anatidae), showing mitochondrial localization of succinic dehydrogenase activity. × 810. (By kind permission, Chandra-Bose and George, unpublished work.)

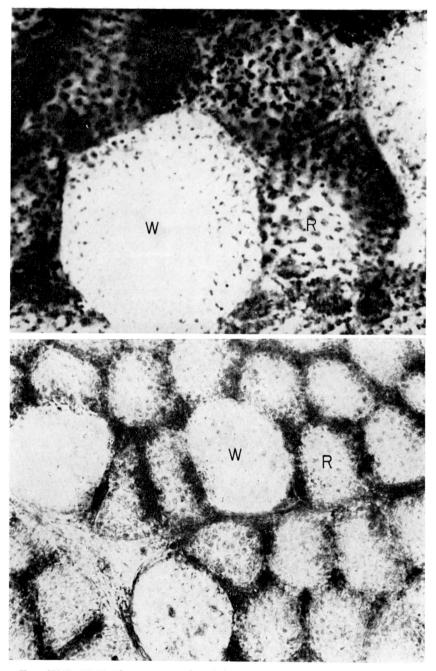

Figs. IV.51–IV.57. Photomicrographs of the transverse section of M. pectoralis of various birds, showing mitochondrial localization of succinic dehydrogenase activity.

Fig. IV.51. (*Above*) Cattle Egret, *Bubulcus ibis* (Ardeidae). × 1140. (By kind permission, Chandra-Bose and George, unpublished work.)

Fig. IV.52. (*Below*) Purple Moorhen, *Porphyrio porphyrio* (Rallidae). × 450. (By kind permission, Chandra-Bose and George, unpublished work.)

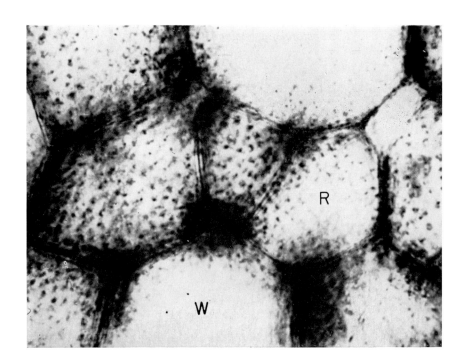

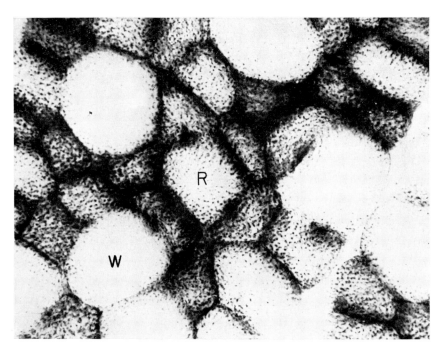

Fig. IV.53. (*Above*) Koel, *Eudynamys scolopacea* (Cuculidae). × 1140. (By kind permission, Chandra-Bose and George, unpublished work.)

Fig. IV.54. (*Below*) Hoopoe, *Upupa epops* (Upupidae). × 450. (By kind permission, Chandra-Bose and George, unpublished work.)

Group 4

The pectoralis muscles of the Pariah Kite, *Milvus migrans* and of the Indian Whitebacked Vulture, *Gyps bengalensis,* have been studied recently (George and Naik, 1959b; Chandra-Bose and George, 1965). The characteristic features of the fibers in the pectoralis muscle in these birds are that they are loosely packed and circular in cross section, considerably larger than the *R* fibers of the pigeon pectoralis and slightly larger than the *I* fibers of the fowl pectoralis (Figs. IV.55, IV.56, and IV.57). In these birds, therefore, the muscle may be considered as con-

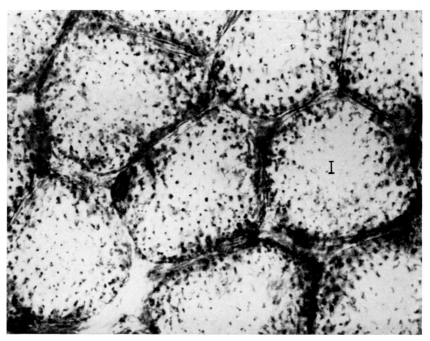

Fig. IV.55. Pariah Kite, *Milvus migrans* (Accipitridae). Central region, × 810. (By kind permission, Chandra-Bose and George, unpublished work.)

sisting of only the *I* type of fibers, but at the same time containing higher concentrations of fat and succinic dehydrogenase than the same type of fibers of the fowl pectoralis. In the lateral part of the muscle near its insertion, the pectoralis of the Pariah Kite contains both the *W* and *I* types (53% and 47% respectively) of fibers (Fig. IV.56). This regional difference is not seen in the pectoralis of the vulture. However, a regional difference in the deep part of the pectoralis of the kite and vulture was noted by George and Naik (1959b). The muscle consists

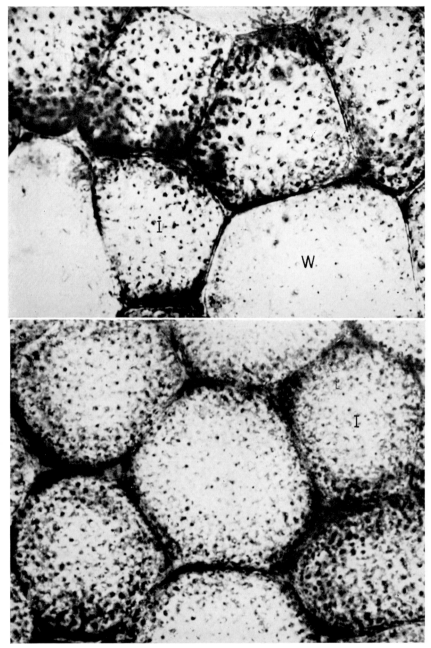

Fig. IV.56. (*Above*) Pariah Kite, *Milvus migrans* (Accipitridae). Lateral region, × 810. (By kind permission, Chandra-Bose and George, unpublished work.)

Fig. IV.57. (*Below*) Indian Whitebacked Vulture, *Gyps bengalensis* (Accipitridae). × 810. (By kind permission, Chandra-Bose and George, unpublished work.)

of a superficial and a deep part, the former being larger, with darker fibers having lesser diameter. On the other hand, in another member of the Order Falconiformes, the hawk, Shikra (*Accipiter badius*), and two members of the Strigiformes, the Great Horned Owl (*Bubo bubo*) and the Spotted Owlet (*Athene brama*), which are not mere soarers but are capable of some versatility in flight, variations are met with. In the Shikra all three types of fibers (*W,I,R*) are present (Fig. IV.58) but are circular in cross section. In the case of the owl and the owlet two types (*I* and *R*) of fibers exist (Figs. IV.59 and IV.60). The

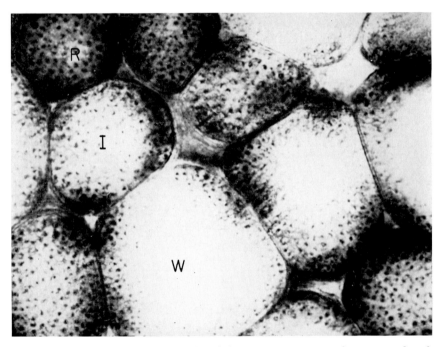

FIGS. IV.58–IV.62. Photomicrographs of the transverse section of M. pectoralis of various birds, showing mitochondrial localization of succinic dehydrogenase activity.

FIG. IV.58. Hawk (Shikra), *Accipter badius* (Accipitridae). × 810. (By kind permission, Chandra-Bose and George, unpublished work.)

relative distribution of the types of fibers in these three birds has been estimated to be: Shikra—*I:* 50.5%, *R:* 29.5%, *W:* 20.0%; Great Horned Owl—*I:* 64.3%, *R:* 35.7%; and Spotted Owlet—*I:* 85.4%, *R:* 14.6%, respectively (Chandra-Bose and George, 1965). The circular, loosely packed fibers may be considered characteristic of soarers and gliders.

Mention should be made here of certain birds, belonging to other orders, which indulge in soaring and gliding flight and also have the

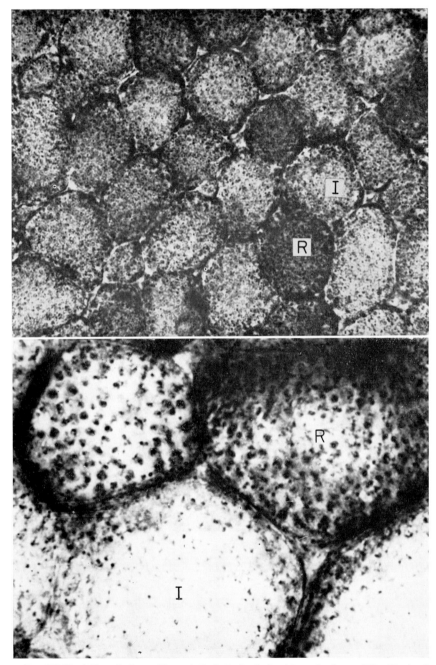

Fig. IV.59. (*Above*) Great Horned Owl, *Bubo bubo* (Strigidae). × 450. (By kind permission, Chandra-Bose and George, unpublished work.)

Fig. IV.60. (*Below*) Spotted Owlet, *Athene brama* (Strigidae). × 1140. (By kind permission, Chandra-Bose and George, unpublished work.)

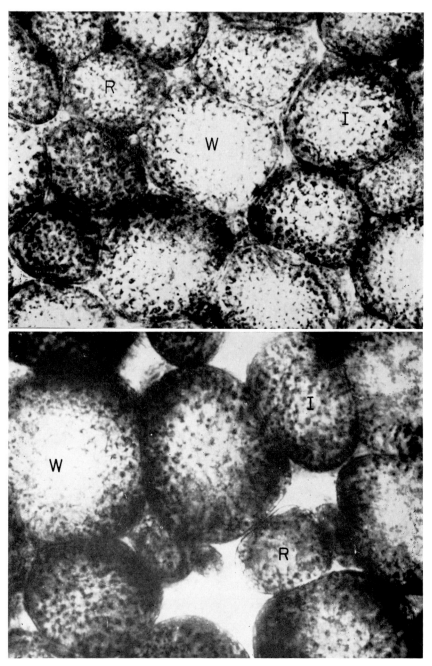

FIG. IV.61. (*Above*) Goldenbacked Woodpecker, *Dinopium benghalense* (Picidae). × 810. (By kind permission, Chandra-Bose and George, unpublished work.)

FIG. IV.62. (*Below*) Crow-Pheasant, *Centropus sinensis* (Cuculidae). × 810. (By kind permission, Chandra-Bose and George, unpublished work.)

characteristic circular fibers loosely packed in the pectoralis muscles (Figs. IV.61 and IV.62): Goldenbacked Woodpecker, *Dinopium benghalense* (Piciformes), and the Crow-Pheasant, *Centropus sinensis* (Cuculiformes). The relative distribution of the three types of fibers in these birds is, *I:* 72.2%, *R:* 27.8%; and *I:* 79.2%, *R:* 20.8%, respectively.

Group 5

This group includes pectoralis muscles having the *R* and *I* types of fibers. Recently Chandra-Bose and George (1964a) observed that two types of pectoralis muscles are found in passerine birds: one consisting of two types of fibers (broad and narrow), and the other of only the narrow type. The pectoralis muscles of the first type (consisting of *R* and *I* types of fibers) are placed in the present group, and those with narrow fibers only in Group 6. The pectoralis muscles of the following birds are in this group (Chandra-Bose and George, 1965; Figs. IV.63–IV.81):

Roseringed Parakeet, *Psittacula krameri* (Psittacidae)
House Swift, *Apus affinis* (Apodidae)
Whitebreasted Kingfisher, *Halcyon smyrnensis* (Alcedinidae)
Common Green Bee-eater, *Merops orientalis* (Meropidae)
Swallow, *Hirundo rustica* (Hirundinidae)
Striated Swallow, *Hirundo daurica* (Hirundinidae)
Whitebellied Drongo, *Dicrurus caerulescens* (Dicruridae)
Rosy Pastor, *Sturnus roseus* (Sturnidae)
Brahminy Myna, *Sturnus pagodarum* (Sturnidae)
Bank Myna, *Acridotheres giginianus* (Sturnidae)
Common Myna, *Acridotheres tristis* (Sturnidae)
House Crow, *Corvus splendens* (Corvidae)
Jungle Crow, *Corvus macrorhynchos* (Corvidae)
Blackheaded Cuckoo-Shrike, *Coracina melanoptera* (Campephagidae)
Small Minivet, *Pericrocotus cinnamomeus* (Campephagidae)
Common Iora, *Aegithina tiphia* (Irenidae)
Redvented Bulbul, *Pycnonotus cafer* (Pycnonotidae)
Jungle Babbler, *Turdoides striatus* (Muscicapidae)
Whitespotted Fantail Flycatcher, *Rhipidura albogularis* (Muscicapidae)
Pied Bush Chat, *Saxicola caprata* (Muscicapidae)
Indian Robin, *Saxicoloides fulicata* (Muscicapidae)
Yellowheaded Wagtail, *Motacilla citreola* (Motacillidae)

According to the data available from Salt (1963), the pectoralis muscle in the American Robin, *Turdus migratorius*, Brewer's Blackbird, *Euphafus cyanocephalus,* and Red-winged Blackbird, *Agelaius phoeniceus,* consists of two types of fibers when stained for fat.

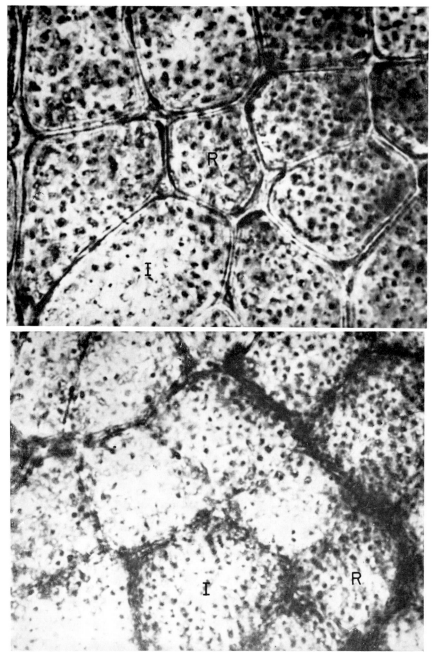

Figs. IV.63–IV.81. Photomicrographs of the transverse section of M. pectoralis of various birds, showing mitochondrial localization of succinic dehydrogenase activity.

Fig. IV.63. (*Above*) Roseringed Parakeet, *Psittacula krameri* (Psittacidae). × 1140. (By kind permission, Chandra-Bose and George, unpublished work.)

Fig. IV.64. (*Below*) House Swift, *Apus affinis* (Apodidae). × 1140. (By kind permission, Chandra-Bose and George, unpublished work.)

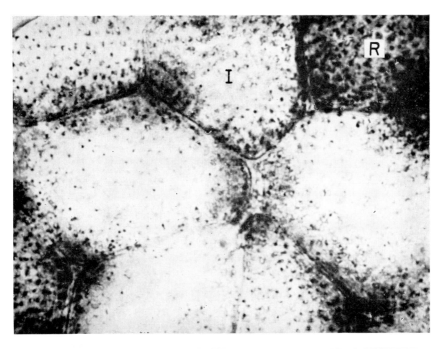

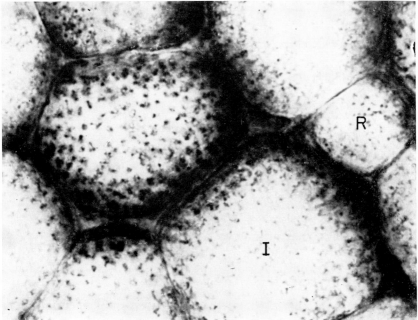

Fig. IV.65. (*Above*) Whitebreasted Kingfisher, *Halcyon smyrnensis* (Alcedinidae). × 1140. (By kind permission, Chandra-Bose and George, unpublished work.)

Fig. IV.66. (*Below*) Green Bee-eater, *Merops orientalis* (Meropidae). × 1140. (By kind permission, Chandra-Bose and George, unpublished work.)

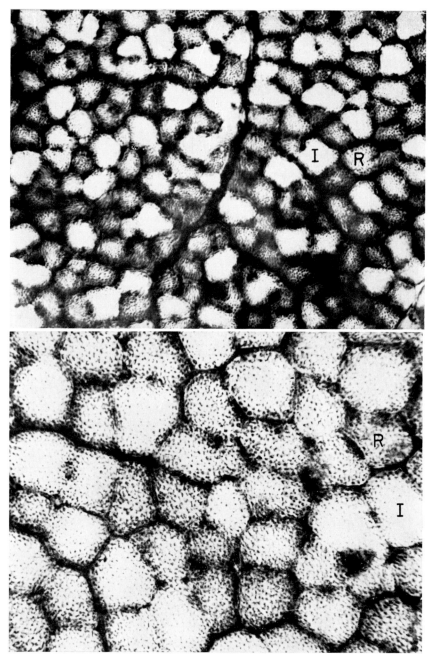

FIG. IV. 67. (*Above*) Striated Swallow, *Hirundo daurica* (Hirundinidae). × 290. (By kind permission, Chandra-Bose and George, 1964a.)

FIG. IV.68. (*Below*) Whitebellied Drongo, *Dicrurus caerulescens* (Dicruridae). × 450. (By kind permission, Chandra-Bose and George, unpublished work.)

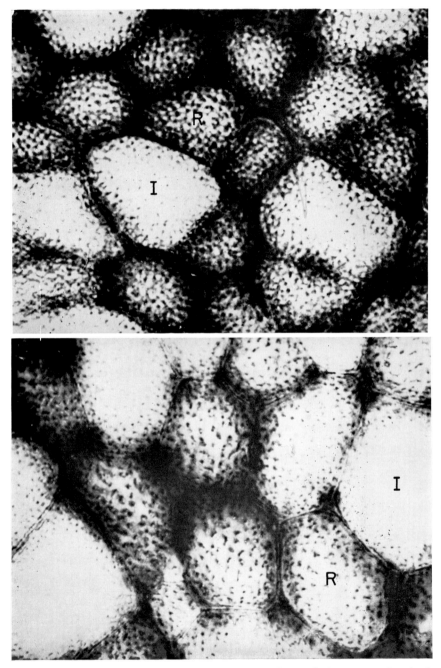

FIG. IV.69. (*Above*) Rosy Pastor, *Sturnus roseus* (Sturnidae). × 720. (By kind permission, Chandra-Bose and George, unpublished work.)

FIG. IV.70. (*Below*) Common Myna, *Acridotheres tristis* (Sturnidae). × 810. (By kind permission, Chandra-Bose and George, 1964a.)

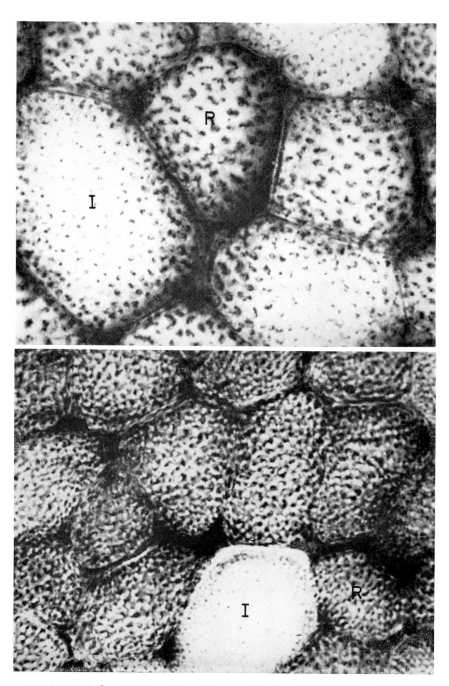

FIG. IV.71. (*Above*) House Crow, *Corvus splendens* (Corvidae). × 1140. (By kind permission, Chandra-Bose and George, 1964a.)

FIG. IV.72. (*Below*) Jungle Crow, *Corvus macrorhynchos* (Corvidae). × 810. (By kind permission, Chandra-Bose and George, unpublished work.)

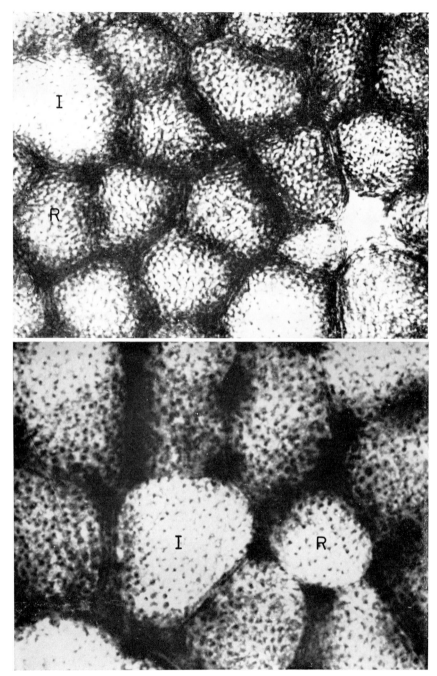

Fig. IV.73. (*Above*) Blackheaded Cuckoo-Shrike, *Coracina melanoptera* (Campephagidae). × 720. (By kind permission, Chandra-Bose and George, unpublished work.)

Fig. IV.74. (*Below*) Small Minivet, *Pericrocotus cinnamomeus* (Campephagidae). × 1140. (By kind permission, Chandra-Bose and George, unpublished work.)

93

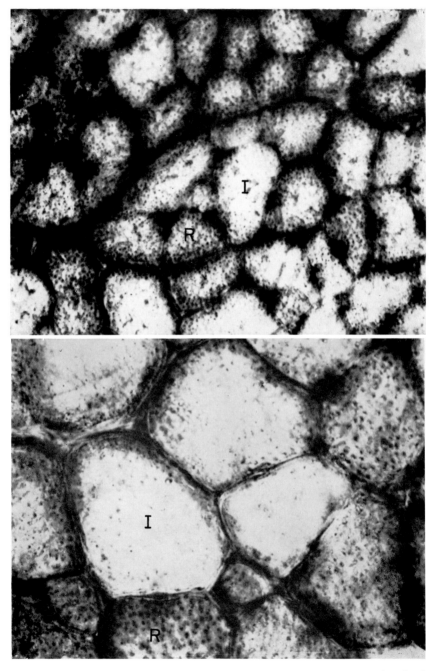

Fig. IV.75. (*Above*) Common Iora, *Aegithina tiphia* (Irenidae). × 450. (By kind permission, Chandra-Bose and George, unpublished work.)

Fig. IV.76. (*Below*) Redvented Bulbul, *Pycnonotus cafer* (Pycnonotidae). × 810. (By kind permission, Chandra-Bose and George, 1964a.)

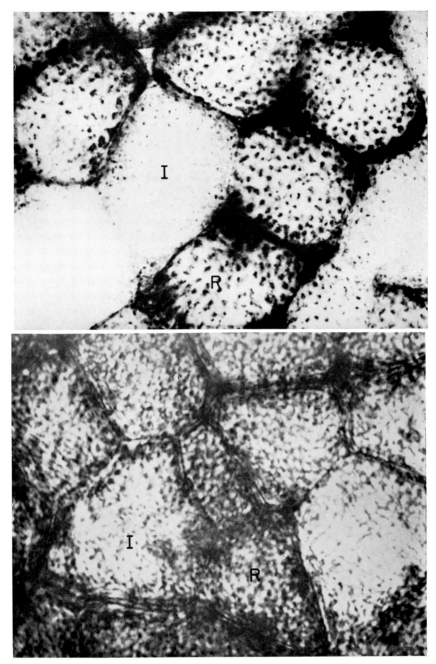

Fig. IV.77. (*Above*) Jungle Babbler, *Turdoides striatus* (Muscicapidae). × 810. (By kind permission, Chandra-Bose and George, 1964a.)

Fig. IV.78. (*Below*) Whitespotted Fantail Flycatcher, *Rhipidura albogularis* (Muscicapidae). × 1140. (By kind permission, Chandra-Bose and George, unpublished work.)

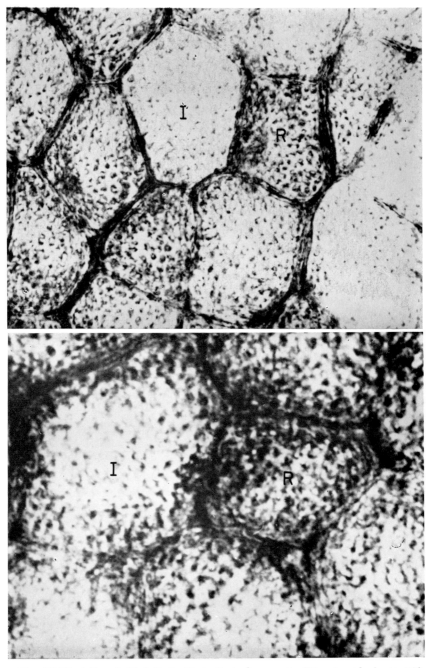

Fig. IV.79. (*Above*) Pied Bush Chat, *Saxicola caprata* (Muscicapidae). × 810. (By kind permission, Chandra-Bose and George, unpublished work.)

Fig. IV.80. (*Below*) Indian Robin, *Saxicoloides fulicata* (Muscicapidae). × 1140. (By kind permission, Chandra-Bose and George, 1964a.)

96

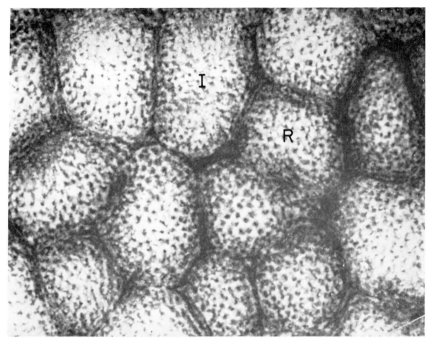

Fɪɢ. IV.81. Yellowheaded Wagtail, *Motacilla citreola* (Motacillidae). × 720. (By kind permission, Chandra-Bose and George, unpublished work.)

Group 6

As mentioned above, this group includes pectoralis muscles containing only the R type fibers. The pectoralis muscles of the following birds examined by Chandra-Bose and George (1964a, 1965) are included in this group (Figs. IV.82–IV.91):

Rubythroated Hummingbird, *Archilochus colubris* (Trochilidae)
Crimsonbreasted Barbet, *Megalaima haemacephala* (Capitonidae)
Yellowfronted Pied or Mahratta Woodpecker, *Dendrocopus mahrattensis* (Picidae)
Dusky Crag Martin, *Hirundo concolor* (Hirundinidae)
Black Drongo, *Dicrurus adsimilis* (Dicruridae)
Large Grey Babbler, *Turdoideus malcolmi* (Muscicapidae)
Tailor Bird, *Orthotomus sutorius* (Muscicapidae)
Purple Sunbird, *Nectarinia asiatica* (Nectariniidae)
White-eye, *Zosterops palpebrosa* (Zosteropidae)
House Sparrow, *Passer domesticus* (Ploceidae)
Whitethroated Munia, *Lonchura malabarica* (Ploceidae)

In the following birds examined by Salt (1963) the pectoralis is reported to consist of only one type of fiber when stained for fat:

Snow Bunting, *Plectorphenax nivalis*
Magnolia Warbler, *Dendroica magnolia*
House Sparrow, *Passer domesticus*
Bohemian Waxwing, *Bombycilla garrula*
Savannah Sparrow, *Passerculus sandwichensis*
Blackthroated Green Warbler, *Dendroica virens*
Swamp Sparrow, *Melospiza georgiana*
Mourning Warbler, *Oporornis philadelphia*
Connecticut Warbler, *Oporornis agilis*
White-winged Crossbill, *Loxia leucoptera*
Brown Creeper, *Certhia familiaris*
White-breasted Nuthatch, *Sitta carolinensis*

The pectoralis of the Rubythroated Hummingbird, *Archilochus colubris* (Trochilidae), also consists of only the *R* type of fibers, but it has the most copious blood supply (Figs. IV.19 and IV.20) hitherto known of any avian pectoralis muscle (Chandra-Bose and George, 1964b).

It is also interesting that whereas one species of woodpecker (Mahratta Woodpecker) falls in Group 6, another (Goldenbacked Woodpecker) is placed in Group 4. Similarly, whereas one species of babbler (Jungle Babbler) and a species of drongo (Whitebellied Drongo) are placed in Group 5, another babbler (Large Grey Babbler) and another drongo (Black Drongo) come under Group 6. This structural variation of the pectoralis is indicative of changes in relation to function even though phylogenetically two species might be very close. This should not appear surprising if it is realized that in the evolution of the bird the most dynamic changes have taken place in those parts of the body that form essential items of the flying equipment. Obviously the pectoral muscles must have been subjected to significant changes in structure in relation to the mode of flight. In no system of bird classification is the structure of the pectoral muscles considered as a factor of diagnostic value. It must, however, be conceded that the classifications of birds, in sharp contrast to those of the other classes of vertebrates, have been based on inadequate anatomical information. The problem has been made more complicated by the many functional adaptations for flight. And, whereas the various vertebrate orders that constitute a class are well defined and distinct, those of the Class Aves are reduced to the status of mere families of the other vertebrate classes.

FIGS. IV.82–IV.91. Photomicrographs of the transverse section of M. pectoralis of various birds, showing mitochondrial localization of succinic dehydrogenase activity.

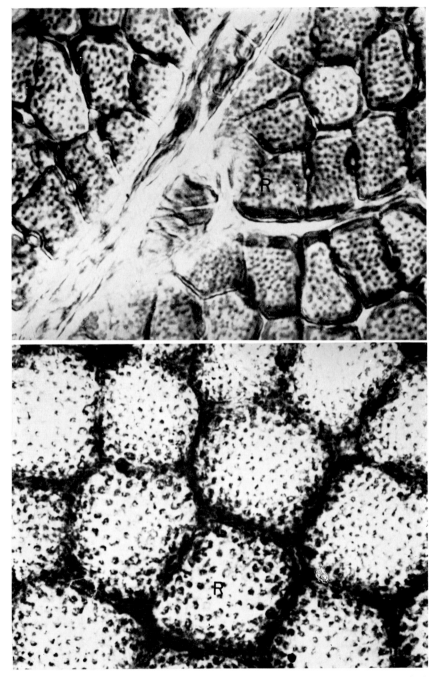

Fig. IV.82. (*Above*) Rubythroated Hummingbird, *Archilochus colubris* (Trochilidae), stained for fat. × 1140. (By kind permission, Chandra-Bose and George, 1964b.)

Fig. IV.83. (*Below*) Crimsonbreasted Barbet, *Megalaima haemacephala* (Capitonidae). × 810. (By kind permission, Chandra-Bose and George, unpublished work.)

99

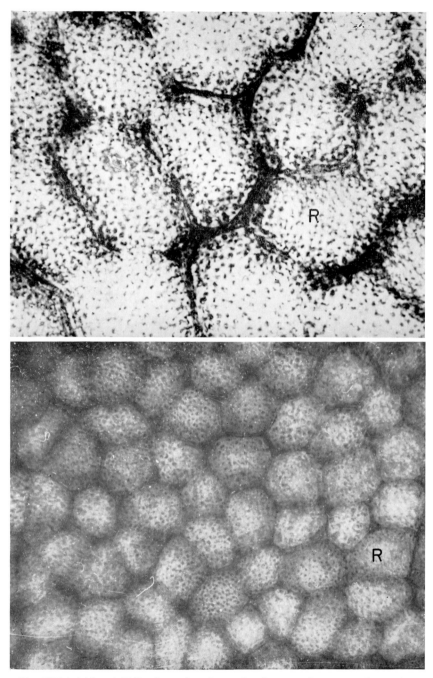

FIG. IV.84. (*Above*) Yellowfronted Pied Woodpecker, *Dendrocopus mahratta* (Picidae). × 720. (By kind permission, Chandra-Bose and George, unpublished work.)

FIG. IV.85. (*Below*) Dusky Crag Martin, *Hirundo concolor* (Hirundinidae). × 450. (By kind permission, Chandra-Bose and George, 1964a.)

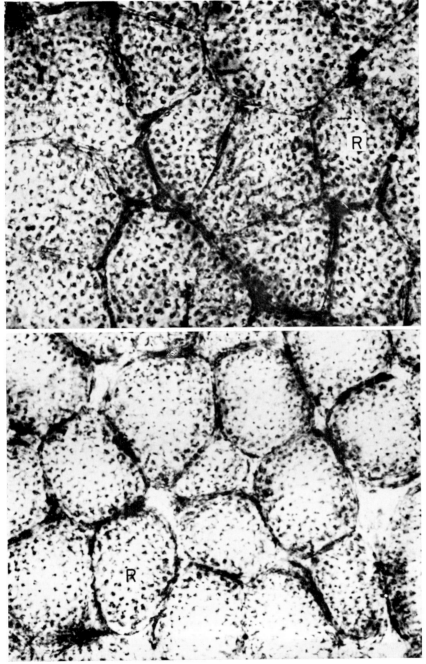

Fig. IV.86. (*Above*) Black Drongo, *Dicrurus adsimilis* (Dicruridae). × 810. (By kind permission, Chandra-Bose and George, 1964a.)

Fig. IV.87. (*Below*) Large Grey Babbler, *Turdoides malcolmi* (Muscicapidae). × 720. (By kind permission, Chandra-Bose and George, unpublished work.)

Fɪɢ. IV.88. (*Above*) Tailor Bird, *Orthotomus sutorius* (Muscicapidae). × 810. (By kind permission, Chandra-Bose and George, unpublished work.)

Fɪɢ. IV.89. (*Below*) Purple Sunbird, *Nectarinia asiatica* (Nectariniidae). × 1140. (By kind permission, Chandra-Bose and George, 1964a.)

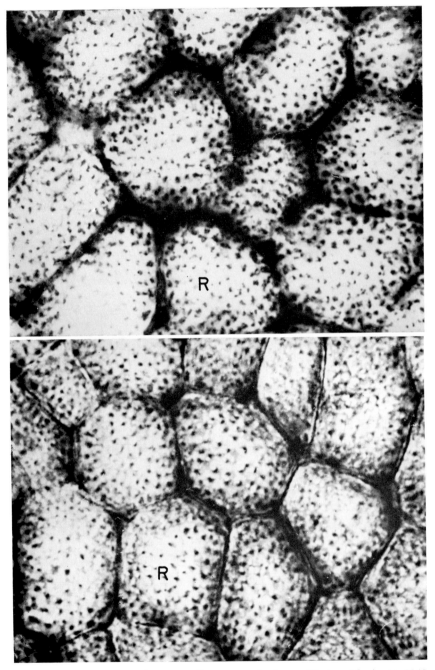

Fig. IV.90. (*Above*) White-Eye, *Zosterops palpebrosa* (Zosteropidae). × 1140. (By kind permission, Chandra-Bose and George, unpublished work.)

Fig. IV.91. (*Below*) House Sparrow, *Passer domesticus* (Ploceidae). × 1140. (By kind permission, Chandra-Bose and George, 1964a.)

Although the pectoralis muscles in Group 6 contain only the narrow R-type fibers, thus exhibiting an apparent homogeneity, there seems to exist a heterogeneity at the biochemical level. It has been shown by George *et al.* (1964) that in the pectoralis of the House Sparrow the fibers in the superficial part contain a considerably greater amount of glycogen and phosphorylase but less of fat and succinic dehydrogenase (Figs. IV.92–IV.95). These authors have suggested that the superficial region of the muscle is adapted for faster contractions and the deeper region for sustained activity. The faster contractions of the superficial region should be particularly effective in taking off and also for the powerful shooting action seen in the sparrow type of flight, which consists of a series of rapid wing beats followed by a shooting glide.

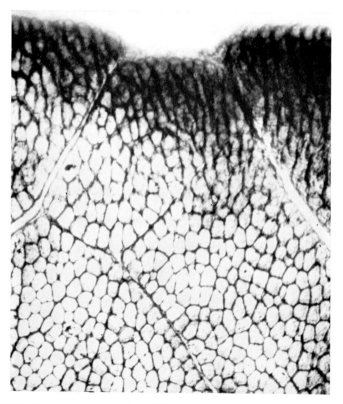

Fig. IV.92. Photomicrograph of a T.S. of M. pectoralis of the House Sparrow stained for glycogen by the PAS technique. Note the greater glycogen deposition in the superficial part of the muscle. × 150. (By kind permission, George *et al.*, 1964.)

The diameter of the fibers of the various birds hitherto studied by Chandra-Bose and George (1965) are presented in Table IV.2. As already mentioned, no information is available on the nature of the fibers in the pectoralis of ratites or the penguins. The pectoralis in ratites, as was perhaps true in *Archaeopteryx* too, might consist of the W, I, and R types of fibers and thus would be placed under Group 1 (George, 1965). Speculation on the structure of the pectoralis muscle in penguins is perhaps more difficult. As indicated by George (1965), there is no doubt that the muscle would have a relatively higher load of myoglobin and fat.

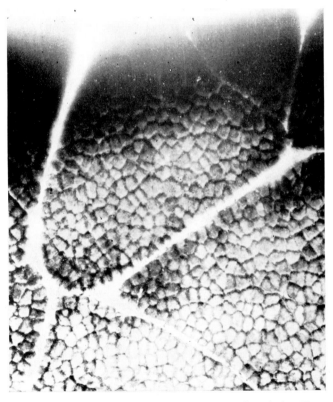

Fig. IV.93. Photomicrograph of a T.S. of M. pectoralis of the House Sparrow stained for phosphorylase. Note the dense staining reaction of the enzyme in the superficial part corresponding to the region deeply stained for glycogen. × 150. (By kind permission, George *et al.*, 1964.)

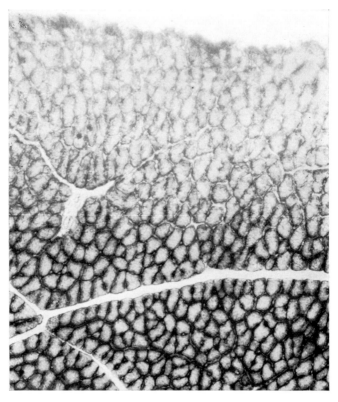

FIG. IV.94. Photomicrograph of a T.S. of M. pectoralis of the House Sparrow stained for fat. The deeper regions are more sudanophilic. × 150. (By kind permission, George *et al.*, 1964.)

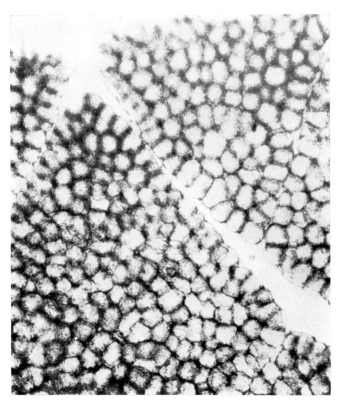

F⸱ɢ. IV.95. Photomicrograph of a T.S. of M. pectoralis of the House Sparrow stained for succinic dehydrogenase. The staining reaction for succinic dehydrogenase is similar to that for fat. × 150. (By kind permission, George *et al.*, 1964.)

TABLE IV.2

DIAMETER OF THE FIBERS IN MICRONS AND THE PROPORTIONS OF THE FIBER TYPES
IN PERCENTAGE IN THE PECTORALIS MUSCLES OF BIRDS.[a]

Name of birds	Fiber diameter (μ) and fiber distribution (%)		
Group 1:	*W*	*I*	*R*
Domestic Fowl (Phasianidae)	75.5 (67.3)[b]	75.0 (21.7)[b]	62.5 (11.0)[b]
Group 2:	*R*	*W*	*I*
Domestic Duck (Anatidae)	32.0 (60.0)	79.0 (23.1)	37.5 (16.9)
Group 3:	*R*	*W*	
Cattle Egret, *Bubulcus ibis* (Ardeidae)	37.5 (77.5)	55.0 (22.5)	
Blue Rock Pigeon, *Columba livia* (Columbidae)	30.0 (85.9)	70.0 (14.1)	
Purple Moorhen, *Porphyrio porphyrio* (Rallidae)	50.0 (80.6)	75.0 (19.4)	
Koel, *Eudynamys scolopacea* (Cuculidae)	40.0 (69.7)	75.0 (30.3)	
Hoopoe, *Upupa epops* (Upupidae)	40.0 (74.0)	70.0 (26.0)	
	R	*I*	
Whitebreasted Kingfisher, *Halcyon smyrnensis* (Alcedinidae)	32.5 (67.7)	57.5 (32.3)	
Green Bee-eater, *Merops orientalis* (Meropidae)	50.0 (52.1)	55.0 (47.9)	
Swallow, *Hirundo rustica* (Hirundinidae)	32.5 (74.0)	35.5 (26.0)	
Striated Swallow, *Hirundo daurica* (Hirundinidae)	32.5 (61.9)	40.0 (38.1)	
Whitebellied Drongo, *Dicrurus caerulescens* (Dicruridae)	42.5 (62.3)	45.0 (37.7)	
Rosy Pastor, *Sturnus roseus* (Sturnidae)	35.5 (69.3)	45.0 (30.7)	
Brahminy Myna, *Sturnus pagodarum* (Sturnidae)	42.5 (57.6)	50.0 (42.4)	
Common Myna, *Acridotheres tristis* (Sturnidae)	42.5 (66.2)	62.5 (33.8)	
Bank Myna, *Acridotheres ginginianus* (Sturnidae)	37.5 (66.7)	50.0 (33.3)	
House Crow, *Corvus splendens* (Corvidae)	37.5 (64.9)	45.0 (35.1)	
Jungle Crow, *Corvus macrorhynchos* (Corvidae)	52.5 (78.0)	65.0 (22.0)	
Blackheaded Cuckoo-Shrike, *Coracina melanoptera* (Campephagidae)	32.5 (68.4)	40.0 (31.6)	
Small Minivet, *Pericrocotus cinnamomeus* (Campephagidae)	40.0 (55.9)	49.0 (44.1)	
Common Iora, *Aegithinia tiphia* (Irenidae)	37.5 (59.6)	55.0 (40.4)	
Redvented Bulbul, *Pycnonotus cafer* (Pycnonotidae)	32.5 (61.2)	50.0 (38.8)	
Jungle Babbler, *Turdoides striatus* (Muscicapidae)	52.5 (54.8)	65.0 (45.2)	
Whitespotted Fantail Flycatcher, *Rhipidura albogularis* (Muscicapidae)	35.0 (60.5)	45.0 (39.5)	

TABLE IV.2 (*Continued*)

Name of bird	Fiber diameter (μ) and fiber distribution (%)		
Group 4:	*I*		
Pariah Kite, *Milvus migrans* (Accipitridae)			
Center	42.5 (100)		
	W	*I*	
Lateral	90.0 (53.2)	60.0 (46.8)	
	I		
Indian Whitebacked Vulture, *Gyps bengalensis* (Accipitridae)			
Center	60.0 (100)		
Lateral	62.0 (100)		
	I	*R*	*W*
Hawk (Shikra), *Accipiter badius* (Accipitridae)	50.0 (50.5)	35.0 (29.5)	70.0 (20.0)
Eagle-Owl, Great Horned Owl, *Bubo bubo* (Strigidae)	53.0 (64.3)	48.0 (35.7)	
Spotted Owlet, *Athene brama* (Strigidae)	58.2 (85.4)	42.0 (14.6)	
Goldenbacked Woodpecker, *Dinopium benghalense* (Picidae)	42.5 (72.2)	25.0 (27.8)	
Crow-Pheasant or Coucal, *Centropus sinensis* (Cuculidae)	46.2 (79.2)	28.0 (20.8)	
Group 5:	*R*	*I*	
Roseringed Parakeet, *Psittacula krameri* (Psittacidae)	32.0 (71.4)	40.0 (28.6)	
House Swift, *Apus affinis* (Apodidae)	37.5 (63.4)	38.0 (36.6)	
Pied Bush Chat, *Saxicola caprata* (Muscicapidae)	40.0 (61.4)	52.5 (38.6)	
Indian Robin, *Saxicoloides fulicata* (Muscicapidae)	32.5 (70.0)	52.5 (30.0)	
Yellowheaded Wagtail, *Motacilla citreola* (Motacillidae)	50.0 (57.3)	67.5 (42.7)	
Group 6:	*R*		
Rubythroated Hummingbird, *Archilochus colubris* (Trochilidae)	25.0 (100)		
Crimsonbreasted Barbet, Coppersmith *Megalaima haemacephala* (Capitonidae)	40.0 (100)		
Yellowfronted Pied Woodpecker, *Dendrocopus mahrattensis* (Picidae)	38.5 (100)		
Dusky Crag Martin, *Hirundo concolor* (Hirundinidae)	32.5 (100)		
Black Drongo or King-Crow, *Dicrurus adsimilis* (Dicruridae)	45.0 (100)		
Large Grey Babbler, *Turdoides malcolmi* (Muscicapidae)	45.0 (100)		

(*Continued*)

TABLE IV.2 (*Continued*)

Name of bird	Fiber diameter (μ) and fiber distribution (%)
Group 6 (*Continued*):	
Tailor Bird, *Orthotomus sutorius*	
(Muscicapidae)	44.0 (100)
Purple Sunbird, *Nectarinia asiatica*	
(Nectariniidae)	32.5 (100)
White-eye, *Zosterops palpebrosa*	
(Zosteropidae)	33.0 (100)
House Sparrow, *Passer domesticus*	
(Ploceidae)	35.0 (100)
Common Silverbill, Whitethroated Munia,	
Lonchura malabarica (Ploceidae)	45.0 (100)

[a] Data from Chandra-Bose and George (1965).
[b] Figures in parentheses denote the respective percentage of the fiber types.

REFERENCES

Beckett, E. B., and Bourne, G. H. (1960). Histochemistry of skeletal muscle and changes in some muscle diseases. *In* "Structure and Function of Muscle" (G. H. Bourne, ed.), Vol. III, pp. 275–320. Academic Press, New York.

Bennett, H. S. (1960). The structure of striated muscle as seen by the electron microscope. *In* "The Structure and Function of Muscle" (G. H. Bourne, ed.), Vol. 1, pp. 137–181. Academic Press, New York.

Bennett, H. S., and Porter, K. R. (1953). An electron microscope study of sectioned breast muscle of the domestic fowl. *Am. J. Anat.* 93: 61–105.

Blanchaer, M. C., and Van Wijhe, M. (1962). Distribution of lactic dehydrogenase in skeletal muscle. *Nature* 193: 877–878.

Bokdawala, F. D., and George, J. C. (1964). Histochemical demonstration of muscle lipase. *J. Histochem. Cytochem.* 12: 768–771.

Bokdawala, F. D., and George, J. C. (1965). Acid and neutral ATPases in skeletal muscle. *J. Animal Morphol. Physiol.* 12: (in press).

Bösiger, E. (1950). Vergleichende Untersuchungen über die Brustmuskulatur von Huhn, Wachtel und Star. *Acta Anat.* 10: 385–429.

Bösiger-Ensner, B. (1961). Comparison de la répartition et du calibre des fibres lentes et rapides du muscle pectoral chez *Coturnix coturnix coturnix* L et la sous-espèce semidomestiquée *Coturnix coturnix coturnix japonica. Compt. Rend.* 253: 2606–2608.

Boyd, J. D. (1960). Development of striated muscle. *In* "Structure and Function of Muscle" (G. H. Bourne, ed.), Vol. 1, pp. 63–85. Academic Press, New York.

Bullard, H. H. (1912). On the interstitial granules and fat droplets of striated muscle. *Am. J. Anat.* 14: 1–46.

Chandra-Bose, D. A., and George, J. C. (1964a). Studies on the structure and physiology of the flight muscles of birds. 11. Cellular organization and distribution of fat and succinic dehydrogenase in the pectoralis of some passerines. *J. Animal Morphol. Physiol.* 11 (C. J. George Felicitation Number): 90–96.

Chandra-Bose, D. A., and George, J. C. (1964b). Studies on the structure and physiology of the flight muscles of birds. 12. Observations on the structure of the pectoralis and supracoracoideus of the Rubythroated Hummingbird. *Pavo* **2**: 111–114.

Chandra-Bose, D. A., and George, J. C. (1965). Studies on the structure and physiology of the flight muscles of birds. 13. Characterization of the avian pectoralis. *Pavo*, **3**: 14–22.

Chandra-Bose, D. A., Chinoy, N. J., and George, J. C. (1964). Studies on the structure and physiology of the flight muscles of birds. 10. Certain biochemical differences in the cellular organization of the fowl pectoralis. *Pavo* **2**: 61–64.

Chappell, J. B., and Perry, S. V. (1953). The respiratory and adenosinetriphosphatase activities of skeletal muscle mitochondria. *Biochem. J.* **55**: 586–595.

Chinoy, N. J. (1963). Histochemical localization of myoglobin in the pigeon breast muscle. *J. Animal Morphol. Physiol.* **10**: 74–77.

Chinoy, N. J., and George, J. C. (1965a). Cholinesterases in the pectoral muscle of some vertebrates. *J. Physiol. (London)* **177**: 346–354.

Chinoy, N. J., and George, J. C. (1965b). Embryonic and postembryonic development of the pigeon pectoralis muscle. *J. Animal Morphol. Physiol.* **12**: 57–68.

Cori, C. F. (1956). Regulation of enzyme activity in muscle during work. *In* "Enzymes: Units of Biological Structure and Function" (O. H. Gaebler, ed.), p. 573. Academic Press, New York.

Dubowitz, V., and Pearse, A. G. E. (1960). A comparative histochemical study of oxidative enzyme and phosphorylase activity in skeletal muscle. *Histochemie* **2**: 105–117.

Fisher, H. I. (1958). The "Hatching Muscle" in the chick. *Auk* **75**: 391–399.

Friedman, D. L., and Larner, J. (1963). Studies on UDPG-α-glucan transglucosylase. III. Interconversion of two forms of muscle UDPG-α-glucan transglucosylase by a phosphorylation-dephosphorylation reaction sequence. *Biochemistry* **2**: 669–675.

George, J. C. (1964). Muscle lipase. *J. Animal Morphol. Physiol.* **11** (C. J. George Felicitation Number): 233–243.

George, J. C. (1965). Evolution of the bird and bat pectoral muscles. *Pavo* **3**: (in press).

George, J. C., and Ambadkar, P. M. (1963). Histochemical demonstration of lipids and lipase activity in rat testis. *J. Histochem. Cytochem.* **11**: 420–425.

George, J. C., and Chinoy, N. J. (1964). Cytochemical evidence for nuclear origin of lipids in cultured muscle cells—A basis for a concept of genetic control in lipid synthesis. *J. Animal Morphol. Physiol.* **11** (C. J. George Felicitation Number): 105–118.

George, J. C., and Iype, P. T. (1960). Improved histochemical demonstration of lipase activity. *Stain Technol.* **35**: 151–152.

George, J. C., and Iype, P. T. (1963). The mechanism of hatching in the chick. *Pavo* **1**: 52–56.

George, J. C., and Jyoti, D. (1955). Histological features of the breast and leg muscles of bird and bat and their physiological and evolutionary significance. *J. Animal Morphol. Physiol.* **2**: 31–36.

George, J. C., and Naik, R. M. (1957). Studies on the structure and physiology of the flight muscles of birds. 1. The variations in the structure of the pectoralis major muscle of a few representative types and their significance in the respective modes of flight. *J. Animal Morphol. Physiol.* **4**: 23–32.

George, J. C., and Naik, R. M. (1958a). The relative distribution and chemical nature of the fuel store of the two types of fibres in the pectoralis major muscle of the pigeon. *Nature* **181**: 709–710.

George, J. C., and Naik, R. M. (1958b). The relative distribution of the mitochondria in the two types of fibres in the pectoralis major muscle of the pigeon. *Nature* 181: 782–783.

George, J. C., and Naik, R. M. (1959a). Studies on the structure and physiology of the flight muscles of birds. 4. Observations on the fiber architecture of the pectoralis major muscle of the pigeon. *Biol. Bull.* 116: 239–247.

George, J. C., and Naik, R. M. (1959b). Studies on the structure and physiology of the flight muscles of birds. 5. Some histological and cytochemical observations on the structure of the pectoralis. *J. Animal Morphol. Physiol.* 6: 16–23.

George, J. C., and Naik, R. M. (1959c). Studies on the structure and physiology of the flight muscles of birds. 6. Variation in the diameter of the fibres of the pectoralis major and its relation to the muscle size and mode of flight. *J. Animal Morphol. Physiol.* 6: 90–94.

George, J. C., and Naik, R. M. (1960). Some observations on the distribution of blood capillaries in the pigeon breast muscle. *Auk* 77: 224–225.

George, J. C., and Pishawikar, S. D. (1959). Studies on the structure and physiology of the flight muscles of birds. 8. Adenosinetriphosphatase activity and sulfhydryl groups in the pigeon breast muscle. *J. Animal Morphol. Physiol.* 6: 103–105.

George, J. C., and Susheela, A. K. (1961). A histophysiological study of the rat diaphragm. *Biol. Bull.* 121: 471–480.

George, J. C., and Talesara, C. L. (1961a). Histochemical observations on the succinic dehydrogenase and cytochrome oxidase activity in pigeon breast muscle. *Quart. J. Microscop. Sci.* 102: 131–141.

George, J. C., and Talesara, C. L. (1961b). A quantitative study of the distribution pattern of certain oxidizing enzymes and a lipase in the red and white fibers of the pigeon breast muscle. *J. Cellular Comp. Physiol.* 58: 253–260.

George, J. C., and Talesara, C. L. (1962a). Histochemical demonstration of certain DPN-linked dehydrogenases and of aldolase in the red and white fibers of pigeon breast muscle. *Quart. J. Microscop. Sci.* 103: 41–46.

George, J. C., and Talesara, C. L. (1962b). Histochemical demonstration of certain oxidizing enzymes in the pectoralis major muscle of the Rosy Pastor (*Pastor roseus*), Goose (*Anser albifrons*) and Fowl (*Gallus domesticus*). *J. Animal Morphol. Physiol.* 9: 59–62.

George, J. C., Susheela, A. K., and Vallyathan, N. V. (1963). Cytoplasmic (non-mitochondrial) lactic and succinic dehydrogenases in the red and white muscle fibres. *J. Animal Morphol. Physiol.* 10: 24–30.

George, J. C., Susheela, A. K., and Vallyathan, N. V. (1964). Histochemical evidence for biochemical differentiation and regional specialization in the breast muscle of the House Sparrow. *Pavo* 2: 115–119.

Gregg, C. T., Heisler, C. R., and Remmert, L. F. (1959). Pyruvate and α-glycerophosphate oxidation in insect tissue. *Biochim. Biophys. Acta* 31: 593–595.

Harman, J. W. (1955). Relation of mitochondria to enzymic processes in muscle. *Am. J. Phys. Med.* 34: 68–88.

Harman, J. W. (1956). The cytochondria of cardiac and skeletal muscle. *Intern. Rev. Cytol.* 5: 89–146.

Hess, R., and Pearse, A. G. E. (1961). Dissociation of uridine diphosphate glucose-glycogen transglucosylase from phosphorylase activity in individual muscle fibers. *Proc. Soc. Exptl. Biol. Med.* 107: 569–571.

Hess, R., Scarpelli, D. G., and Pearse, A. G. E. (1958). Cytochemical localization of oxidative enzymes. II. Pyridine nucleotide-linked dehydrogenases. *J. Biophys. Biochem. Cytol.* **4:** 753–760.

Howatson, A. F. (1956). The structure of pigeon breast muscle mitochondria. *J. Biophys. Biochem. Cytol.* Suppl. **2:** 363–368.

Howatson, A. F., and Ham, A. W. (1957). The fine structure of cells. *Can. J. Biochem. Physiol.* **35:** 549–564.

Huxley, H. E., and Hanson, J. (1960). The molecular basis of contraction in cross-striated muscles. *In* "The Structure and Function of Muscle" (G. H. Bourne, ed.), Vol. 1, pp. 183–227. Academic Press, New York.

Klinar, B., and Župančič, A. O. (1962). Cholinesterases in white and red mammalian skeletal muscle. *Arch. Intern. Pharmacodyn.* **136:** 47–53.

Kölliker, A. (1857). Einige Bemerkungen über die Endigungen der Hautnerven und den Bau der Muskeln. *Z. Wiss. Zool.* **8:** 311–325.

Kölliker, A. (1888). Zur Kenntnis der quergestreiften Muskelfasern. *Z. Wiss. Zool.* **47:** 689–710.

Lasiewski, R. C., Galey, F. R., and Vasquez, C. (1965). Morphology and physiology of the pectoral muscles of hummingbirds. *Nature* **206:** 404–405.

Leloir, L. F., Olavarria, J. M., Goldemberg, S. H., and Carminatti, H. (1959). Biosynthesis of glycogen from uridine diphosphate glucose. *Arch. Biochem. Biophys.* **81:** 508–520.

Naik, R. M. (1961). Pigeon breast muscle as an ideal test material for histochemical demonstration of glycogen. *Stain Technol.* **36:** 247–248.

Nene, R. V., and George, J. C. (1965a). Histochemical localization and distribution of uridine diphosphate glucose-glycogen transglucosylase in pigeon pectoralis muscle. *J. Animal Morphol. Physiol.* **12:** 85–89.

Nene, R. V., and George, J. C. (1965b). A histophysiological study of some muscles of the avian pectoral appendage. *Pavo* **3:** 35–46.

Nene, R. V., and George, J. C. (1965c). Histochemical demonstration of glucose-6-phosphate dehydrogenase in muscle. *J. Animal Morphol. Physiol.* **12:** 90–99.

Ogata, T., and Mori, H. (1964). Histochemical study of oxidative enzymes in vertebrate muscles. *J. Histochem. Cytochem.* **12:** 171–182.

Padykula, H. A., and Gauthier, G. F. (1963). Cytochemical studies of adenosinetriphosphatases in skeletal muscle fibers. *J. Cell Biol.* **11:** 87–107.

Paul, M. H., and Sperling, E. (1952). Cyclophorase system, XXIII. Correlation of cyclophorase activity and mitochondrial density in striated muscles. *Proc. Soc. Exptl. Biol. Med.* **79:** 352–354.

Pearse, A. G. E. (1960). "Histochemistry, Theoretical and Applied." Churchill, London.

Sacktor, B., and Cochran, D. G. (1958). The respiratory metabolism of insect flight muscle. I. Manometric studies of oxidation and concomitant phosphorylation with sarcosomes. *Arch. Biochem. Biophys.* **74:** 266–276.

Salt, W. R. (1963). The composition of the pectoralis muscles of some passerine birds. *Can. J. Zool.* **41:** 1185–1190.

Sasaki, M., and Takeuchi, T. (1963). Histochemical and electron microscopic observations of glycogen synthesized from glucose-1-phosphate by phosphorylase and branching enzyme in human muscle. *J. Histochem. Cytochem.* **11:** 342–348.

Stein, J. M., and Padykula, H. A. (1962). Histochemical classification of individual skeletal muscle fibers of the rat. *Am. J. Anat.* **110:** 103–124.

Takeuchi, T., and Glenner, G. G. (1960). Histochemical demonstration of a pathway for polysaccharide synthesis from uridine-diphosphoglucose. *J. Histochem. Cytochem.* **8:** 227–230.

Vallyathan, N. V., Cherian, K. M., and George, J. C. (1964). Histochemical and quantitative changes in glycogen and phosphorylase during disuse atrophy of the pigeon pectoralis. *J. Histochem. Cytochem.* **12:** 721–728.

Vallyathan, N. V., and George, J. C. (1965). Histochemical demonstration of acid and alkaline phosphatase activity in the red and white fibres of the pigeon pectoralis. *J. Animal Morphol. Physiol.* **12:** 100–103.

Weinreb, S., and Harman, J. W. (1955). Phase and electron microscope studies of the interrelationship of cytochondria and myofibrils in pigeon breast muscle. *J. Exptl. Med.* **101:** 529–538.

Weis-Fogh, T. (1964). Diffusion in insect wing muscle, the most active tissue known. *J. Exptl. Biol.* **41:** 229–256.

Zebe, E. C., and McShan, W. H. (1957). Lactic and α-glycerophosphate dehydrogenases in insects. *J. Gen. Physiol.* **40:** 779–790.

CHAPTER V

The Pectoralis: Biochemical Aspects

I. Myoglobin

In Chapter IV certain histological and histochemical differences between red and white muscles have been considered. It was shown histochemically that the pale fibers of the fowl pectoralis and the red fibers of that of the pigeon contain myoglobin. Earlier studies on the red and white muscles have been reviewed by Needham (1926). The concentration of myoglobin in a muscle is generally regarded as an index of the capacity of the muscle for aerobic metabolism and sustained activity. Lawrie (1950) found that in the fowl there is about 10 times as much myoglobin in the leg muscle (gastrocnemius) as in its pectoralis, while in the pigeon the pectoralis contains about 4 times as much as in the muscle of the leg. It was also observed that the myoglobin content of pigeon pectoralis (0.25%) is about 40 times as great as that of the fowl pectoralis (0.006%).

In the transport of oxygen by hemoglobin or myoglobin and in the transport of electrons to oxygen by the cytochrome system, the porphyrin ring, with its iron moiety, is the key structure. Nair (1952) estimated the iron content in the pectoralis and supracoracoideus muscles of some Indian birds and observed that the latter muscle contained considerably less iron than the former except in the domestic fowl, in which the figures were nearly the same (Table V.1). Highest figures were obtained for the muscles of the sparrow and the least for the domestic fowl and the domestic duck. The kite and the pigeon muscles were close seconds. The high content of iron in the pectoralis muscles of the sparrow and the kite is caused by the fact that these muscles contain only red fibers, the former of the R and the latter of the I varieties, respectively, as explained in Chapter IV. The reason why the figures obtained for the pigeon pectoralis were less than those of the sparrow is because this muscle, as already mentioned, is a mixed one containing the white myoglobin-lacking fibers also. In this context the recent observations of Talesara (1961) on the pigeon pectoralis are of interest. The iron content

115

was found to vary at different depths of the muscle in accordance with the relative distribution of the red and white fibers. The distribution pattern of the two types of fibers has been dealt with in the previous chapter. The iron content was found to be the maximum in the middle of the dorsoventral axis of the muscle where the number of white fibers is least (Fig. V.1). By extending the regression line at either end (Fig. V.1), the author calculated the iron content in the red and white fibers respectively (red fibers: 44.57, and white fibers: 4.97, as mg per 100 gm dry muscle).

TABLE V.1

IRON CONTENT IN THE CHIEF FLIGHT MUSCLES OF SOME BIRDS[a]

| | Iron Content (mg per 100 gm wet tissue) | |
Bird	Pectoralis	Supracoracoideus
Pigeon (*Columba livia*)	8.7	2.5
Parakeet (*Psittacula krameri*)	7.8	2.5
Crow (*Corvus splendens*)	6.4	2.5
Sparrow (*Passer domesticus*)	10.0	5.0
Kite (*Milvus migrans*)	9.0	5.0
Domestic fowl (*Gallus domesticus*)	2.3	2.0
Domestic duck (*Anas platyrhynchos*)	3.3	2.5

[a] Data from Nair, 1952.

It is known that at the venous pressure of oxygen, oxymyoglobin is less dissociated than oxyhemoglobin. This greater affinity of myoglobin for oxygen is of special significance in the physiology of the avian muscle because it facilitates oxygen transfer from oxyhemoglobin to the sites of oxidation in the muscle cell. Lawrie (1952) correlated myoglobin content of the pectoral muscle with the cytochrome oxidase activity of the same muscle preparations. He recorded myoglobin content of 0.69% and 0.22% wet weight and cytochrome c oxidase activity of 1800 and 2300 μl O_2 per mg fat-free dry weight per hour, respectively, in the pectoral muscle of the Manx Shearwater and of the pigeon. The low myoglobin content in the pigeon breast muscle despite the high enzyme activity was attributed to the greater blood flow into this muscle owing to the more rapid wing beats, thus making a higher oxygen store in the muscle unnecessary. On the other hand, in the case of the Manx Shearwater, its wing movements are slow and consequently less blood flows into its muscle. It should be pointed out here that the low myoglobin content of the pigeon breast muscle is due to the presence of the white

fibers in it. We do not know whether the pectoralis of the Manx Shearwater is also a mixed muscle. The Manx Shearwater is an Oceanic bird
which indulges in a considerable amount of fish-hunting activity for its
food. Obviously the higher myoglobin content in its muscle is to provide
a higher oxygen store for such activity. The lower enzyme level in its
muscle supports this suggestion.

The psoas muscle of the Blue Whale, a diving mammal, has a high
myoglobin content of 0.84% but a low cytochrome c oxidase activity of
600 μl O_2 (Lawrie, 1952). The high myoglobin content is obviously for
increased oxygen storage and the low enzyme level for a low rate of

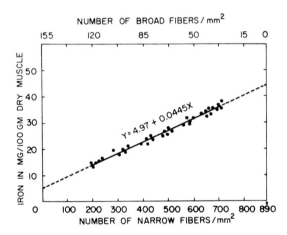

Fig. V.1. Graph showing the relation between the number of red (narrow) and
white (broad) fibers per square millimeter and the iron content as obtained at different depths of M. pectoralis of pigeon. (By kind permission, Talesara, 1961.)

oxygen utilization as an adaptation for diving. Biochemical studies in
relation to the cellular organization of the pectoralis muscle in different
species of birds exhibiting different modes of muscular activity should
throw more light on the metabolism of the muscle.

While considerable advance in our knowledge of the chemical and
physical properties of mammalian myoglobins, as well as the molecular
structure of myoglobin, has been made in recent years, comparatively
little is known of avian myoglobins. Recently myoglobins prepared from
different species of vertebrates, including a cormorant and pelican, were
studied by Brown *et al.* (1962). They found that the fish myoglobins
contain free sulfhydryl groups but not the avian and mammalian myoglobins.

II. Fuel

In the performance of muscular work and the maintenance of muscle tone energy is expended. This energy is generated from a chain of chemical reactions supported by a continuous supply of fuel. Carbohydrates and fats constitute the fuel reserves in all muscles, but properties of these two fuels differ in different muscles depending on the nature of their activity. In the previous chapter histochemical evidence was presented to demonstrate that the chief fuel store in the white fibers of the pigeon pectoralis is glycogen whereas in the red ones it is fat. In this chapter quantitative data are given, on the relative distribution of fat and glycogen in the red and white fibers of the pigeon pectoralis, as well as on the fat content of the pectoralis muscles in several species of birds.

George and Naik (1959) estimated separately the glycogen content of methanol-preserved red and white fibers of the pigeon pectoralis isolated by teasing them out manually with watchmaker's forceps under a binocular dissection miscroscope. The values obtained by them for the glycogen content of the red and the white fibers, calculated on dry weight of the methanol preserved muscle, are, respectively, $2.464 \pm 0.311\%$ and $10.240 \pm 0.093\%$. They estimated glycogen and fat in the different depths of the broad fibers in the muscle, as described in the previous chapter. The region marked A (Fig. IV.14, Chapter IV) was used for the estimations, and the region B, in the same figure, for the count of broad fibers. The results obtained are given in Table V.2. It is

TABLE V.2

THE NUMBER OF WHITE FIBERS PER SQUARE MILLIMETER AND THE PERCENTAGE OF FAT AND GLYCOGEN AT DIFFERENT DEPTHS OF THE PECTORALIS MUSCLE OF THE PIGEON[a]

Depth of the muscle in mm (starting from the ventral face)	Number of white fibers per square mm $\pm$ S.D.	Percentage per dry weight of the muscle $\pm$ S.D.	
		Glycogen	Fat
0—2	90 ± 14	3.655 ± 0.275	10.289 ± 1.942
2—4	63 ± 8	3.175 ± 0.054	12.095 ± 1.056
4—6	48 ± 3	3.102 ± 0.127	14.632 ± 1.752
6—8	51 ± 4	3.409 ± 0.184	13.250 ± 0.571
8—10	72 ± 9	3.588 ± 0.236	11.743 ± 0.572

[a] Data from George and Naik, 1959.

seen that the glycogen content is highest in the most superficial and deepest regions of the muscle where there are more white fibers, whereas the fat content is highest in the middle of the dorsoventral axis of the muscle where the number of the red fibers is the highest.

Although white muscles contain more glycogen, red muscles contain more fat. For sustained activity fat is a better fuel because it yields double the energy and metabolic water obtained from glycogen. It should, therefore, be of considerable interest to have data on the fat content of the locomotor muscles in various birds. George and Naik (1960) recorded the fat content in the pectoralis of a few Indian birds. More extensive data on the fat content of the pectoralis and thigh muscles of a large number of birds belonging to different families were made available by Hartman and Brownell (1961). The data from both these publications have been compiled and presented in Table V.3. The fat content of the pectoralis in two birds (Cattle Egret and Barn Owl) differed markedly in the figures published by the above authors. The figures obtained for the Indian specimens were less than those obtained for the New World specimens. This suggests that the muscles of birds living in cooler regions tend to have a higher fat content. This is in line with Bergmann's rule that warm-blooded animals inhabiting regions of cooler climates and higher altitudes are likely to have larger bodies which conserve heat better than small bodies. The property of fat as an insulator against heat dissipation is well known.

In migratory birds the glycogen and fat content of the pectoralis muscle are almost doubled at the time of migration (Vallyathan, 1963; Vallyathan and George, 1964). The problem of fuel and energy during migration will be dealt with in detail in Chapter VIII.

There is no definite evidence that protein is a fuel for muscular contraction under normal conditions. In the bird muscle, where there are considerable amounts of glycogen and fat, it is most unlikely that protein would be used as fuel except under starvation and complete depletion of the other fuels. With regard to the protein content of the red and white fibers of the pigeon pectoralis muscle, it has been estimated (Pishawikar, 1961) that the white fibers have a higher content of total proteins but less of water soluble proteins than the red fibers (total proteins —white fibers, 89.80 and red fibers, 72.37 gm per 100 gm dry muscle; water soluble proteins—white fibers, 19.56 and red fibers, 37.10 gm per 100 gm dry muscle). This author has suggested that the higher total protein content in the white fibers is due to structural proteins, such as actin and myosin, and the higher water soluble protein content in the red fibers is due to their higher enzyme concentrations.

Tinamidae
   Crypturellus soui (Little Tinamou): pectoralis, 4.27, 4.56; thigh, 1.25
Podicipedidae
   Podiceps dominicus (Least Grebe): pectoralis, 5.12
Phalacrocoracidae
   Phalacrocorax olivaceus (Olivaceous Cormorant): pectoralis, 5.30, 6.72; thigh, 4.08, 4.87
Anhingidae
   Anhinga anhinga (Anhinga): pectoralis, 3.53
Ardeidae
   Casmerodius albus (Common Egret): pectoralis, 3.78; thigh, 2.52
   Leucophoyx thula (Snowy Egret): pectoralis, 4.21; thigh, 3.21
   Bubulcus ibis (Cattle Egret): pectoralis, 4.99, 6.17, 7.33; thigh, 4.88; pectoralis, 3.90,
      4.13[b]
   Tigrisoma lineatum (Banded Tiger-heron): pectoralis, 3.05
   Ixobrychus exilis (Least Bittern): pectoralis, 2.91; thigh, 2.92
Cochleariidae
   Cochlearius cochlearius (Boat-billed Heron): pectoralis, 5.28
Anatidae
   Anas discors (Blue-winged Teal): pectoralis, 4.78
   Aythya affinis (Lesser Scaup): pectoralis, 3.15, 4.45; thigh, 2.22, 3.12
Accipitridae
   Milvus migrans (Pariah Kite): pectoralis, 4.80[c]
   Chondrohierax uncinatus (Hook-billed Kite): pectoralis, 1.04, 2.39, 2.73; thigh, 1.10
   Buteo platypterus (Broad-winged Hawk): pectoralis, 3.22; thigh, 2.98
Falconidae
   Micrastur ruficollis (Barred Forest Falcon): pectoralis, 2.83; thigh, 2.21
Cracidae
   Ortalis garrula (Chestnut-winged Chachalaca): pectoralis, 1.94, 2.00, 2.04; thigh, 2.25
Phasianidae
   Gallus domesticus (Fowl): pectoralis, 0.98[c]
   Odontophorus guttatus (Spotted Wood Quail): pectoralis, 1.96, 3.87
   Coturnix coturnix (Japanese Quail): pectoralis, (11) 3.23 ± 0.19 (S.E.); thigh, (10)
      2.30 ± 0.15
Rallidae
   Aramides cajanea (Gray-necked Wood Rail): pectoralis, 2.52, 2.70, 4.62; thigh, 2.23,
      2.34, 3.68
   Laterallus albigularis (White-throated Crake): pectoralis, 2.68, 2.76, 2.94, 3.53; thigh,
      2.82, 3.16, 4.25
Heliornithidae
   Heliornis fulica (Sungrebe): pectoralis, 2.83
Jacanidae
   Jacana spinosa (American Jacana): pectoralis, 2.99, 3.60, 4.07, 4.51, 4.95; thigh, 1.52,
      2.68, 3.28

TABLE V.3 (*Continued*)

Columbidae

Columba livia (Blue Rock Pigeon): pectoralis, 4.46[c]

Columba speciosa (Scaled Pigeon): pectoralis, 3.90, 4.14, 4.76; thigh, 2.22, 3.15, 4.08

Columba albalinea (White-naped Pigeon): pectoralis, 4.47, 5.10, 5.11; supracoracoideus, 2.40; thigh, 2.72, 3.60, 5.34

Columba subvinacea (Ruddy Pigeon): pectoralis, 3.30; thigh, 3.00

Columbigallina talpacoti (Ruddy Ground Dove): pectoralis, 2.99, 3.08, 3.31, 3.56

Claravis pretiosa (Blue Ground Dove): pectoralis, 2.23, 3.50, 3.64, 4.23

Leptotila verreauxi (White-tipped Dove): pectoralis, 2.62

Leptotila cassinii (Gray-chested Dove): pectoralis, 1.81, 2.80; thigh, 5.81, 6.45

Leptotila rufinucha (Rufous-naped Dove): pectoralis, 2.33; thigh, 1.73

Geotrygon chiriquensis (Rufous-breasted Quail Dove): pectoralis, 2.48, 2.50

Psittacidae

Psittacula krameri (Roseringed Parakeet): pectoralis, 5.33[c]

Brotogeris jugularis (Orange-chinned Parakeet): pectoralis, 4.81, 5.03, 5.27

Pionopsitta haematotis (Brown-hooded Parrot): pectoralis, 5.00, 5.57, 5.72; thigh, 3.35, 3.73, 4.10

Amazona autumnalis (Red-lored Parrot): pectoralis, 4.90

Cuculidae

Clamator jacobinus (Pied-crested Cuckoo): pectoralis, 6.35[b]

Cuculus varius (Hawk-Cuckoo): pectoralis, 4.61, 4.83[b]

Eudynamys scolopacea (Koel): pectoralis, 2.43, 3.00[b]

Crotophaga ani (Smooth-billed Ani): pectoralis, 3.27, 3.85

Tytonidae

Tyto alba (Barn Owl): pectoralis, 5.40; thigh, 1.93; Pectoralis, 3.69[b]

Strigidae

Otus choliba (Tropical Screech Owl): pectoralis, 2.76

Ciccaba nigrolineata (Black and White Owl): pectoralis, 2.10; thigh, 1.80

Rhinoptynx clamator (Striped Owl): pectoralis, 3.10

Nyctibiidae

Nyctibius griseus (Common Potoo): pectoralis, 2.56, 3.86

Caprimulgidae

Chordeiles acutipennis (Lesser Nighthawk): pectoralis, 6.94

Nyctidromus albicollis (Parauque): pectoralis, 3.78, 3.86

Trochilidae

Campylopterus hemileucurus (Violet Sabrewing): pectoralis, 4.50, 4.66, 5.06, 5.18, 5.23, 5.32

Phaeochroa cuvierii (Scaly-breasted Hummingbird): pectoralis and supracoracoideus, 5.24, 5.31

Damophila julie (Violet-bellied Hummingbird): pectoralis and supracoracoideus, 5.05, 5.39, 5.62

Amazilia tzacatl (Rufous-tailed Hummingbird): pectoralis and supracoracoideus, 4.72

Lampornis castaneoventris (White-throated Mountain Gem): pectoralis and supracoracoideus, 5.05

TABLE V.3 (*Continued*)

Trogonidae
  Pharomachrus mocinno (Quetzal): pectoralis, 3.55, 3.93
  Trogon strigilatus (White-tailed Trogon): pectoralis, 2.99, 3.40; thigh, 5.32, 7.12
  Trogon rufus (Black-throated Trogon): pectoralis, 3.77
  Trogon violaceus (Violaceous Trogon): pectoralis, 3.56
Alcedinidae
  Halcyon smyrnensis (Whitebreasted Kingfisher): pectoralis, 3.55, 4.51[b]
  Ceryle torquata (Ringed Kingfisher): pectoralis, 3.72; thigh, 4.08
  Chloroceryle amazona (Amazon Kingfisher): pectoralis, 4.49, 4.76, 5.32
  Chloroceryle americana (Green Kingfisher): pectoralis, 4.15, 4.42, 5.27
Momotidae
  Momotus momota conexus (Blue-crowned Motmot): pectoralis, 2.04
  Momotus momota lessonii: pectoralis, 3.91
Meropidae
  Merops superciliosus (Bluecheeked Bee-eater): pectoralis, 4.00, 4.26[b]
Upupidae
  Upupa epops (Hoopoe): pectoralis, 2.75[b]
Capitonidae
  Eubucco bourcierii (Red-headed Barbet): pectoralis, 3.23
  Semnornis frantzii (Prong-billed Barbet): pectoralis, 2.91; thigh, 3.40, 3.80
Ramphastidae
  Pteroglossus torquatus (Collared Aracari): pectoralis, 2.92
  Pteroglossus frantzii (Fiery-billed Aracari): pectoralis, 3.15; thigh, 3.25
  Ramphastos swainsonii (Chestnut-mandibled Toucan): pectoralis, 2.78; thigh, 1.93
Picidae
  Dendrocopos mahrattensis (Mahratta Woodpecker): pectoralis, 2.65, 2.88[b]
  Picumnus olivaceus (Olivaceous Piculet): pectoralis, 3.84, 3.86
  Piculus rubiginosus (Golden-olive Woodpecker): pectoralis, 4.14; thigh, 3.11
  Dryocopus lineatus (Lineated Woodpecker): pectoralis, 3.54, 3.63; thigh, 3.15
  Centurus rubricapillus (Red-crowned Woodpecker): pectoralis, 3.09, 4.07; thigh, 5.85, 6.32
  Centurus pucherani (Black-cheeked Woodpecker): pectoralis, 3.42, 4.10; thigh, 4.39, 4.73
  Phloeoceastes melanoleucos (Crimson-crested Woodpecker): pectoralis, 3.22, 3.60; thigh, 2.20, 3.39
Dendrocolaptidae
  Xiphorhynchus guttatus (Buff-throated Woodhewer): pectoralis, 2.46; thigh, 5.09
  Lepidocolaptes affinis (Spot-crowned Woodhewer): pectoralis, 2.78, 2.80
Furnariidae
  Synallaxis brachyura (Slaty Spinetail): pectoralis, 3.40
  Anabacerthia striaticollis (Scaly-throated Foliage-gleaner): pectoralis, 4.20
Formicariidae
  Cymbilaimus lineatus (Fasciated Antshrike): pectoralis, 2.56
  Thamnophilus doliatus (Barred Antshrike): pectoralis, 2.81
  Dysithamnus mentalis (Plain Antvireo): pectoralis, 3.40
  Cercomacra tyrannina (Dusky Antbird): pectoralis, 3.99

TABLE V.3 *(Continued)*

Pipridae

   Corapipo leucorrhoa (White-ruffed Manakin): pectoralis, 5.11

   Manacus vitellinus (Golden-crowned Manakin): pectoralis, 4.32

Cotingidae

   Tityra semifasciata (Masked Tityra): pectoralis, 4.45

   Querula purpurata (Purple-throated Fruitcrow): pectoralis, 3.69

Tyrannidae

   Miodynastes maculatus (Streaked Flycatcher): pectoralis, 2.89, 3.01; thigh, 3.45

   Megarhynchus pitangua (Boat-billed Flycatcher): pectoralis, 3.42; thigh, 2.80

   Rhynchocyclus brevirostris (Eye-ringed Flatbill): pectoralis, 2.72, 2.75

   Lophotriccus pileatus (Scale-crested Pygmy Tyrant): pectoralis, 3.75

   Elaenia frantzii (Mountain Elaenia): pectoralis, 4.04

   Myiopagis viridicata (Greenish Elaenia): pectoralis, 3.71

Hirundinidae

   Progne chalybea (Gray-breasted Martin): pectoralis, 5.50, 6.00, 6.31

Dicruridae

   Dicrurus adsimilis (King Crow): pectoralis, 4.14, 5.64[b]

Oriolidae

   Oriolus oriolus (Golden Oriole): pectoralis, 2.89, 3.01[b]

Corvidae

   Corvus splendens (House Crow): pectoralis, 4.17, 5.26[b]

   Corvus macrorhynchos (Jungle Crow): pectoralis, 3.61[b]

Pycnonotidae

   Pycnonotus cafer (Redvented Bulbul): pectoralis, 2.18, 2.25[b]

Troglodytidae

   Thryothorus modestus (Plain Wren): pectoralis, 3.27

Turdidae

   Turdus plebejus (Mountain Robin): pectoralis, 3.18; thigh, 2.24

   Hylocichla ustulata (Olive-backed Thrush): pectoralis, 3.81

Sturnidae

   Sturnus roseus (Rosy Pastor): pectoralis, 4.78, 5.27[b]

   Sturnus pagodarum (Brahminy Myna): pectoralis, 3.44, 4.26[b]

   Acridotheres tristis (Common Myna): pectoralis, 2.53[b]

Coerebidae

   Cyanerpes cyaneus (Red-legged Honeycreeper): pectoralis, 4.56

   Cyanerpes lucidus (Shining Honeycreeper): pectoralis, 4.90, 5.46, 5.70, 6.24

Parulidae

   Myioborus miniatus (Slate-throated Redstart): pectoralis, 4.89

Icteridae

   Zarhynchus wagleri (Chestnut-headed Oropendola): pectoralis, 3.18, 3.89; thigh, 2.24, 3.44

Thraupidae

   Tangara larvata (Golden-masked Tanager): pectoralis, 3.60, 3.81

   Tangara gyrola (Bay-headed Tanager): pectoralis, 3.55

   Thraupis virens (Blue-gray Tanager): pectoralis, 3.64

TABLE V.3 (*Continued*)

Thraupidae (*Continued*)
  Piranga rubra (Summer Tanager): pectoralis, 3.70
  Chlorospingus ophthalmicus (Common Bush Tanager): pectoralis, 3.00, 3.88
Fringillidae
  Passer domesticus (House Sparrow): pectoralis, 2.63, 2.77[b]
  Saltator albicollis (Streaked Saltator): pectoralis, 3.20
  Pheucticus ludovicianus (Rose-breasted Grosbeak): pectoralis, 3.99, 4.28
  Passerina cyanea (Indigo Bunting): pectoralis, 3.85; thigh, 3.83
  Arremonops conirostris (Green-backed Sparrow): pectoralis, 2.25
  Spizella pusilla (Field Sparrow): pectoralis, 2.44

[a] Data from Hartman and Brownell, 1961 (except where otherwise noted).
[b] George and Naik, 1960.
[c] George and Jyoti, 1955.

III. Enzymes

The histochemical localization of enzyme systems involved in the metabolism of glycogen and fat in muscle have been discussed in the previous chapter. We shall now consider certain quantitative aspects of these enzyme levels in the pigeon pectoralis. The pigeon pectoralis is particularly suitable for the present discussion because the red and white fibers that constitute the muscle represent two different systems, of metabolism, namely, of fats and carbohydrates, respectively. Moreover, there is no other skeletal muscle that has received so much attention from biochemists and physiologists and of which so much is known.

A. GLYCOLYTIC ENZYMES

The localization of uridine diphosphate glucose (UDPG)-glycogen transglucosylase in the sarcotubular system has been discussed in the previous chapter. In the pigeon pectoralis muscle this system is prominently seen in the white fibers, and, obviously, the activity of this enzyme is also greater in them. It is now becoming established that this enzyme in the sarcotubular system has a direct role in glycogenogenesis (Andersson-Cedergren and Muscatello, 1963; Margreth *et al.*, 1963).

Phosphorylase activity has also been shown histochemically to be greater in the white fibers of the pigeon pectoralis (Chapter IV). In a quantitative study (Vallyathan and George, 1963) of phosphorylase *a* at different depths of the pigeon pectoralis, it became possible to establish that in the superficial part of the muscle, where the number of white fibers is greater, the enzyme activity is also higher (Fig. V.2). These authors calculated from the regression line in Fig. V.2 the enzyme activity as 45.61 and 4.69 μg phosphorus per mg dry muscle per 15 minutes for white and red fibers, respectively.

In a comparative study (Vallyathan and George, 1963) of phosphorylase activity in the pectoralis muscle of different birds [the domestic fowl (a poor flier), the Common Myna (a nonmigratory starling) and the Rosy Pastor (a migratory starling)] and of a bat, it was found that the fowl muscle, which consists mostly of white fibers, showed the highest enzyme activity (29.37 as compared to 28.53, 22.10, and 4.98 μg phosphorus per mg dry muscle per 15 minutes respectively in the others). The low enzyme activity in the bat muscle was attributed to the fact that the assay was done on specimens killed during the daytime when bats are known to be inactive.

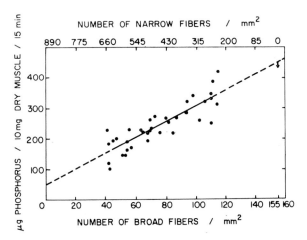

Fig. V.2. Graph showing the relation between the number of white and red fibers per square millimeter area and the phosphorylase activity as obtained at different layers of the M. pectoralis of pigeon. (By kind permission, Vallyathan and George, 1963.)

The higher phosphorylase activity seen in the muscle of the nonmigratory starling as compared to that in the migratory starling is interesting. This indicates that there is greater glycogen utilization in the nonmigratory starling than in the migratory species. However, it should also be of interest to know whether the enzyme activity in the Rosy Pastor is always lower than that of the Myna. The same authors (Vallyathan and George, 1964) reported that during the premigratory period, when the bird is fattening in preparation for migration, the enzyme activity is nearly doubled (43.86 μg phosphorus per mg dry muscle per 15 minutes). This appears to be an instance of metabolic adaptation for increased glycogen metabolism for the conservation and storage of fat. This aspect will be discussed further in Chapter VIII.

B. Certain Oxidizing Enzymes and Lipase

A quantitative assessment of the distribution pattern of the oxidizing enzyme succinic dehydrogenase (SDH), the key enzyme in the Krebs cycle, in the pigeon pectoralis muscle was first made by George and Talesara (1960) using a colorimetric method. The calculation of the enzyme activity was based on a study of the distribution pattern of the red and white fibers at different depths of the muscle.

The investigation was carried out in two regions of the muscle through a depth of 10 mm at every millimeter level. It was observed that in the superficial part of the muscle, where the number of white fibers is highest (132 per sq mm) and that of the red fibers lowest (131 per sq mm), the enzyme activity is lowest (15.5 ± 2.17 μg formazan per 100 mg wet muscle per 15 minutes). On the other hand, in deeper parts of the muscle, where the number of white fibers is the lowest (40 per sq mm) and that of the red fibers the highest (662 per sq mm), the enzyme activity is highest (78.77 ± 1.32 μg formazan per 100 mg wet muscle per 15 minutes). This showed that in contrast to phosphorylase activity the main bulk of SDH activity resides in the red fibers.

Subsequently, George and Talesara (1961a) made a more extensive study of the levels of some oxidizing enzymes (cytochrome oxidase, succinoxidase, malic oxidase, and lactic dehydrogenase) and a lipase in

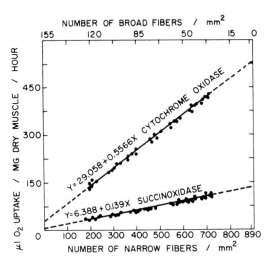

Fig. V.3. Graph showing the relation between the number of red and white fibers per square millimeter and cytochrome oxidase and succinoxidase activity as obtained at different depths of M. pectoralis of pigeon. (By kind permission, George and Talesara, 1961a.)

the pigeon pectoralis using manometric methods. The calculations were again based on the distribution pattern of the red and white fibers in the muscle. The relation between the fiber distribution per unit area of the muscle and the corresponding activity of the various enzymes is shown in Figs. V.3, V.4, and V.5. The results obtained are presented

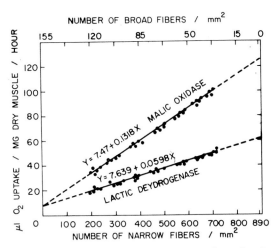

Fig. V.4. Graph showing the relation between the number of red and white fibers per square millimeter and malic and lactic dehydrogenase activity as obtained at different depths of M. pectoralis of pigeon. (By kind permission, George and Talesara, 1961a.)

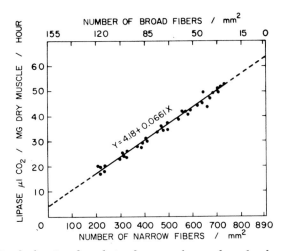

Fig. V.5. Graph showing the relation between the number of red and white fibers per square millimeter and lipase activity as obtained at different depths of M. pectoralis of pigeon. (By kind permission, George and Talesara, 1961a.)

TABLE V.4

DISTRIBUTION PATTERN OF THE VARIOUS ENZYMES IN THE DIFFERENT LAYERS OF THE PECTORALIS MUSCLE OF THE PIGEON AND ITS RELATION TO THE NUMBER OF MUSCLE FIBERS[a]

Experiment	Depths (mm) of the muscle starting from the superficial side (ventral face)	Number of fibers per mm²		Oxidizing enzymes (μl O_2 uptake per mg dry muscle per hour)				Lipase activity (μl CO_2 per mg dry muscle per hour)
		Broad	Narrow	Cytochrome oxidase	Succin-oxidase	Malic oxidase	Lactic de-hydrogenase	
1	0–0.5	119 ± 11	214	146.59	37.90	35.98	20.44	19.08
	0.5–1.0	88 ± 9	385	238.24	60.76	57.52	30.34	29.31
2	0–1	102 ± 8	301	198.86	48.74	45.34	25.90	24.64
	1–2	78 ± 6	471	295.28	68.40	70.77	35.52	35.40
	2–3	56 ± 7	567	340.54	86.03	81.76	42.07	41.46
	3–4	44 ± 3	640	387.95	93.92	91.70	46.18	46.54
	4–5	34 ± 6	696	416.15	104.55	98.73	49.24	51.18

[a] Data from George and Talesara, 1961a.

in Tables V.4 and V.5. It is clear from the results that the oxidizing and the lipolytic enzymes studied are confined mainly to red fibers. This is also in agreement with the histochemical observations (George *et al.,* 1963) discussed in the previous chapter. The question of lactic dehydrogenase (LDH) activity, however, needs to be explained. It has already been pointed out in Chapter IV that by using phenazine methosulfate as a direct electron acceptor (thereby avoiding the histochemical demonstration of the enzyme via the diaphorase system) the activity of the enzyme in the pigeon pectoralis could be shown to be greater in the white fiber than in the red ones. Quantitative estimations of the enzyme in the red and white muscles of the guinea pig showed that the enzyme of the white fibers is of the same order as that of the red

TABLE V.5

ACTIVITY OF THE VARIOUS ENZYMES IN THE RED AS WELL AS THE WHITE FIBERS OF THE PECTORALIS MUSCLE OF THE PIGEON AS DERIVED FROM THE EQUATION OF THE REGRESSION LINE[a]

Muscle	Oxidizing enzymes (μl O_2 uptake per mg dry muscle per hour)				Lipase activity (μl CO_2 per mg dry muscle per hour)
	Cytochrome oxidase	Succinoxidase	Malic oxidase	Lactic dehydrogenase	
Red	524.43	130.10	124.77	60.87	63.00
White	29.05	6.38	7.47	7.63	4.18

[a] Data from George and Talesara, 1961a.

(Blanchaer and Van Wijhe, 1962). In the present discussion it should be reiterated that the higher level of lactic dehydrogenase shown in the red fibers is actually a measure of the mitochondrial activity of the enzyme. The higher level of cytoplasmic lactic dehydrogenase activity shown in the white fibers (as compared with the red fibers) of the pigeon pectoralis we believe is localized in the sarcoplasmic reticulum, which is more prominent in the white fibers (George *et al.,* 1963).

It is now well recognized that LDH is a tetrameric molecule made up of four subunits of two parent molecules (Dawson *et al.,* 1964). The parent ones have been called H (heart) and M (muscle) after their source tissue. The so-called pure H type consists of four H units (H_4) and the M type four M units (M_4), whereas the other three forms are molecular hybrids of the subunits namely M_3H, M_2H_2, and MH_3. The H form was found to show maximal activity at low concentrations of pyruvate but was strongly inhibited by high concentrations of pyruvate. On the other hand, the M form was found to be highly active at relatively high concentrations of pyruvate. These observations indicated different functional roles for the two forms of LDH. In a continuously contracting system like the heart, the property of the LDH of being inhibited by high concentrations of pyruvate should promote complete and continuous oxidation of pyruvate and lactate, which is necessary for a steady flow of energy. In skeletal muscle, contractions are sporadic, and energy is obtained through glycolysis with large amounts of pyruvate being formed to be reduced to lactate.

Evidently the H enzyme is predominant in the heart muscle which is well adapted for an aerobic metabolism, and the M enzyme in the skeletal muscle is adapted for anaerobic metabolism. However, the possibility of a considerable amount of the H enzyme being present in any skeletal muscle which is well adapted for an aerobic metabolism should be recognized. In this regard the breast muscles of birds of different flying abilities should be excellent experimental material for investigation. Wilson *et al.* (1963) studied the five electrophoretic forms of LDH (M_4, M_3H, M_2H_2, MH_3, and H_4) and the degree of substrate (pyruvate) inhibition of the enzyme in the pectoralis muscle of some forty species of adult birds (Table V.6). They observed that in poor fliers (such as the pheasant, grouse, guinea fowl, partridge, and the domestic fowl), pyruvate does not inhibit the breast muscle enzyme. In the more active fliers, increased substrate inhibition was noticed. The highest inhibition, similar to that shown by the heart, was obtained in the breast muscle of the Storm Petrel, a sustained flier. Strong substrate inhibition was also observed in the case of hummingbird and swift muscles. In the case of a soarer or glider, such as the Rough-legged Hawk, the extent of substrate inhibition was moderate. Among the passerines, those that indulge in sustained flight (e.g., the jay, sparrow, starling, and grackle) gave higher values. Some passers (the warbler, vireos, chickadees, and kinglet), which continuously hunt insects in foliage, also gave high values. On the other hand, the towhee, a ground finch which is a reluctant flier, gave a very low value.

Another interesting observation was that no substrate inhibition was noted in the domestic duck and the Laysan Duck, which have lost the capacity for sustained flight.

The same authors investigated the possibility of finding a change in the degree of substrate inhibition at the time of migration. They found in White-crowned Sparrows exhibiting migratory restlessness that there was a twofold increase in the concentration of lactic dehydrogenase but there was no change in the degree of substrate inhibition. No change in substrate inhibition was recorded even in the sparrows captured during actual migration.

The electrophoretic pattern of the breast muscle extracts revealed that the differences observed in the different levels of substrate inhibition in the various birds studied were due to the different proportions of the M and H subunits (Table V.6). The domestic fowl and other galliform birds as well as the domestic duck show low substrate inhibition and have the pure M enzyme (M_4) with perhaps some trace of the M_3H hybrid. Considerable amounts of the M_4 and M_3H forms and a little of M_2H_2 form, are present in the rail and the towhee. In species showing intermediate substrate inhibition, nearly equal amounts of the sub-units of both M and H forms are present, whereas in those showing strong substrate inhibition mostly H sub-units are present.

The important studies of Wilson *et al.* summarized above, have opened yet another new line of investigation in the study of the evolution of the avian pectoralis. George (1965) has discussed some of the aspects of the evolution of the avian pectoralis muscle. He has pointed out that the pectoralis muscle of the fowl type tallies with the M_4, and of the sparrow type with the H_4 types of Wilson *et al.* (1963), whereas the others broadly correspond to intermediate types at different levels of variation. Mention should also be made of the recent attempt of Gysels (1963) to study the electrophoretic mobility of protein fractions of avian pectoralis muscles with a view to obtaining taxonomic data on birds. It is too early to make definite comments on his findings. Nevertheless, his observations have certainly shown promise of new possibilities. Similar studies on the electrophoretic patterns of the avian egg-white proteins have already yielded very interesting results (Sibley, 1960).

The level of succinic dehydrogenase (SDH) activity in a muscle is an index of its capacity for oxidative metabolism. SDH activity in the pectoralis and supracoracoideus muscles of some birds have been determined by George and Talesara (1961b). Their data, as well as similar data on the muscles of three species of hummingbirds (Lasiewski *et al.*, 1965), are presented in Table V.7. The pectoralis muscles of the Calliope Hummingbird and Costa's Hummingbird have the highest enzyme activity; the former has considerably higher enzyme activity than does the latter. The muscle of the Anna's Hummingbird, however, comes next to the Rosy Pastor. The lowest figures were obtained for poor fliers: the domestic fowl, Crowpheasant, and the Jungle Babbler. The supracoracoideus muscle has considerably less enzyme activity than the pectoralis muscle in all cases with the exception of the three hummingbirds. The enzyme level in the supracoracoideus muscle is considerably higher than that of the pectoralis in the hummingbirds. This suggests that the supracoracoideus muscle in hummingbirds has a higher oxidative capacity than

TABLE V.6

LACTIC DEHYDROGENASES OF AVIAN PECTORALIS MUSCLE[a]

Common name	Scientific name	Substrate inhibition NADH L / NADH H	Electrophoretic forms[b]				
			M4	M3H	M2H2	MH3	H4
Wilson's Petrel	Oceanites oceanicus	3.8	−	−	−	+	++
Ruby-throated Hummingbird	Archilochus colubris	2.8	−	+	++	++	++
Chimney Swift	Chaetura pelagica	2.2	++	++	++	++	++
Dovekie	Plautus alle	2.2	−	−	−	−	−
Black-bellied Plover	Squatarola squatarola	2.1	−	−	−	−	−
Golden-crowned Kinglet	Regulus satrapa	2.1	−	−	−	−	−
Black-capped Chickadee	Parus atricapilla	1.9	−	−	−	−	−
Woodcock	Philohela minor	1.9	++	++	++	++	++
Herring Gull	Larus argentatus	1.8	++	++	++	++	++
Brunnich's Murre	Uria lomvia	1.7	−	−	−	−	−
Warbling Vireo	Vireo gilvus	1.7	++	++	++	++	+
Common Pigeon (wild)	Columba livia	1.6	++	++	+	+	−
Black Duck	Anas platyrhynchos	1.6	++	++	++	+	−
White-crowned Sparrow	Zonotrichia leucophrys	1.6	−	−	−	−	−
Black and white Warbler	Mniotilta varia	1.6	++	++	++	++	−
Pintail Duck	Anas acuta	1.6	++	++	++	+	−
Bronzed Grackle	Quiscalus quiscula	1.5	++	++	++	+	−
Starling	Sturnus vulgaris	1.5	++	++	−	+	+
House Sparrow	Passer domesticus	1.5	−	−	−	−	−
Sparrow Hawk	Falco sparverius	1.5	++	++	++	+	−

Common name	Scientific name	Substrate inhibition NADH L / NADH H	Electrophoretic forms[b]				
			M$_4$	M$_3$H	M$_2$H$_2$	MH$_3$	H$_4$
Yellow-shafted Flicker	*Colaptes auratus*	1.5	++	++	++	+	−
Mourning Dove	*Zenaidura macroura*	1.4	−	−	−	−	−
Rough-legged Hawk	*Buteo lagopus*	1.4	++	++	++	+	−
Mallard Duck (wild)	*Anas platyrhynchos*	1.4	++	++	+	+	+
Great Blue Heron	*Ardea herodias*	1.3	−	−	−	−	−
Blue Jay	*Cyanocitta cristata*	1.3	++	++	+	−	−
Horned Grebe	*Podiceps auritus*	1.3	++	++	+	−	−
Black-billed Cuckoo	*Coccyzus erythrophthalmus*	1.3	++	++	+	−	−
Belted Kingfisher	*Megaceryle alcyon*	1.2	++	++	+	−	−
Towhee	*Pipilio erythrophthalmus*	1.2	++	++	+	−	−
Barred Owl	*Strix varia*	1.2	−	−	−	−	−
Virginia Rail	*Rallus limicola*	1.1	++	++	+	−	−
Laysan Duck	*Anas platyrhynchos*	1.08	−	+	−	−	−
Domestic Duck	*Anas platyrhynchos*	1.08	++	++	−	−	−
Domestic Fowl	*Gallus gallus*	0.95	++	−	−	−	−
Chinese Partridge	*Bambusicola thoracica*	0.9	−	−	−	−	−
Guinea Fowl	*Numida meleagris*	0.8	++	−	−	−	−
Ruffed Grouse	*Bonasa umbellus*	0.8	++	−	−	−	−
Ring-necked Pheasant	*Phasianus colchicus*	0.7	−	−	−	−	−
Reeve's Pheasant	*Syrmaticus reevesi*	0.7	−	−	−	−	−
Domestic Fowl, pure M$_4$		0.95	++	−	−	−	−
Domestic Fowl, pure H$_4$		3.4	−	−	−	−	++

[a] Data from Wilson *et al.*, 1963.

[b] The intensity with which the various electrophoretic forms were stained by nitro blue tetrazolium is indicated by: ++, intense staining; +, weak staining; −, little or no staining.

the pectoralis muscle. That hummingbirds indulge in sustained hovering flight is well known. In this type of flight the action of the supracoracoideus muscle as the elevator of the wings is an equally powerful action. It has already been mentioned that the supracoracoideus muscle of hummingbirds is nearly as large as the pectoralis. It will be seen in the next chapter that the hummingbird is the only one thus far studied in which the supracoracoideus muscle consists of only one (R) type of fiber. In the sparrow the supracoracoideus consists of two (R and I) types of fibers, whereas the pectoralis muscles in both birds are similar in the sense that both consist of one (R) type of fiber.

TABLE V.7

SUCCINIC DEHYDROGENASE ACTIVITY IN THE PECTORALIS AND SUPRACORACOIDEUS MUSCLES OF SOME BIRDS[a]

| Species | SDH activity (in μg formazan per mg dry muscle per 30 minutes) | |
	Pectoralis	Supracoracoideus
Fowl	0.47	0.31
Blue Rock Pigeon	8.48	3.84
Cattle Egret	5.22	2.09
Crow-pheasant	3.41	1.76
Roseringed Parakeet	9.50	3.61
Common Myna	6.22	2.86
Rosy Pastor	11.50	4.90
Jungle Babbler	3.97	1.64
House Sparrow	10.04	4.06
Calliope Hummingbird[b]	18.50	23.00
Costa's Hummingbird[b]	12.20	15.00
Anna's Hummingbird[b]	10.90	11.50

[a] Data from George and Talesara, 1961b.
[b] Lasiewski et al., 1965.

Lipase and SDH activities of the whole homogenate and the particulate fractions of the pigeon pectoralis muscle (Table V.8) have been estimated by George and Talesara (1962). SDH activity was largely confined to the mitochondrial fraction; the enzyme concentration in the microsomal and soluble fractions was only negligible. Lipase activity, however, was highest in microsomal fraction. Lipase activity in the mitochondrial fraction was less than half that of the microsomal fraction; the enzyme activity in the soluble fraction was still less. On the basis of histochemical observations, it was suggested in the previous chapter that a higher lipase capable of attacking glycerides of long-chain fatty

TABLE V.8

LIPASE AND SUCCINIC DEHYDROGENASE ACTIVITY OF THE PIGEON PECTORALIS MUSCLE HOMOGENATE FRACTIONS[a]

Fraction	Lipase (Unit: $\mu l\ CO_2$/hour)			Succinic dehydrogenase (Unit: μg formazan/hour)		
	Activity (units)	Specific activity (units per mg protein)	Yield (%)	Activity (units)	Specific activity (units per mg protein)	Yield (%)
Homogenate	997.33	44.15 (38.3–52.8)	100	227	12.47 (9.7–14.0)	100
Myofibrils[b] (600 × g)	231.67	—	23.23	56.95	—	25
Mitochondria (7,500 × g)	181.30	47.05 (36.2–59.6)	18.18	123.10	35.56 (30.0–44.3)	54
Microsomes (40,000 × g)	190.90	103.84 (87.94–120.5)	19.15	5.83	6.37 (4.86–8.93)	3
Soluble (40,000 × g)	326.11	31.26 (26.34–36.84)	32.70	7.10	1.82 (1.53–2.04)	3
Sum of fractions	929.98	—	93.26	192.98	—	85

[a] Data from George and Talesara, 1962.
[b] This fraction also contains some mitochondria, cell debris, and traces of microsomes.

acids resides mainly in the mitochondria, whereas a lower lipase for splitting glycerides of short-chain fatty acids is present in the microsomes (George, 1964).

IV. Metabolism

It is seldom realized that the foundations of our present knowledge of aerobic metabolism were laid by studies in which the pigeon breast muscle was used as the experimental material. The observations of Szent-Györgyi that minced pigeon breast muscle respires very actively by the complete oxidation of pyruvic acid, producing little or no lactic acid (provided catalytic quantities of dicarboxylic acids, such as succinate, fumarate, malate, and oxaloacetate were added), stimulated a rapid flow of important investigations, culminating in the monumental work of Hans Krebs. Krebs showed that, in addition to succinate, fumarate, malate, and oxaloacetate, α-ketoglutaric and citric acids also act catalytically on the respiring muscle-mince, and that their effects are inhibited by malonate. On the other hand, when pyruvate and oxaloacetate were incubated together with the minced muscle under anaerobic conditions, an accumulation of considerable amounts of citric acid resulted. These discoveries enabled him to postulate in 1937 the cycle of reactions called the tricarboxylic acid cycle (Krebs cycle), which brings about the oxidation of pyruvic acid to carbon dioxide and water (Krebs, 1954). We shall have occasion to consider the significance of this cycle in muscle metabolism (in Chapter VIII).

It is now well established that mitochondria contain the complete enzymatic machinery for the operation of the Krebs cycle and for the generation of high energy phosphate bonds. The respiratory activity of different types of muscle has been correlated with the mitochondrial density and the color of the muscle (Paul and Sperling, 1952). Respiratory activity, expressed as μl O_2 per hour per gram wet weight of the tissue (when α-ketoglutarate was used as substrate), was found to be highest in the pigeon breast muscle (with highest color and mitochondrial density) among the breast muscles of the three birds studied (pigeon, 1830; Mallard, 875; and chicken, 110). For detailed information on the biochemistry of muscle mitochondria or sarcosomes, in general, the account given by Slater (1960) should be consulted.

In the light of the histochemical and biochemical observations on the red and white muscles, as well as red and white fibers within muscles, it is clear that the red muscle with its red fibers is adapted for aerobic metabolism and that the white muscle and white fibers are adapted for anaerobic metabolism. The predominant metabolite in the red muscle fibers is fat whereas in the white muscle fibers it is glycogen. Obviously, fat should be the chief fuel for energy in the red fibers and glycogen in the white. As far as our present knowledge goes, fat cannot be metabolized in the absence of oxygen. There is no reliable evidence for anaerobic energy production from fat. One report of anaerobic disappearance of fat in an insect pupa has been refuted and shown to be ill-founded (Gilmour, 1960).

It was shown by Weinhouse *et al.* (1950) that the pigeon breast muscle is capable of metabolizing fat. George and Jyoti (1957) studied the relative reductions in fat and glycogen in an exercised pigeon pectoralis muscle and estimated that over 70% of the energy expended is derived from fat. George and Vallyathan (1964) have shown that when the pectoralis muscle of a pigeon is electrically stimulated, fat in the form of free fatty acids is transported to the muscle from the liver and adipose tissue. In a recent histochemical study of the pectoralis muscle of the Rubythroated Hummingbird, Chandra-Bose and George (1964) have shown that the prominent sarcoplasmic reticulum inside the muscle fibers stain for lipids (Fig. V.6). They have, therefore, indicated that

Fig. V.6. Photomicrograph of a T.S. of M. pectoralis of Rubythroated Hummingbird treated with Nile blue sulfate. The mitochondria, blood capillaries, and sarcoplasmic reticulum are seen. × (By kind permission, Chandra-Bose and George, 1964.)

lipids are transported through the sarcoplasmic reticulum to the mitochondria for oxidation.

If fat is to be utilized for energy, it has first of all to be broken down
to fatty acids and glycerol so that the fatty acids released can undergo
β-oxidation. George and Talesara (1962) demonstrated that the pigeon
breast muscle is incapable of direct oxidation of triglycerides. They,
therefore, suggested that fats will have to be acted upon first by the
muscle lipase, which will split fat into the component fatty acids as the
first step for the utilization of fat. Muscle lipase capable of hydrolyzing
glycerides of long-chain fatty acids has been localized in the mitochondria of skeletal muscles (Bokdawala and George, 1964). In a recent review on muscle lipase George (1964) has suggested that a higher
lipase capable of hydrolyzing esters of long-chain fatty acids resides
in the mitochondria and that another lipase, which acts on those of
short-chain fatty acids, is present in the microsomes. George and Talesara (1962) also found that the highest lipase activity (Table V.8) was
in the microsomal fraction (103.84 μl CO_2 per hour per mg protein),
the next being in the mitochondrial fraction (47.05 μl CO_2 per hour
per mg protein). From these observations they suggested that the
function of the microsomal lipase is the esterification of fatty acids with
glycerol to form neutral lipids, and that perhaps it also effects the splitting up of fat into fatty acids thereby rendering the products of hydrolysis suitable for oxidation by the mitochondria. The problem of fat
utilization for muscular energy will be discussed at greater length in
Chapter VIII.

It should be of considerable interest to know how the two types of
fibers with two different metabolic adaptations, but existing side by side
in the same muscle, function. The red fibers by virtue of their heavy fat
load and dense cellular inclusions indulge in sustained tonic contractions. The white ones, on the other hand, possess the necessary qualities
for rapid tetanic contractions. George and Nene (1965) have shown
that when the pigeon breast muscle is electrically stimulated the white
fibers are completely depleted of their glycogen store within a few
minutes of continuous contraction, but this is not true of the red fibers
(Fig. V.7 A,B). These observations indicate that the white fibers, by
their rapid contractions, should enable the bird to have a quick take-off
and also to manipulate sudden turns while in flight. The red fibers on
the other hand, indulge in slower contractions and in sustained flight. It
is probable that during continuous flight the white fibers remain
passive. We certainly need to know more about the action of these two
types of fibers.

A muscle which indulges in sustained activity requires a continuous

generation of high energy compounds. Such a muscle has a high myoglobin content and cytochrome oxidase activity but a low ATP (adenosinetriphosphate) and creatine phosphate content and low myofibrillar
ATPase (adenosinetriphosphatase) activity (Lawrie, 1953a,b). On the

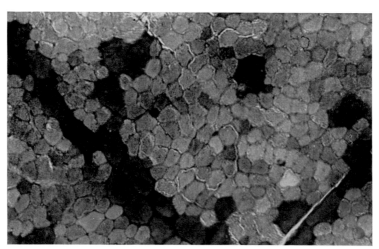

FIG. V.7A. Photomicrograph of a T.S. of M. pectoralis of pigeon stained for the
demonstration of glycogen by the PAS technique. Note the higher concentration of
glycogen in the white fibers. × 260. (By kind permission, George and Nene, 1965.)

FIG. V.7B. Photomicrograph of a T.S. of M. pectoralis of pigeon treated for the
demonstration of glycogen after 10 minutes of electrical stimulation of the pectoral
muscles. Note the depletion of glycogen from the white fibers. A slight increase in the
PAS-positive staining is observed in the red fibers. × 260. (By kind permission,
George and Nene, 1965.)

other hand, a muscle capable of fast contractions for short periods of time utilizes for energy mainly its store of ATP and creatine phosphate. According to Lawrie (1953a,b), a muscle of this kind has low myoglobin content and cytochrome oxidase activity but high ATP and creatine phosphate content and high myofibrillar ATPase activity. The same characteristics are applicable to the red and white fibers, respectively, of the pigeon pectoralis muscle.

The enzyme ATPase, which hydrolyzes the terminal phosphate of ATP to release chemical energy, is known to occur in muscle in three different forms: mitochondrial, myofibrillar, and sarcotubular. Chappell and Perry (1953) noted high ATPase activity in muscle mitochondria. Tonzetich and Kare (1960) differentiated the ATPase of the breast muscle from the leg muscle in the fowl on the basis of their solubility. The ATPase activity in the different fractions of the pigeon breast muscle was studied by Kityakara and Harman (1953). Recently Bokdawala and George (1965) demonstrated histochemically the presence of acid and neutral ATPases in the pigeon pectoralis muscle. The concentration of the former was found to be considerably greater in the white fibers and that of the latter in the red fibers. These authors have suggested that the higher level of acid ATPase in the white fibers is an adaptation for the high rate of glycolysis and possible lactic acid accumulation in these fibers (Chapter IV).

REFERENCES

Andersson-Cedergren, E., and Muscatello, U. (1963). The participation of the sarcotubular system in glycogen metabolism. *J. Ultrastruct. Res.* **8:** 391–401.

Blanchaer, M., and Van Wijhe, M. (1962). Distribution of lactic dehydrogenase in skeletal muscle. *Nature* **193:** 877–878.

Bokdawala, F. D., and George, J. C. (1964). Histochemical demonstration of muscle lipase. *J. Histochem. Cytochem.* **12:** 768–771.

Bokdawala, F. D., and George, J. C. (1965). Acid and neutral ATPases in skeletal muscle. *J. Animal Morphol. Physiol.* **12:** (in press).

Brown, W. D., Martinez, M., Johnstone, M., and Olcott, H. S. (1962). Comparative biochemistry of myoglobins. *J. Biol. Chem.* **237:** 81–84.

Chandra-Bose, D. A., and George, J. C. (1964). Studies on the structure and physiology of the flight muscles of birds. 12. Observations on the structure of the pectoralis and supracoracoideus of the Rubythroated Hummingbird. *Pavo* **2:** 111–114.

Chappell, J. B., and Perry, S. V. (1953). The respiratory and adenosinetriphosphatase activities of skeletal muscle mitochondria. *Biochem. J.* **55:** 586–595.

Dawson, D. M., Goodfriend, T. L., and Kaplan, N. O. (1964). Lactic dehydrogenases: Functions of the two types. *Science* **143:** 929–933.

George, J. C. (1964). Muscle lipase. *J. Animal Morphol. Physiol.* **11** (C. J. George Felicitation Number): 233–243.

George, J. C. (1965). Evolution of the bird and bat pectoral muscles. *Pavo* **3:** (in press).

George, J. C., and Jyoti, D. (1955). The lipid content and its reduction in the muscle and liver during long and sustained muscular activity. *J. Animal Morphol. Physiol.* **2:** 38–45.

George, J. C., and Jyoti, D. (1957). Studies on the structure and physiology of the flight muscles of birds. 2. The relative reduction of fat and glycogen in the pectoralis major muscle during sustained activity. *J. Animal Morphol. Physiol.* **4:** 119–123.

George, J. C., and Naik, R. M. (1959). Studies on the structure and physiology of the flight muscles of birds. 4. Observations on the fiber architecture of the pectoralis major muscle of the pigeon. *Biol. Bull.* **116:** 239–247.

George, J. C., and Naik, R. M. (1960). Intramuscular fat store in the pectoralis of birds. *Auk* **77:** 216–217.

George, J. C., and Nene, R. V. (1965). Effect of exercise on the glycogen content of the red and white fibers of the pigeon pectoralis muscle. *J. Animal Morphol. Physiol.* **12:** (in press).

George, J. C., and Talesara, C. L. (1960). Studies on the structure and physiology of the flight muscles of birds. 9. A quantitative study of the distribution pattern of succinic dehydrogenase in the pectoralis major muscle of the pigeon. *Biol. Bull.* **118:** 262–268.

George, J. C., and Talesara, C. L. (1961a). A quantitative study of the distribution pattern of certain oxidizing enzymes and a lipase in the red and white fibers of the pigeon breast muscle. *J. Cellular Comp. Physiol.* **58:** 253–260.

George, J. C., and Talesara, C. L. (1961b). The succinic dehydrogenase levels in the pectoral muscles of a few representative types of birds and a bat in relation to the fiber diameter, muscle weight and body weight. *Comp. Biochem. Physiol.* **3:** 267–273.

George, J. C., and Talesara, C. L. (1962). Lipase activity of the particulate fractions of the pigeon breast muscle and its significance in the metabolism of the muscle. *J. Cellular Comp. Physiol.* **60:** 33–40.

George, J. C., and Vallyathan, N. V. (1964). Effect of exercise on the free fatty acid levels in the pigeon. *J. Appl. Physiol.* **19:** 619–622.

George, J. C., Susheela, A. K., and Vallyathan, N. V. (1963). Cytoplasmic (non-mitochondrial) lactic and succinic dehydrogenases in the red and white muscle fibers. *J. Animal Morphol. Physiol.* **10:** 24–30.

Gilmour, D. (1960). "Biochemistry of Insects." Academic Press, New York.

Gysels, H. (1963). New biochemical techniques applied to avian systematics. *Experientia* **19:** 107–111.

Hartman, F. A., and Brownell, K. A. (1961). Lipids in the locomotor muscles of birds. *Condor* **63:** 403–410.

Kitiyakara, A., and Harman, J. W. (1953). The cytological distribution in pigeon skeletal muscle of enzymes acting on phosphorylated nucleotides. *J. Exptl. Med.* **97:** 553–572.

Krebs, H. A. (1954). "Chemical Pathways of Metabolism." Academic Press, New York.

Lasiewski, R. C., Galey, F. R., and Vasquez, C. (1965). Morphology and physiology of the pectoral muscles of hummingbirds. *Nature* **206:** 404–405.

Lawrie, R. A. (1950). Some observations on factors affecting myoglobin concentrations in muscle. *J. Agr. Sci.* **40:** 356–366.

Lawrie, R. A. (1952). Biochemical differences between red and white muscle. *Nature* **170**: 122.

Lawrie, R. A. (1953a). The activity of the cytochrome system in muscle and its relation to myoglobin. *Biochem. J.* **55**: 298–305.

Lawrie, R. A. (1953b). The relation of energy-rich phosphate in muscle to myoglobin and to cytochrome-oxidase activity. *Biochem. J.* **55**: 305–309.

Margreth, A., Muscatello, U., and Andersson-Cedergren, E. (1963). A morphological and biochemical study on the regulation of carbohydrate metabolism in the muscle cell. *Exptl. Cell Res.* **32**: 484–509.

Nair, K. K. (1952). The chemical composition of the pectoral muscles of some Indian birds and its bearing on their flight. *J. Univ. Bombay* **21**: 90–98.

Needham, D. M. (1926). Red and white muscle. *Physiol. Rev.* **6**: 1–27.

Paul, M. H., and Sperling, E. (1952). Cyclophorase system XXIII. Correlation of cyclophorase activity and mitochondrial density in striated muscle. *Proc. Soc. Exptl. Biol. Med.* **79**: 352–354.

Pishawikar, S. D. (1961). A study of the phosphates, phosphatases and certain inorganic ions in the pectoralis muscle of some birds with special reference to that of the pigeon. Doctoral Thesis, M.S., University of Baroda, Baroda, India.

Sibley, C. G. (1960). The electrophoretic patterns of avian egg-white proteins as taxonomic characters. *Ibis* **102**: 215–284.

Slater, E. C. (1960). Biochemistry of sarcosomes. *In* "Structure and Function of Muscle" (G. H. Bourne, ed.), Vol II, pp. 105–140. Academic Press, New York.

Talesara, C. L. (1961). A quantitative study of the distribution pattern of iron in the red and white fibers of the pigeon breast muscle. *J. Animal Morphol. Physiol.* **8**: 149–154.

Tonzetich, J., and Kare, M. R. (1960). Adenosinetriphosphatase in red and white muscle. *Arch. Biochem. Biophys.* **86**: 195–200.

Vallyathan, N. V. (1963). On the lipid content and lipase activity in the breast muscle of *Sturnus roseus* (Linnaeus). *Pavo* **1**: 106–109.

Vallyathan, N. V., and George, J. C. (1963). Phosphorylase 'a' in bird and bat breast muscles. *J. Animal Morphol. Physiol.* **10**: 15–23.

Vallyathan, N. V., and George, J. C. (1964). Glycogen content and phosphorylase activity in the breast muscle of the migratory starling, *Sturnus roseus* (Linnaeus). *Pavo* **2**: 55–60.

Weinhouse, S., Millington, R. H., and Volk, M. E. (1950). Oxidation of isotopic palmitic acid in animal tissues. *J. Biol. Chem.* **185**: 191–200.

Wilson, A. C., Cahn, R. D., and Kaplan, N. O. (1963). Functions of the two forms of lactic dehydrogenase in the breast muscle of birds. *Nature* **197**: 331–334.

CHAPTER VI

The Supracoracoideus:
Histophysiological Aspects

The supracoracoideus muscle, the principal elevator of the wing, is considerably less developed than the pectoralis, which is the most powerful muscle in the avian body (Chapter III). This muscle is very poorly developed in soarers like the kite and most highly developed in hummingbirds and penguins.

The histological and histochemical studies of the pectoralis muscle have shown that the cellular organization of this muscle differs in different birds (Chapter IV). The heterogeneity of the component fibers has been established on the basis of the fiber diameter and the mitochondrial density, and three types of fibers (W, I, and R) have been recognized. According to the nature and the relative distribution of these fiber types, the types of pectoralis muscle have been characterized as belonging to six different groups, and these characteristics have been correlated with the corresponding mode of flight (Chapter IV). In the present chapter similar observations made on the supracoracoideus muscle (Chandra-Bose and George, 1965) will be discussed.

I. Characterization of the Supracoracoideus

On the basis of the fiber diameter and the mitochondrial density, as revealed by the intensity of staining for succinic dehydrogenase activity, the avian supracoracoideus muscle may be classed under the following nine groups (Figs. VI.1–VI.30). The diameter of the fibers as well as the relative distribution of the fiber types is presented in Table VI.1.

Group 1. Fowl type (W, I, and R, fibers)
Group 2. Kite type (W and I fibers)
Group 3. Hawk type (W, R, and I fibers)
Group 4. Owl type (R, W, and I fibers)
Group 5. Pigeon type (R, I, and W fibers)

143

Group 6.   Egret type (*R* and *W* fibers)
Group 7.   Swift type (*I* and *R* fibers)
Group 8.   Sparrow type (*R* and *I* fibers)
Group 9.   Hummingbird type (*R* fibers)

Group 1

The supracoracoideus and the pectoralis muscles of the domestic fowl (Fig. VI.1) contain all three types of fibers, *W*, *I*, *R*, in the order of predominance.

Group 2

The supracoracoideus muscles of the kite and the vulture (Figs. VI.2 and VI.3) come under this group in which the *W* and *I* fibers are represented but not the *R* type; the *W* fibers are more numerous than the *I* fibers. The pectoralis muscles of these birds possess only the *I* fibers.

Group 3

The Shikra (Fig. VI.4) supracoracoideus muscle consists of *W*, *R*, and *I* fibers (listed in the order of relative abundance). This pattern of fiber composition is a reversal of the pattern (*I*, *R*, and *W*) in the pectoralis muscle of the same bird. The supracoracoideus muscle of the Whitebreasted Kingfisher (*Halcyon smyrnensis*, Fig. VI.5) also comes under this group. In this bird the fiber composition of the pectoralis muscle is *R* and *I*. The predominant *W* fibers in addition to the *R* and *I* ones in the supracoracoideus should effect faster movement of the muscle in its action of elevating the wings.

Group 4

The fiber pattern of the supracoracoideus in this group resembles that of the previous one except that the *R* fibers number more than the *W* and *I* types. This group includes (Figs. VI.6–VI.8) the supracoracoideus of the domestic duck, Great Horned Owl (*Bubo bubo*), Spotted Owlet (*Athene brama*), and the Crow-Pheasant (*Centropus sinensis*).

The pectoralis muscles of the Pariah Kite, Indian Whitebacked Vulture, Shikra (Hawk), Great Horned Owl, Spotted Owlet, and the Crow-Pheasant were placed in one group in which the *I* fibers predominate and all fibers are characteristically circular in cross section and rather loosely packed. These characteristics have been attributed to the soaring or gliding type of flight (Chapter IV). As far as the supracoracoideus is concerned, although the fibers in all these birds are circular in cross section, the nature of the fibers differs. Consequently, the muscles of the first two (the kite and the vulture) are placed in Group 2; of the third (Shikra), in Group 3; and of the remaining three (the owl, owlet, and Crow-Pheasant), in the present group (Group 4). In addition, the supracoracoideus muscle of the kingfisher is placed in Group 3 and of the domestic duck in Group 4. It is interesting that the pectoralis muscle of the kingfisher (having R and I fibers) comes under the starling type of pectoralis (Group 5), and that both the pectoralis and the supracoracoideus consist of R, W, I fibers in the duck. This means that the supracoracoideus muscle of the kingfisher is capable of quicker activity than that of the starling, whose supracoracoideus muscle consists of only R and I fibers. On the other hand, the supracoracoideus muscle of the domestic duck is capable of greater sustained activity than the muscles discussed above under Groups 1, 2, and 3.

Group 5

The pigeon supracoracoideus contains R, I, and W fibers, and the following birds (Figs. VI.9–VI.13) having the same muscle composition come under this group:

Hoopoe, *Upupa epops* (Upupidae)
Redvented Bulbul, *Pycnonotus cafer* (Pycnonotidae)
Jungle Babbler, *Turdoides striatus* (Muscicapidae)
Indian Robin, *Saxicoloides fulicata* (Muscicapidae)

Among these birds, the pectoralis muscle of the Hoopoe is similar to that of the pigeon in having R and W fibers, whereas the pectoralis muscles of the others consist of R and I fibers.

Group 6

The supracoracoideus muscles of the Cattle Egret, *Bubulcus ibis* (Ardeidae), the Purple Moorhen, *Porphyrio porphyrio* (Rallidae), and the Koel, *Eudynamys scolopacea* (Cuculidae) consist of R and W fibers (Figs. VI.14–VI.16). The fact that both the pectoralis and the supracoracoideus consist of the same fiber types (R and W) in these birds deserves special mention.

Group 7

The Swift-type supracoracoideus muscles, consisting of I and R fibers, are met with in the House Swift, *Apus affinis* (Apodidae), the Green Bee-eater, *Merops orientalis* (Meropidae), the Whitebellied Drongo, *Dicrurus caerulescens* (Dicruridae), and the Crimsonbreasted Barbet,

Megalaima haemacephala (Capitonidae). Of these four birds (Figs. VI.17–VI.20) the first three have R and I fibers in their pectoralis muscle whereas the fourth has only the R fibers.

Group 8

The supracoracoideus muscles of the following birds contain R and I fibers (Figs. VI.21–VI.29):

Roseringed Parakeet, *Psittacula krameri* (Psittacidae)
Rosy Pastor, *Sturnus roseus* (Sturnidae)
Brahminy Myna, *Sturnus pagodarum* (Sturnidae)
Common Myna, *Acridotheres tristis* (Sturnidae)
Bank Myna, *Acridotheres ginginianus* (Sturnidae)
House Crow, *Corvus splendens* (Corvidae)
Jungle Crow, *Corvus macrorhynchos* (Corvidae)
Yellowheaded Wagtail, *Motacilla citreola* (Motacillidae)
Tailorbird, *Orthotomus sutorius* (Muscicapidae)
Purple Sunbird, *Nectarinia asiatica* (Nectariniidae)
House Sparrow, *Passer domesticus* (Ploceidae)

The pectoralis muscles of the first eight birds consist of R and I fibers, which means that in these birds both the pectoralis and the supracoracoideus muscles have the same type of fiber content. On the other hand, the pectoralis muscles in the remaining three birds have only the R fibers.

Group 9

The lone example thus far discovered of a supracoracoideus muscle consisting of only R fibers (Fig. VI.30) is that of the Rubythroated Hummingbird, *Archilochus colubris* (Trochilidae). This unique feature appears to be characteristic of all hummingbirds. The fact that both the pectoralis and the supracoracoideus muscles consist of only the R fibers shows that this bird has reached the very summit of cellular specialization for sustained muscular activity (Chandra-Bose and George, 1964b).

In characterizing the supracoracoideus muscle in terms of its cellular organization, it is realized that this muscle shows a wider spectrum of variations than the pectoralis muscle between the primitive muscle composition of W, I, and R fibers and the advanced one of R fibers only (Chandra-Bose and George, 1965; George, 1965). In comparing the fiber composition of the pectoralis with that of the supracoracoideus in the various groups of birds, certain interesting facts have been brought forth. The fowl, egret, and the sparrow types (Groups 1, 6 and 8) of the supracoracoideus muscles have the same fiber composition as that of their corresponding pectoralis muscles except in three birds of the sparrow type (Group 8); the House Sparrow, Tailorbird, and the Purple Sunbird have a pectoralis consisting of R fibers only. The only other group in which the fiber composition of the two muscles is identical is that of the hummingbird (Group 9). Considering the two muscles together, four types of pectoral muscles are recognized: WIR, R W, RI, and R, respectively. However, it may be stated that, in general, the supracoracoideus muscle has fewer R fibers than the pectoralis muscle.

In a study of the supracoracoideus muscles in some passerine birds, Salt (1963) distinguished dark and pale fibers by staining them for fat with Sudan black B. The dark and pale fibers described by Salt correspond to the R and I fibers, respectively. Salt also estimated the percentage of each fiber type in the different birds examined (Table VI.2). It is seen from his data that there is a gradual decrease in dark fibers and a corresponding increase in the pale fibers from the first to the last bird in the table. There are more dark (R) fibers in the first eight birds, whereas in the last two birds there are more pale (I) fibers. The fiber composition of the muscle in the former case may be designated as of R and I fibers (Sparrow type; Group 8) and the latter as I and R fibers (Swift type; Group 7). It should, however, be mentioned that in characterizing a muscle on the basis of the nature of its component fibers, staining for succinic dehydrogenase activity is a better index than staining for fat. Fat is a metabolite for muscular energy and is likely to show variations in different fibers of the same type. This is revealed in a recent study by Chandra-Bose and George (1964a) on the pectoralis muscle of some passerine birds.

II. Metabolism

The evolution of the R fiber is to be regarded as an adaptation for sustained muscular activity. In birds indulging in sustained flight the predominance of these fibers in the pectoralis and the supracoracoideus muscles is a clear instance of nature's *modus operandi* in selection. The crux of the problem of oxidative metabolism in the muscles involved in sustained flight is, therefore, the extent to which the R fibers are represented in the muscle. A greater number of these fibers also means greater mitochondrial density and fuel (fat) supply.

Nair (1952) estimated the fat content of the pectoralis and supracoracoideus muscles of a few Indian birds (pigeon, parakeet, crow, sparrow, kite, domestic fowl, and the domestic duck) and found that, in all the birds studied except the domestic duck, the supracoracoideus muscle contained less fat than the pectoralis. In the domestic duck, however, the fat content was found to be slightly higher in the supracoracoideus. The difference between the fat content of the two muscles was most conspicuous in the kite (pectoralis: 3.13%; supracoracoideus: 0.83%). This is not surprising if we take note of the fact that the W type fibers, which contain very little fat, predominate in the supracoracoideus whereas they are absent in the pectoralis. The same author also showed that the iron content of the supracoracoideus muscle is considerably less than that of the pectoralis in all the above mentioned birds (Chapter V, Table V.1).

The level of succinic dehydrogenase activity in a muscle can be regarded as an index of the capacity of the muscle for oxidative metabolism. George and Talesara (1961) estimated this enzyme activity in the pectoralis and supracoracoideus muscles in several birds. Lasiewski, *et al.* (1965) assessed the enzyme level in the two muscles of three species of hummingbirds. The data obtained by these four authors are presented in Table V.7, Chapter V. It is seen that the enzyme activity is considerably less in the supracoracoideus muscle of all the birds studied except in the hummingbirds. In the hummingbirds the supracoracoideus muscle has a higher enzyme level than the pectoralis. This is a very interesting and significant finding indeed. It shows that the supracoracoideus muscle in hummingbirds has a higher capacity for aerobic metabolism. It also shows that the action of this muscle in the elevation and rotation of the humerus in these birds is not just a passive process as a result of the relaxation of the pectoralis muscle but is an equally active one; if, indeed, it is not more active. This may be regarded as an adaptation at the biochemical level for the hovering mode of flight exhibited by hummingbirds.

Harman and his associates studied the relative oxidative activity in various pigeon muscles and correlated it with mitochondrial density (Harman, 1956). The pectoralis muscle was shown to have double the mitochondrial content of the supracoracoideus (pectoralis: 6.9×10^{10}; supracoracoideus: 33×10^{10} mitochondria per gram wet weight of muscle). Oxidative activity expressed in terms of oxygen uptake for the oxidation of a-ketoglutarate used as substrate, was found to be about one and a half times as high in the pectoralis (pectoralis: 6.5×10^3; supracoracoideus: 4.4×10^3 μl O_2 per hour per gram wet weight of muscle). It is also desirable to assess the relative capacity of the two muscles for the oxidation of fatty acids inasmuch as fat is the chief fuel for sustained activity. Such a study in the hummingbirds should be especially revealing and rewarding.

TABLE VI.1

DIAMETER OF THE FIBERS IN MICRONS AND THE PROPORTIONS OF THE FIBER TYPES IN PERCENTAGE IN THE SUPRACORACOIDEUS MUSCLES OF BIRDS[a]

Name of bird	Fiber diameter (in μ) and fiber distribution (%)		
Group 1:	*W*	*I*	*R*
Domestic Fowl (Phasianidae)	95.0 (59.2)[b]	75.0 (24.5)[b]	55.0 (16.3)[b]
Group 2:	*W*	*I*	
Pariah Kite, *Milvus migrans* (Accipitridae)	70.0 (54.5)	45.0 (44.5)	
Indian Whitebacked Vulture, *Gyps bengalensis* (Accipitridae)	74.0 (52.0)	60.0 (48.0)	
Group 3:	*W*	*R*	*I*
Shikra, *Accipiter badius* (Accipitridae)	95.0 (43.6)	60.0 (37.2)	80.0 (19.2)
Whitebreasted Kingfisher, *Halcyon smyrnensis* (Alcedinidae)	60.0 (44.5)	42.5 (31.8)	54.0 (23.7)
Group 4:	*R*	*W*	*I*
Eagle-Owl, Great Horned Owl, *Bubo bubo* (Strigidae)	55.0 (39.6)	90.2 (37.7)	80.0 (22.7)
Spotted Owlet, *Athene brama* (Strigidae)	45.0 (40.6)	92.0 (31.4)	60.5 (28.0)
Crow-Pheasant or Coucal, *Centropus sinensis* (Cuculidae)	42.5 (42.0)	72.5 (38.7)	60.0 (19.3)
	R	*W*	*I*
Domestic Duck (Anatidae)	42.0 (48.3)	94.0 (29.3)	75.0 (22.4)
Group 5:	*R*	*I*	*W*
Blue Rock Pigeon, *Columba livia* (Columbidae)	35.0 (59.2)	52.0 (28.0)	80.0 (12.8)
Hoopoe, *Upupa epops* (Upupidae)	30.0 (46.3)	41.0 (29.1)	85.0 (23.6)
Redvented Bulbul, *Pycnonotus cafer* (Pycnonotidae)	40.0 (40.0)	55.0 (37.5)	70.0 (22.5)
Jungle Babbler, *Turdoides striatus* (Muscicapidae)	38.5 (42.5)	60.0 (34.3)	75.0 (23.2)
Indian Robin, *Saxicoloides fulicata* (Muscicapidae)	40.0 (47.0)	51.0 (37.8)	62.5 (15.2)

(*Continued*)

TABLE VI.1 (Continued)

Name of bird	Fiber diameter (in μ) and fiber distribution (%)	
Group 6:	R	W
Cattle Egret, *Bubulcus ibis* (Ardeidae)	47.0 (69.8)	80.0 (30.2)
Purple Moorhen, *Porphyrio porphyrio* (Rallidae)	50.0 (52.1)	92.5 (47.9)
Koel, *Eudynamys scolopacea* (Cuculidae)	55.0 (61.7)	95.0 (38.3)
Group 7:	I	R
House Swift, *Apus affinis* (Apodidae)	50.0 (57.5)	39.0 (42.5)
Green Bee-eater, *Merops orientalis* (Meropidae)	55.0 (55.5)	35.0 (44.5)
Whitebellied Drongo, *Dicrurus caerulescens* (Dicruridae)	55.0 (56.2)	42.0 (43.8)
Crimsonbreasted Barbet, *Megalaima haemacephala* (Capitonidae)	65.0 (58.0)	45.0 (42.0)
Group 8:	R	I
Roseringed Parakeet, *Psittacula krameri* (Psittacidae)	45.0 (75.2)	52.5 (24.8)
Rosy Pastor, *Sturnus roseus* (Sturnidae)	37.0 (55.5)	75.0 (44.5)
Common Myna, *Acridotheres tristis* (Sturnidae)	50.0 (52.7)	65.0 (47.3)
Brahminy Myna, *Sturnus pagodarum* (Sturnidae)	37.5 (52.6)	55.0 (47.4)
Bank Myna, *Acridotheres ginginianus* (Sturnidae)	42.5 (55.7)	47.5 (44.3)
House Crow, *Corvus splendens* (Corvidae)	44.0 (58.5)	65.0 (41.2)
Jungle Crow, *Corvus macrorhynchos* (Corvidae)	35.0 (56.5)	70.0 (43.5)
Tailor Bird, *Orthotomus sutorius* (Muscicapidae)	45.0 (65.9)	70.0 (34.1)
Purple Sunbird, *Nectarinia asiatica* (Nectariniidae)	39.0 (63.1)	58.0 (36.9)
House Sparrow, *Passer domesticus* (Ploceidae)	42.0 (63.6)	56.0 (36.4)
Yellowheaded Wagtail, *Motacilla citreola* (Motacillidae)	40.0 (52.9)	60.0 (47.1)
Group 9:	R	
Rubythroated Hummingbird, *Archilochus colubris* (Trochilidae)	22.5 (100)	

[a] Data from Chandra-Bose and George, 1965.
[b] Figures in parentheses denote the respective percentage of the fiber types.

TABLE VI.2

PROPORTIONS OF DARK AND PALE FIBERS IN THE SUPRACORACOIDEUS MUSCLES[a]

	Dark fibers (%)	Pale fibers (%)
Snow Bunting, *Plectrophenax nivalis*	68	32
Magnolia Warbler, *Dendroica magnolia*	63	37
House Sparrow, *Passer domesticus*	62	38
Bohemian Waxwing, *Bombycilla garrula*	61	39
Savannah Sparrow, *Passerculus sandwichensis*	60	40
Black-throated Green Warbler, *Dendroica virens*	58	42
Swamp Sparrow, *Melospiza georgiana*	55	45
Mourning Warbler, *Oporornis philadelphia*	54	46
Connecticut Warbler, *Oporornis agilis*	53	47
White-winged Crossbill, *Loxia leucoptera*	51	49
Brown Creeper, *Certhia familiaris*	46	54
White-breasted Nuthatch, *Sitta carolinensis*	34	66

[a] Data from Salt, 1963.

Figures VI.1–VI.30

Figs. VI.1–30. Photomicrographs of T.S. of M. supracoracoideus of various birds, showing the mitochondrial localization of succinic dehydrogenase activity. *W*, white fiber type; *I*, intermediate fiber type; *R*, red fiber type.

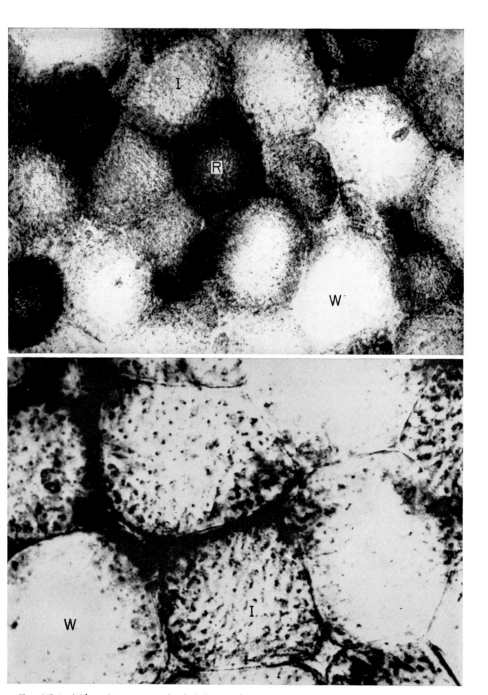

Fig. VI.1. (*Above*) Domestic fowl (Phasianidae). × 290. (By kind permission, Chandra-Bose and George, unpublished work.)

Fig. VI.2. (*Below*) Pariah Kite, *Milvus migrans* (Accipitridae). × 810. (By kind permission, Chandra-Bose and George, unpublished work.)

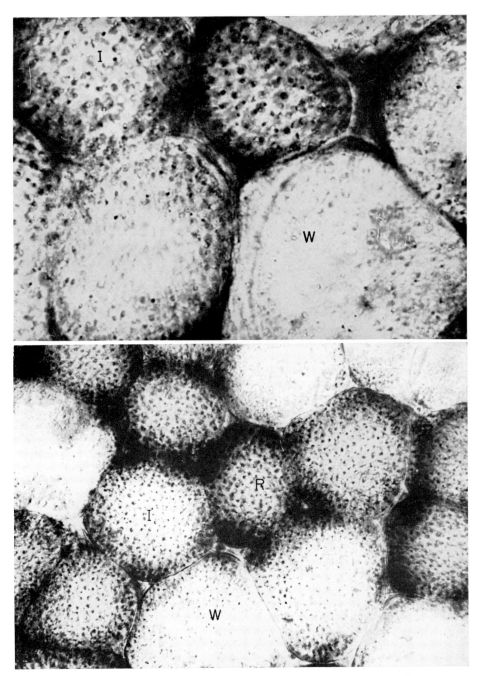

Fig. VI.3. (*Above*) Indian Whitebacked Vulture, *Gyps bengalensis* (Accipitridae). × 810. (By kind permission, Chandra-Bose and George, unpublished work.)

Fig. VI.4. (*Below*) Shikra, *Accipiter badius* (Accipitridae). × 450. (By kind permission, Chandra-Bose and George, unpublished work.)

154

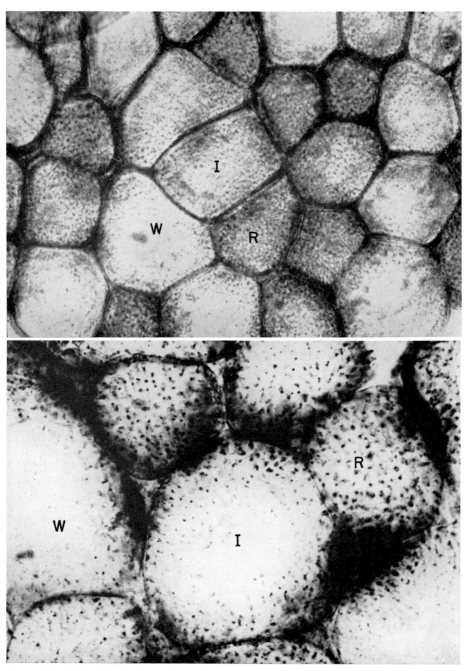

Fɪɢ. VI.5. (*Above*) Whitebreasted Kingfisher, *Halcyon smyrnensis* (Alcedinidae). × 450. (By kind permission, Chandra-Bose and George, unpublished work.)

Fɪɢ. VI.6. (*Below*) Spotted Owlet, *Athene brama* (Strigidae). × 810. (By kind permission, Chandra-Bose and George, unpublished work.)

155

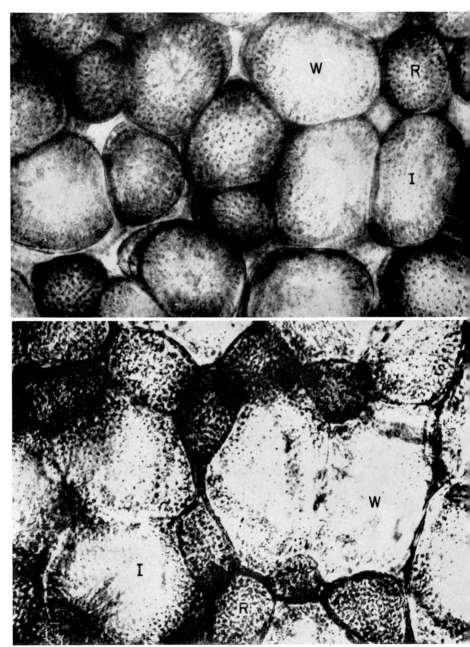

Fig. VI.7. (*Above*) Crow-Pheasant, *Centropus sinensis* (Cuculidae). × 450. (By kind permission, Chandra-Bose and George, unpublished work.)

Fig. VI.8. (*Below*) Domestic duck (Anatidae). × 450. (By kind permission, Chandra-Bose and George, unpublished work.)

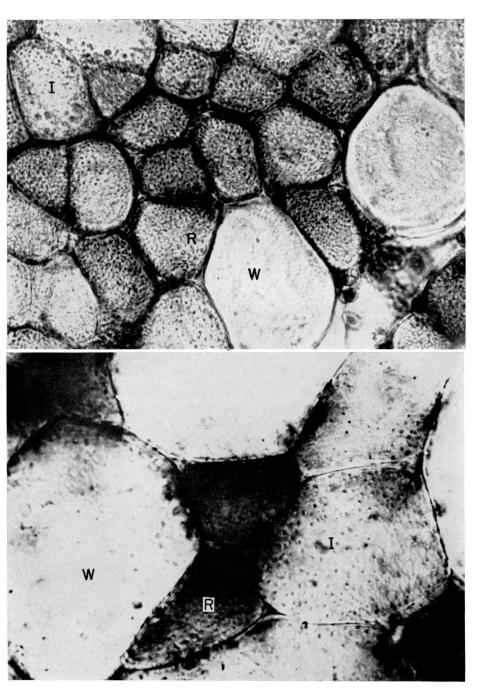

Fig. VI.9. (*Above*) Blue Rock Pigeon, *Columba livia* (Columbidae). × 450. (By kind permission, Chandra-Bose and George, unpublished work.)

Fig. VI.10. (*Below*) Hoopoe, *Upupa epops* (Upupidae). × 810. (By kind permission, Chandra-Bose and George, unpublished work.)

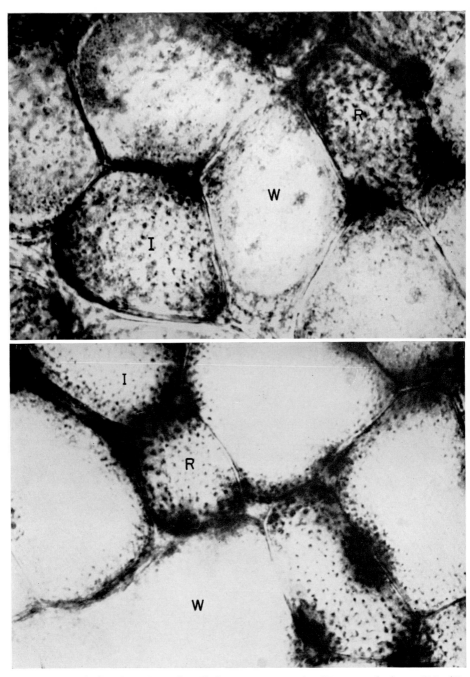

Fig. VI.11. (*Above*) Redvented Bulbul, *Pycnonotus cafer* (Pycnonotidae). × 810. (By kind permission, Chandra-Bose and George, unpublished work.)

Fig. VI.12. (*Below*) Jungle Babbler, *Turdoides striatus* (Muscicapidae). × 810. (By kind permission, Chandra-Bose and George, unpublished work.)

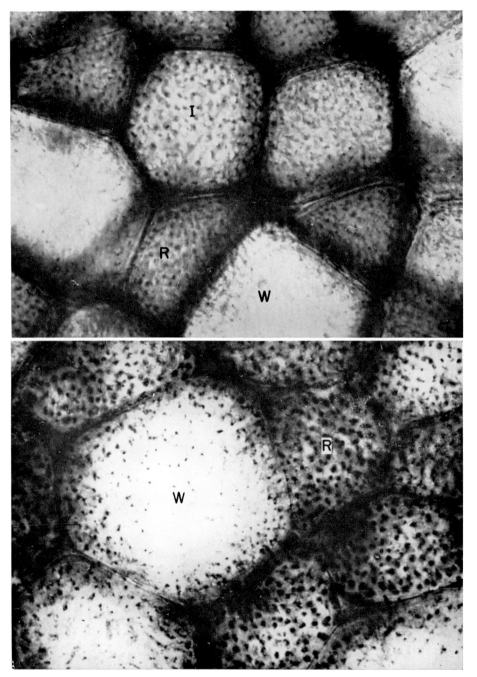

FIG. VI.13. (*Above*) Indian Robin, *Saxicoloides fulicata* (Muscicapidae). × 810. (By kind permission, Chandra-Bose and George, unpublished work.)

FIG. VI.14. (*Below*) Cattle Egret, *Bubulcus ibis* (Ardeidae). × 810. (By kind permission, Chandra-Bose and George, unpublished work.)

159

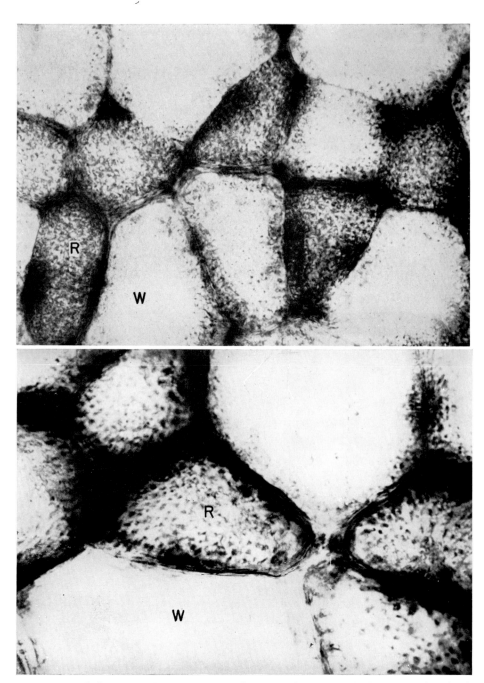

FIG. VI.15. (*Above*) Purple Moorhen, *Porphyrio porphyrio* (Rallidae). × 450. (By kind permission, Chandra-Bose and George, unpublished work.)

FIG. VI.16. (*Below*) Koel, *Eudynamys scolopacea* (Cuculidae). × 810. (By kind permission, Chandra-Bose and George, unpublished work.)

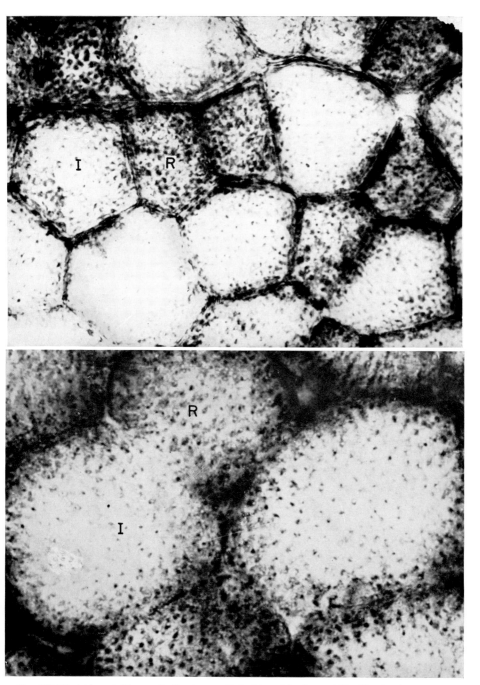

Fig. VI.17. (*Above*) House Swift, *Apus affinis* (Apodidae). × 810. (By kind permission, Chandra-Bose and George, unpublished work.)

Fig. VI.18. (*Below*) Green Bee-eater, *Merops orientalis* (Meropidae). × 1140. (By kind permission, Chandra-Bose and George, unpublished work.)

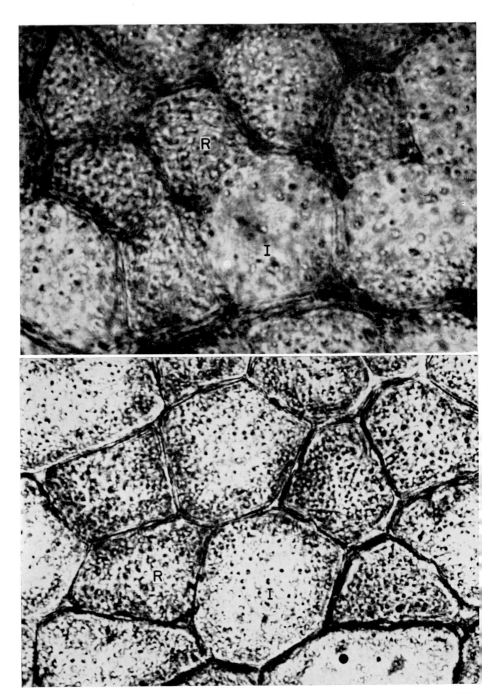

FIG. VI.19. (*Above*) Whitebellied Drongo, *Dicrurus caerulescens* (Dicruridae). × 810. (By kind permission, Chandra-Bose and George, unpublished work.)

FIG. VI.20. (*Below*) Crimsonbreasted Barbet, *Megalaima haemacephala* (Capitonidae). × 810. (By kind permission, Chandra-Bose and George, unpublished work.)

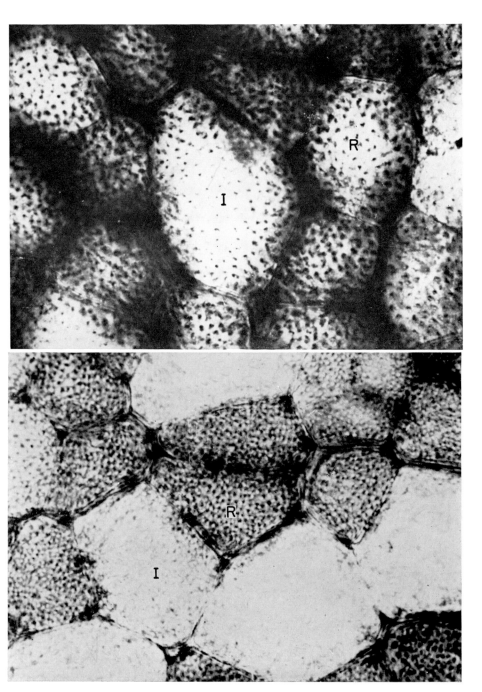

Fɪɢ. VI.21. (*Above*) Roseringed Parakeet, *Psittacula krameri* (Psittacidae). × 810. (By kind permission, Chandra-Bose and George, unpublished work.)

Fɪɢ. VI.22. (*Below*) Rosy Pastor, *Sturnus roseus* (Sturnidae). × 720. (By kind permission, Chandra-Bose and George, unpublished work.)

163

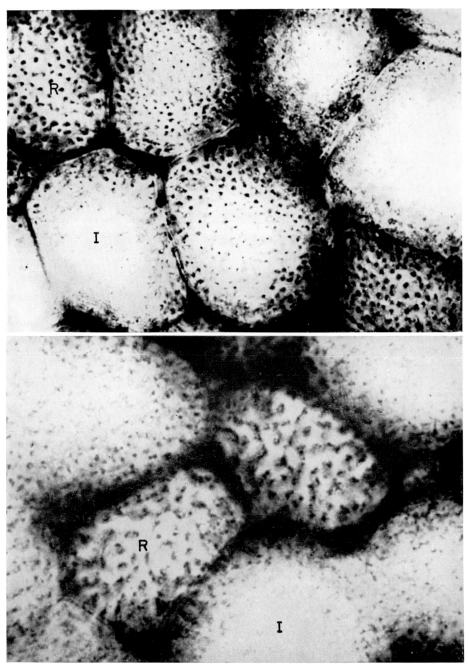

Fɪɢ. VI.23. (*Above*) Common Myna, *Acridotheres tristis* (Sturnidae). × 810. (By kind permission, Chandra-Bose and George, unpublished work.)

Fɪɢ. VI.24. (*Below*) House Crow, *Corvus splendens* (Corvidae). × 1140. (By kind permission, Chandra-Bose and George, unpublished work.)

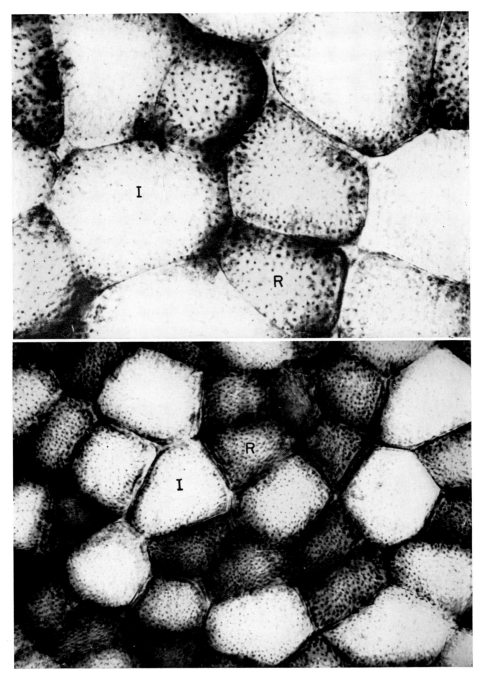

FIG. VI.25. (*Above*) Jungle Crow, *Corvus macrorhynchos* (Corvidae). × 810. (By kind permission, Chandra-Bose and George, unpublished work.)

FIG. VI.26. (*Below*) Yellowheaded Wagtail, *Motacilla citreola* (Motacillidae). × 450. (By kind permission, Chandra-Bose and George, unpublished work.)

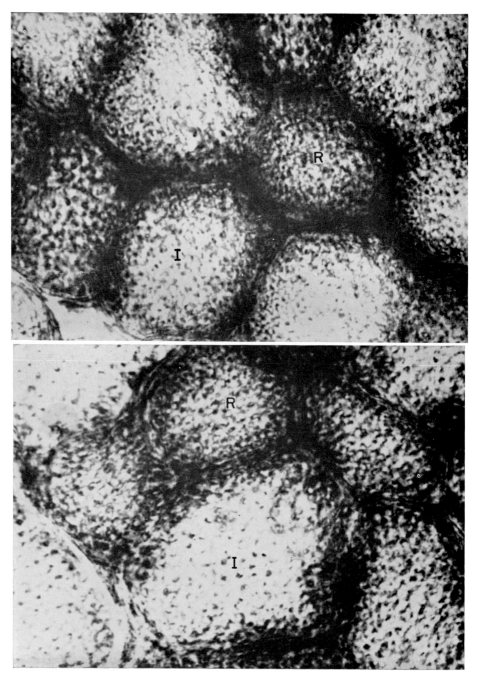

Fig. VI.27. (*Above*) Tailor Bird, *Orthotomus sutorius* (Muscicapidae). × 810. (By kind permission, Chandra-Bose and George, unpublished work.)

Fig. VI.28. (*Below*) Purple Sunbird, *Nectarinia asiatica* (Nectariniidae). × 810. (By kind permission, Chandra-Bose and George, unpublished work.)

Fig. VI.29. (*Above*) House Sparrow, *Passer domesticus* (Ploceidae). × 810. (By kind permission, Chandra-Bose and George, unpublished work.)

Fig. VI.30. (*Below*) Rubythroated Hummingbird, *Archilochus colubris* (Trochilidae). Stained for fat. × 1920. (By kind permission, Chandra-Bose and George, 1964b.)

REFERENCES

Chandra-Bose, D. A., and George, J. C. (1964a). Studies on the structure and physiology of the flight muscles of birds. 11. Cellular organization and distribution of fat and succinic dehydrogenase in the pectoralis of some passerines. *J. Animal Morphol. Physiol.* **11** (C. J. George Felicitation Number): 90–96.

Chandra-Bose, D. A., and George, J. C. (1964b). Studies on the structure and physiology of the flight muscles of birds. 12. Observations on the structure of the pectoralis and supracoracoideus of the Rubythroated Hummingbird. *Pavo* **2**: 111–114.

Chandra-Bose, D. A., and George, J. C. (1965). Studies on the structure and physiology of the flight muscles of birds. 14. Characterization of the avian supracoracoideus. *Pavo* **3**: 23–28.

George, J. C. (1965). Evolution of the bird and bat pectoral muscles. *Pavo* **3**: (in press).

George, J. C., and Talesara, C. L. (1961). The succinic dehydrogenase levels in pectoral muscles of a few representative types of birds and a bat in relation to the fiber diameter, muscle weight and body weight. *Comp. Biochem. Physiol.* **3**: 267–273.

Harman, J. W. (1956). The cytochondria of cardiac and skeletal muscle. *Intern. Rev. Cytol.* **5**: 89–146.

Lasiewski, R. C., Galey, F. R., and Vasquez, C. (1965). Morphology and physiology of the pectoral muscles of hummingbirds. *Nature* **206**: 404–405.

Nair, K. K. (1952). The chemical composition of the pectoral muscles of some Indian birds and its bearing on their flight. *J. Univ. Bombay* **21**: 90–98.

Salt, W. R. (1963). The composition of the pectoralis muscles of some passerine birds. *Can. J. Zool.* **41**: 1185–1190.

CHAPTER VII

Certain Other Wing and Abdominal Muscles: Some Histophysiological Aspects

In the previous chapters certain histophysiological and biochemical aspects of the pectoralis and the supracoracoideus, the two principal flight muscles in the avian body, have been dealt with. In Chapter IX detailed accounts of the gross morphology of the appendicular muscles are given. However, we have very little information on the histophysiological aspects of the appendicular muscles, other than the pectoralis and supracoracoideus, and of the trunk muscles. More information along these lines on the appendicular muscles, especially those of the wing, should be of value in understanding their precise role during flight. For example, in a soarer like the vulture, the musculature of the manus is considerably more developed than in a flapping type of flier such as the sparrow (Abraham, 1963).

In the present chapter we propose to deal with the histological structure and histochemical features of some of the wing muscles. Mm. latissimus dorsi anterior and posterior have been used by neurophysiologists as material for the exposition of the neural end plates in muscle. A brief account of some of the histophysiological aspects of these two muscles, too, will be given. Recently the abdominal muscles of the avian body have attracted some attention because of their possible role in respiration. These muscles will also be dealt with briefly.

I. Wing Muscles

A. GENERAL

We characterized the red (R) and white (W) fibers of the pigeon pectoralis muscle (Chapter IV, Table IV.1) on the basis of diameter, color (myoglobin content), metabolite load (glycogen and fat), and certain enzyme levels (lipase, phosphorylase, and succinic dehydrogenase). In the pectoralis muscle of the domestic fowl a third, intermediate type of fiber (I) was distinguished. On conducting a survey of the distribution pattern of these fiber types in the pectoralis muscles of various birds it became possible to characterize the pectoralis muscle as a whole on the basis of its fiber architecture (Chapter IV). Similarly, the characterization of the supracoracoideus muscle was also possible (Chapter VI).

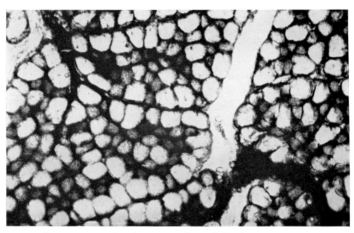

Fig. VII.1. Photomicrograph of a T.S. of M. deltoideus major of pigeon stained for myoglobin by employing the modified method of Chinoy. Note the greater concentration of myoglobin in the red fibers than in the intermediate fibers. $\times$ 130. (By kind permission, Nene and George, 1965.)

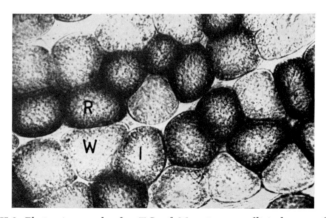

Fig. VII.2. Photomicrograph of a T.S. of M. extensor pollicis longus of domestic fowl stained for succinic dehydrogenase. Note the greater concentration of the enzyme in the narrow, red fibers and a lesser concentration in the broad, white fibers. The intermediate fibers show an intermediate reaction. $\times$ 185. W, white fiber type; I, intermediate fiber type; R, red fiber type. (By kind permission, Nene and George, 1965.)

Investigations on the histophysiological characteristics of some of the other wing muscles in the pigeon and the fowl have brought forth some interesting results (Nene and George, 1965). The three types of fibers (*W*, *I*, and *R*) are present in all muscles (Figs. VII.1 and VII.2) with at least one exception, such as M. biceps of the fowl but not of the pigeon, in which the *I* type fibers are absent. The main difference between the muscles of the fowl and the pigeon are that the red fibers of the fowl are paler and contain slightly less enzyme activity than those of the pigeon. It is also found that all fibers of the fowl muscles are larger than the corresponding types of the pigeon (Table VII.1). The most striking difference between the pectoralis or supracoracoideus and the other wing muscles is that the red fibers, which contain less glycogen than the white (or the intermediate ones in the two former muscles), generally contain more glycogen than the white or intermediate fibers in the latter muscles (Fig. VII.3). The scapular head of M. triceps is, however, an exception: among the fibers attached to the humerus by an apo-neurotic anchor, the white ones have more glycogen. This is a fundamental point of difference between the metabolism of the red and white types of fibers in the two categories of muscles. It has been suggested that the red fibers of the wing muscles other than in the two breast muscles have a higher glycogen synthesizing system than the red fib-

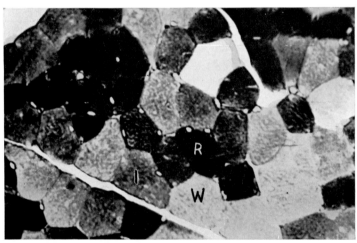

Fig. VII.3. Photomicrograph of a T.S. of M. biceps brachii (coracoidal head) of pigeon stained for glycogen by the PAS technique. Note the greater concentration of glycogen in the narrow, red fibers than in the intermediate fibers which in turn have a greater concentration than the broad, white fibers. × 400. *W*, white fiber type; *I*, intermediate fiber type; *R*, red fiber type. (By kind permission, Nene and George, 1965.)

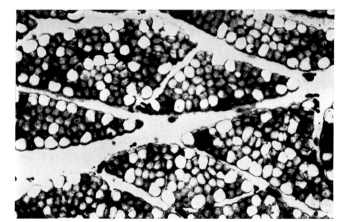

FIG. VII.4

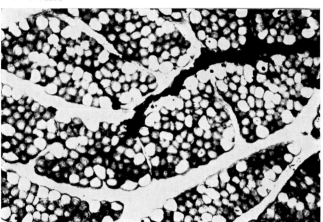

FIG. VII.5

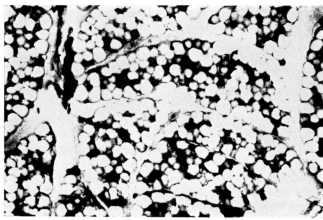

FIG. VII.6

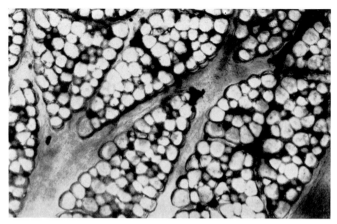

Fig. VII.7

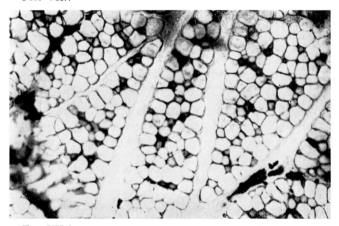

Fig. VII.8

Figs. VII.4–VII.8. Photomicrographs of a T.S. of M. tensor patagii of pigeon stained with Fettrot 7 B. Figure 4 represents the prepatagial part of the muscle and Fig. 8 represents the postpatagial part. Note the greater number of narrow red fibers in the prepatagial part (Fig. 4). The number of red fibers gradually decreases toward the postpatagial part (Fig. 8) where the broad, white fibers predominate. Note the gradual change in the diameter of the white fibers. × 100. (By kind permission, Nene and George, 1965.)

ers of the breast muscles (Nene and George, 1965). This seems to be a characteristic of all the appendicular muscles of the avian body. The functional basis of this characteristic difference among the red fibers is well worth exploring.

A variation from the general pattern of the red fibers is seen in the supinator muscle of the pigeon where the red fibers are larger than the

Table VII.1

Fiber Diameter in Microns of the Various Wing Muscles of the Pigeon and Fowl[a]

Name of muscle	Pigeon			Fowl		
	W fiber	I fiber	R fiber	W fiber	I fiber	R fiber
M. tensor patagii longus	60.9 (55–70)	47.3 (40–50)	37.4 (25–40)	83.9 (75–95)	72.0 (65–75)	53.5 (50–60)
M. tensor patagii brevis	75.5 (70–80)	65.5 (40–75)	39.0 (25–50)	98.7 (90–110)	62.7 (60–85)	60.7 (50–75)
M. deltoideus major	73.7 (60–85)	55.4 (40–65)	40.0 (30–50)	92.4 (60–110)	73.5 (50–85)	77.2 (55–85)
M. triceps scapular head	66.5 (60–70)	54.7 (50–60)	43.5 (35–50)	98.1 (80–110)	83.2 (75–95)	65.9 (50–80)
M. triceps humeral head (ventral)	84.0 (75–100)	64.3 (55–70)	52.0 (45–60)	114.0 (100–125)	93.2 (80–120)	75.2 (60–100)
M. triceps humeral head (dorsal)	87.1 (75–100)	69.0 (65–75)	62.4 (60–65)	115.2 (75–140)	93.6 (65–120)	71.5 (50–80)
M. biceps brachii						
Coracoidal head	78.3 (65–90)	56.0 (50–75)	50.7 (35–65)	69.2 (60–75)	—	56.9 (45–65)
Humeral head	55.1 (50–60)	44.5 (40–50)	38.6 (35–45)	70.6 (65–80)	—	60.5 (50–70)
M. biceps slip	75.0 (60–90)	57.1 (55–70)	41.8 (35–50)	85.4 (80–100)	72.5 (70–75)	65.2 (60–70)
M. extensor metacarpi radialis						
Palmar head	73.7 (60–85)	57.4 (50–60)	44.0 (40–50)	82.4 (75–90)	72.2 (70–75)	60.5 (50–70)
Anconal head	59.3 (50–65)	47.5 (45–50)	37.3 (35–45)	79.1 (65–90)	71.4 (60–75)	60.1 (50–70)
M. extensor digitorum communis	73.3 (55–80)	60.0 (55–65)	50.7 (35–55)	85.4 (75–95)	71.4 (60–80)	51.8 (40–60)
M. extensor metacarpi ulnaris	70.2 (60–75)	50.0 (45–55)	39.1 (35–45)	104.4 (100–125)	81.5 (75–100)	70.9 (60–100)
M. anconeus	70.5 (60–75)	57.1 (50–60)	43.8 (40–50)	102.6 (100–125)	95.0 (90–100)	81.9 (80–100)
M. extensor pollicis longus	72.5 (65–80)	60.0 (55–65)	46.9 (40–50)	101.0 (100–110)	87.8 (80–90)	73.4 (70–85)
M. flexor digitorum superficialis	68.5 (60–75)	49.4 (40–60)	35.1 (30–45)	80.4 (70–90)	64.7 (60–70)	62.4 (50–70)
M. flexor digitorum profundus	70.6 (60–90)	53.5 (50–55)	44.2 (40–50)	97.4 (90–100)	74.6 (70–80)	62.6 (60–80)
M. pronator profundus	69.5 (60–75)	53.3 (50–55)	44.1 (35–50)	100.0 (90–110)	77.5 (75–80)	69.4 (60–75)
M. pronator superficialis	74.6 (70–80)	57.9 (55–75)	40.9 (35–50)	100.0 (80–120)	89.0 (50–95)	66.2 (50–70)
M. ulnimetacarpi ventralis	77.1 (75–85)	63.3 (60–65)	48.5 (40–50)	110.7 (100–125)	102.0 (100–125)	80.0 (75–100)

[a] Data from Nene and George (1965).

white fibers (Nene and George, 1965). This observation also calls for further investigation.

The relative distribution of the three types of fibers that constitute a muscle is not the same in all parts of the muscle. Regional differences in the same muscle have been observed (Nene and George, 1965). For example, M. tensor patagii consists predominantly of the red fibers in its prepatagial part but the pattern gradually changes to predominantly white fibers on its postpatagial side (Figs. VII.4–VII.8). In the case of

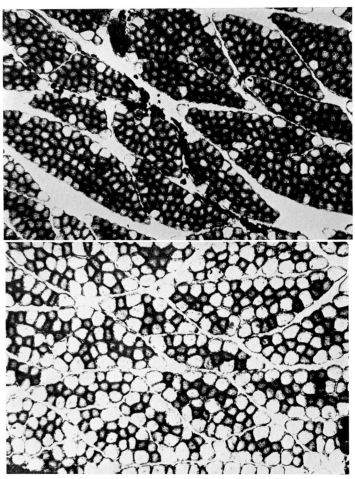

Figs. VII.9 (*above*) and VII.10 (*below*). Photomicrographs of the T.S. of M. extensor metacarpi radialis of pigeon stained with Sudan black B for fat. Figures 9 and 10 represent the anconal and palmar parts of the muscle respectively. Note the predominance of narrow, red fibers in the former and the predominance of the broad, white fibers in the latter. × 100. (By kind permission, Nene and George, 1965.)

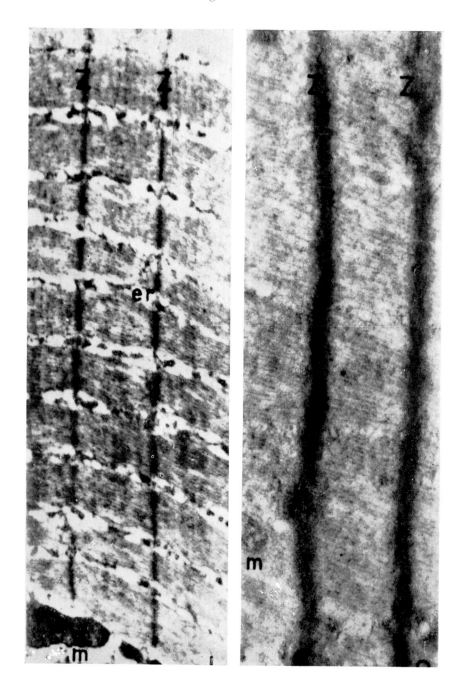

M. biceps and M. extensor metacarpi radialis of the pigeon, the humeral head of the former and the anconal head of the latter consist predominantly of red fibers, whereas the other heads (coracoidal and palmar, respectively) in either muscle consist more or less equally of red and white fibers (Figs. VII.9 and VII.10). This is yet another aspect of muscle structure which calls for further research in order to understand its functional significance.

B. Mm. Latissimus Dorsi Anterior and Latissimus Dorsi Posterior

There has been a considerable amount of interest in Mm. latissimus dorsi anterior and latissimus dorsi posterior ever since Krüger (1950) made the important, observation that the anterior muscle consists of fibers with "felderstruktur" and the posterior of fibers with "fibrillenstruktur." Ruska (1958) confirmed this in an electron microscopic study of these muscles of a crow (Figs. VII.11 and VII.12). It is found that

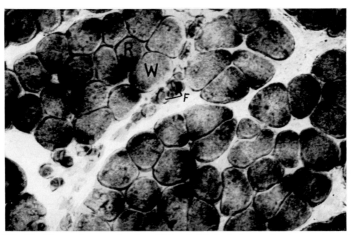

Fig. VII.13. Photomicrograph of a T.S. of M. latissimus dorsi anterior of Cattle Egret (*Bubulcus ibis*) stained for succinic dehydrogenase activity. Note the two types of fibers and the aggregation of mitochondria near the blood capillaries. × 185. W, white fiber type; R, red fiber type; F, interfascicular fat. (By kind permission, Nene and Chinoy, 1965.)

Fig. VII.11. (*Left*) Electron micrograph of M. latissimus dorsi posterior of a crow. L.S. of contracted phasic fiber showing three myomeres with two Z bands (Z) of eleven fibrils, separated by endoplasmic reticulum (er). Mitochondria (m) at the lower left. × 9800. (By kind permission, Ruska and Moore, from Ruska, 1958.)

Fig. VII.12. (*Right*) Electron micrograph of the M. latissimus dorsi anterior of a crow. L.S. of contracted tonic fiber showing three myomeres with two Z bands (Z) but no fibrillation. Mitochondrion (m) at the lower left. × 13,600. (By kind permission, Ruska and Moore, from Ruska, 1958.)

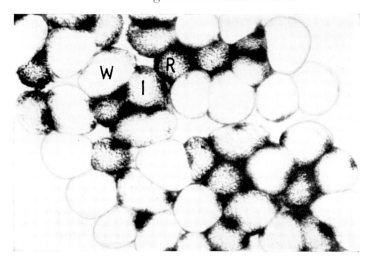

Fɪɢ. VII.14. Photomicrograph of a T.S. of M. latissimus dorsi posterior of Cattle Egret (*Bubulcus ibis*) stained for the demonstration of succinic dehydrogenase activity. Note three types of fibers and the aggregation of mitochondria near the blood capillaries. × 185. W, white fiber type; I, intermediate fiber type; R, red fiber type. (By kind permission, Nene and Chinoy, 1965.)

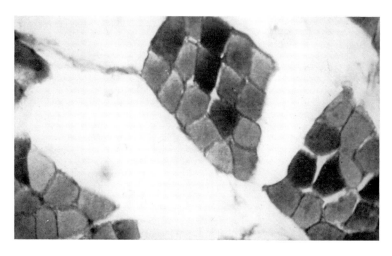

Fɪɢ. VII.15. Photomicrograph of a T.S. of M. latissimus dorsi anterior of domestic fowl stained for glycogen by the PAS technique. Note the two types of fibers and the greater concentration of glycogen in the narrow red fibers. × 320. (By kind permission, Nene and Chinoy, 1965.)

the fibrillar separation of the contractile material is lacking in the former and there is also less sarcoplasmic reticulum in these fibers.

Krüger (1950) showed in birds of different species that the nerve endings in the anterior muscle, which consists of "felderstruktur" fibers, are of the "en grappe" type and those of the posterior muscle, which consists of "fibrillenstruktur" fibers, are of the "en plaque" variety.

FIG. VII.16. Photomicrograph of an isolated muscle fiber from M. latissimus dorsi anterior of domestic fowl stained for the demonstration of acetylcholinesterase. Incubation time: 6 hours. × 510. (By kind permission, Nene and Chinoy, 1965.)

In M. pectoralis of the Blackbird all fibers were found to be of "fibrillenstruktur" with "en plaque" endings (Krüger and Günther, 1958). Ginsborg (1960a) studied the spontaneous electrical activity by intracellular recording at the neuromuscular junction in single fibers of the skeletal muscles of the chicken. He observed that only "slow" fibers are present in the anterior muscle and only "fast" fibers in the posterior muscle. It was also found that some fibers are innervated focally whereas others are innervated at numerous points (multiply innervated) along the fiber (Ginsborg, 1960b). The two types of innervation were then demonstrated histochemically employing the cholinesterase technique

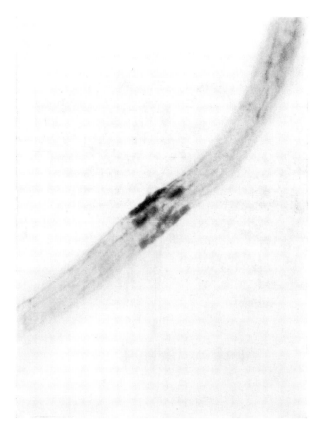

Fig. VII.17. Photomicrograph of an isolated muscle fiber from M. latissimus dorsi anterior of domestic fowl stained for the demonstration of butyrylcholinesterase activity. Incubation time: 22 hours. × 510. (By kind permission, Nene and Chinoy, 1965.)

(Ginsborg and Mackay, 1960). It was found that all fibers in the anterior latissimus dorsi of the chick and the single latissimus dorsi muscle of the pigeon were multiply innervated, whereas the fibers of the posterior muscle were focally innervated. The same authors observed both focally and multiply innervated fibers in the biventer cervicis, semi-spinalis cervicis, gastrocnemius, and sartorius muscles of the chick.

Observations have also been made on the anterior and posterior latissimus dorsi muscles of the chicken from hatching to 1 week of age, from 2 weeks to 3 months of age, and in the adult (Hess, 1961). The anterior

Fig. VII.18. Photomicrograph of an isolated muscle fiber from M. latissimus dorsi posterior of domestic fowl showing the activity of acetylcholinesterase. Incubation time: 4 to 6 hours. × 810. (By kind permission, Nene and Chinoy, 1965.)

muscle was found to consist entirely of fibers of "felderstruktur." Several "en grappe" endings were observed on each muscle fiber along its length at regular intervals of about 250–350 μ in 1- to 7-day-old chickens, and at intervals of about 1000 μ in adults. In the posterior muscle, on the other hand, almost all fibers were found to be of "fibrillenstruktur" in the chicken from hatching to the adult and to have one "en plaque" ending on each fiber. A few fibers probably of "felderstruktur," receiving "en grappe" endings, were also observed.

In both the anterior and posterior muscles of the chick butyrylcholinesterase activity could not be histochemically detected (Silver, 1963). Recently both acetylcholinesterase and butyrylcholinesterase were histo-

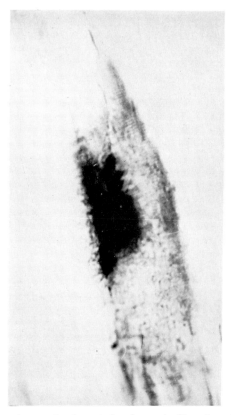

Fig. VII.19. Photomicrograph of an isolated muscle fiber from M. latissimus dorsi posterior of domestic fowl showing the locus of butyrylcholinesterase activity. × 720. Incubation time: 22 hours. (By kind permission, Nene and Chinoy, 1965.)

chemically demonstrated in the pectoral muscles of vertebrates (Chinoy and George, 1965). From the same laboratory, Nene and Chinoy (1965) have shown that the anterior muscle consists of two types of fibers (a broad and a narrow type), whereas the posterior muscle has two types and an intermediate type in addition (Figs. VII.13–VII.15; Table VII.2). The broad fibers contain considerably less myoglobin, fat, and succinic dehydrogenase activity than the narrow ones. This difference is more conspicuous in the fibers of the posterior muscle. On the basis of these observations, the authors have considered the former muscle as red mixed and the latter as white mixed. With respect to the nerve endings, the former has "en grappe" and the latter "en plaque" endings. Both acetylcholinesterase and butyrylcholinesterase are present at the endings in the fibers of both muscles (Figs. VII.16–VII.19). Acetylcholinesterase activity is, however, found to be higher than that of butyrylcholinesterase in both muscles.

TABLE VII.2

THE DIAMETER IN MICRONS OF THE DIFFERENT TYPES OF FIBERS IN *M. latissimus dorsi* *anterior* AND *posterior* OF THREE BIRDS[a]

Bird	M. latissimus dorsi anterior		M. latissimus dorsi posterior		
	W fiber	*R* fiber	*W* fiber	*I* fiber	*R* fiber
Domestic fowl	100 (75–125)	67 (55–80)	153.6 (120–200)	102.5 (90–115)	67.5 (50–85)
Pigeon	70 (60–80)	50 (40–60)	Muscle absent		
Cattle Egret	62 (50–80)	45 (40–50)	87 (70–100)	70 (60–80)	45 (40–50)

[a] Data from Nene and Chinoy (1965).

II. Abdominal Muscles

It is well known that birds lack a respiratory muscle comparable to the diaphragm in the mammals, but they possess air sacs, which the mammals lack. Obviously there should exist significant differences between birds and mammals with regard to the mechanics of respiration. The earliest study on the respiratory movement in birds that we have on record is of Soum (1896). Interest in the subject was revived by Zimmer (1935). Some interesting observations on the anatomy of the ventrolateral abdominal muscles were made by Fisher and Goodman (1955). All these anatomical studies have indicated that the muscles of the abdominal wall have a significant role in the respiratory movements in birds.

Recently, a Japanese group (Kadono *et al.*, 1963) employed electromyographic techniques in order to ascertain the function of the respira-

tory muscles in the chicken during quiet breathing. The external intercostal muscles of the 2nd, 3rd, and 4th intercostal spaces were found to
be concerned with inspiration and those of the 5th and 6th intercostal
spaces with expiration. Internal intercostals posterior to the 3rd intercostal space were observed to be expiratory, but the muscle in the 2nd
intercostal space was inspiratory. They also showed that all four ab-

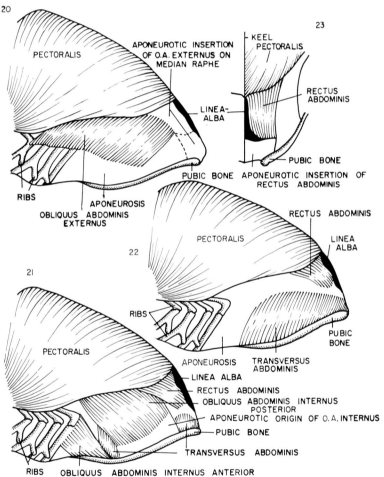

Figs. VII.20–VII.22. The right lateral view of Mm. obliquus abdominis externus,
obliquus abdominis internus, and the transversus abdominis of the pigeon. (By kind
permission, Chinoy and George, 1964.)

Fig. VII.23. Ventral view of the rectus abdominis muscle of pigeon. (By kind
permission, Chinoy and George, 1964.)

dominal muscles of the chicken (namely Mm. obliquus abdominis externus and internus, transversus abdominis, and rectus abdominis) form the principal expiratory muscles. With regard to the trunk muscles, they observed that the main function of "M. serratus dorsalis" is to elevate the external intercostal muscle and that of "M. serratus ventralis" is to depress

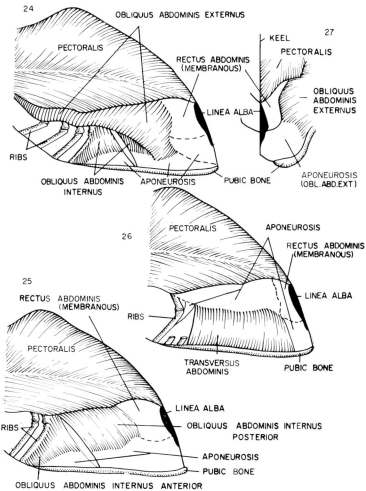

Figs. VII.24–VII.26. The right lateral view of the obliquus abdominis externus, obliquus abdominis internus, and the transversus abdominis muscles of the domestic fowl. (By kind permission, Chinoy and George, 1964.)

Fig. VII.27. Ventral view of the rectus abdominis muscle of domestic fowl. Note the membranous nature of this muscle. (By kind permission, Chinoy and George, 1964.)

the scapula, thus indirectly effecting inspiratory and expiratory movements of the thorax. As for the other thoracic muscles, Mm. transversus
thoracis, scalenus, and levatores costarum were found to be active during
inspiration. No definite conclusions could be arrived at regarding the
action of the dorsal muscles (Mm. trapezius, latissimus dorsi, rhomboideus, longissimus dorsi, and semispinalis dorsi) but they seemed to
assist expiration.

A comparative histophysiological study of the abdominal muscles of
the chicken (a poor flier) and the pigeon (a good flier), was carried out
recently by Chinoy and George (1964) with a view to understanding
their nature and possible role in the respiratory movements of the two
birds. They observed that in the chicken M. rectus abdominis is absent
and its place is taken by a membrane, whereas in the pigeon all four
muscles are well represented (Figs. VII.20 to VII.27). M. obliquus
abdominis internus in both birds consists of two parts, an anterior and a
posterior part. It is likely that Kadono *et al.* (1963) actually made their
electromyographic observations on the posterior part which adjoins the
membrane of the rectus muscle and not on this muscle itself, inasmuch
as it does not exist in the chicken. However, their observation that the
abdominal muscles are expiratory in function is important. The finding
that the rectus muscle is absent in a poor flier suggests that the loss of
this muscle is due to the bird's low respiratory activity. The contraction
of the rectus together with the other abdominal muscles should bring
about a more or less complete replacement of the air in the abdominal
air sac. This device for increased ventilation should be a definite ad-
vantage in an actively flying bird like the pigeon.

The histochemical and quantitative data obtained by Chinoy and
George (1964) on the chicken and pigeon abdominal muscles (Tables
VII.3 and VII.4) with regard to fiber diameter, metabolite load (glycogen and fat), and enzyme levels (lipase and succinic dehydrogenase)
have shown that there exist two patterns of metabolic adaptation at the
cellular level. Some fibers are mainly fat metabolizing fibers whereas
others metabolize chiefly glycogen for energy (Figs. VII.28–VII.45).
M. obliquus abdominis externus and M. transversus abdominis of the
pigeon consist of fibers which are narrower and contain more myoglobin,
fat, lipase, and succinic dehydrogenase than those of Mm. obliquus abdominis internus and rectus abdominis and also of Mm. obliquus abdominis externus and transversus of the fowl. These muscles in the pigeon
should be capable of greater sustained activity than their counterparts
in the fowl. In the pigeon itself, M. transversus, consisting of broader
red and broader white fibers, is considered faster in action than M. obliquus abdominis externus. M. obliquus abdominis internus of the fowl,

TABLE VII.3

THE RELATIVE DISTRIBUTION AND DIAMETER OF THE RED AND WHITE FIBERS IN THE ABDOMINAL MUSCLES OF PIGEON AND FOWL[a]

	Diameter of the fibers in μ		Diameter ratio W.F.	Number of fibers in % per unit area		Number of W.F.
	White fibers (W.F.)	Red fibers (R.F.)	R.F.	W.F.	R.F.	Number of R.F. in an area
PIGEON						
M. o. a. externus	30.13	37.50	1.24:1	11.41	88.59	1:7.76
M. o. a. internus	68.56	44.34	1:1.54	48.11	51.21	1:1.06
M. transversus abdominis	32.66	49.60	1.52:1	8.00	91.95	1:11.4
M. rectus abdominis	68.80	53.18	1:1.29	38.91	60.94	1:1.64
FOWL						
M. o. a. externus	73.00	55.47	1:1.49	65.38	34.61	1:1.88
M. o. a. internus	87.50	64.62	1:1.35	69.62	30.37	1:2.29
M. transversus abdominis	71.42	59.79	1:1.19	62.67	37.32	1:1.67

[a] Data from Chinoy and George (1964).

TABLE VII.4

THE METABOLITE LOAD AND ENZYME (LIPASE AND SUCCINIC DEHYDROGENASE) ACTIVITY IN THE ABDOMINAL MUSCLES OF PIGEON AND FOWL[a]

	Succinic dehydrogenase μg formazan per mg dry weight per hour	Lipase μl CO_2 per mg protein per hour	Glycogen % on wet weight of muscle	Fat % per dry weight of muscle
PIGEON				
M. o. a. externus	7.04 ± 0.48	17.40 ± 0.88	0.13 ± 0.03	14.39 ± 0.70
M. o. a. internus	4.57 ± 0.34	13.29 ± 0.14	0.25 ± 0.03	11.14 ± 0.61
M. transversus abdominis	7.33 ± 0.26	18.15 ± 0.63	0.16 ± 0.03	15.72 ± 0.85
M. rectus abdominis	4.22 ± 0.43	14.56 ± 1.98	0.29 ± 0.05	11.16 ± 0.83
FOWL				
M. o. a. externus	2.96 ± 0.82	6.70 ± 0.55	0.18 ± 0.033	11.27 ± 1.61
M. o. a. internus	1.42 ± 0.18	6.20 ± 0.97	0.12 ± 0.044	8.54 ± 1.53
M. transversus abdominis	3.53 ± 0.36	6.38 ± 0.58	0.28 ± 0.053	12.66 ± 2.23

[a] Data from Chinoy and George (1964).

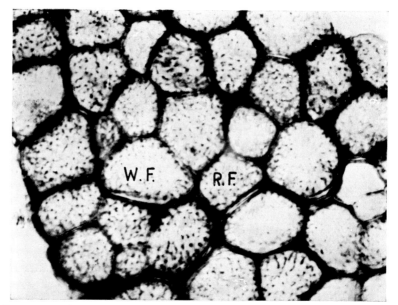

Fɪɢ. VII.28. Photomicrograph of a T.S. of M. obliquus abdominis externus of pigeon stained with Sudan black B for fat. The red fibers (R.F.) are more sudanophilic than the white fibers (W.F.). × 450. (By kind permission, Chinoy and George, 1964.)

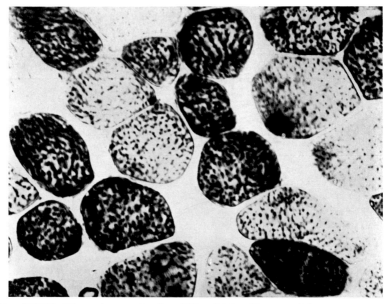

Fɪɢ. VII.29. Photomicrograph of a T.S. of M. obliquus abdominis internus of pigeon stained for the demonstration of fat. × 450. (By kind permission, Chinoy and George, 1964.)

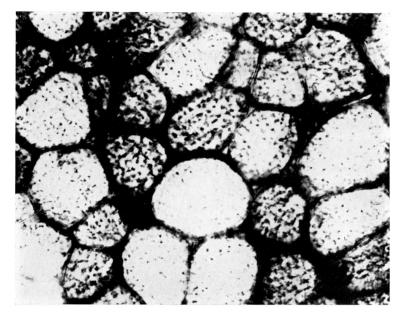

Fig. VII.30. Photomicrograph of a T.S. of M. transversus abdominis of pigeon stained for fat. × 450. (By kind permission, Chinoy and George, 1964.)

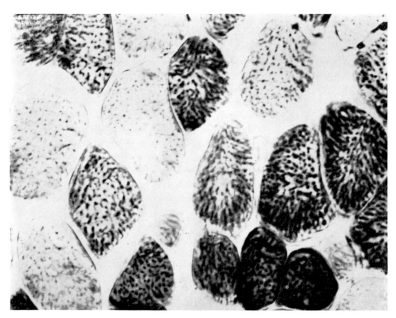

Fig. VII.31. Photomicrograph of the T.S. of M. rectus abdominis of pigeon stained with Sudan black B for fat. × 450. (By kind permission, Chinoy and George, 1964.)

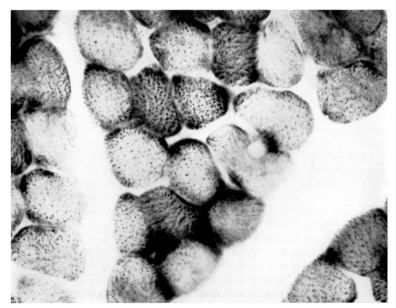

Fig. VII.32. Photomicrograph of a T.S. of M. obliquus abdominis externus of the domestic fowl stained with Sudan black B for fat. × 450. (By kind permission, Chinoy and George, 1964.)

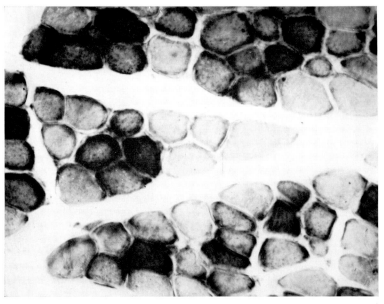

Fig. VII.33. Photomicrograph of a T.S. of M. obliquus abdominis internus of the domestic fowl stained for fat. × 450. (By kind permission, Chinoy and George, 1964.)

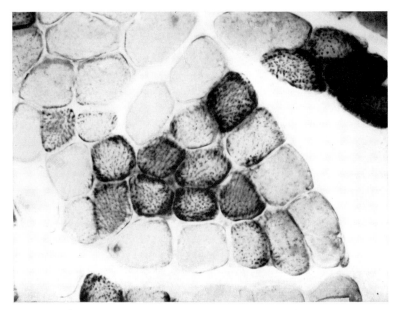

FIG. VII.34. Photomicrograph of a T.S. of M. transversus abdominis of the domestic fowl stained for fat. × 450. (By kind permission, Chinoy and George, 1964.)

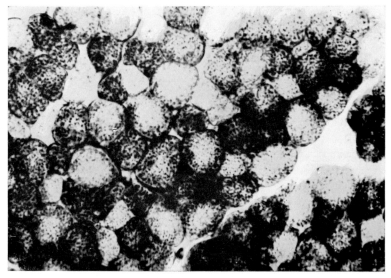

FIG. VII.35. Photomicrograph of a T.S. of M. obliquus abdominis externus of pigeon showing succinic dehydrogenase activity. The red fibers show a greater deposition of the diformazan granules. × 450. (By kind permission, Chinoy and George, 1964.)

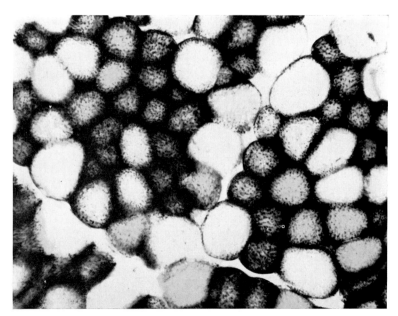

Fig. VII.36. Photomicrograph of a T.S. of M. obliquus abdominis internus of pigeon showing the localization of succinic dehydrogenase activity. × 450. (By kind permission, Chinoy and George, 1964.)

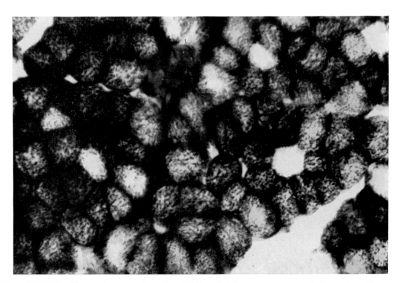

Fig. VII.37. Photomicrograph of a T.S. of M. transversus abdominis of pigeon treated for the demonstration of succinic dehydrogenase activity. × 450. (By kind permission, Chinoy and George, 1964.)

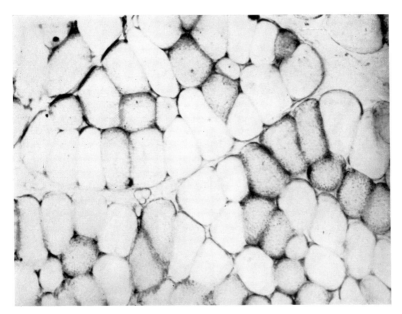

Fig. VII.38. Photomicrograph of a T.S. of M. rectus abdominis of pigeon treated for the demonstration of succinic dehydrogenase activity. × 450. (By kind permission, Chinoy and George, 1964.)

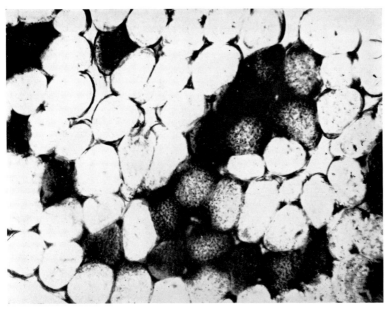

Fig. VII.39. Photomicrograph of a T.S. of M. obliquus abdominis externus of domestic fowl treated for succinic dehydrogenase. × 450. (By kind permission, Chinoy and George, 1964.)

193

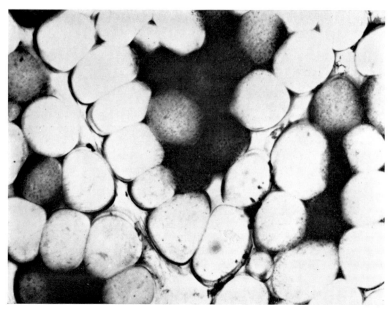

Fig. VII.40. Photomicrograph of a T.S. of M. obliquus abdominis internus of domestic fowl treated for succinic dehydrogenase. × 450. (By kind permission, Chinoy and George, 1964.)

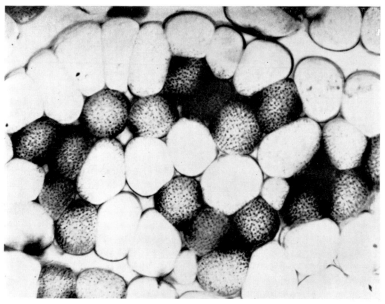

Fig. VII.41. Photomicrograph of a T.S. of M. transversus abdominis of domestic fowl treated for demonstration of succinic dehydrogenase activity. × 450. (By kind permission, Chinoy and George, 1964.)

Fig. VII.42. Photomicrograph of a T.S. of M. obliquus abdominis internus of pigeon stained for glycogen by the PAS technique. The red fibers contain a higher concentration of glycogen than the white fibers. × 1000. (By kind permission, Chinoy and George, 1964.)

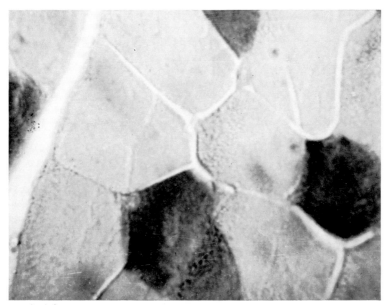

Fig. VII.43. Photomicrograph of a T.S. of M. obliquus abdominis internus of domestic fowl stained for glycogen. × 1000. (By kind permission, Chinoy and George, 1964.)

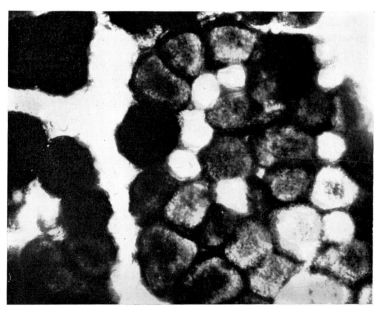

Fig. VII.44. Photomicrograph of a T.S. of M. obliquus abdominis internus of pigeon stained for the demonstration of phosphorylase activity by the method of Eränkö and Palkama. × 450. (By kind permission, Chinoy and George, 1964.)

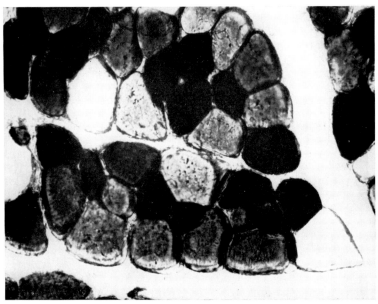

Fig. VII.45. Photomicrograph of a T.S. of M. obliquus abdominis internus of domestic fowl showing phosphorylase activity. × 450. (By kind permission, Chinoy and George, 1964.)

composed of mainly white fibers, should be the fastest muscle in the abdominal wall of the fowl, whereas M. rectus abdominis on the same basis should be the fastest abdominal muscle in the pigeon. Electromyographic studies on these muscles should throw more light on these aspects. However, it is of interest to note that M. rectus abdominis, which is the fastest muscle in a good flier like the pigeon, is lacking in the domestic fowl and another galliform bird (the peafowl), both of which are poor fliers (Chinoy and George, 1964).

The electromyographic studies of Kadono *et al.* (1963) have shown that the abdominal muscles effect expiration. In the flying bird, therefore, the fast contractions of M. rectus abdominis should substantially contribute to a more complete replacement of air in the abdominal air sac and thereby promote greater ventilation of the lungs. This will have to be demonstrated experimentally. By attaching a balloon on the bill of a pigeon and taking moving pictures while it is in flight, it was shown that the bird inhales on the upstroke and exhales on the downstroke (Tomlinson and Mckinnon, 1957; Tomlinson, 1963). Hence, the abdominal muscles should be contracting with the pectoralis muscle during downstroke. We would further like to know whether all the abdominal muscles contract simultaneously or whether there is a time lag between the contractions of the individual muscles so as to present a wave action. Perhaps the three muscles on the lateral abdominal wall contract first and when they are still in the contracted state the rectus abdominis then contracts rapidly, so that there is a more complete expiration of the air from the abdominal air sacs. Direct experimental work on these aspects should provide answers to these and other related questions. In this context it should be mentioned that thirty years ago Bloor and Snider (1934) emphasized the relationship between phospholipid content and muscular activity as observed in the case of the respiratory muscles like the diaphragm in mammals and the abdominal muscles in birds. They obtained in the abdominal muscles of the pigeon a greater phospholipid content than that of either the rooster or the owl, and attributed the low phospholipid level in the latter two birds to their poor flying ability.

REFERENCES

Abraham, S. (1963). A comparison of the muscles involved in the movement of the manus in the House Sparrow with those of the Blue Rock Pigeon and the Black Vulture. *Pavo* 1: 120–123.
Bloor, W. R., and Snider, R. H. (1934). Phospholipid content and activity in muscle. *J. Biol. Chem.* 107: 459–470.
Chinoy, N. J., and George, J. C. (1964). Cellular organization and certain histophysiological features of the avian abdominal musculature. *Pavo* 2: 12–25.

Chinoy, N. J., and George, J. C. (1965). Cholinesterases in the pectoral muscle of some vertebrates. *J. Physiol. (London)* **177**: 346–354.

Fisher, H. I., and Goodman, D. C. (1955). "Myology of the Whooping Crane, *Grus americana.*" Univ. of Illinois Press, Urbana, Illinois.

Ginsborg, B. L. (1960a). Spontaneous activity in muscle fibres of the chick. *J. Physiol. (London)* **150**: 707–717.

Ginsborg, B. L. (1960b). Some properties of avian skeletal muscle fibres with multiple neuromuscular junctions. *J. Physiol. (London)* **154**: 581–598.

Ginsborg, B. L., and Mackay, B. (1960). A histochemical demonstration of two types of motor innervation in avian skeletal muscle. *Bibliotheca Anat.* **2**: 174–181.

Hess, A. (1961). Structural differences of fast and slow extrafusal fibres and their nerve endings in chicken. *J. Physiol. (London)* **157**: 221–231.

Kadono, H., Okada, T., and Ono, K. (1963). Electromyographic studies on the respiratory muscles of the chicken. *Poultry Sci.* **42**: 121–128.

Krüger, P. (1950). Untersuchungen am Vogelflügel. *Zool. Anz.* **145**: 445–460.

Krüger, P., and Günther, P. G. (1958). Innervation und pharmakologisches Verhalten des M. gastrocnemius und M. pectoralis major der Vögel. *Acta Anat.* **33**: 325–338.

Nene, R. V., and Chinoy, N. J. (1965). Histochemical observations on the avian Mm. latissimus dorsi anterior and posterior. *Pavo* **3**: 29–34.

Nene, R. V., and George, J. C. (1965). A histophysiological study of some muscles of the avian pectoral appendage. *Pavo* **3**: 35–46.

Ruska, H. (1958). The morphology of muscle fibers and muscle cells with different properties of conduction of excitation. *Exptl. Cell Res.* Suppl. 5: 560–567.

Silver, A. (1963). A histochemical investigation of cholinesterases at neuromuscular junctions in mammalian and avian muscle. *J. Physiol. (London)* **169**: 387–393.

Soum, M. (1896). Recherches physiologiques sur l'appareil respiratoire des oiseaux. *Ann. Univ. Lyon* **28**: 1–126.

Tomlinson, J. T. (1963). Breathing of birds in flight. *Condor* **65**: 514–516.

Tomlinson, J. T., and Mckinnon, R. S. (1957). Pigeon wing-beats snychronized with breathing. *Condor* **59**: 401.

Zimmer, K. (1935). Beitrage zur Mechanik der Atmung bei den Vögeln in Stand und Flug. *Zoologica* **33**: 1–69.

CHAPTER VIII

The Energy Problem in Bird Migration

The phenomenon of migration though most conspicuous and specialized among birds, is a general feature of all groups of animals. Among the invertebrates, the movements of crabs from the intertidal zone to the deep seas, the migrations of insects such as that of the monarch butterfly from the region of the Great Lakes in North America to as far south as the Gulf of Mexico and of locusts through thousands of miles in every continent, are all well known. The migratory travels of the Atlantic salmon, the hump-back whale, and certain species of bats, among the vertebrates other than birds, are also a matter of common knowledge.

Migrant birds fly over vast expanses of land and sea to reach their destination. The Golden Plover flies over the Atlantic Ocean covering a distance of nearly 2400 miles without stopping for food or rest and then proceeds southward to its destination in Argentina, over land for more than 2000 miles. It spends the winter there and is back in its northern home for the spring. The Pacific Golden Plover leaves its breeding grounds in Alaska for its winter home in the Hawaiian Islands flying in a single hop of at least 2000 miles. The greatest of the feathered marathon travelers is the Arctic Tern which nests near the North Pole. In the fall the Arctic Terns go southward passing through the hot regions near the equator to reach their cool summer home near the South Pole thus completing an 11,000 mile journey. In spring they take another 11,000 mile journey back to the arctic regions.

Of the several questions that could be raised on the subject of bird migration, the question as to what is the source of energy for such sustained flight and how it is harnessed has been one of the most intriguing. In recent years, a considerable amount of work has been done on this aspect of bird migration, not merely because the subject is of general interest to ornithologists but also for its fundamental value to medical science in learning more about problems such as muscular efficiency, physical endurance, obesity, etc., which are of considerable importance to human welfare.

199

I. Premigratory Fat Deposition

The most conspicuous change noticed in a migratory bird toward migration is the enormous amount of fat deposition in the subcutaneous and visceral depots. Liebelt and Eastlick (1954) described sixteen regions of fat storage in the chick embryo. On the basis of this study McGreal and Farner (1956) described fifteen regions of subcutaneous fat depots in the migratory finch, *Zonotrichia leucophrys gambellii*. The superficial pectoral fat depot described in the chick embryo was not sufficiently well defined in the White-crowned Sparrow to warrant the distinction of being called a fat depot. The claviculocoracoid fat body, located cephalad in the region of the clavicle and lateral to the coracoid, was the largest, while the ophthalmic fat body was the smallest. The lateral thoracic fat body, lying superficial to the pectoralis muscle, was found to be most well defined and at the same time one of the largest. Although such deposition of fat has long been known (Wachs, 1926; McCabe, 1943; Odum, 1949), Odum and Perkinson (1951) were the first to determine quantitatively by actual extraction the fat content of a migratory bird (the White-throated Sparrow, *Zonotrichia albicollis,*) in four different seasons: postmigration (October–November), midwinter (January–February), molt (March–April), and premigration (April–May). In the postmigratory period when the birds arrived at their wintering grounds, the total body lipid was as low as 6% of the body weight, whereas in the premigratory period a threefold increase (17% of body weight) was registered. An increase to 12% of the body weight was seen in the midwinter, and during molt the lipid level came down to even lower than the postmigratory figure. Odum and Perkinson also observed that, except for the heart which showed hardly any seasonal variation in its lipid content, all other body parts varied considerably. Subcutaneous fat formed about 40% of the total lipids while the peritoneal fat was found to be highly variable but substantially greater in amount in the premigratory period.

The peritoneal fat or "migratory fat" is distinguished from the subcutaneous fat or "winter fat." The former accumulates rapidly in large amounts just prior to migration and is spent by the end of migration (Odum and Perkinson, 1951). It is also likely that in some species which feed en route, the fat deposits are replenished. The newly arriving Savannah Sparrows and shrikes were found to possess easily detachable fat amounting to about one-fifth of the body weight (McCabe, 1943). In the case of the White-throated Sparrow, Odum and Perkinson (1951) observed that females possessed a higher lipid content during the postmigratory and molt periods whereas males acquired a greater amount of fat and fattened more rapidly than females in the premigratory period. This difference in fat content, however, was not a sex difference in lipid metabolism but rather a difference in migratory behavior. As indeed it was, the males migrated earlier than females. The premigratory fat deposition, therefore, has been emphasized as a prerequisite for migration (Odum and Perkinson, 1951).

Considerable increase in fat deposition in the liver prior to migration has been noted in the White-throated Sparrow (Odum and Perkinson, 1951) and the Rosy Pastor (Naik, 1963). Naik recorded in the Rosy Pastor a sudden rise in the fat and glycogen levels of the liver and a drop in protein and water, in the premigratory period. A reduction in the absolute water content of the lateral thoracic fat body during the premigratory fat deposition, was noted in the White-crowned Sparrow (McGreal and Farner, 1956). Marked premigratory fat deposition has also been reported in the pectoralis muscle of the Rosy Pastor (Vallyathan, 1963). Thus fat is stored in practically all parts of the body. It is, however, interesting that, unlike humans in whom an obese condition often results in a fatty heart, in the migratory bird the heart is the only major part or organ that does not increase in weight owing to fat deposition (Odum and Connell, 1956).

The main fat storage in the bird body prior to migration is in the adipose tissue, though considerable increase in fat also takes place in the liver. The recent discovery (George and Naik, 1962) of the occurrence of hematopoietic nodules as centers of fat synthesis as well as erythrocyte production in the liver of the migratory starling, *Sturnus (Pastor) roseus*, is pregnant with new possibilities in understanding the capacity of the avian liver for increased fat synthesis and erythropoiesis. But in this bird, too, the adipose tissue is where most of the fat is stored. The time-honored notion regarding the adipose tissue as being merely an inert storage tissue has now given place to the new concept of its being a dynamic system concerned with the synthesis, oxidation, storage, and release of lipids. Although this new knowledge is based on extensive experimental work done during the past twenty years, practically all investigations have been on mammalian material and comparatively little on avian. George and Eapen (1958a,b, 1959a,b, 1960) have recently shown that the adipose tissue in birds, is also well organized and metabolically highly active. However, we need to know much more about the avian adipose tissue.

II. Fat Levels and Weight Loss during Migration

With the premigratory deposition of fat, there is also an increase in the body weight. If this fat is to be the fuel for the energy required in migratory flight, a decrease in body weight as well as in the lipid level in the body of the birds actually in migration, and more conspicuously those at the end of migration, is to be expected. Odum and Connell (1956) compared the average lipid levels (percentage of wet weight) of birds (seven species of warblers, vireos, and tanagers) in actual state of migration with those of premigrant, postmigrant, and experimental birds of species of various migratory status. Their data showed highest lipid levels (one-third of the wet weight or two-thirds of the dry weight just prior to migration or during migration in species that winter in Central or South America. In contrast, these long distance migrants during nonmigratory activity and the nonmigratory species possessed only 6 or 7% fat. The White-throated Sparrow which does not migrate beyond southern United States was intermediate between the two extremes. In the same species it was observed in an earlier study (Odum and Major, 1956) that the maximum lipid level in the premigratory period in the wild population was the same as that obtained in those kept in captivity and in which lipid deposition was experimentally induced by subjecting them to long photoperiods.

Odum (1958) in a subsequent report on the lipid content of 45 White-throated Sparrows, 29 warblers, and 101 Red-eyed Vireos killed by flying into a TV tower near Tallahassee (Florida) during the 1956 fall migration, noted that many of them (White-throats) were relatively very lean having less than 2% fat. Evidently, these birds had come almost to the end of their migratory flight. The Red-eyed Vireos and the warblers on the other hand were fat, having the high fat level of 40% for sustaining them in their flight over the Gulf of Mexico.

The outcome of these observations was the realization that the distance the bird would be able to cover (flight range) is dependent on the level of fat deposition. On the basis of the fat levels in the body, Odum et al. (1961) estimated the flight ranges of several species of migrant birds including that of the Rubythroated Hummingbird (Archilochus colubris). They based their calculations on the assumption that the energy required for migratory flight at an average speed of about 30 miles per hour is thrice the existence level. These calculations led them to conclude that tanagers, thrushes, and warblers considered to be trans-Gulf (Gulf of Mexico) migrants have ample fat to make the nonstop over-water journey. They also pointed out that the Rubythroated Hummingbird has more than enough fat reserves to accomplish the trans-Gulf flight.

Nisbet et al. (1963), who made a close study of the migration of the Blackpoll Warblers, observed that these birds remain in New England for some weeks to fatten prior to their migration toward the West Indies. Some of these birds that were caught at the lighthouse in Bermuda were found to be still considerably fat thereby indicating that they would have continued their flight had they not been stopped there. The authors (Nisbet *et al.*, 1963) in estimating the weight loss, found that in a bird of average weight (17.3 gm) the loss was about 0.56 ± 0.07% of the mean body weight per hour. At this rate, it was calculated, that these birds had enough fat reserves for a continuous flight of 105 to 120 hours without stopping in Bermuda, which would have taken them to the main land of South America. Nisbet (1963) in comparing the rate of weight loss obtained from eight previous field studies of migrating birds, to that in the Blackpoll Warbler, arrived at a reasonable average for energy consumption of migrating passerines as 0.076 Kcal per gm total weight per hour.

In estimating the flight ranges of birds Odum *et al.* (1961) distinguished three patterns of premigratory fat deposition. (1.) Short-range migrants in which fat deposition does not reach its peak at the start of migration (e.g., Savannah Sparrow). (2.) Short-range migrants in which the peak fat deposition is reached when migration begins (e.g., White-throated Sparrow). (3.) Long-range migrants that become extremely fat, by as much as 50% more of body weight, prior to migration (e.g., Scarlet Tanager). In a recent communication emerging from the same school, Caldwell *et al.* (1964) have provided indirect evidence that long-range northern migrants start their southward migration with a low to moderate fat-store but increase their reserves with every halt until the peak level is built up at the near points, such as the Gulf Coast from where the long nonstop flights are begun.

Although ornithologists believe that the Rubythroated Hummingbird does indeed fly across the Gulf of Mexico, a distance of over 500 miles, physiologists had not been able to demonstrate convincingly its energy potential to accomplish it. The first attempt to do so was the classic experiment of Pearson (1950) on the Anna and Allen Hummingbirds (*Calypte anna* and *Selasphorus sasin*), in which he had the bird hover under a bell jar and measured the rate of oxygen consumption. Assuming the flight speed of a migrating hummingbird to be 50 miles per hour and its fat reserve 1 gm, he estimated that a metabolic rate of 80 cc O_2 per gm per hour would account for a flight range of only 385 miles (1 gm fat = 9 Kcal, 1 liter of oxygen consumed = 4.69 Kcal). Odum and Connell (1956) pointed out that *Archilochus colubris* actually builds up a fat reserve of 2.1 gm (over 40% of its body weight) prior to migration. But studies on the flight speed of hummingbirds showed the correct speed to be around 25 instead of 50 per hour and so Pearson (1961) maintained that his earlier estimate of 385 miles as the flight range still held good. Recently, Lasiewski (1962, 1963), experimenting with hummingbirds using Pearson's techniques, succeeded in having a bird hover in the metabolic chamber for 50 minutes and thereby obtained direct measurement of oxygen consumed during flight. He obtained an average value of flight metabolism of 42.4 cc O_2 per gm per hour and estimated that a supply of 2 gm of fat would sustain a male for 26 hours of flight and a female for 24.3 hours. A separate calculation for the male and for the female was necessitated by the findings of Connell *et al.* (1960) that the fat-free weight of the male (2.50 gm) is less than that of the female (2.76 gm). Assuming the flight speed to be 25 miles per hour, Lasiewski (1962) estimated the flight range of the male as 650 miles and of the female at 610. The energy potential of that delightful little bird marvel, to fly nonstop across the Gulf of Mexico, was thus experimentally demonstrated.

III. The Fuel for Muscular Energy

From what has been discussed above, there appears to be not even the possible shadow of doubt that the fuel for muscular energy during migration is chiefly fat. It should, however, be mentioned that as migration time approaches glycogen is also increased in the liver as well as in muscle. Naik (1963) has shown that the glycogen content of the liver in the Rosy Pastors, which arrive in Baroda (India) about August/September from Southern Europe and the U.S.S.R. and leave for their breeding grounds there in April, is actually doubled (from 0.26 to 0.62 gm per 100 gm wet weight in April) within a week prior to migration while protein and water are gradually reduced (from 23.58 and 70.05 in October to 17.67 and 65.66 per 100 gm wet weight respectively in April). In the pectoralis muscle of this bird the glycogen content is increased from 0.93 in December to 1.82 gm in April per 100 gm wet muscle (Vallyathan and George, 1964a), and fat from 10.20 in December to 16.75 per 100 gm dry muscle in April (Vallyathan, 1963). Vallyathan and George (1964a) also found that in this starling, during the premigratory period (March/April), the activity of phosphorylase, is doubled (postmigratory, December: 21.86, and premigratory, March/April: 43.86 µg phosphorus per mg dry muscle per 15 minutes). It is likely that fat is synthesized from glycogen and protein. Such a possibility has been suggested by Merkel (1958b) from his observations that during the period of fattening the afternoon respiratory quotients in several species of birds exceeded 1.0 indicating the synthesis of fat from carbohydrate.

Caged photosensitive White-crowned Sparrows deposit large amounts of fat in the subcutaneous and visceral fat depots when subjected to long daily photoperiods (Farner *et al.*, 1961). According to these authors, during this period of fattening, in both the caged birds and the wild population, there is a considerable reduction of glycogen in the liver and also in the pectoralis muscle. They suggested that this is due to increased glycolysis which in turn could act as an acetate-sparing effect, thus providing more acetate for fat synthesis. These findings are contrary to those that have been made in studies of wild populations of Rosy Pastor (Naik, 1963; Vallyathan and George, 1964a; George and Chandra-Bose, unpublished work, 1965). It is most unlikely that this is a case of species difference. Increase in liver and muscle glycogen near migration time, therefore, seems to be a general feature in migratory birds. However, as for the fate of this increased glycogen further investigation is necessary.

Although it has long been known that migratory birds deposit large amounts of fat before migration and some at stopovers during migration, and that the stored fat is almost completely depleted by the end of migration, the various biochemical mechanisms by which fat is metabolized to energy have remained obscure. However, much new light on this aspect has been thrown in recent years (Drummond and Black, 1960; George, 1962).

George (1947, 1952) studied the chemical composition of the skeletal muscles of various representative vertebrate types and observed that of all muscles the pigeon breast muscle contains the highest amount of fat. George (1952) postulated that fat should be the chief fuel for muscular energy in migrating birds. Later, on electrically stimulating the pigeon breast muscle as well as on subjecting the bird to forced flight, it was shown that there is a reduction in the free lipid content of the liver and muscle (George and Jyoti, 1953, 1955b). From the loss of weight observed in a migratory bird (*Carduelis flammea*) which was flown in an empty tube for 10 minutes, it has been calculated that 1 gm of fat is burned in 2–3 hours of continuous flight or the bird undergoes a loss of 2% in its body weight in 1 hour. It was also estimated that its usual fat reserve of 20–25% should be sufficient for 8–12 hours of nonstop flight (Dolnik, 1961).

As a form of reserve fuel, fat has certain definite advantages over carbohydrates and proteins. Since fat has more carbon and hydrogen, 1 gm of fat actually yields more energy than an equal amount of the other two materials put together (1 gm fat = 9.3 Kcal; 1 gm carbohydrate = 4.2 Kcal; 1 gm protein = 4.1 Kcal). When fat is metabolized, it also yields twice as much water as each of the other two substances (1 gm fat = 1.07 gm water; 1 gm carbohydrate = 0.55 gm water; 1 gm protein = 0.41 gm water). The latter feature is of particular significance in terrestrial animals. In these animals conservation of water is very necessary since they have to face severe water shortage and the metabolic water resulting from the combustion of fat becomes a life-saving product. Metabolic water should be especially important in migratory birds as they fly across an ocean like the Atlantic or a desert like the Sahara.

George and Jyoti (1955b) considered the ether-extractable lipid as free lipid and that extracted by an alcohol-ether mixture as total lipid, the difference being the bound lipid. When these experiments were repeated, by estimating the relative reductions in fat and carbohydrate and calculating the energy expended, it was found that in the electrically stimulated pigeon 71% of the total energy expended was derived from free fat and in the pigeon subjected to flight continuous to exhaustion 77% (George and Jyoti, 1957). George and Jyoti (1957) also observed that when the breast muscles of two other birds, a soarer (kite) and a nonflier (domestic fowl), were subjected to electrical stimulation 61% of the energy in each case was derived from free fat. It should be mentioned here that the free lipid contents of the pigeon, kite, and fowl before stimulation, were found to be 2.75%, 3.0%, and 0.55% respectively and total lipids 4.50%, 4.75%, and 1.0% respectively. The reduction in the lipid content was found to be only in the free lipid in the pigeon and kite but in the fowl a reduction in the bound lipid also was indicated. From the considerable reduction in fat in the fowl muscle which has a very low lipid content, it appears reasonable to state that any muscle when subjected to prolonged exercise would utilize fat as the chief fuel. In support of this, may be cited the work of Young and Price (1961) which showed that all of the energy expended in dogs under severe exercise was derived from fat even though dog muscles unlike those of birds have a low fat content. Recently Spitzer and Gold (1964) showed that free fatty acids are oxidized by electrically stimulated dog muscle.

George and Jyoti (1955a) reported two distinct types of fibers in the pigeon breast muscle, one a broad type with clear sarcoplasm and the other a narrow one with dense inclusions of fat globules. It was shown that under starvation, as well as when the muscle was continuously exercised, there appeared to be a reduction in the fat inclusions in the narrow fibers, thereby rendering clearly the otherwise not quite clear, striations in these fibers. Using histochemical and microphotographic techniques, George and Naik (1958, 1959) presented a comprehensive picture of the two types of fibers. They characterized the broad type as glycogen-loaded and the narrow ones as fat-loaded. In the earlier chapters (IV, V) the histochemical and biochemical features of these fiber types have been dealt with in detail. It suffices to state that the broad glycogen-loaded fibers are adapted for an anaerobic metabolism using glycogen as the chief fuel and the narrow fat-loaded ones for an aerobic metabolism using fat.

IV. Combustion of Fat

If fat is to be used as fuel, it has first to be broken down to fatty acids and glycerol (Figs. VIII.1 and VIII.2). Occurrence of a lipase in high concentrations in the fat-loaded fibers of the pectoralis muscle of the pigeon and that of other birds have been demonstrated, using histochemical and biochemical techniques, by George and his associates in a series of publications. The biochemical nature, precise histochemical localization, and the physiological role of lipase in muscle, have been discussed in a recent review (George, 1964). It has been shown that the level of lipase activity in a muscle is an index of the extent of fat utilization and the capacity of the muscle for sustained activity. From histochemical preparations it is now known that lipase activity is localized in the mitochondria (Bokdawala and George, 1964). Studies on the particulate fractions of the pigeon breast muscle (George and Talesara, 1962) showed the highest yield of lipase activity in the soluble fraction whereas the mitochondrial and microsomal fractions showed in each case nearly half the activity of the soluble fraction. However, specific activity of lipase was found to be maximum in the microsomes (103.84 μl CO_2 per mg protein per hour) and next the mitochondria (47.05 μl CO_2 per mg protein per hour) while the concentration of the oxidative enzyme, succinic dehydrogenase was highest (35.56 μg formazan per mg protein per hour) in the mitochondrial fraction and almost negligible in the microsomal fraction (6.37 μg formazan per mg protein per hour) and in the soluble fraction (1.82 μg formazan per mg protein per hour). In the histochemical technique, "Tween 85" (polyoxyethylene sorbitan trioleate) was used as substrate. In the earlier work (George and Iype, 1960), the substrate used was "Tween 80" (polyoxyethylene sorbitan monooleate). With "Tween 80" and still lower "Tweens," such as "40" (polyoxyethylene sorbitan monopalmitate) and "20" (polyoxyethylene sorbitan monolaurate), precipitates of lead sulfide, denoting lipase activity, were found outside the mitochondria also. It is therefore possible that a higher lipase acting on triglycerides of long-chain fatty acids is localized in the mitochondria and a lower lipase acting on those of short-chain fatty acids in the microsomes. In the quantitative estimations of lipase (George and Talesara, 1962) the substrate used was tributyrin which is a triglyceride of shorter chain fatty acids than triolein.

That fats are hydrolytically broken down to glycerol and free fatty

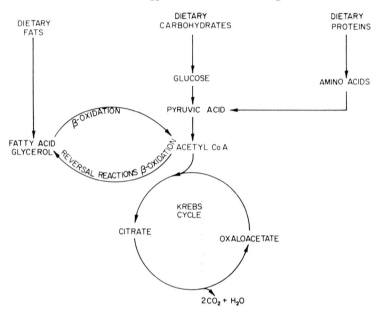

Fɪɢ. VIII.1. Showing the metabolic interrelationships of the three major metabolites.

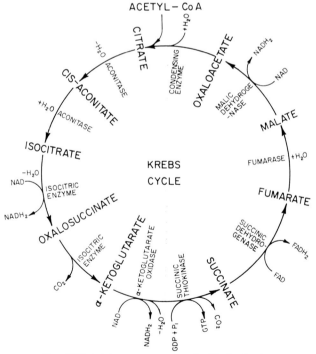

Fɪɢ. VIII.2. Major reactions in the Krebs Cycle.

acids before any oxidative process could take place, had only been assumed and not demonstrated. George and Talesara (1962) recently
tried direct *in vitro* oxidation of two triglycerides (tributyrin and triolein) by the pigeon breast muscle mitochondria as well as whole muscle
homogenate. Both of the triglycerides used were not oxidized but, on the
contrary, the oxidation of a Krebs (tricarboxylic or citric acid) cycle
intermediate, malate, used as sparker, which was found necessary for
fatty acid oxidation, was actually inhibited. This may be attributed to the
liberation of free fatty acids through lipase action which changed the
pH of the medium in the Warburg reaction flask. There is no evidence
that neutral fat, as such, could be directly oxidized. Therefore, lipase action as the first step prior to oxidation should be considered as essential
and a normal process *in vivo*.

The next step in the utilization of fat for energy is the oxidation of
fatty acids to carbon dioxide and water. The mechanism of fatty acid
oxidation involves a stepwise process of cleavage of 2-carbon fragments
(Fig. VIII.3) beginning from the carboxyl end of the fatty acid chain
and is now known to require the action of five different enzymes (thiokinase, acyl dehydrogenase, enoyl hydrase, β-hydroxyacyl dehydrogenase,
β-ketoacyl thiolase). It thus yields at every stage a molecule of 2-carbon
fragments and a fatty acid with the 2-carbon substance less. This mechanism was first postulated by Franz Knoop who gave it the name β-oxida-
tion, and he considered the 2-carbon substance to be acetic acid. The
end result of β-oxidation is the generation of acetyl coenzyme A (acetyl
CoA) which enters the Krebs cycle for final oxidation to carbon dioxide
and water.

Acetyl CoA is also the product of carbohydrate and protein degradation. Glucose, through a process of glycolysis, is broken down to pyruvic
acid, which in turn is oxidized to acetyl CoA. Essentially all amino acids
yield either acetyl CoA or an intermediate of the Krebs cycle (oxaloacetate, or α-ketoglutarate). It may therefore be stated that, in metabolism, all roads lead to acetyl CoA (Fig. VIII.1). Acetyl CoA could
undergo oxidation via the Krebs cycle to form finally carbon dioxide and
water, or undergo a series of condensing reactions to form the higher
fatty acids. Carbohydrate could thus be converted to fat. It should be of
considerable interest to know why it is that under certain circumstances
acetyl CoA gets oxidized to yield energy and in other cases it condenses
to form long-chain fatty acids which in turn go to form fats. We have
no definite answer to this. It is however suggested as a possible explanation that the conversion of acetyl CoA to fat or carbohydrate is
brought about if there is a shortage of oxaloacetate at the first step
where acetyl CoA is condensed with oxaloacetate with the aid of a condensing enzyme to form citrate.

The Krebs cycle is thus the wheel of cellular metabolism which, when it turns, brings about the oxidation of carbohydrates, fats, and also some of the protein intermediates of the cell. The possibility of interconversions of the three foodstuffs, is now well established. The energy in one could be stored in a more convenient form in another for future use.

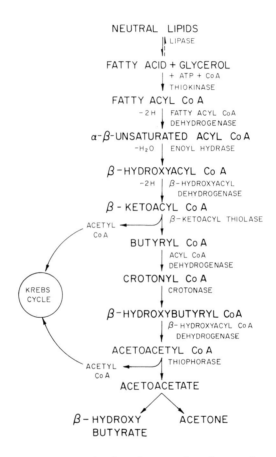

Fig. VIII.3. Major steps in the degradation and oxidation of neutral lipids.

For example the energy in carbohydrates could be stored as fat. This is indeed what migratory birds do prior to migration. It is also the function of the cycle to make the chemical energy thus stored available to the cell in a form that can be easily used when needed for performing the various functions.

V. Generation of Free Chemical Energy

Nearly three decades ago Szent-Györgyi showed that minced pigeon breast muscle could oxidize pyruvate completely provided catalytic amounts of dicarboxylic acids such as succinate, malate, and oxaloacetate were added. So in the aerobic metabolism of glucose to form carbon dioxide and water, formation of lactic acid is not necessary. Pyruvate could be converted to acetyl CoA by an enzyme complex known as pyruvic oxidase.

Acetyl CoA is the link between the two chief metabolic cycles, the tricarboxylic and fatty acid cycles, in the mitochondrion. When acetyl CoA, the end product of fatty acid oxidation, condenses with oxaloacetate to form citrate and enters the Krebs cycle, CoA is released and made available for the esterification of another fatty acid molecule. A continuous flow of oxaloacetate is considered essential to "spark" the oxidation of acetyl CoA and the generation of CoA. Therefore, the role of a Krebs cycle intermediate preferably one preceding oxaloacetate, such as malate, as a "sparker," is well recognized.

When acetyl CoA enters the Krebs cycle and forms citrate, the latter is acted upon by an enzyme aconitase to form cis-aconitate and iso-citrate (Fig. VIII.2). Isocitrate is attacked by the isocitrate dehydrogenase and brings about the oxidative decarboxylation of isocitrate to form a-ketoglutarate and carbon dioxide. Initially the reaction is oxidation with a pyridine nucleotide acting as a coenzyme to produce oxalo-succinate. This is followed by the decarboxylation of oxalosuccinate by the same enzyme to give a-ketoglutarate and carbon dioxide. It is believed that oxalosuccinate if formed as an intermediate does not exist in the free state. Owing to the dual role of the enzyme, the name iso-citric enzyme, has been suggested to cover both the activities. The action of a separate enzyme oxalosuccinate decarboxylase for decarboxyla-tion had also been suggested. The pyridine nucleotide required by the isocitrate dehydrogenase of the heart and skeletal muscle mitochondria was found to be nicotinamide-adenine-dinucleotide (NAD), formerly called diphosphopyridine nucleotide (DPN), while that for the soluble liver enzyme, nicotinamide-adenine-dinucleotide phosphate (NADP) formerly called triphosphopyridine nucleotide (TPN). Isocitrate when oxidized to oxalosuccinate loses two hydrogen atoms to the coenzyme NAD which becomes $NADH_2$ or in the case of NADP, forms $NADPH_2$. The carbon dioxide resulting from the decarboxylation process is derived from the oxidation of one of the carbon atoms of the original oxaloace-tate. After the formation of $NADH_2$, its oxidation results in the genera-tion of energy.

The next step is the formation of succinate and carbon dioxide by the oxidative decarboxylation of a-ketoglutarate catalyzed successively by a-ketoglutarate oxidase complex and succinic thiokinase. In the first reaction coenzyme A also takes part with the result that what is actually formed is succinyl coenzyme A and not succinate. It is also aided by NAD forming $NADH_2$ which in turn is oxidized to provide energy. In the second reaction coenzyme A is enzymatically removed from succinyl coenzyme A with the aid of guanosine diphosphate (GDP) and inorganic phosphate to form guanosine triphosphate (GTP) which is a high-energy compound. This GTP could react enzymatically with adenosine diphosphate (ADP) to form GDP and adenosine triphosphate (ATP). This important substance adenosine triphosphate bearing high-energy phosphate bonds may be called the storage battery of the cell.

In the next reaction two hydrogen atoms are removed enzymatically by succinic dehydrogenase from succinate to form fumarate. This enzyme may be considered the prime mover in the citric acid cycle because of its powerful action in the removal of two hydrogen atoms. These hydrogen atoms are taken up by an electron carrier, cytochrome *b* to form reduced cytochrome *b*.

The fumarate thus formed takes up a molecule of water and with the aid of fumarase forms malate. Malic dehydrogenase with NAD as cofactor is then responsible for the oxidation of malate to form $NADH_2$ and oxaloacetate. This new oxaloacetate has the same two carbon atoms of the old acetate molecule and by accepting another molecule of acetyl CoA, it could start the cycle over again (Loewy and Siekevitz, 1963).

Inside the cell the energy stored in the various substrates is tapped by a series of oxidation-reduction reactions through an electron transport chain consisting of pyridine nucleotides, flavins, cytochromes, and molecular oxygen. In the process of electron transport, a donor transfers a pair of electrons to an acceptor through the agency of an enzyme. Fundamentally the electron donor undergoes oxidation and the electron acceptor reduction, and the process becomes essentially an oxidation-reduction reaction. In the oxidation of pyruvate a pair of electrons are transferred by the coenzyme NAD which is an electron acceptor and becomes reduced NAD or $NADH_2$. Within the Krebs cycle many substrates are oxidized by enzymes known as dehydrogenases, such as isocitrate dehydrogenase, a-ketoglutarate dehydrogenase, succinate dehydrogenase, and malate dehydrogenase. Some dehydrogenases are specifically NAD-linked, others NADP-linked while still others with both the coenzymes.

The oxidation of $NADH_2$ which is the next step in the electron transport chain, is accomplished by an $NADH_2$ reductase. This enzyme is a flavoprotein, in which the flavine-adenine-dinucleotide (FAD) forming

the prosthetic group, becomes reduced, thus participating in the oxidation reaction. In the case of succinic dehydrogenase, electrons from succinate are directly transferred to the flavoprotein instead of through
NAD as from $NADH_2$ to FAD like the other dehydrogenases. This is
realized from the fact that for the oxidation of succinate by succinic
dehydrogenase *in vitro*, the enzymatic reaction does not need the cofactor NAD. It appears therefore that there are two flavoproteins, one
that requires the mediation of NAD and the other that does not. Electrons from the reduced flavoproteins are then taken up by an electron
acceptor, cytochrome *b*. From the reduced cytochrome *b* electrons are
transferred to cytochrome c_1, cytochrome *c*, cytochrome *a*, and cytochrome a_3 in a succession of oxidations and reductions. Cytochromes are
heme proteins in which iron forms the core of the heme and it is the
iron that is oxidized and reduced in electron transport. Recently a new
electron carrier, coenzyme Q_{10} which is a quinone operating in the respiratory chain, has been discovered. Cytochrome *a* and cytochrome a_3
known together as cytochrome oxidase, are responsible for the final
transfer of electrons and hydrogen to oxygen to form water. The transport of electrons from the different substrates to the electron carriers is
dependent on the energy potential of the carriers. Electrons move from
a substance with higher reducing potential to one with a lower reducing
potential. The various steps in the electron transport chain can be compared to a series of cascades in which water starts from a high energy
level (substrate) and ends up at a lower energy level (oxygen). These
cascades are the routes along which ATP production is achieved by the
phosphorylation of adenosine diphosphate (ADP) by inorganic phosphate.

Living organisms have thus developed the ability to generate free energy in the form of ATP by three different methods: (1) through the
process of glycolysis, which is the most primitive and by which sugar is
broken down by enzymes in the absence of free oxygen yielding only
one molecule of ATP for each pair of electrons that are released;
(2) through oxidative phosphorylation in the mitochondrion yielding
three molecules of ATP for each pair of electrons released; (3) and
through chloroplasts, also giving as many molecules of ATP for every pair
of electrons released by light. This threefold increase of energy output
by the chloroplast and the mitochondrion has set the plant and animal
worlds in their respective favored positions.

VI. Energy for Migration

The mitochondrion is very aptly called the powerhouse of the cell. It
has a complex machinery for the generation of power. Its fuel consists
chiefly of carbohydrates and fats. The furnace is the citric acid cycle.

The main product is ATP, the "energy coin of the biological realm," and the byproducts are carbon dioxide and water. In those avians which indulge in sustained flight, the breast muscle consists of cells studded with large mitochondria (Chapter IV). These specialized organelles of the avian muscle cell are the sites of fat combustion. That the pigeon breast muscle has a high oxidative capacity and is capable of metabolizing fat has been demonstrated (Weinhouse et al., 1950; George and Talesara, 1962). The mammalian skeletal muscle also has been found to possess the adequate enzymatic machinery to oxidize short-chain fatty acids to carbon dioxide (Fritz et al., 1958). Such a system is all the more important in the migratory bird in which fat is the chief reserve material.

In the case of a migratory bird, Sturnus roseus, it was observed (George and Talesara, 1961) that the level of the oxidative enzyme, succinic dehydrogenase in the pectoralis muscle, rose from 7.7 μg formazan per mg dry muscle per 30 minutes in the month of November to as high as 16.8 μg formazan per mg dry muscle per 30 minutes in April just prior to migration. This indicates that as the time for migration approaches the oxidative capacity of the pectoralis muscle is increased and that the muscle would increasingly metabolize fat. But in vitro experiments, with added fatty acid, on the capacity for fatty acid oxidation of the breast muscle homogenates of a migratory (Sturnus roseus) and a nonmigratory starling (Acridotheres tristis) during the premigratory phase of the former, showed that the extent of fatty acid oxidation in the former was actually lower than that of the latter (George and Iype, 1964). George and Vallyathan (1964c) conducted similar experiments on the muscle homogenate of the starling (Sturnus roseus) during the pre- and postmigratory periods. They observed that the oxygen uptake due to added fatty acid in the manometric system during the premigratory period was considerably lower than that in the postmigratory period. However, malate oxidation was higher than in the complete system with added fatty acid, in the premigratory period. This diminished capacity for fatty acid oxidation is indicative of a low degree of fat utilization during the premigratory period. This is indeed to be expected because that is the time during which there is rapid synthesis of fat. It is also indicative of the existence of a control mechanism, possibly a hormonal one, to promote fat synthesis and at the same time minimize fat utilization. However, the muscle of the migratory starling in the postmigratory period showed an over-all higher oxidative metabolism than that of the nonmigratory one (George and Iype, 1964).

It is interesting that the capacity for fatty acid oxidation of the pectoralis in the premigratory period is low even though the level of oxidative enzyme activity is highest at that time. The level of lipase activity in a muscle has been shown to be an index of the capacity of the muscle for the utilization of fat (George, 1964). In studying the lipase activity of the pectoralis of *Sturnus roseus* (Vallyathan, 1963), it was observed that during the premigratory period the enzyme activity (26.70 μl CO_2 per mg protein per hour) was lower than that in the postmigratory period (35.91 μl CO_2 per mg protein per hour). These observations further support the suggestion that there exists a control mechanism for minimizing fat utilization and thereby enhancing fat storage. Does such a system, if it exists, also stimulate fat synthesis? Or is it merely the inhibitory action of high fat and free fatty acid levels on lipase and the oxidative system? We need to have more information to arrive at definite conclusions.

The problem of energy for sustained flight during migration is no more a matter of speculation and hypothesization as it was a few years ago. We now do know that fat is the fuel and that muscle has the requisite machinery for the combustion of fat and the generation of free chemical energy. Yet like all scientific enquiries, the more we learn about life processes, the more we become aware of what is yet to be known.

We know that the bird undergoes a period of premigratory hyperphagia which induces voracious feeding and leads to enormous deposition of fat in the body (Odum, 1960a,b). But, we need to know a lot more about the various factors that influence hyperphagia and fat deposition. We know that fat gets accumulated in the adipose tissue, liver, and muscles. Are these tissues actual sites of fat synthesis? What are the different processes involved in the synthesis of fat? If fat is oxidized in the muscle for energy, when the muscle fat gets depleted, how is fat from the other parts made available to the muscle for combustion? Several other questions could be raised.

It is now well established that the adipose tissue in general is a dynamic system where synthesis, storage, oxidation, and release of fats take place (Jeanrenaud, 1961). However, very little information on avian adipose tissue (George and Eapen, 1958b) is available. The liver of at least one migratory bird is now known to possess special sites for fat synthesis (George and Naik, 1962). Lipid synthesis by the rat skeletal muscle has been recently demonstrated (Neptune *et al.*, 1963). Fat synthesis in avian muscle (chicken pectoralis) cells has also been demonstrated (Jordan and Kratzer, 1963).

Increased caloric intake through forced feeding in rats has been shown to result in increased traffic of glucose over an alternate metabolic pathway, the hexosemonophosphate shunt (pentose cycle) leading to enhanced lipogenesis (Cohn and Joseph, 1959). In recent years important contributions have been made on the significance of this metabolic pathway for the generation of $NADPH_2$, on which several biochemical processes depend. The demonstration that reduced NADP is essential for certain steps in the synthesis of fatty acids has clearly indicated that the most important function of this pathway is to supply $NADPH_2$ for lipogenesis (Wakil, 1960; Jeanrenaud, 1961). The initial step in the pathway is the dehydrogenation of glucose-6-phosphate to 6-phosphogluconate. The dehydrogenation of the latter to ribulose-5-phosphate require NADP as hydrogen acceptor while dehydrogenations occurring during glycolysis are linked with NAD. The level of glucose-6-phosphate dehydrogenase, could therefore be regarded as indicative of the extent of $NADPH_2$ production as well as that of fat synthesis. The operation of the pentose cycle in the skeletal muscles of vertebrates, and especially in the avian pectoralis, has been recently demonstrated histochemically (Nene and George, 1965). These authors have shown a high activity of glucose-6-phosphate dehydrogenase in the fat-loaded fibers of the pigeon pectoralis.

It has been mentioned earlier that the microsomal fraction of the pigeon breast muscle was found to have the highest lipase activity but extremely low oxidative enzyme activity. But the mitochondrial fraction showed the highest oxidative enzyme activity and about half the lipase activity of the microsomal fraction (George and Talesara, 1962). These authors suggested for lipase a dual role of hydrolysis of fat into fatty acids and glycerol and of esterification of fat from the two components. According to them the high concentration of lipase in the microsomes could bring about the esterification of the fatty acids synthesized as well as hydrolyze triglycerides and thus render fatty acids available to the mitochondria for oxidation. It is also known that microsomes are the sites of fat synthesis (Green, 1960), and mitochondria for fatty acid oxidation (Kennedy and Lehninger, 1949; Green, 1951). While a very high degree of esterification and hydrolysis of fat with hardly any oxidation of fatty acids, are possible in the microsomes, very high oxidative activity and a considerable amount of hydrolytic and esterifying activity, are possible in the mitochondria. Evidence has now become available of the existence in the liver of two distinct systems, a mitochondrial and a nonmitochondrial one, for the synthesis of fatty acids (Green and Wakil, 1960; Wakil, 1960). These systems should also be present in the muscle. Similarly the existence of a nonmitochondrial oxidating system, probably for the oxidation of some of the products of carbohydrate metabolism and short-chain fatty acids, has recently been shown histochemically in the pigeon breast muscle (George *et al.*, 1963). It should be mentioned, however, that some authors have raised doubts regarding the esterifying action of lipase *in vivo*.

Studies similar to those on the pigeon breast muscle, mentioned above, have been carried out on the pectoralis muscle of wild populations of Rosy Pastors during the premigratory and postmigratory periods and in the early morning as well as late evening hours (George and Vallyathan, 1964a). The results obtained from these studies have enabled the authors to confirm at the subcellular level, earlier observations on the whole muscle homogenates of the same bird. They have concluded that there exists a more favorable set-up of enzymatic levels in these birds for increased biosynthesis of fat and at the same time decreased fat utilization during the premigratory period. The increased glycogen content and phosphorylase activity (Vallyathan and George, 1964a) in the pectoralis of this bird during the premigratory period suggests the possibility of lipid synthesis from carbohydrates which form the main bulk of their food during this period. It has also been suggested (George and Vallyathan, 1964a) that in the premigratory period active fat synthesis takes place during the night.

From the discussion above, it is clear that the muscle cell can synthesize its own fat. We have also considered the mechanism by which fat is metabolized by the muscle cell. It is therefore logical to expect that during muscular activity the intracellular fat should be the immediate source of energy. It has been clearly shown in the rat diaphragm *in vitro* that this is indeed so and that the cells of the diaphragm could respire for relatively long periods using only their endogenous fat as substrate (Neptune *et al.*, 1959). The next question that arises is how fat from extramuscular fat reserves (liver and adipose tissue) is transported to the muscle as the intra- and extracellular muscle fat gets depleted. The answer to this question is available from the recent work of George and Vallyathan (1964b). They have provided evidence to show that when a pigeon is exercised the fat from the fat depots is transported as free fatty acids to the muscle through the blood. However, the mechanism of the transport of fatty acids through the interstitial space to the sites of fatty acid oxidation in the muscle cell remains to be discovered. Some new light on this important problem is now being shed by the studies on the role of carnitine in muscle metabolism. Carnitine, the richest known source of which is muscle, has been shown to stimulate fatty acid oxidation and the possibility of its having a role in the transfer of fatty acids to the sites of fatty acid oxidation has also been indicated (Fritz and McEwen, 1959; Fritz, 1961, 1964). Carnitine has been found to stimulate the oxidation of palmityl CoA and also to augment the rate of palmitate incorporation into mitochondrial phospholipids, primarily lecithin (Bressler and Friedberg, 1964). They (Bressler and Friedberg, 1964) have also indicated a role for carnitine in the translocation of palmityl CoA from extramitochondrial to intramitochondrial sites. Beenak-kers and Klingenberg (1964) have suggested that acetyl carnitine forms a complex with coenzyme A to facilitate fatty acid transfer and that an enzyme carnitine-coenzyme A transacetylase is necessary for the transfer of the acetyl group from carnitine to coenzyme A to form acetyl CoA. They have further suggested that the same enzyme can also transfer acyl groups of medium and long carbon chains. It should be of con-siderable interest to note that in assaying the level of this enzyme ac-tivity in the mitochondria from various organs, that from the pigeon breast muscle was found to possess the highest enzyme level (Been-akkers and Klingenberg, 1964).

The same might be the mechanism of lipid transport in the migratory bird also. With continued flight the oxidation system of the muscle should also become more active, since it is shown that with exercise the succinic dehydrogenase activity of the pectoralis is enhanced in the pigeon (Vallyathan and George, 1964b). It has been demonstrated that the rate of succinate oxidation by rat-liver mitochondria prepared at night, when rats are active, is 41% higher than that prepared in the day-time when rats rest (Glick and Cohen, unpublished, cited by Glick and Bronk, 1964). That with exercise the rate of oxidation of a variety of substrates by rat-liver mitochondria is increased has also been demon-strated (Glick and Bronk, 1964).

It is well known that for efficient oxidative metabolism, in any organ or tissue a copious blood supply is an essential prerequisite. The breast muscles of birds indulging in sustained activity are not an exception to this general rule, rather they are one of the best examples to illustrate it. The fat-loaded fibers in the pigeon pectoralis have been shown to have for their size a greater blood supply than the glycogen-loaded fibers (George and Naik, 1960). But of all the birds hitherto examined, both the pectoralis and the supracoracoideus muscles of the Ruby-throated Hummingbird (Chapters IV and VI) have strikingly profuse blood supply (Chandra-Bose and George, 1964). Menon (1954) who estimated the levels of glucose and fat in the blood of representative vertebrates, found that the bird (pigeon) blood contained the highest. George and Menon (1954) attributed the low glucose and fat levels in the blood of the domestic fowl to its inability to fly and suggested a physiological lag in this bird. It may also be mentioned that the serum lipase activity of the blood of the Rosy Pastor is considerably higher than that of the pigeon which in turn is higher than that of the domestic fowl (George and Vallyathan, 1961). A high lipolytic activity should facilitate the release and movement of free fatty acids for oxidation. However, it should be mentioned that if the products of fat catabolism are produced at a rate faster than the capacity of the system to oxidize them, the acetic acid residues condense to form ketones. For preventing the accumulation of ketone bodies in the blood, it is necessary that the avian body should possess adequate equipment for the prevention of such accumulations as well as for oxidizing them if formed. There seems to be no doubt that such a system does exist in the avian body but we need more experimental evidence to establish it.

The premigratory period is a period of elaborate preparation for migration. We have discussed within the limits of our meager knowledge some of the metabolic adaptations in the muscle during this period. There is the quick build-up of fat in the muscle and elsewhere. We have suggested the existence of a control system which during this time depresses fat utilization in the muscle, in spite of the fact that the oxidative enzymatic machinery is maintained to full capacity in readiness to act when triggered. It is well known to ornithologists that before actual migration there is a sudden spurt of activity which they call, "migratory restlessness," or "Zugunruhe" of caged migrants. Thyroidal activity has been suggested to be the stimulus for this migratory impulse (Merkel, 1958a). Recently it has been shown (George and Naik, 1964) that in the Rosy Pastor the thyroidal secretion that has been stored in the cells of the thyroid is suddenly released from the gland a few days prior to actual migration. It is known that tissues from animals fed on desiccated thyroid tissue show increased oxygen consumption and fatty acid oxidation probably as a result of increased mitochondrial number (Lardy and Maley, 1954). The release of the thyroidal secretion and its influence in increasing the oxidative metabolism of the muscles and the heart could well be one of the major factors acting as the trigger for migration.

REFERENCES

Beenakkers, A. M. T., and Klingenberg, M. (1964). Carnitine-Coenzyme A transacetylase in mitochondria from various organs. *Biochem. Biophys. Acta* **84:** 205–207.

Bokdawala, F. D., and George, J. C. (1964). Histochemical demonstration of muscle lipase. *J. Histochem. Cytochem.* **12:** 768–771.

Bressler, R., and Friedberg, S. J. (1964). The effect of carnitine on the rate of palmitate incorporation into mitochondrial phospholipids. *J. Biol. Chem.* **239:** 1364–1368.

Caldwell, L. D., Odum, E. P., and Marshall, S. G. (1964). Comparison of fat levels in migrating birds killed at a Central Michigan and a Florida Gulf coast television tower. *Wilson Bull.* **75:** 428–434.

Chandra-Bose, D. A., and George, J. C. (1964). Studies on the structure and physiology of the flight muscles of birds. 12. Observations on the structure of the pectoralis and supracoracoideus of the Rubythroated Hummingbird. *Pavo* **2:** 111–114.

Cohn, C., and Joseph, D. (1959). Effect of rate of ingestion of diet on hexosemono-phosphate shunt activity. *Am. J. Physiol.* **197:** 1347–1349.

Connell, C. E., Odum, E. P., and Kale, H. (1960). Fat-free weights of birds. *Auk* **77:** 1–9.

Dolnik, V. R. (1961). Mekhanizm energeticheskoi podgotovki ptits k pereletu i faktory, ee opredelyayushchie. *In* "Ekologiya i migratsii ptits pribaltiki," pp. 281–288. Akad. Nauk Latv. S.S.R., Riga.

Drummond, G. I., and Black, E. C. (1960). Comparative physiology: fuel of muscle metabolism. *Ann. Rev. Physiol.* **22:** 169–190.

Farner, D. S., Oksche, A., Kamemoto, F. I., King, J. R., and Cheyney, H. E. (1961). A comparison of the effect of long daily photoperiods on the pattern of energy storage in migratory and non-migratory finches. *Comp. Biochem. Physiol.* **2:** 125–142.

Fritz, I. B. (1961). Factors influencing rates of fatty acid oxidation and synthesis in mammalian systems. *Physiol. Rev.* **41:** 52–129.

Fritz, I. B. (1964). Carnitine and its role in fatty acid metabolism. *Advan. Lipid Res.* **1:** 285–334.

Fritz, I. B., and McEwen, B. (1959). Effects of carnitine on fatty acid oxidation by muscle. *Science* **129:** 334–335.

Fritz, I. B., Davis, D. G., Holtrop, R. H., and Dundee, H. (1958). Fatty acid oxidation by skeletal muscle during rest and activity. *Am. J. Physiol.* **194:** 379–389.

George, C. J., and Menon, K. R. (1954). The physiological lag in the domestic fowl. *J. Animal Morphol. Physiol.* **1:** 77.

George, J. C. (1947). The evolutionary significance of the variation in the chemical composition of the skeletal muscle in the vertebrate series of animals. *J. Univ. Bombay* **16:** 34–40.

George, J. C. (1952). Biochemical evolution of the skeletal muscle in vertebrates. *J. Maharaja Sayajirao Univ. Baroda* **1:** 25–33.

George, J. C. (1962). Some dynamic aspects of muscle metabolism. Presidential Address (Physiology Section). All-India Congress of Zoology 1962. Zoological Society of India, Calcutta. (in press).

George, J. C. (1964). Muscle lipase. *J. Animal Morphol. Physiol.* **11** (C. J. George Felicitation Number): 233–243.

George, J. C., and Eapen, J. (1958a). Certain histochemical and physiological observations on the adipose tissue of the pigeon. *J. Animal Morphol. Physiol.* **5:** 49–56.

George. J. C., and Eapen, J. (1958b). Histochemical demonstration of certain enzymes in the adipose tissue of the fowl (*Gallus domesticus*), Rosy Pastor (*Pastor roseus*). *J. Animal Morphol. Physiol.* **5:** 101–105.

George, J. C., and Eapen, J. (1959a). Further histochemical observations on the adipose tissue of the pigeon. *J. Animal Morphol. Physiol.* **6:** 30–33.

George, J. C., and Eapen, J. (1959b). Lipase activity in the adipose tissue of vertebrates. *J. Animal Morphol. Physiol.* **6:** 119–122.

George, J. C., and Eapen, J. (1960). Oxygen consumption and oxidation of various metabolites by the pigeon adipose tissue, *in vitro*. *J. Animal Morphol. Physiol.* **7:** 32–36.

George, J. C., and Iype, P. T. (1960). Improved histochemical demonstration of lipase activity. *Stain Technol.* **35:** 151–152.

George, J. C., and Iype, P. T. (1964). Fatty acid oxidation by breast muscle homogenates of a migratory and a non-migratory starling. *Pavo* **2:** 84–87.

George, J. C., and Jyoti, D. (1953). On the reduction of fat in the liver and in the flight muscle (pectoralis major) of *Columba livia* during flight. *J. Univ. Bombay* **21:** 72–73.

George, J. C., and Jyoti, D. (1955a). Histological features of the breast and leg muscles of bird and bat and their physiological and evolutionary significance. *J. Animal Morphol. Physiol.* **2:** 31–36.

George, J. C., and Jyoti, D. (1955b). The lipid content and its reduction in the muscle and liver during long and sustained muscular activity. *J. Animal Morphol. Physiol.* **2:** 37–45.

George, J. C., and Jyoti, D. (1957). Studies on the structure and physiology of the flight muscles of birds. 2. The relative reduction of fat and glycogen in the pectoralis major muscle during sustained activity. *J. Animal Morphol. Physiol.* **4:** 119–123.

George, J. C., and Naik, R. M. (1958). Relative distribution and chemical nature of the fuel store of the two types of fibres in the pectoralis major muscle of the pigeon. *Nature* **181:** 709–710.

George, J. C., and Naik, R. M. (1959). Studies on the structure and physiology of the flight muscles of birds. 4. Observations on the fiber architecture of the pectoralis major muscle of the pigeon. *Biol. Bull.* **116:** 239–247.

George, J. C., and Naik, R. M. (1960). Some observations on the distribution of the blood capillaries in the pigeon breast muscle. *Auk* **77:** 224–225.

George, J. C., and Naik, D. V. (1962). Hematopoietic nodules as centers of fat synthesis in the liver of the migratory starling, *Pastor roseus*. *Quart. J. Microscop. Sci.* **104:** 393–399.

George, J. C., and Naik, D. V. (1964). Cyclic changes in the thyroid of the migratory starling *Sturnus roseus* (Linnaeus). *Pavo* **2:** 37–47.

George, J. C., and Talesara, C. L. (1961). The succinic dehydrogenase levels of the pectoral muscles of a few representative types of birds and a bat in relation to the fiber diameter, muscle weight and body weight. *Comp. Biochem. Physiol.* **3:** 267–273.

George, J. C., and Talesara, C. L. (1962). Lipase activity of the particulate fractions and its significance in the metabolism of the muscle. *J. Cellular Comp. Physiol.* **60:** 33–40.

George, J. C., and Vallyathan, N. V. (1961). A comparative study of the lipase activity in the blood sera of three representative birds. *J. Animal Morphol. Physiol.* **8:** 48–52.

George, J. C., and Vallyathan, N. V. (1964a). Lipase and succinic dehydrogenase activity of the particulate fractions of the breast muscle homogenate of the migratory starling *Sturnus roseus* in the pre-migratory and post-migratory periods. *J. Cellular Comp. Physiol.* **63:** 381–392.

George, J. C., and Vallyathan, N. V. (1964b). Effect of exercise on the free fatty acid levels in the pigeon. *J. Appl. Physiol.* **19:** 619–622.

George, J. C., and Vallyathan, N. V. (1964c). Capacity for fatty acid oxidation by the breast muscle of the starling (*Sturnus roseus*) in the pre- and post-migratory periods. *Can. J. Physiol. Pharmacol.* **42:** 447–452.

George, J. C., Susheela, A. K., and Vallyathan, N. V. (1963). Cytoplasmic (non-mitochondrial) lactic and succinic dehydrogenases in the red and white muscle fibres. *J. Animal Morphol. Physiol.* **10:** 24–30.

Glick, J. L., and Bronk, J. R. (1964). Effect of exercise on the rate of oxygen uptake by rat-liver mitochondria. *Biochim. Biophys. Acta* **82:** 165–167.

Green, D. E. (1951). The cyclophorase complex of enzymes. *Biol. Rev. Cambridge Phil. Soc.* **26:** 410–419.

Green, D. E. (1960). The synthesis of fat. *Sci. Am.* **202:** 46–51.

Green, D. E., and Wakil, S. J. (1960). Enzymatic mechanisms of fatty acid oxidation and synthesis. *In* "Lipide Metabolism" (K. Bloch, ed.) pp. 1–40, Wiley, New York.

Jeanrenaud, B. (1961). Dynamic aspects of adipose tissue metabolism: A review. *Metab., Clin. Exptl.* **10:** 535–581.

Jordan, J. P., and Kratzer, F. H. (1963). Malonyl-Coenzyme A as an intermediate in fatty acid synthesis by skeletal muscle mitochondria. (Abstract.) *J. Arkansas Med. Soc.* **160:** 55.

Kennedy, E. P., and Lehninger, A. L. (1949). Oxidation of fatty acids and tricarboxylic acid cycle intermediates by isolated rat liver mitochondria. *J. Biol. Chem.* **179:** 957–972.

Lardy, H. A., and Maley, G. F. (1954). Metabolic effects of thyroid hormones *in vitro. Recent Progr. Hormone Res.* **10:** 129–155.

Lasiewski, R. C. (1962). The energetics of migrating hummingbirds. *Condor* **64:** 324.

Lasiewski, R. C. (1963). Oxygen consumption of torpid, resting, active and flying hummingbirds. *Physiol. Zool.* **36:** 122–140.

Liebelt, R. A., and Eastlick, H. L. (1954). The organ-like nature of the subcutaneous fat bodies in the chicken. *Poultry Sci.* **33:** 169–179.

Loewy, A. G., and Siekevitz, P. (1963). Cell Structure and Function. Holt, New York.

McCabe, T. T. (1943). An aspect of the collectors' technique. *Auk* **60:** 550–558.

McGreal, R. D., and Farner. D. S. (1956). Premigratory fat deposition in the Gambel White-crowned Sparrow: Some morphologic and chemical observations. *Northwest Sci.* **30:** 12–23.

Menon, K. R. (1954). The glucose and fat levels in the blood of five representative vertebrates. *J. Animal Morphol. Physiol.* **1:** 65–68.

Merkel, F. W. (1958a). Untersuchungen zur künstlichen Beeinflussung der Aktivität gekäfigter Zugvögel. *Vogelwarte* **19:** 173–185.

Merkel, F. W. (1958b). Untersuchungen über tages- und jahresperiodische Änderungen in Energiehaushalt gekäfigter Zugvögel. *Z. Vergleich. Physiol.* **41:** 154–178.

Naik, D. V. (1963). Seasonal variation in the metabolites of the liver of the Rosy Pastor, *Sturnus roseus* (Linnaeus). *Pavo* **1:** 44–47.

Nene, R. V., and George, J. C. (1965). Histochemical demonstration of glucose-6-phosphate dehydrogenase in muscle. *J. Animal Morphol. Physiol.* **12:** 85–89.

Neptune, E. M., Jr., Sudduth, H. C., and Foreman, D. R. (1959). Labile fatty acids of rat diaphragm muscle and their possible role as the major endogenous substrate for maintenance of respiration. *J. Biol. Chem.* **234:** 1659–1660.

Neptune, E. M., Jr., Sudduth, H. C., Brigance, W. H., and Brown, J. D. (1963). Lipid glyceride synthesis by rat skeletal muscle. *Am. J. Physiol.* **204:** 933–938.

Nisbet, I. C. T. (1963). Weight-loss during migration—Part 2: Review of other estimates. *Bird Banding* **34:** 139–159.

Nisbet, I. C. T., Drury, W. H., Jr., and Baird, J. (1963). Weight-loss during migration—Part 1: Deposition and consumption of fat by the Blackpoll Warbler, *Dendroica striata. Bird Banding* **34:** 107–138.

Odum E. P. (1949). Weight variations in wintering white-throated sparrows in relation to temperature and migration. *Wilson Bull.* **61:** 3–14.

Odum. E. P. (1958). The fat deposition picture in the White-throated Sparrow in comparison with that in long-range migrants. *Bird-Banding* **29:** 105–108.

Odum, E. P. (1960a). Lipid deposition in nocturnal migrant birds. *Proc. 12th intern. Ornithol. Congr. Helsinki, 1958* pp. 563–576.

Odum, E. P. (1960b). Premigratory hyperphagia in birds. *Am. J. Clin. Nutri.* **8:** 621–629.

Odum, E. P., and Connell, C. E. (1956). Lipid levels in migrating birds. *Science* **123:** 892–894.

Odum, E. P., and Major, J. C. (1956). The effect of diet on photoperiod-induced lipid deposition in the White-throated Sparrow. *Condor* **58:** 222–228.

Odum, E. P., and Perkinson, J. D., Jr. (1951). Relation of lipid metabolism to migration in birds: Seasonal variation in body lipids of the migratory white-throated sparrow. *Physiol. Zool.* **24:** 216–230.

Odum, E. P., Connell, C. E., and Stoddard, H. L. (1961). Flight energy and estimated flight ranges of some migratory birds. *Auk* **78:** 515–527.

Pearson, O. P. (1950). The metabolism of hummingbirds. *Condor* **52:** 145–152.

Pearson, O. P. (1961). Flight speeds of some small birds. *Condor* **63:** 506–507.

Spitzer, J. J., and Gold, M. (1964). Free fatty acid metabolism by skeletal muscle. *Am. J. Physiol.* **206:** 159–164.

Vallyathan, N. V. (1963). On the lipid content and lipase activity in the breast muscle of *Sturnus roseus* (L.) *Pavo* **1:** 106–109.

Vallyathan, N. V., and George, J. C. (1964a). Glycogen content and phosphorylase activity in the breast muscle of the migratory starling, *Sturnus roseus* (Linnaeus). *Pavo* **2:** 55–60.

Vallyathan, N. V., and George, J.C. (1964b). Effect of exercise on the phosphorylase and succinic dehydrogenase levels in the pigeon breast muscle. *J. Animal Morphol. Physiol.* **11** (C. J. George Felicitation Number): 186–191.

Wachs, H. (1926). Die Wanderungen der Vögel. *Ergeb. Biol.* **1:** 479–637.

Wakil, S. J. (1960). The mechanism of fatty acid synthesis. *Am. J. Clin. Nutri.* **8:** 630–644.

Weinhouse, S., Millington, R. H., and Volk, M. E. (1950). Oxidation of isotopic palmitic acid in animal tissues. *J. Biol. Chem.* **185:** 191–199.

Young, D. R., and Price, R. (1961). Utilization of body energy reserves during work in dogs. *J. Appl. Physiol.* **16:** 351–354.

CHAPTER IX

The Musculature

I. Introduction

The monumental works of Fürbringer (1888, 1902) and of Gadow and Selenka (1891) continue to be invaluable references because of their scholarly treatment of the myology of the major groups of birds. These classic studies are difficult to obtain except in the larger libraries. It is true, as well, that such books lose some of their importance as new information is published and as concepts (both morphological and taxonomic) change. Moreover, it soon becomes evident to anyone who studies the earlier literature that very few ornithologists or anatomists dissected all of the muscles of the wing or leg; even fewer concerned themselves with the musculature of the head and axial skeleton. Most early papers discussed only those muscles which were thought at the time to have taxonomic value. This accounts for the undue emphasis placed on Garrod's leg-muscle formulas by some taxonomists. Garrod (1881: pp. 211–212) realized the limitations of such formulas to a greater extent than have many later workers.

Several excellent papers on the myology of birds have been published during the past 35 years. These papers are of special value because they discuss particular species in detail or because they examine many species of a single family. These comparative studies are essential if we are to learn how much variation occurs in the muscle pattern and in the relative development of muscles within a family. Such data are prerequisite to an intelligent interpretation of the significance of differences in the musculature among the genera of different families.

A number of bird muscles are relatively similar in configuration throughout nearly the entire class. Still other muscles exhibit many peculiar modifications. In order to understand a muscle and its relations, therefore, it is necessary to have information on that muscle from genera of several families. In the following summary of our current knowledge of the avian muscular system we have placed special emphasis on those muscles which are known to exhibit the greatest variation in configuration among the families of birds.

A number of errors in the literature stem from a lack of knowledge of the pattern and relative development of certain muscles in different families. Other errors have been perpetuated by graduate students and taxonomists who have relied on Shufeldt's (1890) descriptions of the muscles of the Raven. Engels (1938) found "eight major errors" in Shufeldt's descriptions of the tongue muscles alone. Hudson and Lanzillotti (1955) commented that Shufeldt "also failed to differentiate between the flexor carpi ulnaris and the flexor digitorum sublimus. His description of the flexor digitorum sublimus makes it quite apparent that he did not find any such muscle." The beginning student of avian myology would do well to ignore Shufeldt's book. We have referred to Shufeldt's nomenclature of muscles, but only because several American authors have followed Shufeldt. We have intentionally refrained from citing or quoting from certain published papers, feeling that they are unreliable.

A statement on muscle terminology is pertinent. The different names applied to avian muscles are, for the most part, a reflection of the several schools of thought on how a muscle should be named, and this depends, in large measure, on whether the anatomist is interested in pure descriptive anatomy or in functional anatomy. One may, for example, establish a set of names based on the functions of the muscles, or one may name the muscles according to their origin and insertion. Ideally every avian anatomist would like to have a set of names which would indicate the homology of each muscle, not only among all birds but also in other vertebrate classes. If Straus (1946: p. 89) is correct in stating that Fürbringer's theory of nerve-muscle specificity "is founded upon a false embryological concept and is completely negated both by comparative and experimental data," then attempting to homologize avian muscles with those of reptiles and mammals becomes exceedingly difficult, if not impossible. In any event, we must know far more about avian myology, neurology, and embryology before such comparisons can be attempted with much confidence.

Hudson (1948: pp. 103, 126) and Hudson and Lanzillotti (1955: p. 43) emphasized the need for further work on the homology and innervation of bird muscles and quoted the innervation of appendicular muscles from Gadow and Selenka (1891) and Fisher (1946). Hudson adopted the names of muscles employed by Gadow except "where this does not appear to be expedient," but he did not adopt the names proposed by Howell (1937, 1938) because "it should be emphasized that investigation of a single species cannot be considered as an adequate basis for renaming muscles" (Hudson, 1948: p. 103). This, of course, is true. One cannot hope to solve the complicated problem of homologies by reference to a

single species, despite Howell's broad background in comparative anatomy. We are, however, not impressed by criticism of the first two criteria
(function; origin and insertion) for naming bird muscles because they
do, or may, ignore innervation. Very little is known about the avian
spinal cord (Huber, 1936; Portmann and Stingelin, 1961), and there apparently have been no attempts to localize within the spinal cord by
means of nerve-degeneration experiments the nuclear groups related to
the appendicular muscles. The gross pattern of the brachial and lumbosacral plexuses (which is known for very few birds) can provide certain
information, which, by itself, may be of doubtful value; see the excellent
study by Baumel (1958) on variation in the brachial plexus of *Progne
subis.*

Obviously, one must adopt a set of names in order to convey information to other anatomists. We have retained some old names because they
have been used by avian anatomists and taxonomists for nearly 100
years. We have adopted a conservative approach in selecting a "preferred list" of names for bird muscles, believing that a knowledge of the
muscles is more important than the names used for them. We have, for
example, retained the traditional concept of the numbering of the digits
of the bird hand: pollex, digit II, digit III. Montagna (1945) presented a
good case for considering the digits in the fowl to be II, III, and IV.
Holmgren (1955: p. 275), however, said that "any investigation of the
morphology of the carpus must begin at a less advanced stage than that
used by Montagna." Holmgren added that "Montagna has taken the
somewhat independent rudiment of the epiphysis of the metacarpale 3
for a distal carpale. In the common fowl (and also in *Anser*) this rudiment is more strongly developed than in other birds and later joins on to
the diaphysis." Nevertheless, Holmgren also concluded (primarily on the
basis of a study of *Larus*) that the hand digits should be numbered II,
III, and IV. He added (Holmgren, 1955: p. 281): "The last step in the
development of the 1st finger is taken, for instance, in a 25 mm. *Larus*
embryo, where there is a small cartilage on the outside of metacarpale
2. Into this cartilage the m. flexor metacarpi radialis is inserted, and
this cartilage must consequently represent the 1st finger." His reasoning
in reaching this conclusion, however, is obscure and escapes us. Holmgren proposed that the first digit fuses with the carpometacarpus and
becomes the extensor process of that bone. Unfortunately, Holmgren did
not live to complete his studies.

We do not consider the question of the numbering of the hand digits
settled to the point where muscle names should be changed. Although
Hudson wrote specifically about myological studies, the same concept
applies to the embryological development of the bird hand. We agree

wholeheartedly with Hudson's comments (1948: p. 103): "Although Dr. Howell is eminently qualified to make such a study, it should be emphasized that investigation of a single species cannot be considered an adequate basis for renaming muscles. I would like to urge Dr. Howell or some other qualified comparative anatomist to carry out similar studies on representatives of fifteen or twenty orders of birds. If this were done any changes in terminology of muscles that might be indicated by such a comprehensive investigation could be adopted with confidence. However, until such a study is made I do not believe that any radical changes in the names used for bird muscles are justified. Such changes only add to the confusion and make more difficult an already complicated field of study."

Fisher and Goodman (1955: p. 39) adopted the evidence on the hand digits presented by Montagna and changed the names of the muscles inserting on those digits (e.g., M. extensor pollicis longus became M. extensor longus digiti II). New names were coined in order to avoid switching a specific name from one muscle to an entirely different muscle. Before publishing these changes, Fisher wrote to avian anatomists, asking for comments and suggestions on the proposed name changes. The published changes are presumed to represent the consensus of American avian anatomists. It is recommended that these names be adopted by those who prefer to follow Montagna and Holmgren on the numbering of the wing digits.

In his excellent paper on the development of the wing musculature of *Gallus*, Sullivan (1962) renamed certain muscles inserting on the hand digits. Sullivan informed us (1962) that his study did not include an investigation of the bony elements of the hand and that he had accepted Montagna's evidence for considering the wing digits to be II, III, and IV.

Although the purpose is self-evident, there is good reason to suggest that the beginning student of avian myology first acquaint himself with the general plan of the muscular system of man or subhuman mammals. Many of the superficial flexor and extensor muscles of the forearm in man and other mammals, for example, share more or less common flexor and extensor tendons of origin. The origins and bellies of several muscles are so intimately related that the individual muscles do not obtain their integrity for some distance down the forearm; one finds many minor variations in length of belly and in the presence of accessory slips. These variations are of no significance taxonomically. A similar pattern of origin is found among the muscles of the bird crus (tibiotarsus). From these areas of common origin in both birds and mammals, discrete separate bellies and tendons of insertion are formed.

Many of the bird's appendicular muscles have short bellies and very long tendons of insertion. The fleshy bellies occupy a proximal location near the center of gravity. The tendons of many of the leg muscles and some of the wing muscles are calcified or contain sesamoid bones, especially in cranes and gallinaceous birds. Hudson *et al.* (1959) described these features in detail in gallinaceous birds.

The student of avian myology encounters two problems both in his own work and in attempting to interpret the published results of others: normal anatomical variation; and the excessive subdivision of certain muscles by some authors and, especially, the taxonomic significance attributed to those subdivisions. Berger (1956d) summarized available information on anatomical variation in the avian skeletal, muscular, nervous, and vascular systems. Baumel (1958) described variation in the brachial plexus in a series of *Progne subis*.

Many of the misconceptions found in the literature probably stem from the author's failure to understand the nature and significance of aponeuroses, raphes, and fascial planes. The structure of a muscle (e.g., parallel, bipennate) is a reflection of the function that the muscle performs. The tripartite structure of M. depressor mandibulae in some birds (Beecher, 1953; Berger, 1957), for example, means only that the muscle is composed of several pennate parts. The tendinous septa that both separate and interconnect these parts of a single muscle may be very strong and conspicuous or they may consist of little more than thin fascial planes. The minute details of the architecture of a given muscle are of critical importance in analyzing the functions of the muscle, but overemphasis on these details in postulating phylogenetic relationship is, to put it mildly, open to question. The pterygoid muscle-complex has presented authors with many problems in their attempts to describe their findings for publication. Zusi (1962) stated that "because of the complexity of this muscle and its superficial variability within the class Aves, the terminology of the pterygoideus group is almost as varied and confusing as that of the adductor mandibulae externus complex. . . . Unfortunately, this muscle has seldom been studied in terms of its major aponeuroses, and the variability of its basic structure in birds is not known." Zusi, therefore, considered the pterygoideus complex to consist of three major parts (M, N, and O), which "are readily separable in terms of aponeuroses, although the fibers of the different parts merge in several places." Zusi identified the multiple aponeuroses of origin by letters (A, B, C, etc.) and aponeuroses of insertion by other letters (M, N, O, etc.). This approach recognizes that the muscle is a complex (not a series of individual muscles) and that the architecture of the complex is important functionally but of doubtful value when taken as an isolated character in determining phylogenetic relationships (see Zusi's discussion, 1962: p. 95).

There appears to be no "best" sequence for discussing the muscles. The sequence may be based on embryological development, on innervation, on the easiest sequence for dissecting the muscles, etc. Usually an author adopts an order which involves two or more of these criteria, in part because of inadequate data on the embryonic development of the muscular system. To discuss the muscles in the precise order of dissection would result in a hodge-podge, suitable only in a laboratory dissection manual. We have discussed the muscles (particularly those of the limbs) partly on developmental groups and partly on the sequence of dissection (that is, the more superficial muscles are described before the deeper muscles).

There is a great need for four types of research on the avian muscular system:

1. Descriptions of the complete appendicular myology of all genera in different families of birds in order to learn more about the amount of intergeneric variation in circumscribed groups of birds.

2. Comparisons of the wing myology of flightless (or nearly flightless) genera with flying genera in the same family. This would provide some information on the type and rate of degeneration of muscles correlated with function or loss of function, as well as on the possible disappearance of muscles in flightless forms.

3. Nerve-muscle experiments on living birds: that is, cutting nerves or tendons of muscles in an effort to learn what effect there is on the flight of the bird (see Fisher, 1957c).

4. Studies of the gross pattern of the brachial and lumbosacral plexuses and the muscles they innervate, as well as nerve-degeneration experiments in order to ascertain the relations of the plexus nerves to the nuclear columns in the spinal cord.

A. Muscles Used in the Classification of Birds

Four groups of muscles have been used in attempts to determine the phylogenetic relations among birds: muscles of the jaws, trachea and syrinx, pectoral appendage, and pelvic appendage. Unfortunately, one is forced to conclude that the addition of myological data to taxonomic diagnoses is, for the most part at present, mere "window dressing." At the same time, we are convinced that this need not be so; but, in order to correct the situation, we must have many more studies of the type published during the past 30 years.

B. THE JAW MUSCLES

Several excellent studies of these muscles have been published in recent years. The development of the jaw muscles must be related to feeding habits, as are the shape of the bill, the shape and structure of the tongue, and the pattern of both the horny and the bony palate. Hence, the analysis of this complex of structures is very difficult. Indeed, one must have, as Beecher (1951b: p. 274) pointed out, "sound criteria for clearly distinguishing between adaptation and phylogeny." Taxonomists have concluded that the data published to date on jaw muscles have not been satisfactorily applied to the classification of birds. For a discussion of the problems involved see Tordoff (1954b) and Mayr (1955).

C. THE SYRINGEAL MUSCLES

The muscles of the trachea and syrinx may be divided into extrinsic and intrinsic groups. The extrinsic tracheal muscles have one attachment to a nontracheal structure. With one exception (M. sternotrachealis), these muscles have not been used thus far in systems of classification.

The intrinsic tracheal, or syringeal, muscles arise and insert on some part of the tracheobronchial tree, including the bony or cartilaginous rings and semirings which form part of the syrinx. The syringeal muscles have been used primarily in the classification of passerine birds. Current systems of taxonomy, however, rely almost entirely on data published during the last century. One looks forward with considerable anticipation to the publication of a modern study of this problem recently completed by Dr. Peter Ames.

Two difficult problems confront the student of the tracheal muscles: synonymy and homology. Both result, in part, from the wide variation in pattern of these muscles among the orders of birds. One encounters serious contradictions in the basic phylogenetic and embryological treatises on the development and homology of tracheal muscles. There is little doubt that the same name has been applied to nonhomologous muscles throughout the orders of birds.

Miskimen's (1951) study suggests that the number of muscles alone is a poor criterion for judging closeness of relationship. She found from three to five pairs of intrinsic syringeal muscles in fringillid genera alone. Much additional information is needed on the pattern of the syringeal muscles in passerine birds, however, before meaningful conclusions can be drawn. Nevertheless, it can be asserted strongly that there is no justification for such published statements as the following concerning passerine birds: "We had constant characters tying the families together (the hind limb and syringeal musculature)." One is inclined to ask: What are these "constant" characters? The mere presence of muscles?

D. Muscles of the Pectoral Appendage

Fürbringer (1888: pp. 816–821) tabulated special features of 15 muscles and muscle slips related to the wing musculature which he thought might be of taxonomic use. Most of these are dermal slips, some of which have since been shown to exhibit individual variation within a species. Beddard (1898) referred primarily to seven wing muscles in his technical diagnoses of the families and orders of birds: pectoralis, tensores patagii longus et brevis (patagialis), deltoideus major, scapulotriceps ("anconaeus longus"), cucullaris pars propatagialis, the biceps slip, and the expansor secundariorum. Most of the standard taxonomic references mention only the last two muscles. Berger (1956c) has shown that most statements in these references pertaining to M. expansor secundariorum are unreliable because the muscle has been found in all birds examined carefully.

Few people have described the muscles distal to the elbow, and several excellent papers on the shoulder musculature have been little used (e.g., Buri, 1900; Fürbringer, 1902). Detailed descriptions of the total wing myology are available for so few birds that no one has proposed a series of muscle formulas which summarize the muscle pattern of the wing and which might be useful in determining relations on an ordinal or lower level. It seems possible that the evolution of the wing in flying birds has almost reached a stage wherein the minimum number of muscles to accomplish flight are present. In any event, the adaptations for flight make it difficult to identify differences of phylogenetic significance. The problem is intensified because we know relatively little about the intricate interrelationships of the muscles in maintaining flight.

It may not be instructive or intelligent to dismiss consideration of a muscle with the simple statement that the degree of development is correlated with flight pattern. The problem is not that simple and, furthermore, such an answer may not be an answer at all. Let us consider the relative development of Mm. pronator superficialis and pronator profundus. Because of their origin and insertion, these muscles pronate the radius on the ulna (or depress the leading edge of the wing) and flex the forearm. This does not fully explain the actions of these muscles, however, when coupled with the actions of other synergistic, antagonistic, and fixator muscle groups. Moreover, other factors may be of equal or greater importance to muscle development in analyzing flight pattern: for example, total length and intramembral proportions of the wing; wing, body, and tail supporting surface; shape of wing; and perhaps an inherent behavior pattern. In his discussion of the pronator muscles in the Cathartidae, Fisher (1946: p. 620) commented that "no correlation with type of flight is possible because the upward force of air beneath the distal tips of the secondaries in all cases tends to depress the anterior edge of the forearm without the intervention of muscular action." In fact, the bird might have to "fight against" such depression of the anterior margin of the wing. This may be an oversimplification of a complicated problem, but the fact remains that these two muscles do exhibit striking differences in development in some birds. In three genera of cuckoos (*Coccyzus, Crotophaga, Geococcyx*), where the pattern of flight is distinctly different in each, the pronator profundus muscle extends about three-fourths the length of the forearm. In analyzing these and other wing muscles, Berger (1954) concluded that although an increase in development of some muscles in *Geococcyx*, in comparison with the other genera, may be an adaptation for its mode of flight, basically the increase may be simply a reflection of the greater amount of work required of its muscles in order to maintain flight in a heavy bird with a relatively short, small wing. Therefore, the "differences in flight pattern in the three genera may best be explained in terms of a progressive reduction in relative wing area and a progressive increase in body size from *Coccyzus* to *Geococcyx*."

Still another factor must be considered. A long, fleshy belly is more efficient for extent of contraction, but a shorter, more bulky muscle is more efficient for power and speed of contraction. The tendency for concentration in the proximal half (or less) of the forearm of muscle bellies in passerine birds presumably is correlated to the power required for rapid wing beats. Because of the relatively short geological age of passerine birds, however, it cannot be assumed that there has been a drastic reduction in muscular development in sedentary passerine species. It would, for example, be interesting to compare the appendicular muscles of such a sedentary species as the Zapata Wren (*Ferminia cerverai*) with those of a migratory wren. Many other examples could be cited. In another connection, Beddard (1898: p. 501) stated that it appears "that, in spite of the small size of the manus in the ostrich relative to that of flying birds, there is but little if any evidence of degeneration in its musculature."

Despite the many problems involved in attempts to separate functional from phylogenetic features of the wing muscles, current information suggests that studies of the comparative development of the following muscles would be profitable: pectoralis pars propatagialis; cucullaris pars propatagialis; latissimus dorsi; tensores patagii longus et brevis; deltoideus major; deltoideus minor; biceps brachii and the biceps slip;

coracobrachialis anterior; proscapulohumeralis; subcoracoideus; scapulo-triceps; anconaeus coracoideus; expansor secundariorum; pronator super-ficialis; pronator profundus; flexor digitorum superficialis; flexor carpi ulnaris; ulnimetacarpalis ventralis; extensor metacarpi ulnaris; and ex-tensor indicis longus, especially the presence or absence of its distal head (= flexor metacarpi brevis).

E. MUSCLES OF THE PELVIC APPENDAGE

The pelvic musculature is much better known than is the wing myol-ogy. Hudson's (1937) excellent analysis of the leg myology of American genera led him to modify the leg-muscle formulas introduced by Gar-rod. Berger (1959a) proposed three additions based on the study of Old World genera. These muscles and their letter designations are given in Table IX.1 (see Fig. IX.1). Table IX.2 presents expanded myological formulas of species studied in recent years.

TABLE IX.1

SYMBOLS FOR FORMULA MUSCLES

Code letter	Name of muscle
A	Piriformis pars caudofemoralis (= femorocaudal)
B	Piriformis pars iliofemoralis (= accessory femorocaudal)
C	Iliotrochantericus medius
D	Gluteus medius et minimus (= "piriformis" of Fisher)
E	Iliacus (= "psoas" of Fisher)[a]
F	Plantaris
G	Popliteus
X	Semitendinosus (= flexor cruris lateralis of Fisher)
Y	Accessory semitendinosus
Am	Ambiens
V	Vinculum (between the tendons of Mm. flexor perforatus digiti III and flexor perforans et perforatus digiti III)[b]

[a] M. iliacus of Fisher equals M. iliotrochantericus anterior of Hudson and Berger.

[b] This vinculum (a tendinous connection) is not to be confused with the vinculum be-tween the tendons of Mm. flexor digitorum longus and flexor hallucis longus.

Much additional information is needed before one can comment with much confidence on the significance of leg-muscle formulas for taxo-nomic purposes. In addition to the many genera that have never been studied, we must have information on the presence or absence of the formula muscles in most of the genera reported on in the earlier litera-ture. The touracos and the cuckoos would appear to be closely related on the basis of Garrod's formula muscles but not closely related on the basis of the expanded formula (Berger, 1960a).

TABLE IX.2

MYOLOGICAL FORMULAS OF SELECTED SPECIES

Family and species	Formula
Gaviidae	
Gavia immer	ABCDEFGXAmV
Podicipedidae	
Podiceps caspicus	BCEFGX
Sulidae	
Sula leucogaster	ADEFGXAmV
Fregatidae	
Fregata magnificens	ADEFGAm
Ardeidae	
Ardea herodias	ADEFGXY
Butorides virescens	ADEFGXY
Anhimidae	
Chauna torquata	ABCDEFGXAmV
Anatidae	
Chen hyperborea	ABC($\pm$)DEFGXAmV
Cathartidae	
Cathartes, Coragyps	ACDEFGXYAmV
Sarcoramphus, Vultur, Coragyps	CDEFGXYAmV
Sagittariidae	
Sagittarius serpentarius	BDEGXYAmV
Falconidae	
Falco sparverius	ADEFGAm
Falco columbianus	ADEFGAm
Polihiërax semitorquatus	ADEFGAm
Accipitridae	
Accipiter cooperii	ADEGAm
Buteo jamaicensis	ADEGAm
Aquila chrysaëtos	ADEGAm
Circus cyaneus	ADEGAm
Pandionidae	
Pandion haliaetus	ADEGAm
Megapodiidae	
Megapodius pritchardii	ABCDEFGXYAmV
Leipoa ocellata	ABCDEFGXYAmV
Cracidae	
Crax nigra	ABCDEFGXYAmV
Ortalis vetula	ABCDEFGXYAmV
Tetraonidae	
Dendragapus obscurus	ABCDEFGXYAmV
Phasianidae	
Oreortyx picta	ABCDEFGXYAmV
Numididae	
Numida meleagris	ABCDEFGXYAmV
Meleagrididae	
Meleagris gallopavo	BCDEFGXYAmV

TABLE IX.2 (*Continued*)

Family and species	Formula
Opisthocomidae	
Opisthocomus hoazin	ABDEFGXYAm
Gruidae	
Grus americana	ABCDEFGXYAmV;
	BCDEFGXYAmV
Grus canadensis	ABC($\pm$)DEFGXYAmV
Rallidae	
Fulica americana	ABDEFGXYAmV
Scolopacidae	
Totanus melanoleucus	ADEFGXYAmV
Laridae	
Larus pipixcan	ACDEFGXYAmV
Alcidae	
Uria aalge	ABDEFGXAm
Columbidae	
Goura victoria	ABCEFGXYV
Columba livia	ABCEFGXYAmV
Zenaidura macroura	ABCEFGXYAmV
Gallicolumba luzonica	ABCEFGXYAmV
Musophagidae	
Tauraco leucotis	ABDFGXYAmV
Cuculidae	
Cuculus canorus	AFGXYAm
Piaya cayana	AEFGXYAm
Coua caerulea	ABFGXYAm
Geococcyx californianus	ABEFGXYAm
Strigidae	
Otus asio	ADEG
Bubo virginianus	ADEG
Caprimulgidae	
Chordeiles minor	AEFGXY
Apodidae	
Chaetura pelagica	AE
Trochilidae	
Eugenes fulgens	AC
Trogonidae	
Pharomachrus mocino	ACEFX
Alcedinidae	
Chloroceryle americana	ACEFX
Coraciidae	
Coracias abyssinica	ACEFGXY
Upupidae	
Upupa epops	ACFXY
Bucerotidae	
Aceros undulatus	ACEXY
Indicatoridae	
Indicator variegatus	ACXY

TABLE IX.2 (*Continued*)

Family and species	Formula
Picidae	
Colaptes auratus	ACEFXY
Dendrocopos villosus	ACEFX
Cotingidae	
Procnias nudicollis	ACEFXY
Tyrannidae	
Tyrannus tyrannus	ACEFXY[a]

[a] The same formula muscles have been found in representatives of all other passerine families thus far examined: Corvidae, Paradisaeidae, Vangidae, Sturnidae, Vireonidae, Parulidae, Icteridae, Ploceidae, Fringillidae.

It is obvious that a leg-muscle formula tells nothing about the relative development or peculiarities of structure of the muscles, nor does it reveal anything about the approximately 36 other muscles of the pelvic limb. For understanding functional anatomy as well as phylogenetic relations, a knowledge of the complete myology is essential (see the discussion in Newton and Gadow, 1893: pp. 603–604). It is obvious, as well, that myological data must be used in conjunction with other information, both anatomical and biological, in order to ascertain phylogenetic relationships. Muscle formulas may yet prove useful in technical diagnoses of families or other taxonomic categories, but how useful remains to be determined.

Certain interesting intergeneric and interspecific differences in muscle pattern have been described. The cranes offer one striking example. Fisher and Goodman (1955: pp. 85, 123) emphasized the amount of individual variation they found in M. piriformis pars caudofemoralis in three specimens of the Whooping Crane (*Grus americana*), and they discussed other differences found by other authors. Both pars caudofemoralis and pars iliofemoralis of M. piriformis were found in two specimens of the Whooping Crane, but only pars iliofemoralis was found in a third specimen. Berger (1956e) found both parts of the muscle in three specimens of the Sandhill Crane (*Grus canadensis tabida*). Fisher and Goodman stated: "Thus it is impossible with the information at hand to set up any definite formula for the family Gruiidae, or apparently even for the genera *Grus* and *Balearica* as now known. One would not expect intraspecific variation of the sort we noted or that found by Mitchell and Beddard in *Balearica*. . . . The variation in *G. leucogeranus* from the *Grus* line is not unexpected, for this crane also differs in many other ways." If leg-muscle formulas were as diagnostic as they have long been thought to be, however, these differences would not be found. As far as these muscles are concerned, it seems likely that the cranes are one of the more troublesome groups. Moreover, one is inclined to feel that considerable variation in a muscle might be expected in a muscle if it were in the process of "dropping out" phylogenetically. The relative development of pars caudofemoralis suggests that the muscle might be in

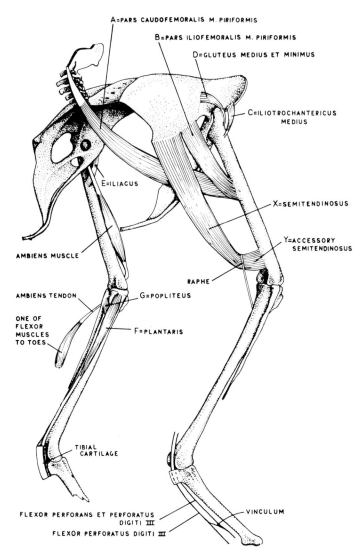

FIG. IX.1. The formula muscles of Garrod (1881), Hudson (1937), and Berger (1959a).

the process of becoming vestigial in certain groups of birds. In a bird the size of the Sandhill Crane, for example, the belly of pars caudofemoralis is only 9 cm long and has a maximum width of less than 1 cm; the tendon of origin is only 0.5 mm in diameter. Relative to its development in many birds, pars caudofemoralis might well be considered vestigial in the cranes.

At the same time, we do not know how much of the variation in the cranes falls under the heading of anomaly. The early literature does not specify how many specimens of a species were dissected. One surmises that the "normal" or "typical" pattern for the genus *Grus* is the presence of both parts of M. piriformis. The absence of a given muscle in a single specimen of a species or genus does not necessarily mean that that muscle is not characteristic for the species or the genus, or that the muscle is useless as a taxonomic character, either for that group or for other groups of birds. After one dissects a number of closely related genera, one quickly recognizes deviations from the typical pattern. Unless one can dissect several specimens of the species, one must realize that he may be dealing with an anomaly, a situation which does not negate all of the other evidence. It seems reasonable to assume that the configuration or the absence of certain muscles might be taxonomically useful in some groups of birds but not in other groups.

Berger (1960a) found what would appear to be an unusual pattern in the development of M. femorotibialis internus in two distantly related cuckoos (*Cuculus* and *Coua*). In these two genera alone, the muscle has two independent heads, each of which inserts by its own tendon; in all other cuculine genera dissected, the muscle is single from origin to insertion.

Two examples may suffice to dispel the long held notion that all passerine birds exhibit a uniformity in muscle pattern. Stallcup (1954) reported that M. obturator externus is represented by a single belly in *Passer, Estrilda, Peophila, Hesperiphona, Carpodacus, Pinicola, Leucosticte, Spinus,* and *Loxia.* The muscle consists of two bellies in all other genera he examined. Berger (1957) pointed out that M. flexor hallucis brevis is found in certain passerine birds (e.g., Corvidae, *Paradisaea, Artamella, Agelaius*) but absent in others (e.g. *Fregilupus, Sturnus, Aplonis*).

The major variations in pattern and relative development of the muscles of the pelvic appendage are described in detail in a later section. Table IX.3 lists a series of questions about some of the muscles. Such a check-list can readily be expanded from the comparative data on the individual muscles, and should be of considerable assistance to the beginning student.

TABLE IX.3

A Partial Check List for Leg Muscle Dissections

1. Does M. sartorius have an origin from the spine of the last dorsal vetebra?
2. Does the origin of M. femorotibialis internus extend proximally to the level of insertion of M. iliacus?
3. Does M. femorotibialis internus consist of a single head? or of two heads?
4. Does M. piriformis pars iliofemoralis arise exclusively from the ilium, or does the origin extend downward onto the ischium?
5. Does M. piriformis pars caudofemoralis arise directly from the pygostyle, or from aponeuroses or ligaments ventral to the pygostyle?
6. Is there any connection between the tendons of insertion of Mm. semitendinosus and semimembranosus?
7. Does the aponeurosis of origin of M. biceps femoris extend anterior to the acetabulum?
8. What is the configuration of the biceps loop?
9. Is M. obturator internus triangular or oval in shape?
10. Does M. obturator externus consist of a single head or of two heads?
11. What is the relationship between the insertion of Mm. adductor longus et brevis and accessorius semitendinosi to the origin of M. gastrocnemius pars media?
12. What is the relative development of Mm. peroneus longus and peroneus brevis?
13. Does the belly of M. peroneus longus conceal most of the belly of M. tibialis anterior?
14. Do the three parts of M. gastrocnemius consist of a single head or of two heads?
15. Does M. flexor perforatus digiti II arise from the intercondyloid region of the femur as well as from the ambiens tendon?
16. Does the distal head of M. flexor perforatus digiti III arise from the fibula, the ambiens tendon complex, etc.?
17. Does M. flexor digitorum longus have a femoral origin?
18. What is the course of the flexor tendons through the tibial cartilage?
19. What is the course of the flexor tendons through the intertarsal space?
20. What is the structure of the hypotarsus? Does it contain any bony canals?
21. What is the course of the flexor tendons through the hypotarsus.
22. Do the tendons of all of the "perforating" muscles actually perforate the tendon of its corresponding "perforated" muscle?
23. Does the tendon of M. flexor hallucis brevis ensheathe the tendon of insertion of M. flexor hallucis longus?
24. What is the relative development of M. extensor proprius digiti III?
25. Is there an automatic flexor of the hallux?

II. Muscles of the Head and Visceral Compartment of the Neck

A. Muscles of the Orbit

The muscles of the orbit include six extra-ocular muscles, two muscles which act on the nictitating membrane, and three muscles in the eyelids. The few published details available on these muscles are given by Shufeldt (1890), Gadow and Selenka (1891), Slonaker (1918), Wedin (1953), and Fisher and Goodman (1955). Lord (1956) and Goodge

(1960) have described the finer structure of the eyeball itself and the specialized muscles of the avian ciliary body and the choroid layer.

1. Extra-ocular Muscles

The six extrinsic or extra-ocular muscles correspond closely to those in mammals: *rectus internus (medialis), rectus externus (lateralis), rectus superior, rectus inferior, obliquus superior, obliquus inferior.* The flat, ribbonlike rectus (straight) muscles arise from the thickened periorbita surrouning the optic nerve just after its entrance into the orbit. The fleshy part of each muscle is confined to approximately the proximal two-thirds of the muscle in *Passer domesticus;* the distal (lateral) one-third is aponeurotic. Each aponeurosis inserts into the outer coat of the eyeball a short distance lateral to the equator of the eyeball.

Both the superior oblique and the inferior oblique muscles arise from the bone on the nasal (anterior) side of the bony wall of the orbit. Fisher and Goodman (1955: Fig. 2), however, show the origin of the inferior oblique on the bone inferior to the optic foramen and the optic nerve in *Grus americana.* The superior oblique muscle passes backward and outward deep to the aponeurosis of the superior rectus muscle and inserts by a very broad aponeurosis medial and anterior to the area of insertion of the superior rectus muscle. It may be noted that the avian superior oblique muscle differs from that in man in that it does not give rise to a tendon which passes through a fibrous trochlea (pulley) to make a sharp turn backward to its insertion on the eyeball posterior to the equator. The inferior oblique muscle passes backward below the eyeball and inserts lateral and mostly anterior to the area of insertion of the inferior rectus muscle.

The eyeball in owls is enclosed in a bony sclerotic tube and is capable of very limited movement. Nevertheless, the extra-ocular muscles are fairly well developed.

2. Muscles of the Nictitating Membrane

Mm. quadratus nictitantis and pyramidalis nictitantis lie on the medial (deep) or posterior (in owls) surface of the eyeball (Fig. IX.2). They can be exposed to full view only by cutting the optic nerve and severing the rectus and oblique muscles near their origin and reflecting them outward.

M. quadratus (in *Columba livia*) has a wide (12 mm) origin from the superior surface of the eyeball just medial to the area of insertion of the superior oblique muscle. The fleshy belly curves downward around the back of the eyeball and appears to insert on the tendon of M. pyramidalis just dorsal to the optic nerve. In *Passer domesticus, Larus argen-*

tatus, Otus asio, and presumably in most birds, the inferior border of M. quadratus forms a sling through which the tendon of M. pyramidalis curves from anterior to posterior around the dorsal border of the optic nerve.

M. quadratus in *Otus asio* is a very wide (19 mm), bilobed muscle, which extends almost the complete width of the eyeball dorsal to the optic nerve. The inferior margin of the muscle forms a sling for the tendon of M. pyramidalis.

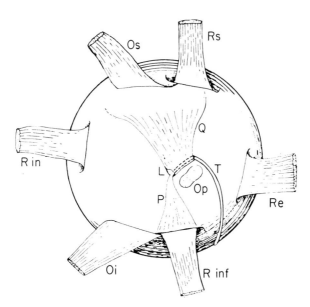

Fig. IX.2. Posterior surface of the right eyeball of the House Sparrow (*Passer domesticus*) with the rectus muscles reflected. Legend: Re, rectus externus; R in, rectus internus; R inf, rectus inferior; Rs, rectus superior; Oi, inferior oblique; Os, superior oblique; Op, optic nerve; P, pyramidalis; Q, quadratus; L, loop of quadratus for passage of tendon (T) of M. pyramidalis. (By permission, Slonaker, 1918.)

M. pyramidalis (in *Columba livia*) arises from the inferior surface of the eyeball just medial and dorsal to the area of insertion of the inferior rectus muscle. The flat, fleshy belly (3.5 mm wide at its origin and 8 mm long) of M. pyramidalis curves upward around the deep or medial surface of the eyeball anterior (medial in owls) to the optic nerve. The muscle tapers to a rounded tendon at the anterodorsal corner of the optic nerve. The tendon curves posteriorly and downward (through the muscular sling of M. quadratus in most birds) around the superior and posterior surface of the optic nerve and gradually becomes flattened. The tendon continues outward around the posterior surface of the eyeball, then passes anteriorly (nasalward) deep to the lower eyelid, and inserts in the inferior margin of the nictitating membrane.

Contraction of Mm. quadratus and pyramidalis draws the transparent nictitating membrane posteriorly (temporalward) over the cornea of the eyeball. Upon relaxation of the two muscles, elastic tissue within the nictitating membrane returns it nasalward to the resting position (Newton and Gadow, 1893: Slonaker, 1918). Some authors have reported smooth muscle fibers in the nictitating membrane but Slonaker did not find any in the House Sparrow. So little work has been done on the ocular muscles that there is need for a thorough comparative study of the subject.

3. *Muscles of the Eyelids*

M. *orbicularis palpebrarum* is the intrinsic muscle of the eyelids. It is, according to Slonaker, composed of smooth muscle fibers arranged primarily parallel to the lid margins. The muscle is a sphincter and closes the lids. Fisher and Goodman (1955) show an extensive origin for the muscle from the bony wall of the anteroventral part of the orbit, but they do not describe the nature of the muscle in *Grus americana*. The bony attachments (the orbit and the maxillojugal), of course, suggest that M. orbicularis in *Grus americana* (and other birds?) is composed of striated fibers and, therefore, corresponds in configuration to the palpebral portion of M. orbicularis oculi in man.

Birds have a levator of the upper eyelid and a depressor of the lower eyelid. Slonaker gave the origin of the two muscles in the House Sparrow as being "at the posterior part of the eye socket just back of the region of the origin of the rectus muscles." This does not fit the description in *Columba livia, Larus argentatus,* or *Grus americana*. In these genera, M. *levator palpebrae superioris* arises by an aponeurosis either from the superior rim of the orbital margin or from the anterior part of the roof of the orbit. In *Larus* the muscle also seems to have some origin by an aponeurosis attached to the outer superior surface of the eyeball. M. levator palpebrae superioris inserts near the marginal fold of the upper eyelid. The upper eyelid is only slightly movable in most birds and, apparently, is immovable in some. Slonaker and others have described a tarsal plate in the lower eyelid but not in the upper eyelid.

M. *depressor palpebrae inferioris* arises by a strong aponeurosis from the posteroinferior bony wall of the orbit in *Larus argentatus*. The belly passes forward and outward under the eyeball and inserts into the anteroinferior border of the tarsal plate. The aponeurosis and belly are fused with the orbital fascia under the eyeball and appear to form with it a functional suspensory ligament of the eyeball.

B. The Muscles of the Middle Ear and the External Acustic Meatus

Newton and Gadow (1893: p. 180) describe a tensor tympani muscle in birds. This muscle "arises near the occipital condyle, passes through a hole into the tympanic cavity, attaches its tendon to the ends of the columellar processes, and also spreads over the tympanum itself." This muscle must be so small in most birds that histological techniques are required to demonstrate it.

One doubts the existence of any muscle which Shufeldt (1890: p. 62) described under the heading of "tensor tympani." Shufeldt (1890: p. 4) also described a dermo-osseous muscle (M. circumconcha) "which surrounds the periphery of the ear-conch." Gadow and Selenka (1891: p. 463) describe (after Tiedemann and Merrem) three small muscles which arise from the bone surrounding the outer end of the external auditory meatus and insert into the skin covering it, particularly when the skin forms a discrete auricular fold.

C. The Jaw Muscles

The jaw muscles have been described in a wide variety of birds by Gadow and Selenka (1891), Lakjer (1926), Moller (1930, 1931), Hofer (1950), Beecher (1951a, 1953), Fiedler (1951), Prins (1951) Barnikol (1953a,b), Starck and Barnikol (1954), Sims (1955), Fisher and Goodman (1955) and Zusi (1962). Important discussions on the movements of the mandible are found in the papers by Fisher (1955a,b), Bock (1960a,b), and Zusi (1959, 1962).

Fisher and Goodman (1955) state precisely the current situation with respect to terminology and identification of certain jaw muscles in different papers: "The nomenclature of the muscles of the adductor and pterygoideus groups is in a state of vast confusion, despite the major studies by Lakjer (1926), Edgeworth (1935), Fiedler (1951), and Hofer (1950). Because of interspecific variation and lack of agreement between previous workers it is virtually impossible to assign names with confidence." There is, indeed, a great need for a monograph on the jaw muscles of birds, particularly in view of attempts to classify passerine birds on the basis of jaw-muscle patterns (e.g., Beecher, 1953).

1. M. Depressor Mandibulae

This muscle (also called the digastric muscle) arises from the posterior or posterolateral surface of the occipital region of the skull (Fig. IX.3).

The belly passes downward around the posterolateral surface of the skull and inserts by fleshy or tendinous fibers on the retroarticular process of the mandible.

Beecher (1953) illustrated M. depressor mandibulae (and the other jaw muscles) in a large number of passerine species (Fig. IX.4). Berger (1957) illustrated the muscle in *Fregilupus, Sturnus, Aplonis,* and *Artamella,* and concluded that the relative development of M. depressor mandibulae alone would be a poor criterion for assigning a genus to one family or another (Fig. IX.4).

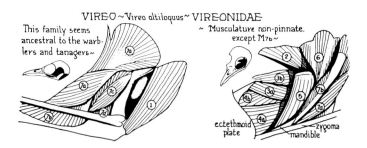

FIG. IX.3. Jaw muscle-pattern of *Vireo altiloquus* depicted in functional groups. Key to numbers on fig.: 1, M. depressor mandibulae; 2, protractor quadrati; 3, pterygoideus dorsalis (a) anterior, (b) posterior; 4, pterygoideus ventralis (a) anterior, (b) posterior; 5, pseudotemporalis profundus; 6, pseudotemporalis superficialis; 7, adductor mandibulae (a) externus superficialis, (b) externus medialis, (c) externus profundus, (d) posterior. (By permission, Beecher, 1951b.)

2. M. Adductor Mandibulae

This is a complex rather than a single muscle. Its four main parts have been called *superficialis, medialis, profundus,* and *posterior;* these have been further subdivided in some genera (see Beecher, 1951a, 1953; Fisher and Goodman, 1955; Zusi, 1962) (Figs. IX.5 and IX.6). The several parts of the complex arise by fleshy fibers or by aponeuroses from the temporal fossa, the zygomatic process, the otic and orbital processes of the quadrate bone, or the postorbital ligament. The various layers pass downward and forward to insert on the dorsal and lateral surfaces of the mandible, beginning on the coronoid process (surangular) and extending posteriorly a variable distance in different birds.

3. M. Pseudotemporalis Superficialis

This muscle arises primarily by fleshy fibers from the anterior portion of the temporal fossa (from the pseudotemporal fossa in some birds) and

from the posterior wall of the orbit. The belly (or bellies) passes downward to insert by a tendon or an aponeurosis on the medial surface of
the mandible, about "3 centimeters from the posterior end of the bone"

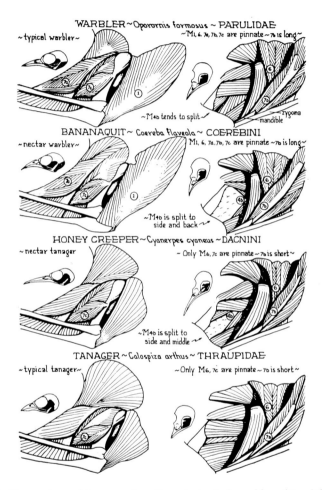

FIG. IX.4. Comparison of jaw muscle-pattern in typical warblers (Parulidae) and
tanagers (Thraupidae) with that of their nectar-adapted forms. See Legend for Fig.
IX.3 for key to numbers on figures. (By permission, from Beecher, 1951b.)

in *Grus americana* (Fisher and Goodman, 1955). In *Thalasseus maximus*
the muscle inserts on a tubercle on the medial surface of the mandible
"at the posterior end of the groove between the surangular and the prearticular" (Zusi, 1962) (Figs. IX.7 and IX.8).

Fisher and Goodman describe a *pseudotemporalis bulbi muscle,* which arises from a small area on the temporal fossa ventral to the posterior portion of M. pseudotemporalis superficialis. The belly passes forward superficial to the latter muscle and inserts on the fascia inferior to the lacrimal gland and the eyeball.

4. M. Pseudotemporalis Profundus

This muscle arises by fleshy fibers and/or by an aponeurosis from the quadrate (primarily its orbital process). The fleshy belly passes downward and forward to insert by fleshy fibers on the medial surface of the

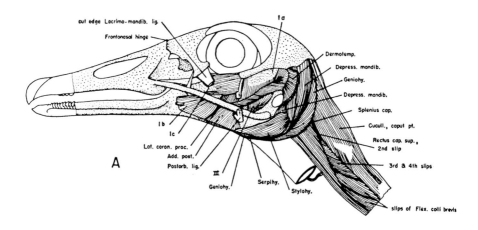

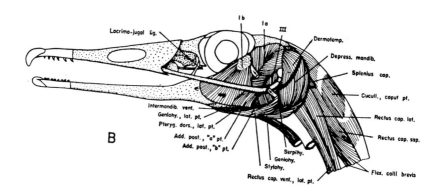

FIG. IX.5. Lateral view of the superficial muscles of the jaws and the anterior third of the neck. (A) *Branta canadensis.* (B) *Mergus merganser.* (By permission, Goodman and Fisher, 1962.)

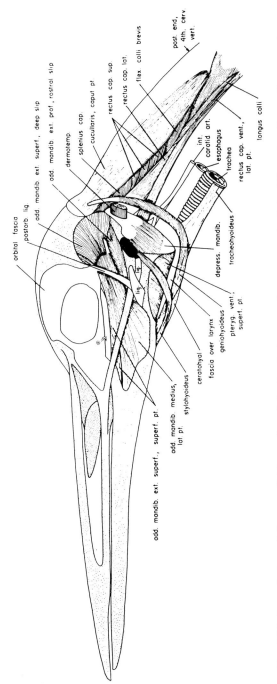

FIG. IX.6. Lateral view of the superficial muscles of the head, throat, and anterior neck of the Whooping Crane, *Grus americana.* (By permission, Fisher and Goodman, 1955.)

mandible, either anterior and ventral, or posterior, to the area of insertion of M. pseudotemporalis superficialis.

5. M. Pterygoideus Ventralis

This part of the pterygoid muscle-complex may be divided into a superficial and a deep layer; the deep layer in some birds is divisible into a medial and a lateral portion. The muscle arises by fleshy and tendinous fibers from the palatine (primarily) and pterygoid bones. The superficial layer inserts on the ventrolateral surface of the posterior end of the mandible. The deep layer inserts on the internal articular process of the mandible and on the medial surface of the bone, anterior to the area of insertion of M. depressor mandibulae.

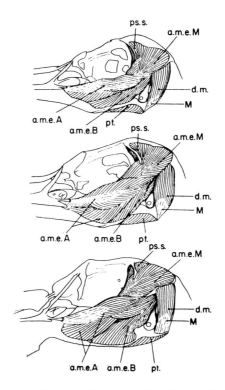

FIG. IX.7. Lateral view of superficial jaw muscles. Above: *Larus atricilla.* Middle: *Thalasseus maximus.* Bottom: *Rynchops nigra.* All are adjusted to the same body size. Key to labels: a.m.e., adductor mandibulae externus (A, B, and M mean part A, part B, and part M); d.m., depressor mandibulae (M = aponeurosis M); ps. s., pseudotemporalis superficialis; pt., pterygoideus. (By permission, Zusi, 1962.)

6. *M. Pterygoideus Dorsalis*

This muscle consists of two heads which arise by fleshy and tendinous fibers from the palatine and pterygoid bones. The two parts of the muscle insert by fleshy fibers, by an aponeurosis, or by a tendon on the medial surface of the mandible anterior to the joint between the mandible and the quadrate.

7. *M. Protractor Quadratus*

This deeply situated muscle arises from the posteroventral corner of the orbit (orbitosphenoid) and the anteroventral region of the pseudo-

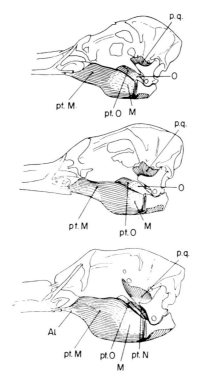

Fig. IX.8. Lateral view of the deep protractors and retractors of the upper jaw. Above: *Larus atricilla*. Middle: *Thalasseus maximus*. Bottom: *Rynchops nigra*. Most of the lower mandible and the jugal strut have been removed. All are adjusted to the same body size. Key: p.q., protractor quadrati; pt. M, pt. N, pt. O mean part M, part N, and part O of the pterygoideus muscle; Al, M, and O indicate aponeuroses. (By permission, Zusi, 1962.)

temporal fossa (parasphenoid). The fleshy belly passes downward and inserts primarily on the medial surface of the body and part of the orbital process of the quadrate; some fibers may insert on the pterygoid.

8. M. Protractor Pterygoideus

Fisher and Goodman (1955) describe this muscle in *Grus americana* as arising primarily by fleshy fibers from the "most lateral protuberance of the basitemporal plate, which point lies at the level of the posterior end of the quadrate." The muscle has a fleshy insertion on the dorsal and medial surfaces of the "anterior third of the length of the pterygoid bone."

D. MUSCLES OF THE TONGUE, LARYNX, AND TRACHEA

The several pairs of muscles which operate the hyoid apparatus in birds have been, as a matter of convenience, referred to as the "tongue" muscles by avian anatomists. These muscles correspond to the mylohyoid muscle and to certain of the extrinsic tongue muscles of mammals, which, in general, are innervated by cranial nerves V, VII, and XII. The "tongue" muscles of birds, therefore, are not to be confused with the intrinsic tongue muscles of mammals. There are very few intrinsic tongue muscles in birds (apparently none in some genera), and little is known about them.

The tongue musculature has been described in a wide variety of birds by Gadow and Selenka (1891), Mudge (1903), Leiber (1907), Moller (1930, 1931), Scharnke (1931, 1932), Steinbacher (1934, 1957), Engels (1938), Fisher and Goodman (1955), and Weymouth, *et al.* (1964). Engels gave a general description of the tongue muscles in passerine birds, presented a partial synonomy of the welter of names used for the tongue muscles, and corrected a "number of bewildering errors in the only extensive description extant of the tongue musculature of the Raven (Shufeldt, 1890), errors both of commission (descriptions and homologies) and of omission (undescribed muscles)."

1. M. Mylohyoideus

This muscle also has been called M. mylohyoideus anterior (Gadow and Selenka, 1891: p. 304; Mudge, 1903: p. 247) and M. intermandibularis (Edgeworth, 1935: p. 278; Fisher and Goodman, 1955).

M. mylohyoideus arises from the medial surface of the ramus of the mandible and passes medially, dorsal to M. geniohyoideus, to insert on a midline raphe shared with the mylohyoid muscle of the opposite side (Fig. IX.9). The mylohyoid muscle is a narrow band (2 mm wide) of fleshy fibers in Rivoli's Hummingbird (*Eugenes fulgens*); it is a long, sheetlike muscle arising throughout most of the length of the mandibular rami in some birds (e.g., the Raven, sunbirds, *Dacnis*, *Zosterops;* see Moller, 1931: pp. 117, 132); the muscle is vestigial in *Grus americana* (Fisher and Goodman, 1955). Mudge (1903) describes an anterior and a posterior belly of the mylohyoid muscle in parrots. The two bellies have

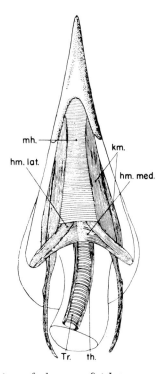

Fɪɢ. IX.9. A ventral view of the superficial tongue muscles of *Dacnis cayana*. Legend: hm. lat., hyomandibularis lateralis; hm. med., hyomandibularis medialis; km., keratomandibularis; mh., mylohyoideus; th., tracheohyoideus; Tr., trachea. (After Moller, 1931.)

a common origin from the anterodorsal "corner of the rami of the lower jaw . . . just behind the line that marks the posterior limit of the bill." The anterior belly corresponds to the typical mylohyoid muscle in most birds; that is, the right and left muscles insert in a midline raphe. The right and left posterior bellies in parrots insert into a bony or cartilaginous nodule "which articulates with the ventral surface of the urohyal," or, rarely, "into the basihyal just at the origin of the urohyal" (Fig. IX.10).

2. M. Serpihyoideus

This is M. hyomandibularis medialis of Moller (1930), M. gularis posterior of Edgeworth (1935: p. 282), and the medial portion of M. mylohyoideus posterior of Gadow and Selenka (1891: pp. 305–307) and of Mudge (1903: p. 253).

M. serpihyoideus arises from the base of the skull (the basitemporal plate) medial to the origin of M. depressor mandibulae in the Raven. The belly fans out as it passes ventrad between the angle of the mandible and the ceratobranchial and inserts in a midline raphe. The belly is continuous near the midline with the posterior margin of M. mylohyoideus in the Raven (Engels, 1938). Moller (1930: p. 710; 1931; pp. 119, 132) says that M. serpihyoideus arises from the caudal end of the

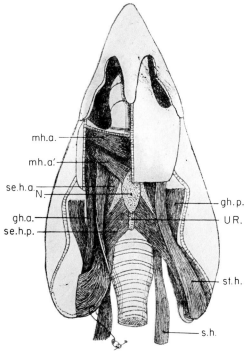

Fig. IX.10. Ventral view of the tongue muscles of *Ara ararauna*. The right half of the mandible has been removed and the right stylohyoid muscle has been reflected to show the course of the geniohyoid muscle. Key to labels: gh. a., geniohyoideus anterior; gh. p., geniohyoideus posterior; mh. a., mylohyoideus anterior; mh. p., mylohyoideus posterior; N., cartilaginous nodule; se. h.a., serpihyoideus anterior se. h. p., serpihyoideus posterior; s.h., sternohyoideus; st. h., stylohyoideus; UR., urohyal. (By permission, Mudge, 1903.)

mandible in the Meliphagidae, in *Dacnis,* and in *Zosterops;* the muscle inserts partly on a midline raphe and partly on the urohyal. M. serpihyoideus also arises from the posterior end of the mandible in parrots; it inserts into a nodule on the ventral surface of the urohyal or on a fascial sheath investing the urohyal (Mudge, 1903). M. serpihyoideus is vestigial in *Grus americana* (Fisher and Goodman, 1955).

3. M. Stylohyoideus

This muscle also has been called M. hyomandibularis lateralis (Moller, 1930) and M. gularis anterior (Edgeworth, 1935: p. 282). Gadow and Selenka (1891: pp. 305–307) and Mudge (1903: p. 253) describe M. stylohyoideus as the lateral and anterior part of the mylohyoideus posterior muscle, and M. serpihyoideus as the medial and posterior part of the same muscle (Figs. IX.11 and IX.12). Inasmuch as birds do not possess a styloid process, the name stylohyoideus undoubtedly was introduced because of its presumed homology with that muscle in mammals. "Hyomandibularis" has much to recommend it if one were to name the muscles on the basis of embryological development. For the vast majority of birds, however, the requisite embryological data are not available.

M. stylohyoideus arises from the lateral or posterolateral surface of the posterior part of the mandible (the angulare portion) anterior to the area of insertion of M. depressor mandibulae in most birds. Fisher and Goodman (1955) found an additional tendinous origin from the opisthotic process of the skull in *Grus americana.* The fleshy belly passes forward and inward to insert on the basihyal (basihyobranchiale of Engels) in the Raven; it inserts on the ceratohyal just posterior to its articulation with the basihyal in *Grus americana.*

In *Eugenes fulgens* M. stylohyoideus arises on the dorsal surface of the skull just posterior to the frontonasal junction. The muscle on the left side of the skull is crossed superficially by the two epibranchials and their covering geniohyoid muscles. M. stylohyoideus passes posteriorly along the skull in close apposition to the lateral border of its corresponding epibranchial. As it reaches the articulation between the epibranchial and the ceratobranchial, M. stylohyoideus passes ventromediad and inserts on the posterior surface of the nearly vertically directed basihyal a short distance ventral to its midlength.

M. stylohyoideus is absent in some parrots (Mudge, 1903).

4. M. Geniohyoideus

This is M. branchiomandibularis of Edgeworth (1935: p. 284) and M. keratomandibularis of Moller (1930, 1931) and Scharnke (1931).

M. geniohyoideus arises from the medial surface of the mandible. The belly passes posteriorly ventral (superficial) to M. mylohyoideus and dorsal (deep) to M. stylohyoideus and inserts on the epibranchial. M. geniohyoideus is said to be "more or less clearly separable" into medial and lateral portions in some birds (Mudge, 1903: p. 261; Moller, 1930; Engels, 1938). The muscle is composed of three parts in most of

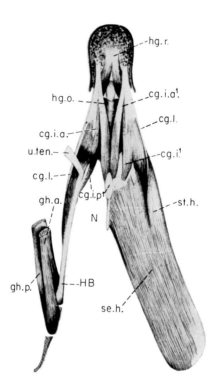

Fig. IX.11. Ventral view of certain tongue muscles of *Cacatua galerita*. The sternohyoid muscles have been removed on both sides. Mm. serpihyoideus, stylohyoideus, and ceratohyoideus have been removed on the right side of the tongue. Key to labels: HB, hypobranchial; cg. i. a., ceratoglossus inferior anticus; gh. a., anterior part of geniohyoideus; gh. p., posterior part of geniohyoideus; hg. o., hyoglossus obliquus; hg. r., hyoglossus rectus; u. ten., urohypobranchial ligament ("tendon," Mudge, 1903: p. 214). (By permission, Mudge, 1903.)

the parrots studied by Mudge; these insert on the hypobranchial (=basibranchial) and the ceratobranchial (the posterior "horns" of the hyoid apparatus in parrots and some other birds consist of three, rather than two, elements).

The epibranchials are greatly elongated in hummingbirds, woodpeckers, and wrynecks. The epibranchials in these birds curve dorsad, follow the contour of the skull, and may extend as far anteriorly as the nostrils. In *Eugenes fulgens* M. geniohyoideus inserts for a short distance on the epibranchial, beginning about 2 mm from its articulation with the cerato-branchial, but then fans out to envelop the epibranchial. The right and left epibranchials and their enveloping geniohyoideus muscles curve dorsad around the back of the skull and meet near the midline at about

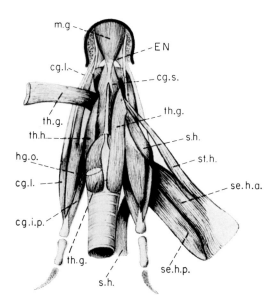

FIG. IX.12. Dorsal view of tongue of *Pezoporus formosus*. Mm. sternohyoideus, stylohyoideus, and serpihyoideus have been removed, and M. thyroglossus has been reflected on the left side. Key to labels: cg. i. p., ceratoglossus inferior posticus; cg. 1., ceratoglossus lateralis; cg. s., ceratoglossus superior; EN, entoglossus; hg. o., hyoglossus obliquus; mg. mesoglossus; th. h., thyrohyoideus; th. g., thyroglossus; other labels as in Figs. IX.10 and 11. (By permission, Mudge, 1903.)

the level of the ridge marking the superior limit of origin of M. adductor mandibulae. From this point anteriad, the two epibranchials pass forward side by side to end on the left side of the median dorsal ridge (culmen) of the maxilla (upper mandible) dorsal to the slitlike nostril (Weymouth *et al.*, 1964). This asymmetry in the termination of the epibranchials (that is, both ending on the same side of the culmen) also occurs in many genera of the Picidae.

5. M. Genioglossus

This muscle arises from the medial or anteromedial surface of the mandible. The fleshy belly passes ventromediad, fans out, and inserts in the connective tissue of the floor of the oral cavity and on the ventral surface of the paraglossal (entoglossum) in *Grus americana* (Fisher and Goodman, 1955). The muscle passes dorsoanteriorly and inserts on a thin ridge "which marks the dorsal limit of the posterior lateral process of the entoglossum" in most parrots (Mudge, 1903). In *Nestor*, however, the two muscles pass dorsal to the entoglossum and "become confluent with each other in the middle line, so that there is no insertion to the entoglossum; the muscle merely forms a loop around it." Moller (1931) describes an insertion on the dorsal and lateral edges of the cerato-branchial (=keratobranchiale) in *Dacnis cayana*; Moller also found the genioglossus muscles in species of the Nectariniidae and Melipha-gidae. Engels (1938) found M. genioglossus to be vestigial in the Raven and other passerines he examined; the muscle is representd by a "few longitudinal fibers in the anterior part of the floor of the mouth, be-

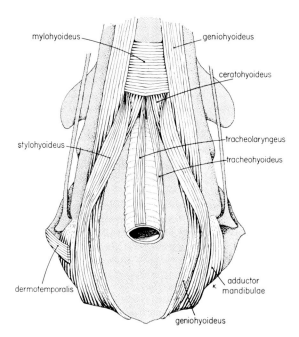

FIG. IX.13. Ventral view of superficial tongue musculature of *Eugenes fulgens* after the skin and subcutaneous connective tissue have been removed. (By permission, Weymouth *et al.*, 1964.)

tween the oral mucosa and the mylohyoideus." The genioglossus muscle
has not been described in hummingbirds.

6. *M. Ceratohyoideus*

This is M. interkeratoideus of Edgeworth (1935: p. 279) and M. keratohyoideus of Scharnke (1931: p. 439). Engels describes M. ceratohyoideus as arising from the lateral surface of the ceratobranchial in the
Raven. The muscle then takes a half turn around the ceratobranchial
and passes toward the midline ventral to the ceratobranchial. The right
and left ceratohyoideus muscles insert in a midline raphe deep to, and
apparently continuous with, the raphe of M. serpihyoideus. There is, according to Engels, no insertion on the urohyal or any other part of the
hyoid apparatus.

In *Eugenes fulgens* M. ceratohyoideus arises by fleshy fibers from
nearly the entire posteromedial surface of the ceratobranchial, extending
posteriorly to the articulation between it and the epibranchial (Figs.
IX.13 and IX.14). The small belly passes forward and inserts on the

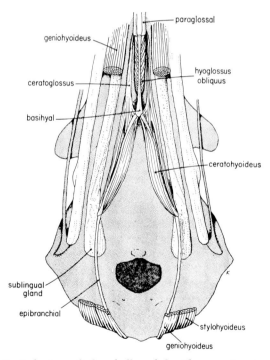

Fig. IX.14. Ventral view of the skull and hyoid apparatus to show the deep
muscles of the tongue region in *Eugenes fulgens.* (By permission, Weymouth *et al.,*
1964.)

lateral surface of the basihyal. The ceratohyoideus muscle is strongly developed in parrots (Mudge, 1903); in many genera, the muscle also attaches to the urohyal (a cartilaginous urohyal articulates with the posterior end of the basihyal in parrots and some other birds). M. ceratohyoideus is absent in *Grus americana* (Fisher and Goodman, 1955) and in many other birds (Newton and Gadow, 1893: p. 620).

7. M. Ceratoglossus

This is M. ceratoglossus posterior of Engels (1938), M. keratohyoideus of Moller (1930, 1931), and apparently M. hyoglossus of Edgeworth (1935: p. 288). The muscle is composed of two parts (pars lateralis and pars inferior, or M. ceratoglossus lateralis and M. ceratoglossus inferior) in cranes, of two parts (superior and inferior) in woodpeckers, and of three parts (superior, inferior, and lateral) in parrots and some other birds (Gadow and Selenka, 1891: pp. 315–316; Mudge, 1903: pp. 214–232).

M. ceratoglossus arises from the dorsal surface of the ceratobranchial in the Raven. The single, cylindrical belly turns ventrad, ends on a tendon, and inserts on a tubercle on the ventromedial corner of the paraglossal. The muscle arises by two heads in *Eugenes fulgens*. The long, lateral head arises from the lateral surface of the ceratobranchial in its caudal half to two-thirds (variation in four specimens). The short medial (and anterior) head arises from the lateral surface of the ceratobranchial for a short distance (about 0.5 mm) just caudal to the articulation of the basihyal with the ceratobranchial; a small bundle of fleshy fibers arises from the basihyal just anterior to its articulation with the ceratobranchial. The two heads pass anteriorly, closely applied to the lateral border of M. hyoglossus obliquus, and the lateral head fuses with the dorsal surface of the medial head. The common belly ends on a tendon which inserts on the ventral border of the paraglossal a short distance beyond its proximal end.

Fisher and Goodman describe two ceratoglossus muscles (lateralis and inferior) in *Grus americana*. Their M. ceratoglossus inferior is composed of three parts (lateral, medial, and posterior). Both Mm. ceratoglossus inferior and ceratoglossus lateralis arise from the ceratohyal; they insert on the basihyal and on the paraglossal (entoglossum). The lateral head of M. ceratoglossus inferior ends on a tendon which also forms the origin of "M. hypoglossus rectus." Mudge (1903) describes in detail the many variations in configuration of inferior, superior, and lateral ceratoglossus muscles in parrots, in which family this complex is very highly developed.

8. M. Hyoglossus Obliquus

This is M. hypoglossus obliquus of Gadow and Selenka (1891), Mudge (1903), and Scharnke (1931: p. 459), M. hypoglossus posterior of Edgeworth (1935), and M. hypoglossus of Moller (1930, 1931). Engels (1938) pointed out that it is incorrect to call this muscle the "hypoglossus," as virtually all authors have done. The correct spelling is *hyoglossus.*

The hyoglossus muscles appear to exhibit considerable variation among different groups of birds, and the homology of the several muscles described by authors remains uncertain. Engels described M. hyoglossus obliquus as "an apparently unpaired, transverse muscle, passing beneath the basihyobranchiale between the posterior ends of the paraglossalia" in the Raven. The muscle is paired in the Whooping Crane and arises by an aponeurosis from the ventrolateral margin of the posterior half of the basihyal; each muscle inserts by fleshy fibers on the ventrolateral corner of the paraglossal.

M. hyoglossus obliquus also is paired in Rivoli's Hummingbird. The muscle arises by fleshy fibers from the lateral surface of the basihyal in most of its anterior half to two-thirds. From the area of origin of the anteriormost fibers, the belly turns outward and inserts by fleshy and tendinous fibers on the ventral and medial surfaces of the paraglossal a short distance anterior to its tip. The precise area of insertion had to be determined by histological sections (Weymouth *et al.*, 1964).

M. hyoglossus obliquus arises from the basihyal and the hypobranchial in parrots; in some genera, the muscle is divided into a medial and a lateral portion, one arising from the basihyal, the other from the hypobranchial. The muscle inserts on the medial surface of the posterior end of the posterior lateral process of the entoglossum. In speaking of parrots, Mudge stated that the muscle varies in three ways: the amount of its extension backward upon the hypobranchial; the degree of development of its tendon or aponeurosis; and whether it is a single muscle or is divided into medial and lateral bellies.

9. M. Hyoglossus Anterior

This is M. hypoglossus rectus of Gadow and Selenka (1891: p. 317), Mudge (1903: p. 247), and Fisher and Goodman (1955). Scharnke (1931: p. 440) describes two separate muscles (Mm. hypoglossus anterior and hypoglossus posterior), but, inasmuch as he probably did not study serial sections, it seems almost certain that Scharnke was dealing with a single muscle. M. hyoglossus anterior corresponds to Engel's M. ceratoglossus anterior.

M. hyoglossus anterior is a complex muscle arising by two heads in *Eugenes fulgens*. Both heads arise and insert on the paraglossal. A dorsal head arises from the dorsal surface of the paraglossal a short distance anterior (distal) to the origin of a ventral head; the dorsal head gradually moves to the medial surface of the paraglossal. The ventral head arises from the ventral suface of the extreme posterior ossified portion of the paraglossal but then passes distad along the lateral surface of the paraglossal. From its position on the lateral side of the paraglossal, the ventral head passes ventral to the paraglossal, becomes semitendinous, and fuses with the dorsal head. The common tendon of insertion passes distad ventromedial to the paraglossal and inserts on the entire dorsal, medial, and ventral surfaces of the anterior cartilaginous portion of the paraglossal.

Engels describes this muscle in the Raven as arising by a "delicate tendon just in front of the tubercle on the paraglossale on which the posterior ceratoglossus inserts; the muscle fibers spread out anteriorly over the under side of the cartilage of the tip of the tongue." M. hyoglossus anterior arises from the posterolateral process of the paraglossal and from the tendon of insertion of M. ceratoglossus inferior in *Grus americana*.

Gadow and Selenka (1891: p. 317) describe their M. hypoglossus rectus as lying on the ventral surface of the tongue, arising from the *basihyal* (anterior to the origin of M. hyoglossus obliquus), and inserting on the anterior end of the entoglossum. Mudge, however, describes the muscle in parrots as arising from the "outer surface of the *posterior lateral process* of the entoglossum" and inserting by tendinous fibers "partly into the apex of the tongue and partly into the fascia of the mesoglossus" muscle.

10. M. Mesoglossus

This intrinsic tongue muscle was described in certain parrots by Mudge (1903: p. 263); it apparently has not been described in any other family. M. mesoglossus is a triangular-shaped muscle lying on the dorsal surface of the paraglossal (entoglossum), and is invested by a dense sheath of connective tissue. The muscle is absent in some species of parrots and then is replaced by a "conical mass of dense connective tissue."

11. M. Dermoglossus

This name was coined by Fisher and Goodman (1955) to describe a muscle in the Whooping Crane (Fig. IX.15). M. dermoglossus arises from the fascia covering the lateral surface of the pharynx. The belly passes anteriorly and inserts by "fleshy and fascial fibers on the dorso-lateral corner of the anterior end of the basihyal."

12. M. Depressor Glossus

Shufeldt (1890) described such a muscle, but Engels (1938) commented that "the fact is that there is no muscle in the Raven which answers this description, or which occupies the position of the muscle shown" in Shufeldt's Figure 17.

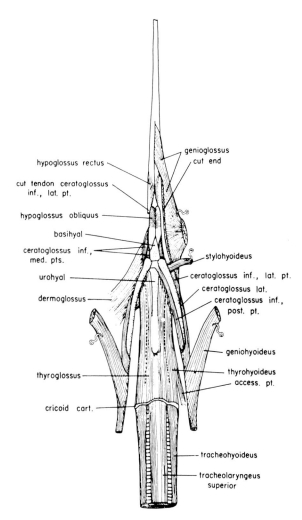

Fig. IX.15. Ventral view of the musculature of the tongue and the anterior part of the trachea in *Grus americana*. (By permission, Fisher and Goodman, 1955.)

13. Mm. Thyroglossus and Thyrohyoideus

Fisher and Goodman (1955) point out that the names "thyroglossus" (=thyreoglossus) and "thyrohyoideus" (=thyreohyoideus) are misleading because the bird larynx does not contain a thyroid cartilage. Both muscles arise from the cricoid cartilage and both pass forward ventral to the pharynx and insert on the basihyal. The paired thyroglossus muscles lie on either side of the ventral midline; the paired thyrohyoideus muscles lie lateral to the thyroglossus muscles.

The two muscles are incompletely separated in some birds (e.g., *Grus americana*), and either or both may be absent. Mudge (1903) describes the considerable variation in the relative development of the two muscles among psittacine genera. Engels describes only a thyrohyoideus muscle in the Raven; it extends from the cricoid cartilage "over the head of the ceratobranchiale, to the dorsal surface of the basihyobranchiale, reaching to its very tip."

An *accessory thyrohyoideus muscle* (Mudge, 1903: p. 232) arises from the fascia of the floor of the oral cavity and the pharynx lateral to the glottis in *Grus americana* (Fisher and Goodman, 1955).

14. M. Tracheohyoideus

This is M. ceratotrachealis of Burt (1930). There is considerable confusion in the literature concerning the tracheal and syringeal muscles, and it is probable that the same name has been applied to nonhomologous muscles throughout the orders of birds. M. tracheohyoideus of Fisher and Goodman (1955) does not fit the description of this muscle as given by earlier authors, nor as implied by the two parts of the name; in the absence of embryological data, one assumes that their tracheohyoideus is a modified portion of M. sternotrachealis. Gadow and Selenka consider Mm. tracheohyoideus, sternotrachealis, cleidotrachealis, thyrohyoideus, etc., to be derived phylogenetically from a primitive sternohyoid layer, which still persists in some birds (e.g., *Apteryx*, parrots). Whether or not this interpretation is correct remains to be proven.

M. tracheohyoideus, by definition, should extend from the trachea to some part of the hyoid apparatus (and not to the larynx). Moller (1930, 1931) reports an insertion on the basihyal, urohyal, and ceratobranchial in the hummingbirds, sunbirds, and honey-eaters examined by him. He described two bellies and a common insertion on the lateral suface of the urohyal in *Zosterops* (although he considered the attachment to the urohyal to be the origin): one belly arises on the trachea, the other on the skin of the neck.

Leiber (1907), Scharnke (1931), and Steinbacher (1934, 1957) discussed and illustrated M. tracheohyoideus in woodpeckers. In most woodpeckers (but not in *Sphyrapicus*) the right and left tracheohyoideus muscles wind around the trachea (from one to two times) before passing anteriorly to insert on the ceratohyal.

Scharnke (1931) described a *laryngohyoideus muscle* (M. *cricohyoideus* of Edgeworth) in *Sphyrapicus varius* extending from the cricoid cartilage to the hyoid apparatus.

15. M. Sternohyoideus

This muscle has been described by Gadow and Selenka (1891) and by Mudge (1903: p. 258). M. sternohyoideus arises from the carina of the sternum and inserts on some part of the hyoid apparatus (e.g., parahyal process, entoglossum, basihyal, hypobranchial) in most parrots. In *Strigops*, "in correlation with the absence of a carini sterni, the muscle arises from the skin of the thorax" (Mudge, 1903). In all parrots except *Strigops*, M. sternohyoideus passes cephalad in contact with the skin of the neck. The muscle has "undergone retrogression" in the mid-cervical region in most parrots. (For other details of this interesting muscle, see the fine paper by Mudge.)

16. M. Sternotrachealis

This muscle apparently has been found in all birds studied. The most common origin is on the sternocoracoidal process of the sternum, but the muscle may arise from the first sternal rib rather than directly from the sternum. M. sternotrachealis inserts on the trachea; the area of insertion may be near the tracheal bifurcation or may be some distance anterior to it. Berger (1960a) illustrated variation in the site of insertion in several cuckoos. Miskimen (1951, 1963) described an insertion on the last tracheal ring (her "first" tracheal ring) or on the syringeal drum in a small series of passerine birds, and anterior to the syrinx in several tyrannids.

17. M. Ypsilotrachealis

Gadow and Selenka (1891: pp. 307, 730) use this name for a muscle which arises on the anterior or medial surface of the clavicle and passes cephalad to insert into the trachea, cricoid cartilage, or the skin of the neck; they discuss many modifications among different genera. Other names used for this muscle are claviculotrachealis (Gadow and Selenka, 1891), cleidotrachealis (Shufeldt, 1890; Burt, 1930), and cleidothyroideus (Leiber, 1907).

The belly of M. ypsilotrachealis is intimately related to the skin of the midneck region and to dermal muscles found there. The muscle would appear to be a modified portion of the sternohyoid-sternotrachealis complex. Leiber reported an insertion on the cricoid cartilage in woodpeckers. Burt described an insertion into the skin of the neck, but his illustration of the muscle suggests an insertion on the anterior part of the trachea or the larynx; one cannot be certain from the drawing. According to Shufeldt, the muscle inserts "on the anterior aspect of the superior larynx, the trachea, and the skin over these parts" in the Raven.

18. M. Thyroarytenoideus

This muscle (more properly called M. cricoarytenoideus) is M. dilatator laryngis of Edgeworth (1935: pp. 285, 440) and M. apertor laryngis of Gadow and Selenka (1891: p. 718). The muscle has been described in very few birds. M. thyroarytenoideus arises from the "posterior edge of the cricoid and from the posterior half of the length of the dorsolateral edge of the lateral cricoid" in *Grus americana*. The fleshy belly passes anteromedially and inserts on the lateral surface of the arytenoid cartilage.

19. M. Constrictor Glottidis

This is M. sphincter laryngis of Gadow and Selenka (1891: p. 718) and M. constrictor laryngis (constrictor dorsalis) of Edgeworth (1935: pp. 285, 440). M. constrictor glottidis, lying deep to M. thyroarytenoideus, arises by fleshy fibers from the "dorsal and lateral surfaces of the medial or middle cricoid cartilage" in *Grus americana*. The belly fans out and inserts primarily in the connective tissue anterior and lateral to the "anterior apex of the arytenoid cartilage," but some fleshy fibers also insert on the dorsomedial edge of the lateral cricoid cartilage (Fisher and Goodman, 1955).

E. The Syringeal Muscles

The muscles of the trachea fall into two groups: extrinsic and intrinsic. The extrinsic muscles have one attachment to a nontracheal structure (e.g., sternum, clavicle, membranes, skin); examples are Mm. sternotrachealis, cleidotrachealis, and tracheohyoideus. The intrinsic tracheal muscles arise and insert on some part of the tracheobronchial tree, including the bony or cartilaginous rings and semirings which form the syrinx. These are the muscles which traditionally are referred to as syringeal muscles (Figs. IX.16–IX.18).

Used primarily in the classification of passerine birds, the structure of the syrinx and its musculature is in great need of intensive study. There have been no thorough and reliable papers on the passerine syrinx since the publication of those by Köditz (1925) and Rüppell (1933). The acromyodian type syrinx (found in oscines or "singing" birds) is characterized by having several distinct pairs of intrinsic muscles "inserted into the ends of the upper three half-rings of the bronchial tubes" (Coues, 1903: p. 245). The mesomyodian syrinx has "less specialized muscles inserted into the middle portion of the upper bronchial half-rings." The Acromyodi also have been called the Polymyodi (with many

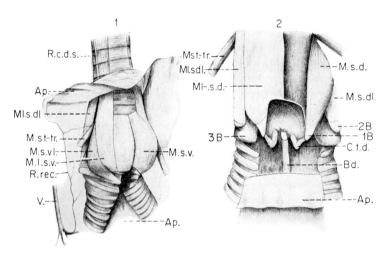

Fɪɢ. IX.16. Ventral (left) and dorsal views of the syrinx of *Pycnonotus atriceps* (Family Pycnonotidae). Key to labels: Ap, aponeurosis; Bd, bronchidesmus; V, vagus nerve; R. rec., recurrent branch of vagus nerve; R. c. d. s., ramus cervicalis descendens superior; 1B, 2B, 3B, first, second, and third bronchial ring; C. t. d., cartilago tensor dorsalis; M. l. s. v., M. laryngosyringeus ventralis; M. l. s. vl., laryngosyringeus ventrilateralis; M. l. s. d., laryngosyringeus dorsalis M. l. s. dl., laryngosyringeus dorsolateralis; M. s. v., syringeus ventralis; M. s. vl., syringeus ventrilateralis; M. s. d., syringeus dorsalis; M. s. dl., syringeus dorsolateralis; M. st. tr., sternotrachealis. (After Köditz, 1925.)

muscles); the Mesomyodi have been called the Oligomyodi (with few muscles). Newton and Gadow (1896: p. 938) state that this distinction is a poor one because the Passeres "includes forms with any number of pairs [of muscles] from 1 to 7." Gadow suggested that the Passeres might better be divided into the following two groups:

1. *Passeres diacromyodi*, in which some of the syringeal muscles are attached to the ventral and some to the dorsal ends of the rings, "those ends being, so to say, equally treated." Such a pattern is found in the Oscines and Suboscines.

2. *Passeres anisomyodi*, in which the muscles are "unequally inserted, either in the middle, or upon only one or the other, dorsal or ventral, end of the semirings." This pattern is found in the Clamatores and Subclamatores.

Gadow stated that there are no Passeres "known to be intermediate between those that are diacromyodian and those that are not." He added that, if followed, his proposal would lead to "a natural classification of the Passeres, and avoid the obviously illogical shortcomings which result from attempts to sort them into two groups by the application of two distinct taxonomic principles, one being the number of the muscles and the other the mode of the insertion" (Newton and Gadow, 1896: pp. 937–942).

Nearly 70 years later, however, we still do not know whether or not

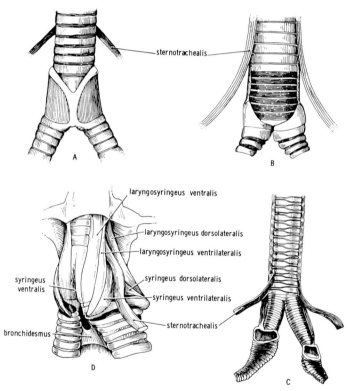

Fig. IX.17. The three types of syringes. A. Tracheobronchial syrinx of *Neodrepanis coruscans* (after Amadon). B. Tracheal syrinx of *Conopophaga aurita* (after Müller). C. Bronchial syrinx of *Steatornis caripensis* (after Garrod). D. Tracheobronchial syrinx of the sunbird *Arachnothera longirostris* (after Köditz). (By permission, Van Tyne and Berger, 1959.)

Gadow was correct in his proposal. Unfortunately, the excellent papers by Müller (1878), Wunderlich (1886), Setterwall (1901), Köditz (1925), Mayr (1931), and Rüppell (1933) have been overlooked or ignored by most recent authors. The coining of new names, without reference to the literature, is regrettable (Miskimen, 1963).

Some nonpasserine birds (e.g., *Struthio, Casuarius, Dromiceius, Apteryx*, Pelecaniiformes, *Scopus;* Gadow and Selenka, 1891: p. 735) and

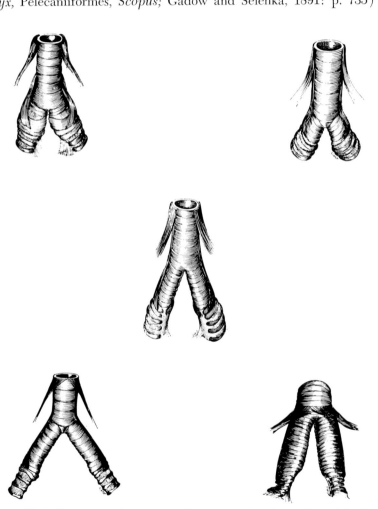

Fɪɢ. IX.18. Variation in the syrinx in five genera of cuckoos. Upper left: Tracheobronchial syrinx of *Piaya cayana.* Upper right: Bronchial syrinx of *Guira guira.* Lower left: Bronchial syrinx of *Morococcyx erythropygus.* Center: Bronchial syrinx of *Crotophaga sulcirostris.* Lower right: Bronchial syrinx of *Centropus superciliosus.* (By permission, Berger, 1960a.)

a few passerine genera (e.g., *Conopophaga*) have no intrinsic syringeal muscles. Turkey Vultures (*Cathartes aura*) are said not to have a syrinx at all.

Most American authors have used Shufeldt's terminology for the syringeal muscles; he adopted names used by Owen in 1866 (Fig. IX.19).

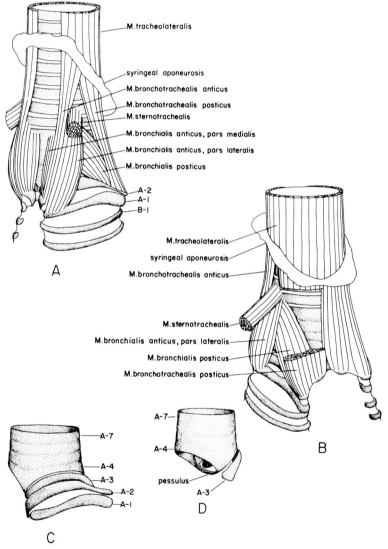

Fɪɢ. IX.19. Four views of an oscine syrinx (*Corvus*); A. left ventrolateral view; B. left dorsolateral view; C. left ventrolateral view of drum and A-elements; D. left dorsolateral view of drum and pessulus. (Courtesy of Peter L. Ames.)

Shufeldt found one pair of extrinsic tracheal muscles (sternotrachealis) and six pairs of intrinsic tracheal muscles in the Raven. From none to nine pairs of intrinsic syringeal muscles have been described in passerine birds (that is, in addition to M. sternotrachealis). Köditz (1925) described eight pairs in certain passerine birds: four pairs of long muscles (Mm. laryngosyringei), which descend along the trachea and insert on the syrinx, and four pairs of short muscles (Mm. syringei), which arise and insert on some part of the syrinx or the tracheal rings immediately anterior to the syrinx. Setterwall (1901) described nine pairs of intrinsic syringeal muscles. Mayr (1931) also found nine pairs of intrinsic syringeal muscles in *Gymnorhina*.

The synonomy of names used for syringeal muscles, so far as can be determined and particularly for passerine birds, is given in Table IX.4. The syringes of many birds, both passerine and nonpasserine, have been illustrated by Garrod (1881), Forbes (1885), Fürbringer (1888), Gadow and Selenka (1891), Beddard (1898), Miller (1934), Miskimen (1951,

TABLE IX.4

SYNONOMY OF SYRINGEAL MUSCLES

1. M. laryngosyringeus ventralis (longus), Köditz (1925)
   M. tracheobronchialis ventralis, Fürbringer (1888: pp. 1087–1092)
   M. bronchotrachealis anticus, Shufeldt (1890), Miskimen (1951)
   M. tracheolateralis (part), Shufeldt, Miskimen
   M. tracheolaryngeus superior and inferior (?), Fisher and Goodman (1955)
2. M. laryngosyringeus ventrolateralis (longus)
   M. tracheobronchialis obliquus
   M. tracheolateralis (part)
3. M. laryngosyringeus dorsolateralis (longus)
   M. tracheobronchialis dorsalis longus
   M. bronchotrachealis posticus
   M. tracheolateralis (part?)
4. M. laryngosyringeus dorsalis (longus)
   M. tracheobronchialis dorsalis brevis
   M. bronchotrachealis brevis
5. M. syringeus ventralis (brevis)
   M. bronchialis anticus
6. M. syringeus ventrilateralis externus (Setterwall, 1901)
   M. syringeus ventrilateralis brevis (Köditz)
   M. tracheobronchialis obliquus (part)
7. M. syringeus ventrilateralis internus (Setterwall, 1901)
   M. syringeus ventrilateralis brevis internus
8. M. syringeus dorsalis (brevis)
9. M. syringeus dorsolateralis (brevis)
   M. bronchialis posticus
10. M. interbronchialis lateralis (Mayr, 1931)

1963), and Berger (1960a), as well as by those authors mentioned previously in this section; each of these authors also cites references to other papers on the syrinx. It may be pointed out that Gadow and Selenka adopted the terminology of Fürbringer (1888), and that most of their illustrations were taken from the earlier literature; moreover, their original drawings of the syrinx of *Corvus corax* (their Plate L) contains several errors.

III. Dermal Muscles

Shufeldt (1890) described 13 muscles as being "true dermal muscles" or "dermo-osseous muscles." Few authors have studied the striated dermal muscles of birds, but reference often is made to one or more of Shufeldt's dermal muscles, nearly all of which are simply specialized slips of well known muscles described by Fürbringer or by Gadow and Selenka. It seems desirable, therefore, to place these muscles in proper perspective.

Mm. dermo-temporalis, dermo-dorsalis, platysma myoides, and dermo-cleido-dorsalis are modified portions of M. cucullaris. M. dermo-tensor patagii is M. cucullaris pars propatagialis.

M. dermo-iliacus is M. latissimus dorsi dorsocutaneous.

M. dermo-ulnaris is M. serratus metapatagialis.

Mm. dermo-humeralis and dermo-pectoralis are parts of M. pectoralis pars abdominalis.

M. cleido-trachealis (= M. ypsilotrachealis) presumably is a specialized portion of the sternohyoid-sternotrachealis complex.

The actual existence as independent muscles of Shufeldt's Mm. dermo-frontalis, circumconcha, and dermo-spinalis remains to be confirmed.

IV. Muscles of the Axial Skeleton

A large group of muscles stabilize and move the skull and the several parts of the vertebral column. Some of these muscles are segmental in nature. Others, presumed to have evolved from segmental muscle masses, are complex muscles composed of several parts, whose origins or insertions are intimately related to the attachments of other muscles. Some of the muscles are primarily fleshy; others contain large aponeurotic or tendinous portions. These muscles have been described for many birds by Garrod (1881: p. 346), Fürbringer (1888), Watson (1883), Gadow and Selenka (1891), Boas (1929), Palmgren (1949), Fisher and Goodman (1955), Kuroda (1962), and Zusi (1962).

1. M. Cucullaris

This is the most superficial muscle in the neck (Fürbringer, 1888: p. 1056; Gadow and Selenka, 1891: pp. 214–216). The nature and relations of M. cucullaris are indicated by some of its other names: constrictor colli, cutaneous colli, and subcutaneous colli. The muscle is not, therefore, a true muscle of the axial skeleton. It is, however, convenient to discuss the muscle here in order to point up the need to clarify the occurrence of M. cucullaris and its relations to the deeper cervical muscles.

According to Gadow and Selenka, M. cucullaris typically consists of two intimately related layers. The superficial layer is composed of circularly arranged fibers lying immediately deep to the skin of the neck. It is this layer primarily which functions as a constrictor colli, particularly when the muscle is strongly developed and the bellies on the right and left sides of the neck meet in the dorsal and ventral midline of the neck. The deep layer of M. cucullaris consists primarily of longitudinal fibers. The composite cucullaris muscle in different birds has attachments to the skull, the mandible, to deeper cervical muscles and to those attached to the hyoid apparatus, to the furculum, and the skin. Certain dermal muscles described by Shufeldt for the Raven are specializations of M. cucullaris: dermotemporalis, dermodorsalis, dermocleidodorsalis, platysma myoides, and dermotensor patagii.

M. dermotemporalis is well developed in *Agelaius phoeniceus*. The muscle arises by fleshy fibers from the dorsal part of the posterior bony rim of the orbit. The belly is 5 mm wide at its origin. The dorsal third of the belly is much thinner than the ventral two-thirds. The belly passes caudally along the lateral surface of the skull and neck, rapidly fans out to a width of about 15 mm, and then splits into two thin fasciculi, both of which are closely applied to the deep surface of the skin. The dorsal fasciculus runs caudally deep to the dorsal cervical feather tract and inserts into the skin of the feather tract at about the midlength of the neck. The ventral fasciculus passes ventrocaudad and inserts into the skin covering the ventrolateral surface of the neck.

M. dermotemporalis in *Eugenes fulgens* (Fig. IX.20) arises from an area about 1 mm wide on the dorsal surface of the skull medial to, and just caudal to the midpoint of, the orbit. At its origin, M. dermotemporalis is covered by the more superficially situated M. stylohyoideus. The belly of the dermotemporalis muscle winds around the bone forming the dorsomedial and posterior rims of the orbit, descending posterior to the external acustic meatus superficial to Mm. stylohyoideus and geniohyoideus. The narrow, thin belly of M. dermotemporalis passes caudad, fans out, and inserts into the skin of the side of the neck at about its midlength.

2. M. Complexus

Most authors have used the name complexus for a muscle which Fürbringer (1888: p. 1056) referred to as the "kopftheil" portion (that is, caput or capitis portion) of his M. cucullaris. It appears more logical not to consider the present muscle as a part of M. cucullaris. M. complexus is a true muscle of the axial skeleton. It is the most superficial of the cervical muscles on the dorsal and lateral surfaces of the neck; it

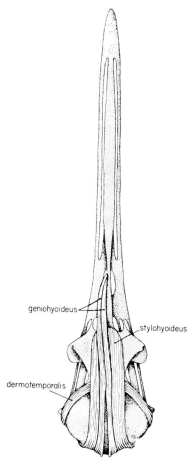

Fig. IX.20. Dorsal view of the skull of *Eugenes fulgens* to show the relations of Mm. geniohyoideus, stylohyoideus, and dermotemporalis. (By permission, Weymouth *et al.*, 1964.)

covers (conceals) Mm. biventer cervicis and spinalis. The muscle is exposed by removing the skin and the subcutaneous portion of M. cucullaris. One assumes that the primary reason why few people have recognized the dermal muscles of birds is that the usual dissecting technique involves skinning the bird before the study is started.

M. complexus arises by fleshy fibers and by aponeuroses from the transverse process (usually cited as the diapophysis, which, precisely, often is defined as the upper articular portion of a transverse process) of one or more cervical vertebrae. Fisher and Goodman give the origin in the Whooping Crane as being primarily from the fourth cervical vertebra. The muscle arises from cervical vertebrae 2, 3, and 4 in *Larus marinus* (Boas, 1929) and from vertebrae 5, 6, and 7 in *Thalasseus maximus* (Zusi, 1962). Boas illustrated differences in origin in a series of birds. M. complexus inserts by fleshy or tendinous fibers on the occipital crest of the skull, just dorsal to the areas of insertion of M. biventer cervicis (medially) and M. splenius capitis (laterally).

Fisher (1958, 1961, 1962) described the development and function of M. complexus (the "hatching muscle") in several birds. Each half of the bilateral muscle usually consists of three segments (sometimes four) separated by tendinous intersections.

3. *M. Biventer Cervicis*

The two parts of this paired muscle lie on either side of the dorsal midline of the neck. The muscle arises from the neural spines of one or more cervical vertebrae (e.g., C16 in *Grus americana;* C16 and C17 in *Thalasseus maximus*), or the first thoracic vertebra (*Corvus corax,* Shufeldt), but the origin typically is shared with the tendons of origin of other muscles (e.g., M. spinalis cervicis, M. longus colli). In some birds (e.g., *Larus, Tetrao*), the muscle is fleshy at both ends and tendinous in the central portion (see Boas, 1929: Plate 10; Palmgren, 1949: Fig. 1). M. biventer cervicis is absent in *Anhinga, Nannopterum,* and *Ardea* (Boas, 1929; Kuroda, 1962). According to Kuroda, M. biventer cervicis in the Adelie Penguin is "uniformly a rather wide flat belt which runs through the whole length of the back (on both sides of the spinal ridge of thoracic vertebrae) to reach the pelvis."

4. *M. Splenius Capitis*

This is M. rectus capitis posticus of Gadow and Selenka. Recent authors, following Boas, call it the splenius capitis (Fig. IX.21).

M. splenius capitis is a well developed muscle arising by tendinous and fleshy fibers from the neural spines of one or two cervical vertebrae (typically from the axis; sometimes also from C3). The belly of M. splenius (a bandage) capitis passes outward and cephalad to insert on the posterior surface of the skull, ventral (deep) to the areas of insertion of Mm. complexus and biventer cervicis. The area of insertion, however, extends ventrad along the lateral surface of the skull, medial to the insertion of M. rectus capitis lateralis, to the base of the opisthotic process (see Fisher and Goodman, 1955: Fig. 4).

Boas, Palmgren, and Fisher and Goodman have described other muscle slips which they name M. splenius accessorius.

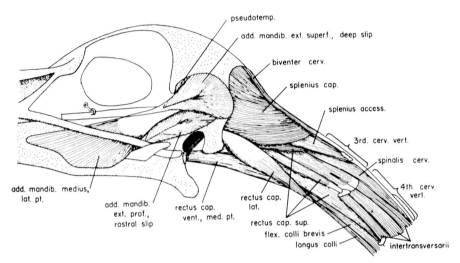

Fig. IX.21. Lateral view of a second layer of muscles of the head and neck of *Grus americana*. (By permission, Fisher and Goodman, 1955.)

5. M. Splenius Colli

This is M. longus colli posticus of Shufeldt. Like many of the deep neck and back muscles, M. splenius colli consists of a series of fleshy and tendinous fascicles whose origin and/or insertion either interdigitates with the attachments of other muscles or is shared with them. In *Thalasseus maximus*, for example, M. splenius colli arises primarily from the neural spines of cervical vertebrae numbers 3 through 7. Zusi (1962) reports that the fleshy slips from "7, 6, 5, and 4 insert in the same sequence on the tendon of M. spinalis cervicis." Boas (1929) gives the origin of M. splenius colli in *Larus marinus* from the third to seventh cervical vertebrae.

Mm. splenius colli and spinalis cervicis are so intimately related in *Grus americana* that Fisher and Goodman described them together. Kuroda (1962) considered M. splenius colli as the anterior (pars anterior) portion of the spinalis muscle complex, as Gadow and Selenka (1891: p. 110) had done; this seems like a more logical interpretation of the complex. Most recent authors have followed Boas in using the name splenius colli. Garrod (1881: pp. 334–346) described and illustrated the specializations of this muscle in *Anhinga*.

6. M. Rectus Capitis Lateralis

This muscle has a deep origin from the hypopophyses of several of the anterior cervical vertebrae (e.g., C3 and C4 in *Grus;* C2–C5 inclusive in *Larus, Thalasseus,* and *Tetrao*). The common belly passes cephalad on the lateral surface of the neck and inserts by a tendon or by tendinous and fleshy fibers on the ventrolateral surface of the skull (on the lateral crest of the exoccipital in *Thalasseus;* on the base of the opisthotic process in *Grus*), lateral to the area of insertion of M. splenius capitis and medial to the origin of M. depressor mandibulae.

7. M. Rectus Capitis Superior

This muscle arises by multiple fasciculi from various parts (e.g., transverse process, lamina, anapophysis, zygopophyseal process, centrum) of several (often C1 through C5) anterior cervical vertebrae. The several fasciculi typically fuse on a common aponeurosis, which inserts on the basitemporal plate of the skull. Fisher and Goodman report that, in the Whooping Crane, the largest slip arises from C5 and "inserts tendinously on the most antero-lateral corner of the axis and the posterolateral aspect of the atlas," as well as on dense fascia extending between these vertebrae and the base of the skull. "Hence the functional insertion of the slip is at least in part on the middle of the posterior edge of the basitemporal plate."

8. M. Rectus Capitis Ventralis

This muscle arises from the midventral surface of the atlas (the *processus latus* of Boas, 1929: p. 194, Plate 6) and from the hypopophyses of several of the following cervical vertebrae (C2 through C5 in *Larus, Thalasseus*); also from the anterolateral surface (*sublateral process,* Boas, Zusi) of C6 in *Larus* and *Thalasseus*. The several fasciculi tend to form two bellies (medial and lateral); the dorsal carotid arteries ascend between the two bellies. Pars medialis inserts primarily by fleshy fibers on the basitemporal plate, posterior to the bony part of the Eustachian tube and anterior to the area of insertion of M. rectus capitis superior. Pars lateralis inserts by tendinous fibers on the lateral surface of the basitemporal plate, or on the posterior surface of the occipital process, and, in part, may insert with pars medialis (Fig. IX.22).

9. M. Flexor Colli Brevis

This muscle arises by several fasciculi from the ventral surface of the atlas (*Grus*) and/or from the transverse processes and other parts of several other cervical vertebrae (C2–C6 in *Spheniscus;* C3–C5 in *Thalas-*

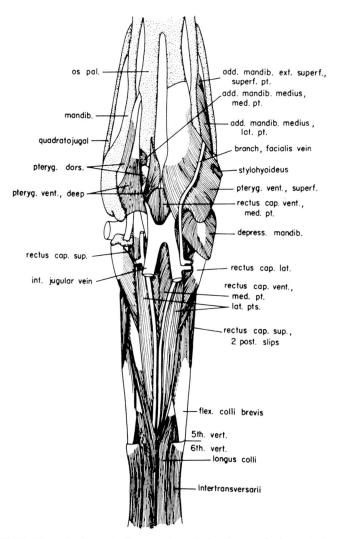

FIG. IX.22. Ventral view of the muscles of the jaw and the anterior cervical region in *Grus americana*. The superficial layer of M. pterygoideus ventralis and M. depressor mandibulae have been removed on the left side. Note the asymmetry of M. rectus capitis ventralis. (By permission, Fisher and Goodman, 1955.)

seus; C5–C6 in *Grus*). The origins of the several fasciculi are intimately fused to, or shared with, the attachments of other muscles (e.g., Mm. rectus capitis superior and intertransversarii). The fasciculi end on a common tendon, which inserts on the ventral surface of the atlas in *Larus* and *Thalasseus*. An anterior fasciculus in *Grus americana* inserts on M. rectus capitis superior, an indirect insertion on the atlas; the posterior fasciculi insert on the transverse process of C3.

10. M. Flexor Colli Profundus

Gadow and Selenka (1891: p. 118) describe this muscle as the anterior portion of M. longus colli anticus. This is the deepest layer of muscles on the ventral surface of the anterior region of the neck. M. flexor colli profundus is composed of a series of fleshy fasciculi which arise from the ventral surfaces of transverse processes, hypopophyses, etc., of several cervical vertebrae. The fasciculi pass cephalad and insert on the ventral surfaces of one or more of the preceding vertebrae; the anteriormost area of insertion is on the axis.

11. M. Longus Colli Ventralis

This muscle, as its name suggests, lies on the ventral surface of the vertebral column. The muscle (also called longus colli anterior or anticus) consists of a series of fasciculi, which arise from the hypopophyses and the centra of the anterior dorsal (thoracic of authors) vertebrae and from most of the cervical vertebrae. The fasciculi pass cephalad and insert on the transverse processes (or costal processes) of most of the cervical vertebrae (C3–C13 in *Thalaseus;* C3–C16 in *Grus*); Shufeldt says that the muscle inserts on the atlas, also, in *Corvus.*

12. M. Spinalis Cervicis

This muscle is called M. longus colli posticus by Shufeldt (1890) and Kuroda (1962); it is, however, sometimes difficult, or impossible, to determine exactly which fasciculi are included in the definition of some of the cervical muscles in different papers. Moreover, M. spinalis cervicis is simply the continuation in the cervical region of the corresponding M. spinalis thoracis in the thoracic region. Kuroda divides the spinalis complex into *pars longa, pars anterior, pars posterior,* and *pars inferior.*

M. spinalis cervicis arises from the neural spines of several cervical and (sometimes) dorsal vertebrae: for example, C15 and D1-D3 in *Thalasseus,* C15 and D1–D2 in *Larus marinus;* C18 in *Grus americana.* The primary area of insertion of M. spinalis is on the axis (C2, epistropheus), but additional tendinous slips insert on the dorsal part (anapophysis) of other cervical vertebrae (C5–C14 in *Thalasseus;* C8–C13 in

Grus). The multiple tendons of insertion are shared with the tendons of origin or insertion of Mm. spinalis thoracis, ascendentes cervicis, dorsales pygmaei, splenius colli.

13. M. Spinalis Thoracis

This muscle also is called M. longissimus dorsi (Shufeldt, 1890; Gadow and Selenka, 1891: p. 106). The muscle arises both by tendinous and by fleshy fibers from the lateral surface of the median dorsal ridge of the synsacrum (and the bony boundaries of the ilioneural canal when present), from the anterior edge of the ilium, and from the neural spines and the dorsal surfaces of the bases of the transverse processes of several or all of the dorsal vertebrae. The belly of M. spinalis thoracis passes anteriorly along the sides of the neural spines of the dorsal vertebrae and medial to M. iliocostalis. The lateral border of the spinalis muscle contacts, and may be fused with, the underlying muscles (e.g., ascendentes thoracis, intertransversarii, and obliquotransversales). Boas wrote that the ventral part of the muscle is a continuation of M. ascendentes. The several heads or aponeurotic slips of origin of M. spinalis thoracis fuse to form a single belly, which, however, has multiple slips of insertion, primarily on several of the posterior cervical vertebrae. At its insertion, M. spinalis thoracis is intimately related to fascicles of origin of M. spinalis cervicis, which is simply the cervical continuation of the same muscle complex.

14. M. Dorsales Pygmaei

This complex consists of four (*Tetrao*), six (*Anhinga, Grus*), or seven (*Ardea, Thalasseus*) separate slips arising from the posterior cervical vertebrae and passing cephalad to insert, in general, on the second or third vertebra anterior to the origin. The slips arise and insert on cervical vertebrae 8–11 in *Tetrao*, 8–13 in *Anhinga*, 8–14 in *Thalasseus*, 9–15 in *Ardea*, and 10–15 in *Grus* (Boas, 1929; Fisher and Goodman, 1955; Zusi, 1962). The tendons or fleshy fibers arise from the nueral spines or the laminae (neural arches), pass cephalad and slightly outward, and insert more laterally (on the transverse oblique crest) on the anterior vertebrae. Mm. dorsales pygmaei are said to be absent in *Rhea, Dromiceius*, and some tinamous (Boas). The muscles are strongly developed in *Struthio* and *Anhinga*.

15. M. Iliocostalis

Shufeldt considered this muscle as part of his M. sacrolumbalis. As a muscle complex, M. iliocostalis extends from the ilium to the base of the neck (Fig. IX.23). The muscle lies both lateral and ventral to M. spinalis

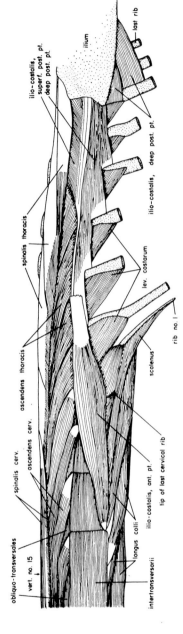

FIG. IX.23. Lateral view of the superficial muscles of the left side of the vertebral column in *Grus americana*. (By permission, Fisher and Goodman, 1955.)

thoracis, and is partially fused with it. The posterior fasciculi arise from the anterior end of the ilium and from the transverse processes of several dorsal vertebrae. Other fibers arise from the anteroventral edge of the ilium and insert on the posterior surface of one or more of the true ribs. Anterior fasciculi arise from the dorsal surface of the tips of several dorsal vertebrae, as well as from the tendons of more posterior portions of the muscle. The multiple fasciculi pass anteriorly; some retain their integrity but others fuse to form common bellies. Insertion is on the true ribs and on the transverse processes of the posterior cervical vertebrae and a variable number of dorsal vertebrae.

16. M. Scalenus

This muscle has been described by Shufeldt (1890), Gadow and Selenka (1891), and Fisher and Goodman (1955). The fleshy belly arises from the transverse processes of one of the posterior cervical vertebrae, passes posteriorly and downward, and inserts on one or more of the cervicodorsal (cervical) ribs (that is, ribs articulating with cervical vertebrae and which do not articulate ventrally with the sternum).

17. M. Levator Costarum

This is a series of fleshy slips which arise from the ventrolateral surface of the transverse processes of the dorsal vertebrae and which insert primarily on the anterior surface of the corresponding true rib. The number of slips, therefore, varies with the number of dorsal vertebrae and true ribs.

18. Mm. Ascendentes

This group of muscles corresponds to M. obliquus colli of Shufeldt and M. cervicales ascendens in the cervical region. The multiple slips of the complex have been subdivided into M. ascendentes cervicis and M. ascendentes thoracis by Fisher and Goodman. The fasciculi lie ventral to M. spinalis and dorsal to M. intertransversarii. The fasciculi arise from the anteroventral surface of the transverse processes of some or all of the dorsal vertebrae and from the diapophyses of most of the cervical vertebrae. Anteriorly, the origin may extend ventrally onto the centra of the vertebrae. The fasciculi pass anteriad and insert on the postzygopophyseal processes or anapophyses of the second and third vertebrae anterior to the vertebra of origin (in general).

19. Mm. Obliquotransversales

Gadow and Selenka (1891: p. 106) call these muscles the transversoobliquus; Boas (1929) considers them a part of his M. ascendens cervicis.

Shufeldt describes these muscles in the Raven as passing "obliquely between the tranverse process of one vertebra to the postzygopophysis on the same side of the vertebra next beyond but one" in the cervical region. Fisher and Goodman describe the muscles in *Grus americana* as arising by fleshy fibers from the "lateral part of the anterior surface of the postzygopophyseal processes and from the fascia overlying the articulation," and as inserting by fleshy and tendinous fibers on the "next anterior postzygopophyseal process." Whether or not these fasciculi deserve to be recognized by a separate name is open to question.

20. Mm. Intertransversarii

This is a series of bilaterally paired muscles that interconnect the transverse processes of adjacent vertebrae in the cervical region; sometimes, also the anterior dorsal vertebra. The anteriormost muscle typically extends between the posterior surface of the axis and C3. The insertion extends from the posterior surface of the transverse process downward onto the centrum in some birds.

21. Mm. Inclusi

These muscles have been considered by some authors as medial portions of Mm. intertransversarii (intertransversales of Shufeldt; intertuberculares of Gadow and Selenka). Boas (1929) introduced the name inclusi, and subdivided the complex into M. inclusi superior and M. inclusi inferior. The topographical relations of the two groups would be indicated better by referring to them as dorsalis and ventralis. The vertebral artery and vein ascend through the neck between the two layers of the muscle.

M. inclusi superior arises from the anterodorsal surface of a transverse process, medial and adjacent to the origin of M. intertransversarius. The belly passes cephalad and inserts by fleshy fibers on the lamina (neural arch) of the next anterior vertebra; the insertion may extend ventrad to the lateral surface of the centrum of the same vertebra.

M. inclusi inferior arises from the anteroventral surface of a transverse process, passes cephalad, and inserts on the lateral surface of the centrum of the next vertebra anteriorly.

22. Mm. Intercristales

This series corresponds to Mm. interarticulares of Shufeldt and M. rotatores s. obliquotransversales of Gadow and Selenka (1891: p. 114). Mm. intercristales lie deep to M. spinalis in the cervical region. The fleshy bellies arise from the postzygopophyseal crests and/or from the anterior surface of the neural spines and the laminae of the vertebrae.

The bellies pass cephalad and insert on the transverse-oblique crests or the postzygopophyseal processes of the next vertebra anterior to the origin.

23. *Mm. Interspinales*

These muscles, as their name implies, interconnect the neural spines of adjacent vertebrae. They occur between the anterior cervical vertebrae (C1–C6 in *Grus;* C2–C5 in *Thalasseus*), between dorsal vertebrae in some birds, and between the free caudal vertebrae. Shufeldt says that the muscles are paired in the cervical region in the Raven; Fisher and Goodman report that the dorsal interspinal muscles of the tail are paired in the Whooping Crane. Fisher and Goodman also consider under the heading of interspinales a series of muscles lying ventral to the free caudal vertebrae and which extend between the hypopophyses of adjacent vertebrae.

24. *Mm. Adductores Rectrices*

These muscles arise from the pygostyle and insert on the medial surface of the rectrices in some birds. Fisher (1946) reports that M. adductor rectricum in the cathartid vultures arises from the pygostyle and inserts only on the innermost (number 1) rectrix. "The muscle originating from the lateral surface of rectrix 1 inserts on the median surface of rectrix 2, and so on."

25. *M. Levator Coccygis*

This is the most superficial muscle on the dorsal surface of the post-acetabular portion of the sacrum and the free caudal vertebrae. The right and left muscles lie on either side of the midline. M. levator coccygis arises by tendinous and fleshy fibers from the dorsomedial surface of the sacrum (primarily the synsacrum), and, in some birds, from the transverse process of one or more of the anterior free caudal vertebrae. The muscle breaks up into several fasciculi, which insert (primarily by tendons) on the neural spines of several free caudal vertebrae; in some birds, also on the pygostyle.

26. *M. Levator Caudae*

This muscle lies on a deeper plane than M. levator coccygis. M. levator caudae arises by fleshy fibers from the posterior edge of the ilium and the posterior fused vertebrae of the synsacrum. The belly (or bellies) passes caudad lateral to the neural spines of the free caudal vertebrae and dorsal to their transverse processes. The muscle gives rise to multiple slips, which insert on the neural spines of the posterior free caudal vertebrae and the pygostyle, on the bases of the rectrices, and on the fascial covering of the uropygial gland. The upper tail coverts are buried in the fleshy and tendinous fibers of insertion.

27. M. Lateralis Caudae

This muscle arises by tendinous and/or fleshy fibers from the transverse processes of the more anterior free caudal vertebrae and from the posterior edge of the ilium, or from a dense aponeurosis extending between the ilium and the free caudal vertebrae. The belly passes caudad and gives rise to multiple tendinous or fleshy fasciculi, which insert primarily on the dorsal surface of the rectrices; additional attachments on the pygostyle or the ventral surfaces of rectrices occur in some birds.

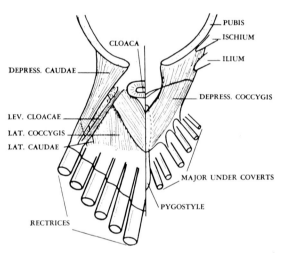

FIG. IX.24. Ventral view of the tail muscles of *Coragyps atratus*. (By permission, Fisher, 1946.)

28. M. Depressor Caudae

This muscle arises primarily by fleshy fibers from the ilium, ischium, and posterior part of the pubis, and from related aponeuroses and ligaments (Fig. IX.24). The belly passes dorsocaudad lateral to M. piriformis pars caudofemoralis and inserts on the ventral surface of one or more of the outer rectrices.

29. M. Levator Cloacae

This muscle lies along the medial border of M. depressor caudae and presumably is derived from it. M. levator cloacae extends between one or more of the outer rectrices to the fascia surrounding the dorsolateral border of the cloacal aperture. Fisher (1946) pointed out that the functional origin is on the rectrix.

30. M. Depressor Coccygis

This muscle arises from an extensive area on the posterior end of the ilium, ischium, and pubis. The belly passes backward dorsal (deep) to the bellies of Mm. depressor caudae and levator cloacae, narrows, and inserts on the ventral margin of the pygostyle and on the bases of the under tail coverts.

31. M. Lateralis Coccygis

This is the deepest of the muscles that lie on the ventral surface of the free caudal vertebrae and the pygostyle. The muscle arises by fleshy fibers from the posteromedial surface of the ilium and from the ventral surfaces of the transverse processes of some or all of the free caudal vertebrae. The main area of insertion is on the ventrolateral surface of the pygostyle, dorsal to the area of insertion of M. depressor coccygis, but additional areas of insertion among different genera include the lateral surface of the pygostyle, the hypopophyses of the more posterior free caudal vertebrae, the lateral surfaces of the centra of caudal vertebrae, and the bases of some of the rectrices and their lower (under) coverts. M. infracoccygis (Shufeldt, 1890: p. 315) and Burt (1930) and M. intercoccygis of Fisher (1946: p. 633) are presumed to be simply the most medial fasciculi of M. lateralis coccygis.

32. M. Transversoanalis

This is M. transversus perinei of Shufeldt (1890: p. 312), so named because of topographical relations similar to those of M. levator ani in mammals. M. transversoanalis is a thin sheet of muscle fibers which bounds the body wall posterior to the pelvis. The muscle arises from the posterior or posteromedial borders of the ilium and ischium, the posterior portion of the pubis, and from one or more of the posterior fused vertebrae in the synsacrum. The sheetlike belly passes caudoventrad and inserts (anterior to the cloaca) on a ventral midline raphe shared with the muscle of the opposite side.

33. M. Obliquus Abdominis Externus

The external abdominal oblique muscle is the most superficial of the three sheetlike muscles which form the ventral and ventrolateral parts of the abdominal wall. The muscle arises by an aponeurosis from the lateral surfaces of the true ribs, inferior to their uncinate processes, and from the ventral margin of the pubis (Fig. IX.25). The belly passes ventrad and inserts by an aponeurosis on the costal margin of the sternum deep to M. pectoralis pars thoracicus. Posterior to the sternum, the belly ends on an aponeurosis which fuses in the ventral midline on a raphe shared with the muscle of the opposite side; the most caudal portion of the muscle may be fleshy at the midline insertion. Anteriorly,

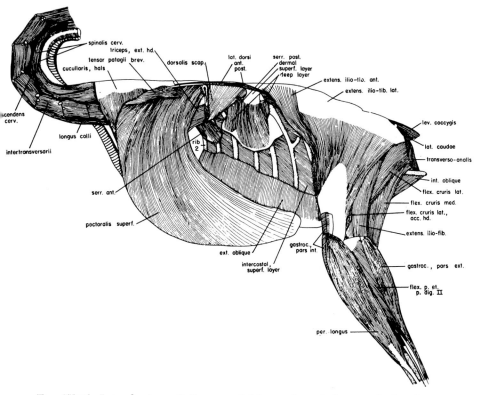

Fig. IX.25. Lateral view of the superficial muscles of the vertebral column, trunk, thigh, and leg of *Grus americana*. (By permission, Fisher and Goodman, 1955.)

the external abdominal oblique muscle lies superficial to the external intercostal muscles; posteriorly, it lies superficial to the anterior portion of the internal abdominal oblique muscle. See Fig. VII.20.

34. M. Obliquus Abdominis Internus

The internal abdominal oblique muscle occupies the interval between the last rib and the caudal end of the pubis. The muscle arises by an aponeurosis from the ventral margin of the pubis throughout all, or nearly all, of its length; occasionally, also, it arises from the ventral margin of the ilium, anterior to the pectineal process of the pubis. The fibers of the internal abdominal oblique muscle pass anteroventrad at approximately a 45 degree angle to the synsacrum. The belly inserts by fleshy fibers on the posterior surface of the last rib, particularly the vertebral portion, but fleshy fibers typically extend downward onto part of the sternal portion of the rib. See Fig. VII.21.

35. M. Transversus Abdominis

This is the deepest of the three flat abdominal muscles. The internal surface of the muscle lies in contact with the transversalis fascia. M. transversus abdominis is covered laterally by the internal abdominal oblique muscle and ventrally by the rectus abdominis muscle. M. transversus adominis arises by fleshy fasciculi from the medial (inner) surfaces of the last two or three ribs and by an aponeurosis and/or by fleshy fibers from the ventral margin of the pubis, medial to the aponeurosis of origin of the internal abdominal oblique muscle. The right and left transversus abdominis muscles insert in a ventral midline raphe (the *linea alba*), which extends from the posterior margin of the sternum to the interpubic ligament. See Fig. VII.22.

36. M. Rectus Abdominis

The straight abdominal muscles lie on either side of the ventral midline raphe and extend between the posterior margin of the sternum and the pubis. The rectus abdominis muscle has an aponeurotic origin from the pubis and the interpubic ligament. The posterior two-fifths to half of the muscle may be aponeurotic before giving rise to fleshy fibers. The muscle inserts primarily by fleshy fibers on the posterior margin of the sternum and the last sternal rib. M. rectus abdominis lies immediately deep to M. obliquus abdominis externus and superficial to M. transversus abdominis. See Fig. VII.23.

37. Mm. Intercostales Externi

The external intercostal muscles occupy the intercostal spaces between adjacent ribs. From their anterior attachment to the posterior surface of a rib, the fibers of the muscle run posteroventrad to their insertion on the following rib. Extensions of the external intercostal muscles pass from the lateral surface of the rib anterodorsal to insert on the uncinate process (epipleural appendage) of the rib next anterior to it; these muscle fasciculi were named Mm. appendicocostales by Shufeldt (1890).

38. *Mm. Intercostales Interni*

The internal intercostal muscles are poorly developed in most birds, and consist primarily of a layer of fascia containing muscle fibers at the anterior attachment of the muscle. The fibers of the internal intercostal muscles run at approximately right angles to the fibers of the external intercostal muscles. Fisher and Goodman (1955) report that the internal intercostal muscles are limited to the spaces between the vertebral ribs; they found only a layer of fascia deep to the external intercostal muscles between the sternal ribs.

39. *Mm. Costopulmonares*

The costopulmonary muscles arise from the medial surface of several (4 in *Columba*) vertebral ribs near their articulation with their sternal counterparts. The fleshy fibers of each belly pass inward and dorsally to insert into the pulmonary aponeurosis. Some of the dorsal fasciculi are intimately related to the necks of the posterior thoracic and abdominal air sacs.

40. *M. Costisternalis*

This muscle (described by Gadow and Selenka, 1891: p. 122) corresponds to M. triangularis sterni of Shufeldt. The muscle lies on the inside of the rib cage and arises by fleshy fibers from the costal process of the sternum. The belly splits into four slips (primarily tendinous), which insert on the medial surface of a corresponding number of sternal (costal) ribs.

41. *M. Costisternalis Externus*

Beddard (1898: p. 107) described this muscle in the Anhimidae (formerly Palamedeidae). "This peculiar muscle, apparently found only in Palamedeidae, replaces physiologically the uncinate processes, as its broad ribbon-like belly runs diagonally across the outer surface of the ribs. It arises by a very thin flat tendon from the third, fourth, and fifth ribs, and from the interspaces between them. It is inserted to the costal edge of the sternum half an inch from the posterior end."

42. *M. Quadratus Lumborum*

This muscle is listed by Gadow and Selenka (1891: p. 126), who report that it is greatly reduced in birds. They describe the muscle in *Rhea.*

V. Muscles of the Wing

1. M. Latissimus Dorsi

a. Columba livia. M. latissimus dorsi pars anterior arises by an aponeurosis from the neural spines of the last cervical and the first dorsal
vertebrae and from the anterior tip of the spine of the second dorsal
vertebra. The sheetlike fleshy belly passes outward and forward, enters
the arm musculature between M. scapulotriceps and M. humerotriceps,
and inserts on the posterior surface of the shaft of the humerus ventral
to the area of insertion of the anterior head of M. deltoideus major.
The 7 mm-wide fleshy insertion on the humerus begins about 9 mm
distal to the articular head of the bone.

M. latissimus dorsi pars posterior, pars metapatagialis, and pars dorsocutaneous are absent.

b. Agelaius phoeniceus. Pars anterior is a thin, flat band of fleshy
fibers about 6 mm in maximum width at its origin from the neural spines
of the last two cervical vertebrae. The belly passes outward superficial
to all the other back muscles except for pars dorsocutaneous. Pars anterior enters the arm by passing between the bellies of Mm. scapulotriceps and humerotriceps and inserts on a curved ridge (1.5 mm long)
on the anterolateral surface of the humerus, beginning 4 mm distal to
the junction of the deltoid crest and the margin of the articular head.
Relative to its relations in many birds, the area of insertion is a considerable distance (2 mm) anterior to the orgin of the dorsal head of M. humerotriceps.

Pars posterior and pars metapatagialis are absent.

M. latissimus dorsi dorsocutaneous arises by fleshy fibers from the
dorsal surface of the anterior iliac process of the pelvis. The fleshy belly
(slightly less than 2 mm wide) passes forward on the deep surface of
the skin lateral to the neural spines of the vertebrae. The belly tapers to
a fibroelastic tendon, which ends at about the midlength of the neck by
inserting into the skin of the dorsal cervical feather tract ventral to the
insertion of the dorsal fasciculus of M. dermotemporalis.

c. Comparative data. M. latissimus dorsi is the most superficial muscle layer in the back (Figs. IX.26–IX.29). The fully developed complex
consists of two independent bellies (*pars anterior* and *pars posterior*)
and two dermal slips (*latissimus dorsi metapatagialis* and *latissimus dorsi
dorsocutaneous*). The dermal components insert into the skin of the
back (usually) or the head in relation to dorsal feather tracts.

Pars anterior arises from the neural spines of a variable number of
cervical and dorsal (thoracic) vertebrae. Fürbringer (1902: p. 484) re-

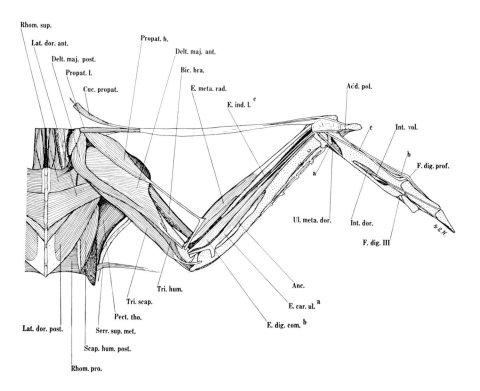

Rhom. sup.

Lat. dor. ant.

Delt. maj. post.

Propat. l.

Cuc. propat.

Propat. b.

Delt. maj. ant.

Bic. bra.

E. meta. rad.

E. ind. l. ^c

Ad'd. pol.

Int. vol.

b

F. dig. prof.

c

a

Ul. meta. dor.

Int. dor.

F. dig. III

Tri. hum.

Tri. scap.

Pect. tho.

Lat. dor. post.

Serr. sup. met.

Scap. hum. post.

Rhom. pro.

Anc.

E. car. ul. ^a

E. dig. com. ^b

FIG. IX.26. Dorsal view of the back and wing of the Common Crow (*Corvus brachyrhynchos*) as seen after the skin and subcutaneous connective tissue have been removed. (By permission, Hudson and Lanzillotti, 1955.)

Abbreviations used in wing muscle drawings: An.—M. anconeus; Anc.—M. anconaeus coracoideus; Cb. ant.—M. coracobrachialis anterior; D. min.—M. deltoideus minor; Del.—M. deltoideus major; Dor. scap.—M. dorsalis scapulae; Exp.—M. expansor secundariorum; Ext. dig.—M. extensor digitorum communis Ext. in. long.—M. extensor indicis longus; Ext. meta.—M. extensor metacarpi radialis; Ext. p. brev.—M. extensor pollicis brevis; Ext. p. long.—M. extensor pollicis longus; Flex. c. u.—M. flexor carpi ulnaris; Flex. d. III—M. flexor digiti III; Flex. dig.—M. flexor digitorum superficialis; Flex. meta.—M. flexor metacarpi radialis; Flex. meta. post.—M. flexor metacarpi posterior; Inter. dor.—M. interosseus dorsalis; Inter. palm.—M. interosseus palmaris; Lat. dor. p. ant.—M. latissimus dorsi pars anterior; Lat. dor. p. post.—M. latissimus dorsi pars posterior; Met.—metapatagium; Pect. pro. brev.—M. pectoralis pars propatagialis brevis; Pect, pro. long.—M. pectoralis pars propatagialis longus; Pro.—M. proscapulohumeralis; Pro. prof.—M. pronator profundus; Pro. sup.—M. pronator superficialis; Rhom. pro.—M. rhomboideus profundus; Rhom. sup.—M. rhomboideus superficialis; Sup.—M. supinator; T. dor.—M. humerotriceps, dorsal head; T. hum.—M. humerotriceps; T. scap.—M. scapulotriceps; T. ven.—M. humerotriceps, ventral head; Tpb.—M. tensor patagii brevis; Tpl.—M. tensor patagii longus; Tr.—M. scapulotriceps.

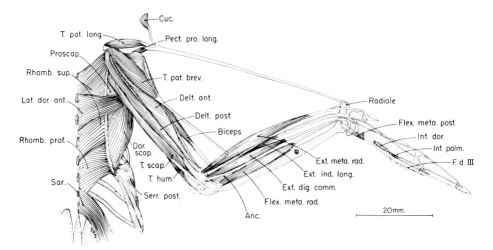

Fig. IX.27. Dorsal view of the back and wing of the Bourbon Crested Starling (*Fregilupus varius*). M. latissimus dorsi pars posterior is absent in this passerine species. (By permission, Berger, 1957.) For Key to Abbreviations see legend to Fig. IX.26.

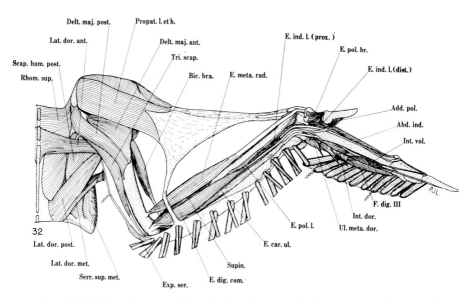

Fig. IX.28. Dorsal view of the back and wing of the Prairie Falcon (*Falco mexicanus*). Note the short distal head of M. extensor indicis longus. (By permission, Hudson and Lanzillotti, 1955.) For Key to Abbreviations see legend to Fig. IX.26.

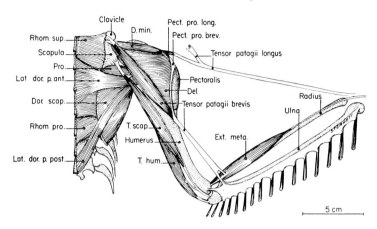

Fɪɢ. IX.29. Dorsal view of the proximal wing muscles of *Aceros undulatus* (Bucerotidae). (By permission, Berger, 1960b.) For Key to Abbreviations see legend to Fig. IX.26.

ported that pars anterior has an accessory origin (*caput accessorium scapulae*) in *Rhea, Casuarius,* and *Dromaeus.*

Pars posterior arises caudal to pars anterior from neural spines of dorsal vertebrae in most birds; it may arise exclusively from the anterior edge of the pelvis and associated fascia (e.g., *Polihiërax*), from the dorsal portions of ribs (*Chauna, Vanellus, Crypturus*), or from both dorsal vertebrae and the ilium (*Rhynochetus,* Beddard, 1891: p. 12; *Pharomachrus mocino, Chloroceryle americana*). Pars posterior in *Otus asio* arises by an aponeurosis from the median dorsal ridge of the synsacrum and by both tendinous and fleshy fibers from approximately the medial half of the anterior iliac process of the ilium. In *Chordeiles minor,* pars posterior arises from the spine of the last dorsal vertebra, from the median dorsal ridge of the synsacrum, and from the entire anterior edge of the anterior iliac process, just anterior to the origin of M. iliotrochantericus posterior. As noted below, pars posterior is absent in hummingbirds (e.g., *Eugenes fulgens*); it is hypertrophied in the Chimney Swift (*Chaetura pelagica*), in which pars posterior arises by an aponeurosis from neural spines of the posterior dorsal vertebrae, from the ilium, and from the last thoracic rib (i.e., a rib articulating dorsally with the anterior end of the synsacrum).

The two main parts of M. latissimus dorsi may form an almost continuous sheet of muscle (*latissimus dorsi communis* of Fürbringer), as in *Spheniscus, Fulmarus, Tauraco leucotis,* and cuckoos (Fürbringer, 1902: p. 489; Berger, 1953: Fig. 3), or the two parts may be widely separated in the back, as in *Polihiërax semitorquatus, Aceros undulatus, Goura victoria, Otus asio, Chloroceryle americana,* and *Procnias nudicollis.*

Both pars anterior and pars posterior of M. latissimus dorsi enter the arm musculature by passing between M. scapulotriceps and M. humerotriceps to insert on the humerus. There is considerable variation in the relationships of the two tendons of insertion. Pars anterior inserts on the humerus by a wide fleshy or semitendinous band; pars posterior most commonly inserts by a small tendon or a flat aponeurosis, either posterior (ventral) or proximal to the insertion of pars anterior. Although the tendons of the two parts typically insert adjacent to each other, I have never seen an instance in which the two tendons fuse completely for a common insertion. Fisher and Goodman (1955) reported that pars posterior in *Grus americana* attaches to the deep side of pars anterior, but also inserts on the humerus beneath the fleshy insertion of pars anterior. In *Grus canadensis tabida,* however, I found that pars posterior inserts proximal to the insertion of pars anterior. Similar variation is found in the pattern of insertion among the cuckoos: in *Crotophaga sulcirostris,* pars posterior inserts immediately posterior to the upper third of pars anterior; in *Coccyzus erythropthalmus,* pars posterior inserts in line with and proximal to the insertion of pars anterior. There is a striking difference in the pattern of insertion of pars anterior and pars posterior between the two starlings, *Sturnus* and *Aplonis.* In *Aplonis* pars posterior inserts immediately posterior to, and in contact with, pars anterior. In *Sturnus* pars anterior inserts on the anterolateral edge of the humerus, whereas pars posterior inserts on the posterolateral edge of the bone, so that there is a space about 3 mm wide between the two areas of insertion (Berger, 1957).

One of the most peculiar patterns of insertion I have seen is found in *Geococcyx califorianus,* in which species the areas of insertion of pars anterior and pars posterior are separated by the dorsal (internal) head of M. humerotriceps. Pars anterior inserts by a broad (7 mm wide), flat tendon dorsal (anterior) to the area of origin of the dorsal head of M. humerotriceps, beginning about 10 mm inferior to the junction of the articular head and the deltoid crest of the humerus. Pars posterior inserts by a strong round tendon immediately distal to the insertion of M. proscapulohumeralis and between the uppermost fibers of origin of the two heads of the humerotriceps (Berger, 1954). A similar pattern of insertion is found in the Chimney Swift (*Chaetura pelagica*), although its shoulder musculature and humerus are greatly modified from the generalized pattern seen in *Geococcyx.* M. latissimus dorsi pars anterior in the swift is a weakly developed fleshy band less than 1 mm wide except at its origin. The ectepicondylar process of the humerus in the swift is located just distal to the midlength of the bone. Pars anterior inserts on the humeral shaft just proximal to the ectepicondylar process and posterior to the areas of insertion of the very large tendon of M. supracoracoideus and the fleshy insertion of the rudimentary M. deltoideus major. Pars posterior is hypertrophied in the swift. The muscle inserts by a large semitendinous mass between the dorsal and ventral heads of M. humerotriceps and just distal to the area of insertion of M. proscapulohumeralis. In contrast to *Geococcyx*, however, the dorsal head of M. humerotriceps is weakly developed in the swift.

An apparently previously undescribed close relationship between the tendon of insertion of pars posterior and an aponeurotic *humeral anchor* of M. scapulotriceps is found in *Gavia immer, Otus asio, Chordeiles minor*, and *Pharomachrus mocino*. In these species, a dense aponeurosis covers the anterior part of the deep surface of the belly of M. scapulotriceps. The aponeurosis is joined at approximately a 45 degree angle by an aponeurotic band (humeral anchor), which is attached to the posterior surface of the shaft of the humerus. The tendon of insertion of pars posterior is partially fused to the deep surface of the humeral anchor, but can be teased away from it.

Pars anterior is said to be absent in *Apteryx* and in *Alcedo bengalensis*, but not in other species of *Alcedo* (Beddard, 1898: p. 80). Pars posterior is absent in *Otis, Pterocles* (Beddard, 1898: pp. 80, 309), *Columba livia, Gallicolumba luzonica, Eugenes fulgens, Indicator variegatus*, the Picidae, *Artamella viridis, Fregilupus varius, Dendroica kirtlandii*, the Pleoceidae, and the Fringillidae. It may be emphasized that pars posterior has been found in all genera of the Corvidae thus far investigated (Hudson and Lanzillotti, 1955) and in the two genera of Sturnidae (*Sturnus vulgaris, Aplonis tabuensis*) studied by Berger (1957). Berger (1956b) also found pars posterior in a specimen of *Paradisaea rubra* (Paradisaeidae).

Latissimus dorsi metapatagialis, a dermal component, typically is a small fleshy band, which usually arises from the superficial surface of pars posterior. The belly passes forward and outward to insert in the skin at the posterior margin of the humeral feather tract, adjacent to the insertion of M. serratus metapatagialis. The muscle is a very wide (1.5 cm) sheet of muscle in the Common Gallinule (*Gallinula chloropus*). Beddard (1898: p. 202) said that the colies, hornbills, swifts, and hummingbirds are the only flying birds that lack this muscle. Hudson and Lanzillotti (1955), however, reported the muscle to be absent in the Corvidae. I did not find the muscle in *Goura victoria, Gallicolumba luzonica, Columba livia, Coracias abyssinica, Upupa epops, Indicator variegatus, Polihiërax semitorquatus, Paradisaea rubra, Sturnus vulgaris*,

Aplonis tabuensis, Artamella viridis, Dendroica kirtlandii, or *Spizella arborea.* A rudimentary latissimus dorsi metapatagialis was present unilaterally in a specimen of *Fregilupus varius,* but its presence had to be confirmed by microscopic examination (Berger, 1957: p. 241). The muscle may be present or absent in *Grus americana* and *Grus canadensis* (Fisher and Goodman, 1955: p. 48; Berger, 1956e: p. 285). Swinebroad (1954) did not mention this muscle in his discussion of several fringillids.

Latissimus dorsi dorsocutaneous ("dermo-iliacus" of Shufeldt, 1890: p. 12), a second dermal component, arises from the anterior end of the ilium. The belly passes craniad along the lateral margin of the dorsal feather tracts to insert into the skin near the base of the neck in most birds. Little specific information is available on the occurrence of this muscle. According to Beddard (1898: p. 80) and Fürbringer (1902: pp. 501–502), the dorsocutaneous component is found in *Apteryx,* Alcidae, Charadriidae, Cracidae, some galliform birds, Piciformes, and Passeriformes. I have found the muscle in *Indicator, Procnias nudicollis, Fregilupus, Sturnus, Aplonis, Artamella, Paradisaea,* and *Dendroica kirtlandii.* In some birds this muscle is partially fused either with latissimus dorsi metapatagialis or with M. cucullaris dorsocutaneous (Fürbringer, 1902).

2. M. Rhomboideus Superficialis

a. Columba livia. The superficial rhomboid muscle arises by an extensive aponeurosis from the neural spines of the last two cervical vertebrae, from the spines of all of the dorsal vertebrae, and by an aponeurosis (shared with M. sartorius) from the median dorsal ridge of the synsacrum and from the anterior iliac process of the ilium. The fleshy fibers pass outward and forward to insert on the dorsomedial edge of the scapula, beginning posterior to the acromion and extending caudally to within 4 mm of the apex of the scapula. M. rhomboideus superficialis conceals all but a small triangular portion of M. rhomboideus profundus at the apex of the scapula.

b. Agelaius phoeniceus. The muscle arises by fleshy fibers and by an aponeurosis from the interspinous ligaments and the neural spines of the last two cervical vertebrae and the first three dorsal vertebrae. The wide, thin belly passes outward and forward to insert on the dorsomedial edge of the scapula in its anterior two-thirds (about 20 mm). M. latissimus dorsi pars anterior crosses superficial to the middle portion of M. rhomboideus superficialis.

c. Comparative data. M. rhomboideus superficialis typically is a thin sheet of muscle, lying deep to M. latissimus dorsi and superficial to M. rhomboideus profundus (Fig. IX.30). In most birds, the superficial rhomboid arises by an aponeurosis from the neural spines of several of the cervical and dorsal vertebrae and from the interspinous ligaments between the spines. In some birds (e.g., *Columba livia*), the muscle also arises from the anterior edge of the synsacrum and from the anterior iliac process of the pelvis. According to Beddard, the superficial rhomboid arises from the ribs in *Casuarius* and in *Apteryx*. The fleshy fibers pass outward and, in general, forward to insert on the dorsomedial edge of the scapula; anteriorly, the muscle may insert on the dorsal end of the clavicle. The insertion on the scapula may begin on the acromion, or just caudal to it, and extend caudally from about two-thirds to nearly the entire length of the blade of the scapula. The superficial rhomboid muscle is relatively weakly developed in *Chaetura pelagica*, in which species the belly inserts on little more than the anterior half of the scapula.

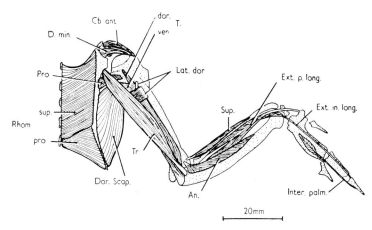

Fig. IX.30. Dorsal view of wing of *Coua caerulea* (Cuculidae) to show a deep layer of muscles. (By permission, Berger, 1953.) For Key to Abbreviations see Fig. IX.26.

3. M. Rhomboideus Profundus

a. Columba livia. The deep rhomboid muscle arises by an aponeurosis from the neural spines of the last two cervical vertebrae and all of the dorsal vertebrae. The fleshy belly passes outward to insert on most of the medial surface of the caudal 25 mm of the blade of the scapula, but anteriorly it inserts on the dorsomedial surface, dorsal to the area of insertion of M. serratus profundus.

b. Agelaius phoeniceus. This muscle arises by fleshy fibers and by an aponeurosis from the interspinous ligaments and from the neural spines of the last two cervical vertebrae (from the posterior tip only of the penultimate vertebra) and the first four dorsal vertebrae. The origin from the fourth dorsal vertebra is intimately related to the origin of M. sartorius. The flat belly (slightly thicker than that of M. rhomboideus superficialis) passes outward and backward to insert on the medial surface of the scapula in its caudal one-third. The fibers insert posterior and dorsal to the area of insertion of M. serratus profundus.

c. *Comparative data.* The deep rhomboid muscle, usually thicker than the superficial rhomboid, also arises from the neural spines of a variable number of cervical and dorsal vertebrae and their interspinous ligaments, sometimes only from the spines of dorsal vertebrae; in *Podargus* the muscle also arises from the ilium. The fleshy fibers of M. rhomboideus profundus pass outward and backward to insert on the dorsomedial surface of the scapula (in some birds, also on the medial surface) in its caudal third or more. The anterior portion of the deep rhomboid is concealed by the belly of the superficial rhomboid muscle in all birds. In some birds (e.g., *Columba livia*) the superficial rhomboid is so extensive that it conceals all but a small, triangular-shaped piece of the deep rhomboid at its attachment to the apex of the scapula. The deep rhomboid muscle is said to be absent in *Apteryx* (Beddard, 1898: p. 504).

4. *M. Serratus Profundus*

a. *Columba livia.* The deep "serrated" muscle arises by separate fleshy fasciculi from the lateral surfaces of the last cervicodorsal rib and the first true rib. The fasciculi pass dorsocaudad to insert fleshily on the medial surface of the scapula in the region of the junction of the anterior two-thirds and the posterior one-third of the blade of the scapula. The muscle is visible in a dorsal view only after Mm. latissimus dorsi, rhomboideus superficialis, and rhomboideus profundus have been reflected or removed.

b. *Agelaius phoeniceus.* This well developed complex arises by several fleshy fasciculi from the transverse processes of the penultimate and the antepenultimate cervical vertebrae and from the lateral surfaces of the last cervicodorsal rib and the first true rib. The anterior fasciculi pass backward and outward; the posterior fasciculi pass backward and upward. There is little fusion among the fasciculi but they insert in sequence on the medial surface of the scapula for a distance of about 9 mm between the origin of the internal head of M. subscapularis (anteriorly) and the insertion of M. serratus posterior (posteriorly).

c. *Comparative data.* This is the "levator scapulae" of Shufeldt (1890: pp. 98, 104) and of Burt (1930: p. 489), but this name is inappropriate. Howell (1937: p. 368) stated that "no bird, so far as I am aware, possesses a true levator scapulae arising from the more cranial of the cervical vertebrae . . . ."

M. serratus profundus arises by multiple fasciculi from any or all of the following structures: the posterior cervical vertebrae, one or more of the cervicodorsal ribs, one or more of the true ribs. Depending on the origin, the fibers pass caudad or dorsocaudad to insert on the medial surface of the scapula deep to the insertion of M. rhomboideus profundus and anterior to the insertion of M. serratus posterior.

In *Aceros undulatus* the fleshy fasciculi arise from the lateral surfaces of both of the cervicodorsal ribs and the first true rib (the smallest component) and from the adjacent area on the respective vertebrae. In *Grus canadensis tabida* M. serratus profundus arises by fasciculi from the transverse process of the last cervical vertebra and from the lateral surface, near the neck, of true ribs numbers 1, 2, and 3. In *Paradisaea* and in the Corvidae, the fasciculi arise from the transverse processes of cervical vertebrae numbers 12 and 13 and from the lateral surface, dorsal to the uncinate processes, of the last cervicodorsal rib and the first true rib. An example of intergeneric variation in origin within a family (Cuculidae) is shown in the accompanying table.

Genus	Cervical vertebrae			Cervicodorsal ribs		True rib
	10	11	12	1	2	1
Crotophaga	x	x	x	x	x	
Geococcyx	x	x	x		x	
Coua		x	x	x	x	
Coccyzus	x	x			x	x

5. M. Serratus Anterior

a. Columba livia. M. serratus anterior arises by two strong fleshy bellies: one from the lateral surface of the first true rib, inferior to its uncinate process; and a second, deeper, belly from the uncinate process of the last cervicodorsal rib and from the shaft of the rib inferior to the uncinate process. The two bellies pass dorsad, fuse, and give rise to a common aponeurosis (about 4 mm wide), which continues upward between the two heads of M. subscapularis and inserts on the ventromedial edge of the scapula, beginning about 5 mm caudal to the posterior lip of the glenoid cavity.

b. Agelaius phoeniceus. This muscle arises by two fleshy fasciculi from the lateral surfaces of the last cervicodorsal rib and the first true rib at the level of its uncinate process. The two flat fasciculi pass dorsally, fuse, and form a flat fleshy belly. The belly gives rise to a thin, bandlike aponeurosis, which passes upward between the two heads of M. subscapularis and inserts on the ventral edge of the scapula a short distance caudal to the glenoid cavity.

c. Comparative data. This is the M. serratus superficialis anterior of Fürbringer (1902) and Hudson and Lanzillotti (1955). Shufeldt (1890: p. 99) called it the "thoraco-scapularis." His descriptions of the serratus muscles and references to the synonomy given by Gadow indicate that Shufeldt did not understand the relationships of the three major serratus muscles. Following Shufeldt, both Berger (1953: pp. 58–59; 1954: pp. 14–15) and Swinebroad (1954: pp. 492, 499) also misinterpreted this complex. The "serratus anterior" of both authors is merely a part of M. serratus profundus (see Berger, 1959b). Swinebroad's "M. serratus posterior, deep layer," actually is M. serratus anterior in the species he dissected.

The serratus anterior is the smallest of the three major serratus muscles. It arises from the lateral surface of one or more of the anterior ribs. In certain cuckoos (e.g., *Coua, Crotophaga*) there is a single fleshy slip, which arises from the last cervicodorsal rib; in *Polihiërax semitorquatus*, the single slip arises from the first true rib. There are two or more slips in many birds. In the following birds, the two slips arise, respectively, from the last cervicodorsal rib and the first true rib: *Geococcyx, Tauraco, Aceros, Paradisaea,* and the Corvidae. In all known instances, the fleshy slip (or slips) gives rise to a wide, bandlike tendon, which passes upward between the two heads of M. subscapularis to insert on the ventral edge (usually) of the scapula; it inserts on the dorsal border in *Rhea* (Beddard, 1898: p. 81). There may be fascial connections with the ventral margin of M. subscapularis.

6. M. Serratus Posterior

a. Columba livia. The posterior serratus muscle is a well developed mass of fleshy fibers about 20 mm in width. It arises primarily by aponeuroses from the lateral surfaces of the first four true ribs, at the level of their uncinate processes, and from the intercostal fascia between the ribs. The origin from the 4th rib lies deep to the anterior border of M. sartorius. The several fleshy fasciculi pass dorsad, fuse, and insert on the ventral edge of the caudal 12 mm of the scapula. The muscle inserts by fleshy fibers on the apex of the scapula and by an aponeurosis anterior to the apex.

b. Agelaius phoeniceus. This relatively wide (9 mm), thick muscle arises from the lateral surfaces of true ribs 2, 3, and 4, ventral to their uncinate processes, and from the external intercostal fascia. As it passes dorsad, the flat belly tapers and inserts by fleshy fibers on the apex of the scapula and by an aponeurosis on the ventral edge of the scapula for a short distance anterior to the insertion of the fleshy fibers.

c. Comparative data. This is M. serratus superficialis posterior of Hudson and Lanzillotti (1955).

M. serratus posterior is the largest of the three serratus muscles. It arises by several fasciculi from the lateral surface of the shafts and uncinate processes of several of the true ribs, and, in some genera, from the intercostal fascia. The fleshy fasciculi usually are separable only at their origin. The common belly inserts primarily by fleshy fibers on the apex of the scapula, but, in many birds by an aponeurosis anteriorly. The insertion may be on the caudal tip only or may occupy the posterior third or more of the scapular blade. In the Cathartidae (Fisher, 1946: p. 586), the Whooping Crane (*Grus americana;* Fisher and Goodman, 1955: p. 54), and some other birds, there is a superficial and a deep layer, but in most birds there is a single layer of muscle.

7. *M. Serratus Metapatagialis*

a. Columba livia. This is relatively a bulky muscle formed by three fleshy bands, which arise from the lateral surfaces of true ribs 2, 3, and 4, inferior to the origin of M. serratus posterior. The three fasciculi fuse to form a common belly, which passes upward to insert into the skin of the humeral feather tract.

b. Agelaius phoeniceus. This dermal component consists of a thin band of fleshy fibers arising from the posteroinferior surface of the most posterior part of M. serratus posterior near its origin from the 4th true rib. The belly passes upward and forward to insert into the skin of the humeral feather tract.

c. Comparative data. This is the serratus superficialis metapatagialis of Hudson and Lanzillotti (1955) and of Fürbringer (1902). It is a dermal component ("dermo-ulnaris" of Shufeldt) of M. serratus posterior.

M. serratus metapatagialis arises from the lateral surface of one or more of the true ribs, inferior to their uncinate processes. The fleshy belly inserts in the skin in the region of the posterior margin of the humeral feather tract. In many birds, a fibroelastic tendon forms at the fleshy insertion and passes distad in the metapatagium. In the Common Loon (*Gavia immer*), this tendon ends near the elbow by fusing with the tendons of Mm. triceps and expansor secundariorum. In the Yellow-shafted Flicker (*Colaptes auratus*), M. serratus metapatagialis gives rise to a wide fibrous band, which runs distad in the metapatagium and changes into a tendon; it ends on a proximally directed fleshy slip of M. expansor secundariorum. In some passerine birds (e.g., *Tyrannus tyrannus, Stelgidopteryx ruficollis, Sitta carolinensis, Bombycilla cedrorum, Dendroica petechia, Molothrus ater,* and *Junco hyemalis*), the tendon of M. serratus metapatagialis reaches the back of the elbow and there ends in relation to the innermost secondary or M. expansor secundariorum. In still other passerine birds (e.g., *Vireo flavifrons, Seiurus aurocapillus, Agelaius phoeniceus, Spinus tristis, Spizella pusilla, Melospiza melodia*), the tendon does not have an attachment at the elbow but ends in the connective tissue of the metapatagial skin fold.

According to Beddard (1898: p. 82), pars metapatagialis is absent in the Ratites (except *Apteryx*), in penguins, and in hummingbirds. I did not find it in *Eugenes fulgens*.

8. M. Proscapulohumeralis (Scapulohumeralis Anterior)

a. Columba livia. M. proscapulohumeralis is absent in the Rock Dove.

b. Agelaius phoeniceus. M. proscapulohumeralis is relatively well developed in the Red-winged Blackbird. The muscle has a fleshy origin from the lateral surface of the scapula for a distance of 6 mm between the posterior rim of the glenoid cavity (anteriorly) and the origin of M. dorsalis scapulae (posteriorly). The flat belly passes outward and forward, becomes rounded, and inserts in the pneumatic fossa of the humerus between the origins of the two heads of M. humerotriceps.

c. Comparative data. M. proscapulohumeralis of Howell (1937) and Berger (1960b) is the same as M. scapulohumeralis anterior of Gadow and Selenka (1891: p. 235), Fürbringer (1902: p. 544), and Hudson and Lanzillotti (1955). Shufeldt (1890: p. 88) called it "M. supraspinatus." The muscle that Fisher (1946: p. 584) and Fisher and Goodman (1955: pp. 52–53) call M. proscapulohumeralis is actually the external head (pars externa) of M. subscapularis. "M. proscapulohumeralis brevis" of Fisher (1946: p. 587) and of Fisher and Goodman (1955: p. 53) is M. proscapulohumeralis in the Cathartidae and in *Grus americana*. Swinebroad (1954: p. 499) also used the term "proscapulohumeralis brevis," citing Shufeldt's "teres minor" as a synonym, which, however, apparently is the dorsal head of M. subcoracoideus. So far as I can determine, Swinebroad's "proscapulohumeralis brevis" is simply one head of M. subcoracoideus.

The small proscapulohumeralis muscle arises from the postglenoid surface of the scapula, usually between the areas of origin of M. scapulotriceps and M. subscapularis (external head). The belly passes downward and forward, superficial to M. subscapularis, to insert in the pneumatic fossa (usually) of the humerus and between the two heads of origin of M. humerotriceps. The pattern of insertion in *Indicator varie-gatus* appears to be identical to that illustrated by Bock (1962: p. 430) in *Coccothraustes*.

Mitchell (1901b: p. 644; 1915: p. 415) discussed the considerable variation in development of M. proscapulohumeralis in gruiform birds. He stated that M. proscapulohumeralis inserts on the humerus "near the forked origin" of M. humerotriceps. He noted also that the muscle is much reduced in *Otis* and "is attached to the humeral anchor" of M. scapulotriceps. Mitchell did not study the genus *Grus*, in which both Fisher and Goodman (1955) and Berger (1956e) found the muscle to be inconstant in occurrence. Berger found M. proscapulohumeralis bi-laterally in one specimen of the Sandhill Crane, unilaterally in a second, and absent bilaterally in a third specimen. The muscle is so small and delicate in the cranes and many other birds, however, that it might be destroyed by shot or be so mutilated in handling a poorly preserved specimen that one might be completely unaware that a separate mus-cle was involved.

In the Sandhill Crane this is a minute band of fleshy fibers 3 cm long and only about 2 mm wide. It arises from the ventral edge of the scapula just caudal to the glenoid cavity and *anteroventral* to the origin of M. scapulotriceps. M. proscapulohumeralis inserts by fleshy fibers (and not by a tendon as in the Whooping Crane) on the humerus about 0.5 cm proximal to the insertion of M. latissimus dorsi pars pos-terior, and anterior to the origin of M. humerotriceps. The area of inser-tion is on the plane of the inferior margin of the pneumatic fossa of the humerus, but is entirely anterior to the humerotriceps muscle.

Fürbringer (1902: p. 547 and Figs. 258–260) also described and illus-trated M. proscapulohumeralis in genera in which it does not insert in the pneumatic fossa. In *Ciconia, Pelecanus,* and some owls, for example, the muscle inserts proximal and/or anterior to most of the origin of M. humerotriceps. In *Otus asio,* M. proscapulohumeralis inserts on the medial bar of bone anterior and proximal to the pneumatic fossa.

M. proscapulohumeralis is said to be absent in the Ratites, penguins, *Fregata, Platalea, Threskiornis, Chauna, Chunga, Psophia, Opisthoco-mus, Pterocles,* Columbidae, *Cacatua, Buceros,* and *Bucorvus* (Für-bringer, 1902: p. 545). I did not find the muscle in *Goura victoria* or *Gallicolumba luzonica* (Columbidae).

9. M. Dorsalis Scapulae (*Scapulohumeralis Posterior*)

a. Columba livia. This well developed muscle arises primarily by fleshy fibers from the lateral surface and by an aponeurosis from the ventral edge of the caudal 30 mm of the blade of the scapula; anteriorly, it arises dorsal to the origin of the external head of M. subscapularis. The belly passes forward to a large tendinous and fleshy insertion on the anconal or dorsal surface of the bicipital crest of the humerus within the large pneumatic fossa. Fleshy and tendinous fibers of origin of M. humerotriceps arise on both sides of the area of insertion of M. dorsalis scapulae.

b. Agelaius phoeniceus. M. dorsalis scapulae arises posterior to the origin of M. proscapulohumeralis from most of the lateral and ventral surfaces of the scapula in approximately its caudal half. The origin from the lateral surface of the scapula is primarily by fleshy fibers; from the ventral edge it is primarily by an aponeurosis. The large belly passes forward and inserts by tendinous fibers on the dorsal surface of the distal end of the bicipital crest of the humerus.

c. Comparative data. Howell, Fisher, and Berger call this muscle dorsalis scapulae. Gadow and Selenka, Fürbringer, and Hudson call it scapulohumeralis posterior.

The dorsalis scapulae muscle has been found in all birds studied; it exhibits relatively little difference in structure throughout the group. It arises primarily by fleshy fibers from the lateral surface and by an aponeurosis from the ventral edge of the caudal half to three-fourths of the blade of the scapula, dorsal and posterior to the origin of M. subscapularis pars externa. The smallest origin I have seen is in *Geococcyx*, in which genus it arises from slightly less than the caudal half of the scapula. The belly is completely concealed by M. latissimus dorsi in some birds (e.g., *Spheniscus, Fulmarus, Tauraco,* cuckoos), but the wide gap between the two parts of the latter muscle leaves much of the dorsalis scapulae muscle exposed in others (e.g., *Polihiërax, Aceros, Goura, Chloroceryle, Procnias*).

M. dorsalis scapulae inserts by fleshy fibers, which are surrounded by a dense tendinous envelope, on the anconal surface of the bicipital crest of the humerus, distal to the attachment of the humeral tendon of M. biceps brachii. The area of insertion may be located opposite or just distal to the plane of the pneumatic fossa.

10. *M. Subscapularis*

a. Columba livia. M. subscapularis arises by two heads from the lateral (*pars externa*) and medial (*pars interna*) surfaces of the anterior portion of the scapula. The external head arises from the lateral surface of the scapula for a distance of about 20 mm, beginning caudal to the origin of M. scapulotriceps. The internal head arises from the medial surface of the anterior 16 mm of the scapula. The two heads fuse on a common tendon, which joins a similar tendon of M. subcoracoideus to form a bilaminar or V-shaped tendon; it inserts on the proximal end of the internal tuberosity of the humerus (*tuberculum mediale humeri* of Hudson and Lanzillotti, 1955).

b. *Agelaius phoeniceus.* The external head of M. subscapularis arises from the lateral and ventral surfaces of the scapula for a distance of about 10 mm, beginning on the posterior rim of the glenoid cavity ventral to the origin of M. proscapulohumeralis. The internal head of the muscle arises by fleshy fibers from the medial and ventromedial surfaces of the blade of the scapula in approximately its anterior half. The aponeurosis of insertion of M. serratus anterior passes upward between the two heads of M. subscapularis. The two heads fuse on a large, flat tendon, which inserts on the proximal surface of the internal tuberosity of the humerus.

c. *Comparative data.* M. subscapularis is so closely related to M. subcoracoideus that Fürbringer (1902: p. 554) called the entire complex M. subcoracoscapularis, which has four heads in many birds: *caput scapulare internum* (M. subscapularis pars interna), *caput scapulare externum* (M. subscapularis pars externa), *caput subcoracoideus posterior*, and *caput subcoracoideus anterior*. It is advantageous, however, to describe two separate muscles, each with two heads, as Howell (1937) and later American workers have done.

M. subscapularis is composed of two heads. I know of no bird in which either head is absent. Beddard's statement (1898: p. 499) that the subscapularis muscle in the cassowary "is a single-headed muscle arising from the scapula only" needs clarification; so far as I know, this muscle has no other origin than from the scapula.

The *external head* (*pars externa*) of M. subscapularis arises from the lateral surface and ventral edge of the scapula caudal to the origins of Mm. scapulotriceps and proscapulohumeralis. Some of the fibers of the external head may arise either dorsal or ventral to the area of origin of M. proscapulohumeralis. The *internal head* (*pars interna*) arises from the medial surface of the scapula. The origin of pars interna may begin on the acromion (e.g., *Crotophaga, Coccyzus*) or at the level of the glenoid cavity (most birds). The internal head may be about the same size as the external head or it may be much longer (e.g., the Corvidae).

The tendon of M. serratus anterior invariably passes upward between the two heads of M. subscapularis before they fuse to insert by a single tendon on the internal tuberosity of the humerus. The tendons of insertion of Mm. subscapularis and subcoracoideus fuse for a common insertion in some birds.

The muscle which Fisher (1946) and Fisher and Goodman (1955) call the "proscapulohumeralis brevis" in the Cathartidae and in the Whooping Crane is actually the external head of M. subscapularis. It is difficult to visualize the origin of M. subscapularis from the "ventral surface" of the os humeroscapulare, as reported in certain Fringillids by Swinebroad (1954: p. 499).

11. M. Subcoracoideus

a. Columba livia. This muscle consists of two well developed heads. The *dorsal* or *transverse head* arises fleshily from the medial surface of the apex of the clavicle, from the coracoclavicular membrane inferior to the apex of the clavicle, and from the ventromedial surface of the anterior 5 mm of the scapula. The large and long *ventral head* arises by fleshy fibers from the posterior surface of the coracoclavicular membrane in approximately its ventral two-thirds and from the anterior edge of the sternum. The two heads fuse and insert on a common tendon shared with M. subscapularis. The portion of the tendon serving for the insertion of M. subcoracoideus is attached to the internal tuberosity of the humerus distal to the attachment for M. subscapularis.

b. Agelaius phoeniceus. The well developed dorsal head of M. subcoracoideus arises by fleshy fibers from the medial surface of the most anterior end of the scapula. The belly winds outward posterior to the coracoid and ventral to the scapula and fuses with the ventral head. The long ventral head arises from the posterior surface of the coracoid in approximately its basal half. The belly passes upward and fuses with the dorsal head at the level of the procoracoid process of the coracoid. The relatively small, flat common tendon inserts on the posteroproximal surface of the base of the internal tuberosity of the humerus posterior and adjacent to the insertion of M. subscapularis.

c. Comparative data. The subcoracoideus muscle ("coracobrachialis" plus "teres minor" of Shufeldt) has two heads in most birds. A *ventral head* arises from the coracoid (usually just dorsal to its sternocoracoidal impression) and/or from the coracoclavicular membrane or the sternum. It arises exclusively from the coracoclavicular membrane in certain cuckoos (e.g., *Coua, Crotophaga, Coccyzus, Chrysococcyx*).

A dorsal or transverse head arises from the medial surface of the apex of the clavicle, the coracoid, the coracoclavicular ligament, or the acromion (scapula). A clavicular origin is said to be uncommon (Gadow and Selenka, 1891: p. 238); it is characteristic of cuckoos. The clavicular head is unusually well developed in *Tauraco leucotis* (Berger, 1960a). In this species the muscle has an extensive origin from an area 17 mm long on the medial surface of the superior end of the clavicle, the coracoclavicular ligament, and the acromion. The ventral head in *Tau-*

raco arises from the basal 10 mm of the posterior face of the coracoid and the adjacent coracoclavicular membrane.

In the Corvidae the ventral head arises from the dorsomedial edge of the coracoid near the sternal end of the bone; the shorter dorsal head arises from a small area on the medial surface of the dorsal end of the coracoid and the adjacent scapula "in intimate contact with the anterior end of pars interna of M. subscapularis" (Hudson and Lanzillotti, 1955). M. subcoracoideus also arises by two heads in *Paradisaea rubra* (Berger, 1956b): the longer ventral head arises from the posterior surface of the base of the coracoid; the shorter dorsal head arises from an area 3 mm wide on the medial surface of the acromion. The two heads of the muscle in *Aceros undulatus* have different origins than those just described: the ventral head arises by a strong tendon (shared with a deep belly of M. supracoracoideus) from the dorsal lip of the coracoidal sulcus of the sternum; the dorsal head arises from the posterior surface of the coracoid just inferior to the coracoscapular articulation.

M. subcoracoideus has a single head, arising from the coracoid, in some birds: e.g., Cathartidae, *Polihiёrax semitorquatus*, *Grus americana*, *Grus canadensis*, and *Goura victoria*. In the Sandhill Crane it is a small triangular-shaped muscle arising from the anteromedial surface of the coracoid, just above the middle of the bone. The subcoracoideus is a strongly developed muscle in *Goura*, arising from the posteromedial edge of the coracoid throughout nearly its entire length.

M. subcoracoideus inserts by a strong tendon on the internal tuberosity of the humerus immediately proximal to the humeral origin of M. biceps brachii.

12. *M. Pectoralis*

a. Columba livia. M. pectoralis pars thoracicus is the most superficial of the muscles arising from the sternum. The muscle arises from approximately the ventral one-fourth of the carina (for a width of 10 mm anteriorly but decreasing to about 2 mm posteriorly); from the body of the sternum lateral to the origin of M. supracoracoideus; and from the posterolateral process and the interosseous membrane between it and the posteromedial process (these processes often are called "xiphoid" processes). The fibers of the bulky belly converge and insert by fleshy fibers surrounded by a dense tendinous envelope on the deltoid crest of the humerus. See Fig. III.1, p. 23.

Mm. pectoralis propatagialis longus et brevis are represented by a single aponeurotic sheet, which leaves the surface of the belly of pars thoracicus near its insertion on the deltoid crest and inserts on the leading edge of the common belly of Mm. tensores patagii longus et brevis.

Three dermal components are more or less closely related to M. pectoralis pars thoracicus and, presumably, correspond to Gadow and Selenka's (1891) pars abdominalis:

(1) A wide (about 9 mm) sheet of fleshy fibers arises by an aponeurosis from the surface of pars thoracicus at about the plane of junction of the anterior one-third and the posterior two-thirds of the sternum. The fleshy fibers pass forward to insert into the skin covering the ventral and lateral surfaces of the neck.

(2) A second sheet of fleshy fibers (about 40 mm long and 6.5 mm in maximum width) arises by a thin aponeurosis from the deep side of the tendinous envelope surrounding the insertion of pars thoracicus. The fibers pass backward and fan out to insert into the skin of the ventral abdominal feather tract. The fleshy fibers end just anterior to the termination of the fleshy fibers of the third dermal component.

(3) The third dermal component, with a belly about 30 mm long and 7 mm in maximum width at its origin, arises from the fascia covering the external abdominal oblique muscle. The sheetlike belly decreases in width as it passes forward to insert into the skin of the posterior part of the ventral abdominal feather tract.

A fourth dermal component consists of a fleshy bundle of fibers (about 3 mm wide), which arises from the anterior surface of the clavicle at about its midlength and from the adjacent fascia overlying M. pectoralis pars thoracicus. The muscle passes forward to the neck, where it fans out to insert into the medial surface of the crop and into the skin on the ventral surface of the neck. Shufeldt might have called such a muscle a dermocleidoventralis.

b. Agelaius phoeniceus. M. pectoralis pars thoracicus has an extensive origin from the following structures: from slightly less than the ventral half of the carina of the sternum, from the posterior and lateral aspects of the ventral surface of the body of the sternum (lateral and posterior to the area of origin of M. supracoracoideus), from the interosseous membrane between the body and the posterolateral process of the sternum, from the anterior and lateral surfaces of the clavicle in its basal four-fifths, from the outer surface of the clavicular portion of the coracoclavicular membrane, and from an aponeurosis which extends dorsally from the lateral margin of the sternum over the lateral surfaces of the sternal ribs and the ventral ends of the costal ribs. The large, bulky belly conceals Mm. supracoracoideus and coracobrachialis posterior. The belly passes forward and inserts by fleshy fibers, surrounded by a dense tendinous envelope, on the deltoid crest of the humerus. The tendon of origin and the proximal end of the belly of M. biceps brachii lie immediately deep to the distal part of the belly of pars thoracicus and its enveloping tendinous sheath.

M. pectoralis propatagialis brevis consists of a small, but long (10 mm), tendon, which arises from the dense fascia on the superficial surface of pars thoracicus near its insertion opposite the deltoid crest of the humerus. The tendon passes distad in the propatagium and fuses with the most proximal end of the tendon of insertion of M. tensor patagii brevis.

M. pectoralis propatagialis longus is a small, dense aponeurosis derived from the anteromedial surface of pars thoracicus a short distance lateral to its clavicular origin. The aponeurosis passes dorsally and fuses with the anterior edge of the small fleshy belly of M. tensor patagii longus.

M. pectoralis pars abdominalis is a wide band of fleshy fibers in the skin covering the lateral wall of the thorax and abdomen. The fibers fan out and terminate in the region of the knee posteriorly. Anteriorly, the belly passes deep to the anterodorsal margin of pars thoracicus and ends on a delicate aponeurosis which fuses with the fasciae in the axillary region.

c. *Comparative data.* It is incorrect to call this muscle the "pectoralis major," as has often been done (e.g., Shufeldt, 1890: p. 69; Lowe, 1931: p. 451). Howell's careful work (1937: p. 371) led him to the conclusion that "the larger, superficial pectoral of birds is not homologous with the superficial (major) division of mammals, but with their pectoralis minor layer. . . . This is indicated, among other things, by the course of the nerves, all of which pass to this division of musculature caudal to the coracoid and its muscles."

The main part of the pectoralis muscle and the several specializations of the complex will be discussed separately.

Pars thoracicus, the largest of all bird muscles, is the major part of M. pectoralis (Gadow and Selenka, 1891: p. 241). This is the pectoralis thoracicus of Buri (1900: p. 512) and Fürbringer (1902: p. 418) and the pectoralis superficialis of Howell (1937), Fisher (1946), and others (Figs. IX.31–IX.33).

Pars thoracicus may arise from any of the following structures: sternum (including the carina, body, "xiphoid" processes, and interosseous membranes), clavicle, coracoid, coracoclavicular membrane, sternocostal membrane, and sternal ribs. In loons, grebes, ducks, some gallinaceous birds, and tinamous the right and left pectoralis muscles also share a common origin from a midline septum that extends inferior to the carina. A superficial and a deep layer have been described in "many Ciconii-

formes," in *Bugeranus, Balearica, Scopus*, and in storks (Beddard, 1898:
pp. 79, 366, 440), in the Cathartidae (Fisher, 1946), in *Grus americana*
(Fisher and Goodman, 1955), and in the Procellariiformes and Pelecani-
formes (Kuroda, 1961a). Kuroda also described and illustrated three
layers of pars thoracicus in the Frigatebird (*Fregata magnificens*). There
is a single layer in most birds.

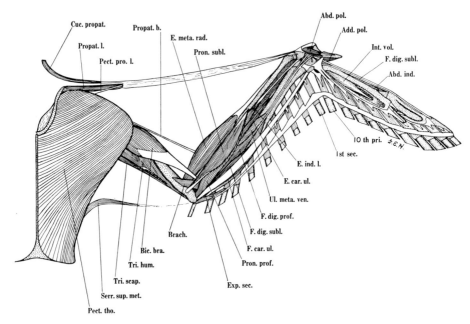

Fig. IX.31. The ventral wing muscles of the Common Crow. Most American
ornithologists call the innermost primary number 1, rather than number 10. (By
permission, Hudson and Lanzillotti, 1955.) For Key to Abbreviations see legend
to Fig. IX.26.

The fleshy fibers of pars thoracicus converge to insert on the ventral
surface of the deltoid crest of the humerus (*crista lateralis humeri* of
Hudson and Lanzillotti, 1955; *pectoral crest* of Shufeldt). The muscle
inserts primarily by fleshy fibers, which, however, usually are surrounded
by a dense tendinous envelope. In *Gavia, Chen, Grus,* and *Goura* there
is a strong tendinous connection between the deep fasciculi of the muscle
and the tendon of origin of M. biceps brachii.

Mm. pectoralis propatagialis longus et brevis are specializations of the
pectoralis complex. Both may consist of fleshy fasciculi or they may be
entirely aponeurotic. They usually arise from the surface of pars thoracicus, typically near its insertion, but in some genera M. pectoralis propa-

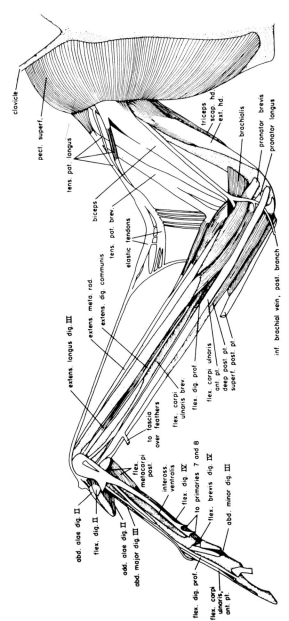

FIG. IX.32. Ventral view of the superficial muscles of the right wing of *Grus americana*. (By permission, Fisher and Goodman, 1955.) For Key to Abbreviations see legend to Fig. IX.26.

tagialis longus arises by fleshy fibers from the apex of the clavicle or the coracoid (e.g., penguins, hawks, owls, *Chaetura pelagica*).

Mm. pectoralis propatagialis longus et brevis may be represented by a single fleshy belly, which gives rise to two tendons, one of which inserts on the belly or tendon of insertion of M. tensor patagii longus, the other inserts on M. tensor patagii brevis, as in *Coua caerulea* (Berger, 1953), *Tauraco leucotis* (Berger, 1960a), and *Podargus* (Beddard, 1898: p. 79). Both of the propatagialis muscles are represented by fleshy bellies in *Accipiter nisus* (Beddard, 1898: p. 79). In many genera (e.g., *Goura*, *Gallicolumba*, *Otus*, *Chloroceryle*, *Coracias*, *Indicator*) M. pectoralis

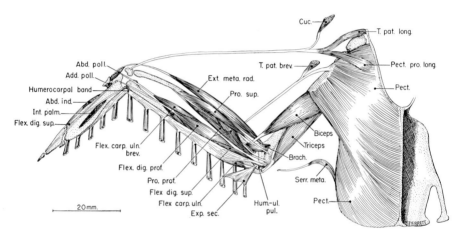

Fig. IX.33. The ventral wing muscles of *Fregilupus varius*. (By permission, Berger, 1957.) For Key to Abbreviations see legend to Fig. IX.26.

propatagialis longus is a fleshy muscle, whereas M. pectoralis propatagialis brevis is represented by a tendon or an aponeurosis. In still other genera (e.g., Corvidae, *Paradisaea rubra*, *Spizella arborea*) both are represented by tendinous bands. Among cuculine genera Mm. pectoralis propatagialis longus et brevis are represented by a single complex, which may be entirely tendinous (*Morococcyx*, *Dromococcyx*, *Tapera*, *Guira*, *Ceuthmochares*, *Centropus*, *Cuculus*, *Piaya*), or which may arise from pars thoracicus as a fleshy bundle (*Geococcyx*, *Coua*, *Carpococcyx*, *Crotophaga*, *Coccyzus*, *Saurothera*, *Clamator*, *Chrysococcyx*, *Surniculus*, and *Phaenicophaeus*; Berger, 1960a).

Beddard (1898) referred to a *propatagialis posticus* muscle in tinamous and in some gallinaceous birds.

Pars abdominalis (pectoralis abdominalis; dermo-humeralis of Shufeldt) was divided into an anterior *subcutaneus thoracis* part and a posterior *subcutaneus abdominalis* part by Gadow and Selenka (1891: p. 245), either of which may be absent. In some birds pars abdominalis is represented by a continuous band of muscle in which the two parts are separated by a tendinous intersection (see Beddard, 1898: p. 79; Gadow and Selenka, 1891: Plate 18b). Depending upon its degree of development, pars abdominalis arises from the subcutaneous tissue of the pelvic region or from the thoracoabdominal region near the knee. The posterior part of the muscle inserts into the skin of the lateral abdominal feather tract. The anterior portion of the muscle gives rise to a tendon which has an attachment on the belly of pars thoracicus, on the tendon of origin of M. biceps brachii, directly on the humerus, or the tendon may become lost in the fascia of the axillary region (as in *Pelecanus, Chauna,* and *Cathartes;* Beddard, 1898: pp. 79, 489). Beddard also reported that in *Crypturus* the tendon inserts on a tendinous bridge shared with Mm. pectoralis pars thoracicus, latissimus dorsi posterior, and expansor secundariorum.

A third slip, *pectoralis abdominalis metapatagialis,* has been found in some birds (Buri, 1900: p. 512; Fürbringer, 1902: p. 440).

13. *M. Supracoracoideus*

a. Columba livia. M. supracoracoideus arises from approximately the dorsal three-fourths of the carina throughout its entire length, from the ventral surface of the body of the sternum, and from a small area (10 mm long) on the base of the coracoclavicular membrane. There is no origin from the coracoid or the clavicle. The fleshy fibers converge on a large tendon, which passes dorsad through the triosseal canal (foramen triosseum; canalis supracoracoideus) to insert on the posterior edge of the humerus just distal to its articular head; the tendon fans out to a width of 4 mm at its insertion. After emerging from the triosseal canal, only the most proximal part of the tendon is concealed by the belly of M. deltoideus minor. See Fig. III.1.

b. Agelaius phoeniceus. M. supracoracoideus arises from slightly more than the dorsal half of the carina, from the anterior portion of the body of the sternum, from the sternocoracoidal process of the sternum, and from the anteromedial surface of the coracoid in approximately its basal half. The fleshy fibers converge on a strong tendon, which passes dorsad through the triosseal canal. After emerging from that canal, the strong, flat tendon of M. supracoracoideus passes diagonally outward and forward deep to the tendon of origin of the posterior fasciculus of the anterior head of M. deltoideus major and the posterior belly of M. deltoideus minor. The tendon inserts on the anterior edge of the head of the hu-

merus at the margin of its articular head. As it crosses the dorsal surface
of the shoulder joint, the tendon of M. supracoracoideus passes through a
fibrous pulley which extends between the os humeroscapulare and the
coracohumeral ligament.

   c. Comparative data. This muscle is still sometimes referred to as the
"pectoralis minor" muscle (e.g., Young, 1950: p. 421; Arvey, 1951; Kuroda,
1961a), but there seems to be no justification for this name. Howell
(1937: p. 372) stated that M. supracoracoideus "is strictly comparable
with the pectoralis major of mammals." Because of its deep position,
however, it seems desirable to retain the traditional name of supracoracoideus for this muscle in birds. The muscle also has been called the
"pectoralis secundus" (Shufeldt) and the "subclavius" (Parker and Haswell, 1947: p. 440).

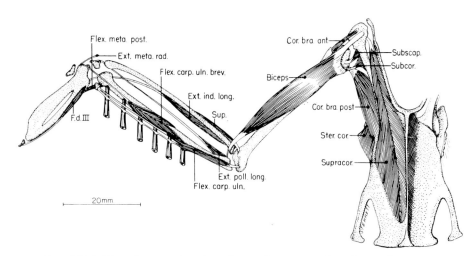

FIG. IX.34. Ventral view of a deep layer of wing muscles of *Fregilupus varius*.
(By permission, Berger, 1957.) For Key to Abbreviations see legend to Fig. IX.26.

   Laterally the belly of M. supracoracoideus is in contact with M.
coracobrachialis posterior and, superficially, both muscles are covered by
M. pectoralis (Fig. IX.34). Typically, the supracoracoideus arises from
the dorsal portion of the carina, the anterolateral aspect of the body of
the sternum, the coracoid, the coracoclavicular membrane, and, in some
genera, from the clavicle (e.g., *Geococcyx*). The usual single tendon of
insertion passes dorsad through the triosseal canal (bounded by coracoid,
clavicle, and scapula in most birds) to insert on the anterior edge of the
humerus near the junction of its articular head and deltoid crest.

Despite the importance of M. supracoracoideus for flight, there is little specific information in the literature on this muscle. Gadow and Selenka (1891: p. 248) reported that the muscle is bipartite in the Rasores (scratching birds) and in *Tinamus* and that the tendons of insertion of the two parts of the muscle remain separated. Berger (1955b) found that the supracoracoideus in *Crax rubra* is composed of two distinct and completely separate bellies and tendons of insertion. The superficial belly is typical in origin and in the course of its tendon dorsolaterad through the triosseal canal. The tendon, however, inserts on the humerus 15 mm *distal* to the junction of the humeral head and the deltoid crest. The deep belly arises exclusively from the coracoclavicular membrane; its tendon also passes through the triosseal canal to insert primarily at the base of the deltoid crest, but a small tendinous branch passes distad to insert proximal to the tendon of the superficial belly. Fisher (1946: p. 579) described a separate thin, but wide, fleshy fasciculus, which arises from the medial edge of the coracoid and the adjacent area on the coracoclavicular membrane in the Cathartidae. The tendon inserts on the proximopalmar surface of the deltoid crest in contrast to the insertion of the main tendon "on the anconal surface of the external tuberosity of the humerus." The bipartite supracoracoideus muscle is hypertrophied in penguins. Kuroda (1961a) reported that M. supracoracoideus is composed of three parts in *Fregata, Sula,* and *Phoenicopterus* and of four parts in *Diomedea*. In most birds, however, there is a single, generally bipennate belly. The tendon of insertion most often forms on the deep or coracoidal aspect of the belly; fleshy fibers may surround the tendon as it passes through the triosseal canal. After its emergence from the canal, the tendon may be concealed by the belly of M. deltoideus minor (e.g., *Chaetura pelagica, Chloroceryle americana, Indicator variegatus, Spizella arborea*). In some genera (e.g., *Pharomachrus*) the deltoideus minor muscle conceals the proximal part of the tendon of M. supracoracoideus but not its distal part; in other genera (e.g., *Goura, Gallicolumba*) the deltoideus minor muscle lies entirely anterior to the supracoracoideus tendon. The tendon has an unusual area of insertion in *Goura victoria*, in which species the tendon inserts at the distal margin of the articular head on the dorsal surface of the humerus about midway between the anterior and posterior edges of the bone. Beddard (1898: p. 310) reported this to be the typical insertion in the Columbidae. Both the belly of M. supracoracoideus and its tendon of insertion are hypertrophied in *Chaetura pelagica* and *Eugenes fulgens*.

14. M. Coracobrachialis Anterior

a. Columba livia. The well developed belly of this muscle arises primarily by tendinous fibers from the lateral surface of the apex of the coracoid. The belly passes outward, embedded in tough fascia, on the ventral surface of the coracohumeral joint capsule and inserts on the anterior corner of the humerus between the articular head and the area of insertion of M. pectoralis pars thoracicus.

b. Agelaius phoeniceus. M. coracobrachialis anterior is absent in this species. There are no muscle fibers visible grossly on the ventral surface of the coracohumeral joint capsule, and none were found by histological examination.

c. Comparative data. Sullivan (1962: p. 468) commented that the homologue for M. coracobrachialis anterior ("coracohumeralis" of Shufeldt) in *Lacerta* and *Didelphys* "is simply termed coracobrachialis. The name coracobrachialis is used also for what is almost certainly the homologous muscle in man. In order to achieve greater uniformity throughout the tetrapods, it seems advisable to drop the word anterior from the name for this muscle in the birds; furthermore this allows the name coracobrachialis anterior to be substituted for deltoideus minor." It is unwise in general, I believe, to shift a well established name from one muscle to an entirely different muscle. As additional embryological evidence becomes available, however, it may be necessary to follow that procedure in order that the names of muscles will reflect more basic relationships than adult position and attachments. In view of the conservative approach followed in this work, however, I have retained the long-used name for the muscle.

M. coracobrachialis anterior is a small muscle located on the ventral surface of the scapulohumeral joint; in many birds the muscle is partly embedded in the joint capsule. The muscle has a fleshy or tendinous origin from the head of the coracoid; in some birds also from the coracohumeral ligament (Corvidae) and/or the deep surface of the biceps tendon (*Chen hyperborea, Coua caerulea*). It inserts on the ventral surface of the humerus, distal to the head and between the areas of insertion of Mm. pectoralis and supracoracoideus.

The belly of this muscle varies considerably in relative development in different birds. In the cuckoos (Berger, 1953, 1954, 1960a), for example, this muscle shows two patterns of development. In *Geococcyx, Morococcyx,* and *Coua* the belly is larger than in most birds, extending dorsad around the anterior edge of the humerus to the dorsal (anconal) surface, where it lies in contact with the belly of M. deltoideus minor. The two muscles conceal the tendon of insertion of M. supracoracoideus. In *Coccyzus, Chrysococcyx,* and all other genera of cuckoos examined the coracobrachialis anterior muscle is a narrow, thin muscle sheet, which does not wrap around the anterior edge of the humerus; the belly is partly embedded in the joint capsule. The muscle also is weakly developed in *Goura victoria, Gallicolumba luzonica, Chloroceryle americana, Indicator variegatus, Procnias nudicollis,* and *Spizella arborea.* M. coraco-brachialis anterior is hypertrophied in *Chordeiles minor, Chaetura pelagica, Upupa epops,* and in *Pharomachrus mocino.* The muscle is said to exhibit its strongest development in tinamous and in ratites (Beddard, 1898: p. 86).

15. *M. Coracobrachialis Posterior*

a. Columba livia. This muscle arises by fleshy fibers from the lateral surface of slightly less than the basal two-thirds of the coracoid and from the anterior edge of the sternocoracoidal process of the sternum, super-ficial to the origin of M. sternocoracoideus. The well developed belly inserts by a strong, flat tendon on the capital groove surface of the in-ternal tuberosity of the humerus.

b. Agelaius phoeniceus. This muscle lies lateral to the anterior part of M. supracoracoideus and deep to the belly of M. pectoralis pars thoracicus. M. coracobrachialis posterior arises by fleshy and tendinous fibers from the lateral surface of the coracoid in its basal three-fifths. The bulky belly passes upward and ends on a strong, flat tendon. It inserts on the capital groove surface of the internal tuberosity of the humerus.

c. Comparative data. This is the "pectoralis tertius" of Shufeldt (1890: p. 74), and it is the second of the muscles which has been called "pectoralis minor" (Watson, 1883; Lowe, 1931).

There appears to be little difference in the development of M. coracobrachialis posterior among birds. The muscle arises from the basal portion of the coracoid (including the sternocoracoidal process of that bone), from the anterolateral edge of the body of the sternum (usually by tendinous fibers), and, in some birds (e.g., *Geococcyx, Crotophaga*), from the coracoclavicular membrane adjacent to the coracoid.

The belly gives rise to a short, stout tendon, which inserts either in a pit on the apex or on the capital groove surface of the internal tuberosity of the humerus.

16. *M. Sternocoracoideus*

a. Columba livia. This muscle arises from the anterior edge of the sternocoracoidal process of the sternum; it inserts on the sternocoracoidal impression or fossa on the posterior surface of the coracoid in slightly less than its basal half (i.e., for a distance of about 15 mm).

b. Agelaius phoeniceus. M. sternocoracoideus arises from the outer surface of the sternocoracoidal process of the sternum. The wide, flat belly passes forward and inward to insert in the sternocoracoidal impres-sion on the posterior surface of the base of the coracoid.

c. *Comparative data*. M. sternocoracoideus exhibits little difference in development among birds. The muscle arises from the sternocoracoidal process of the sternum, in some birds also from the sternal ribs; it inserts in the sternocoracoidal impression on the posterior surface of the base of the coracoid. The muscle is double in *Casuarius* and is said to be absent in swifts and hummingbirds (Beddard, 1898: pp. 85, 224). I did not find it in *Chaetura pelagica* or *Eugenes fulgens*.

17. M. Cucullaris Pars Propatagialis

a. *Columba livia*. Pars propatagialis is absent in this species.

b. *Agelaius phoeniceus*. Pars propatagialis is a well developed muscle, which splits off the surface of M. cucullaris on the lateral surface of the neck. The rounded belly passes posteriorly and outward to enter the propatagium. Some of the fleshy fibers of pars propatagialis insert on the follicles of feathers overlying the shoulder region, but most of the belly continues outward in the propatagium, tapers to a fibroelastic tendon, and fuses with the leading edge of the tendon of insertion of M. tensor patagii longus about a third of the way out the propatagium.

c. *Comparative data*. M. cucullaris is a muscle of the head and neck; its structure has been described for many birds by Fürbringer (1888: pp. 302, 1056; 1902: pp. 361, 367), Gadow and Selenka (1891: pp. 214, 253), Buri (1900: p. 404), Boas (1929: p. 189), Palmgren (1949), and Fisher and Goodman (1955).

In some birds (e.g., parrots, *Upupa*, woodpeckers, passerines) M. cucullaris has a muscular slip whose tendon inserts on the tendon of M. tensor patagii longus. The tendon inserts "mainly on the follicles of the anterior feathers of the humeral feather tract" in the Corvidae (Hudson and Lanzillotti, 1955). Pars propatagialis inserts by fleshy fibers on the tendon of M. tensor patagii longus in *Artamella viridis* (Berger, 1957); it inserts by fleshy fibers into the skin over the shoulder region in *Tyrannus tyrannus* (Stejneger, 1887). Shufeldt (1890: p. 113) stated that the tendon of pars propatagialis does not fuse with the tendon of M. tensor patagii longus in *Progne subis* but remains "distinct as far as the carpus." Swinebroad (1954: p. 505, "dermo-tensor patagii") described the muscle in *Passer domesticus, Richmondena cardinalis, Zonotrichia albicollis,* and *Melospiza melodia*.

After discovering pars propatagialis in *Progne subis*, Shufeldt (1887-a,b,c) thought that he had found a new muscle of taxonomic value; he named it the "dermo-tensor patagii." Stejneger (1887, 1888, 1889) called attention to the synonymy of Shufeldt's muscle, took issue with some of his descriptions, described the muscle in several species (*Tyrannus tyrannus, Gracula religiosa, Passer domesticus,* and *Pheucticus ludovici-*

anus), and illustrated the muscle in *Amazona leucocephala* and *Cola-pates auratus*. Stejneger (1889: p. 16) doubted that the muscle "will be found of much service in defining trenchantly even families or smaller groups, since every possible gradation between the rudimentary stage and the most highly developed condition seems to occur within the same group of unquestionably nearly related birds." The vitriolic exchange between Shufeldt and Stejneger makes interesting reading.

The "dermo-tensor patagii" of Fisher (1946: p. 574; Table 19) in the Cathartidae is not the "dermo-tensor patagii" of Shufeldt but rather appears to be a portion of M. pectoralis pars propatagialis longus.

18. M. Tensor Patagii Longus (Propatagialis Longus)

a. Columba livia. In the Rock Dove, Mm. tensores patagii longus et brevis consist of a single hypertrophied belly, which conceals all but the caudal border of the posterior head of M. deltoideus major. The anterior portion (=M. tensor patagii longus) of the patagial muscle is thin and sheetlike; the posterior portion (=M. tensor patagii brevis) is much thicker. The common belly has an extensive origin from the medial surface of the apex of the clavicle, from the scapuloclavicular ligament, and from the medial surface of the acromion process of the scapula. The tendon of the tensor patagii longus muscle arises as a wide elastic band from the anterior margin of the common belly near the distal end of the deltoid crest. The anterior edge of the fleshy belly of the *biceps slip* fuses with the proximal portion of the elastic band. About three-fourths of the way out the propatagium, the elastic band gives rise to a small anterior inelastic tendon and a larger posterior tendon. The anterior tendon fuses with the tendon of the biceps slip and inserts with it. The posterior tendon inserts on the distal end of the ulna and on the os ulnare, but the tendon also is intimately fused with the deep fascia of the wrist and hand.

Mm. pectoralis propatagialis longus et brevis are represented by an aponeurotic band from the surface of M. pectoralis pars thoracicus; the band inserts on the leading edge of the common belly of Mm. tensores patagii longus et brevis.

b. Agelaius phoeniceus. Mm. tensores patagii longus et brevis are independent except for a small common origin. M. tensor patagii longus is a small muscle about 8 mm long and 4 mm in maximum width. The muscle arises partly by fleshy fibers and partly by a flat tendon (shared with M. tensor patagii brevis) from the dorsomedial surface of the apex of the clavicle; there is also a small origin from the fascia covering the dorsomedial surface of the posterior head of M. deltoideus major near its origin from the apex of the clavicle. The belly of M. tensor patagii longus ends on a small tendon, which passes distad in the leading edge of the propatagium. The tendon is reinforced by the tendon of M. cucullaris pars propatagialis as previously described. As it nears the distal end of the forearm, the tendon expands and encloses a sesamoid where the tendon crosses the anterodorsal surface of the radius. The tendon then passes superficial to the tendon of insertion of M. extensor metacarpi radialis and inserts on both sides of that tendon on the distal end of the radius and on the os radiale. The tendon of M. tensor patagii longus serves as a ligament or vaginal sheath to hold the tendon of M. extensor metacarpi radialis in its groove on the distal end of the radius. Extensions of the tendon of M. tensor patagii longus also pass into the manus and fuse with the deep fascia.

c. *Comparative data.* Beddard (1898: p. 82) referred to Mm. tensores patagii longus et brevis as M. patagialis because in many birds there is a single belly which gives rise to two tendons of insertion. Gadow and Selenka (1891), Fürbringer (1902), and Hudson and Lanzillotti (1955) refer to the muscles as Mm. propatagialis longus et brevis. The muscles undoubtedly are derived from the deltoid complex (Howell, 1937).

Whether Mm. tensores patagii longus et brevis are represented by a single belly or by independent bellies the complex typically arises from the medial or dorsal surface of the apex of the clavicle; when the belly is large, the origin extends posteriorly to the coracoid and the acromion process of the scapula. The two muscles are represented by a single belly in *Crax rubra, Grus canadensis,* Columbidae, Cuculidae, *Tauraco leucotis, Otus asio, Chordeiles minor, Pharomachrus mocino, Coracias abyssinica, Upupa epops,* and *Spizella arborea.* The common belly of the two tensores is hypertrophied in the pigeons and parrots. Beddard (1898: p. 258) reported that the common belly often completely covers M. deltoideus major in parrots. There is a common origin in *Chrysococcyx cupreus,* but two bellies are formed distally. The two muscles are independent throughout in *Chaetura pelagica, Eugenes fulgens, Chloroceryle americana, Indicator variegatus, Procnias nudicollis, Paradisaea rubra, Fregilupus varius, Artamella viridis, Sturnus vulgaris, Aplonis tabuensis,* and *Dendroica kirtlandii.* The only fleshy origin for M. tensor patagii longus in *Aceros undulatus* is pars propatagialis longus of M. pectoralis; there is no independent belly, and there is no connection between the tendon of the tensor patagii longus and the fleshy belly of the tensor patagii brevis muscle. Garrod found the only representative of the tensor patagii longus to be the biceps slip in *Crex pratensis* (Beddard, 1898: p. 82).

The tendon of insertion of M. tensor patagii longus exhibits a relative uniformity in structure among birds. The tendon passes distad in the anterior margin of the propatagium (prepatagial skin fold) as a wide fibroelastic band, which becomes tendinous at a variable distance from the distal end of the forearm. The primary insertion in many birds is on the extensor process of the carpometacarpus, but the tendon usually fans out to fuse with the deep fascia of the manus. There is an insertion on the pollex in the Corvidae (Hudson and Lanzillotti, 1955). In *Aceros undulatus* one extension of the tendon fuses with the muscular fascia covering M. abductor pollicis. In certain cuckoos (*Geococcyx, Crotophaga, Coccyzus, Coua*) extensions of the tendon insert on the bases of the alula quills and the proximal primaries. In other cuckoos (e.g., *Chrysococcyx, Cuculus, Coccyzus*) the tendon bifurcates near the distal end of the radius; the main branch fuses with the deep fascia of the manus and has a minor attachment to the extensor process; the smaller branch serves as the origin for a small fleshy muscle [the *accessory flexor of the pollex* of Berger (1955a: Fig. 70)], which inserts on the posterobasal corner of the pollex superficial to the insertion of M. flexor pollicis. In the penguins the tendon of M. tensor patagii longus "is inserted on to the whole length of the bones of the arm as far as the extremity of the last phalanx" (Beddard, 1898: p. 397).

Shortly after its formation the tendon of insertion of M. tensor patagii longus may be reinforced by pars propatagialis longus of M. pectoralis, by the biceps slip, by the tendon of M. cucullaris pars propatagialis, or by a ligament attached to the deltoid crest.

19. *M. Tensor Patagii Brevis (Propatagialis Brevis)*

a. Columba livia. The common belly of Mm. tensores patagii longus et brevis has been described earlier in this chapter. M. tensor patagii brevis, the thicker posterior portion of the common belly, extends distally almost to the leading edge of M. extensor metacarpi radialis before giving rise to a short, broad and dense tendinous sheet, most of which fuses with the dense fascia covering the surface of M. extensor metacarpi radialis. Extensions of the tensor patagii brevis tendon, however, pass posteriorly over the forearm muscles and become indistinguishable from the dense antebrachial fascia, which attaches to the humerus proximally, extends into the hand distally, and fuses with the fascia surrounding the bases of the secondaries throughout the length of the ulna.

b. Agelaius phoeniceus. M. tensor patagii brevis is a much larger muscle (about 20 mm long and 8 mm in maximum width) than M. tensor patagii longus. M. tensor patagii brevis arises by fleshy fibers and by a flat tendon (shared with part of M. tensor patagii longus) from the dorsal surface of the apex of the clavicle. The bulky belly tapers to a strong, flat tendon 8 mm long. The tendon is anchored to the anterodorsal surface of the belly of M. extensor metacarpi radialis about 6 mm distal to its humeral origin. The tendon of M. tensor patagii brevis then turns sharply proximad, crosses superficial to the belly of M. extensor metacarpi radialis, and inserts on the ectepicondylar process of the humerus. M. pectoralis propatagialis brevis fuses with the proximal end of the tendon of insertion of M. tensor patagii brevis.

c. *Comparative data.* When both the tensor patagii longus and brevis muscles are represented by separate bellies, the brevis is the larger. The fleshy belly of M. tensor patagii brevis ends near the distal end of the deltoid crest in most brids; it extends further down the humerus in some birds (e.g., *Goura victoria, Pharomachrus mocino*). In the swifts (but not the crested-swifts), hummingbirds, and some pigeons (e.g., *Columba, Gallicolumba*) the belly of the tensor patagii brevis muscle extends distad to the leading edge of M. extensor metacarpi radialis, with which it is fused.

The tendon of M. tensor patagii brevis passes distad parallel to the humerus and inserts in a wide variety of patterns primarily on the belly or tendon of origin of M. extensor metacarpi radialis (see Garrod, 1881: pp. 356–360; Forbes, 1885: pp. 390–392). Garrod, Forbes, Beddard, and Lowe placed considerable emphasis on the taxonomic value of the pattern formed by the tendon of insertion. In addition to the main insertion on the belly of M. extensor metacarpi radialis, there are many secondary attachments: the lateral supracondylar ridge of the humerus (*Geococcyx*); the tendon of origin of M. extensor digitorum communis (*Coccyzus, Chrysococcyx*); the ulna (*Cuculus*); the lateral epicondyle of the humerus (*Paradisaea, Corvus*); the tendon of M. triceps (*Polihiërax*). In many birds a posterior extension of the main tendon fans out posteriorly and extends the entire length of the forearm, fusing with the antebrachial fascia and with the fascia surrounding the bases of the secondaries and their upper coverts. The simplest pattern of insertion is found in the toucans (Ramphastidae; Beddard, 1898: pp. 83, 191) and in passerines. The typical passerine pattern is exhibited in *Paradisaea rubra,* in which species the tendon of the tensor patagii brevis sends strong fibrous bands into the belly of M. extensor metacarpi radialis, but the main tendon runs proximad to insert on the lateral epicondyle of the humerus superficial to the tendon of origin of M. extensor metacarpi radialis.

In *Aceros undulatus* the tendon of insertion bifurcates in the distal fourth of the arm. The distal branch inserts on the tendon of M. extensor metacarpi radialis 2 cm distal to its humeral origin. The proximal branch passes posteriorly superficial to the forearm muscles, has an attachment to the distal end of the humerus, and fans out as a discrete tendon, which extends the entire length of the forearm, fuses with the antebrachial fascia, and passes into the manus to fuse with the deep fascia and ligaments there; large aponeurotic slips pass from the posterior edge of the tendon to the bases of all but the two most proximal secondaries; a deep extension of the tendon attaches to the radius posterior to the area of insertion of M. supinator.

In *Coracias abyssinica* Mm. tensores patagii longus et brevis consist of a common belly, which, however, gives rise to three fleshy prongs distally. M. tensor patagii brevis is represented by two of the fleshy prongs, each of which gives rise to an independent tendon: the anteriormost of the two tendons divides to form two tendons about half way down the arm. The three tendons insert into the leading edge of M. extensor metacarpi radialis. From the middle of the three tendons a strong aponeurosis passes posteriorly superficial to the forearm muscles, fuses with the dense antebrachial fascia, and sends slips into the bases of the proximal secondaries.

In *Chordeiles minor* Mm. tensores patagii longus et brevis are represented primarily by a single belly, which is fused with the anterior margin of the anterior head of M. deltoideus major, except distally where the tensor patagii brevis muscle passes superficial to the anterior head of the deltoid muscle. The belly of M. tensor patagii brevis is independent only in its distal 7 or 8 mm, and this part of the belly is bound to M. pectoralis by the aponeurotic M. pectoralis propatagialis brevis; it also is connected to the underlying anterior head of M. deltoideus major by dense fascia. The tendon of insertion of M. tensor patagii brevis splits into two equally developed parts some 10 mm from the insertion on M. extensor metacarpi radialis. The proximal tendon is anchored to the leading edge and dorsal surface of M. extensor metacarpi radialis but then passes proximad to insert on the humerus about 1 mm distal to the origin of that muscle. The distal tendon inserts at right angles on a dense aponeurosis, continuous with a slip from the proximal tendon, on the surface of M. extensor metacarpi radialis. The distal tendon and the aponeurosis serve as a tendon of origin for a fleshy belly (12 mm long), which inserts on the tendon of M. extensor metacarpi radialis.

The most complicated pattern of insertion is found in the Laridae and the Alcidae (Beddard, 1898: Figs. 171–175), in which multiple tendons are formed and there are secondary connections in the propatagium with one or more tendons of M. tensor patagii longus.

Considerable care must be exercised in isolating the tendon of the tensor patagii brevis from the connective tissue of the propatagium. This is especially important in those genera in which the insertion is by a wide aponeurosis rather than by a discrete tendon. In *Tauraco leucotis*, for example, the inserting tendon of M. tensor patagii brevis is a wide sheet (1.5 mm wide); it would be easy to make artificial separations in such a tendon sheet to produce "multiple tendons." This may account for the apparent two distinct tendons in *Tauraco corythaix* as illustrated by Lowe (1943: Fig. 19). Some of the multiple tendons described in literature, therefore, may be artifacts.

20. M. Deltoideus Major

a. Columba livia. The major deltoid muscle is composed of a large posterior head and a small anterior head. All but the posterior margin of the posterior head is concealed by the common belly of Mm. tensores patagii longus et brevis. The *posterior head* arises by fleshy fibers from the lateral and dorsal surfaces of the acromion; it inserts for a distance of about 10 mm near the distal end of the humerus, extending as far distad as the lateral epicondyle. N. brachialis longus superior and accompanying blood vessels pierce the muscle to form a gap near the distal part of the insertion. The *anterior head* of M. deltoideus major lies mostly deep to the posterior head and is fused to its deep surface; it arises by fleshy fibers from the ventrolateral surface of the acromion and from the scapula inferior to the acromion. An os humeroscapulare is absent and there is no origin from the joint capsule. The anterior head inserts by fleshy fibers on the shaft of the humerus, beginning 10 mm distal to the junction of the articular head and the deltoid crest; the muscle inserts entirely distal to the deltoid crest. The two bellies have an over-all continuous insertion on the distal two-thirds of the shaft of the humerus.

b. Agelaius phoeniceus. The major deltoid muscle has two well developed heads. The *anterior head* is composed of two intimately related parts. The largest part arises primarily by fleshy fibers from the very large os humeroscapulare (scapula accessoria) and from the dorsal scapulohumeral ligament. The belly passes forward and downward to insert by fleshy fibers on most of the deltoid crest and on the shaft of the humerus distal to the crest for a distance of about 20 mm. A large posterior fasciculus arises primarily by a strong, flat tendon attached to the ventral edge of the acromion process of the scapula within the triosseal canal. The tendon passes outward deep to the origin of M. deltoideus minor and superficial to the capsule of the shoulder joint, and then fuses, in part, with the os humeroscapulare and associated ligaments. The fleshy fibers of the posterior fasciculus arise from the tendon and from the os humeroscapulare. Part of the posterior fasciculus fuses with the posterior surface of the anterior component of the anterior head in the proximal half of the arm, but the rest of the muscle continues as an independent belly and gives rise to a short (1 mm long) tendon, which inserts on a tubercle on the proximal face of the ect-epicondylar process of the humerus.

The *posterior head* of M. deltoideus major arises primarily by fleshy fibers from the posterior and medial surfaces of the apex of the clavicle and from a small area on the dorsal coracoclavicular ligament. The flattened belly passes distad superficial to the tendon of M. supracoraco-deus and the bellies of Mm. deltoideus minor and scapulotriceps. The belly of the posterior head extends the full length of the arm and inserts by short semitendinous fibers on the humerus just proximal to the base of the ectepicondylar process.

c. Comparative data. The major deltoid muscle exhibits variation in the number of heads, in the relative development of the heads, in the presence or absence of a *scapular anchor,* and in the extent of insertion on the deltoid crest and the shaft of the humerus.

The *anterior head* (*deltoideus major anterior*) arises from the os humeroscapulare (when present), from the scapulohumeral joint capsule, from the apex of the clavicle, or from the anterior end of the scapula (from the acromion or from the lateral surface of the scapula posterior and inferior to the acromion, usually near the glenoid cavity). The anterior head may arise almost exclusively from the os humeroscapulare when it is unusually well developed (e.g., *Otus asio, Tauraco leucotis, Procnias nudicollis*).

The *posterior head* (*deltoideus major posterior*) arises from the acromion (*Otus, Coua, Geococcyx, Coracias*), from the apex of the clavicle (*Chloroceryle, Upupa, Indicator, Procnias,* Corvidae), or the coracoid (*Struthio, Rhea, Aceros*). In many genera (e.g., *Gavia, Chen, Grus, Otus Pharomachrus, Chloroceryle, Coracias, Upupa, Procnias,* Corvidae) there is a secondary tendinous anchor (*Scapular anchor*) extending between the posterior margin of the posterior head and the blade of the scapula, dorsal to the origin of M. dorsalis scapulae; there is some variation among genera in the exact pattern of the scapular anchor. The posterior head has an unusual origin in *Aceros undulatus:* by a strong flat tendon from the procoracoid process of the coracoid; the tendon passes laterad around the anterior edge of the scapula dorsal to the coraco-scapular ligament; the tendon gives origin to fleshy fibers at the lateral surface of the scapula and then fuses with the capsule of the shoulder joint. The small anterior head in *Aceros* arises from the capsule of the shoulder joint and from the very small os humeroscapulare. The two heads fuse after a short independent course and have a continuous insertion on slightly more than the proximal half of the humerus.

The two heads of M. deltoideus major may be about the same size;

the anterior head is larger in some passerines (e.g., *Paradisaea rubra*, Corvidae); the posterior head is larger in cuckoos and in *Chordeiles minor;* relative development of the two heads varies intergenerically in the Psittacidae (Beddard, 1898: p. 260). In some genera (e.g., *Galli-columba, Pharomachrus, Chloroceryle*) the major deltoid muscle is composed of a large superficial head and a much smaller deep head. In *Chloroceryle americana*, for example, the deep head is a small band of muscle 10 mm in length and little more than 1 mm in width, except at its insertion. The deep head arises exclusively from the dorsal ligaments of the shoulder joint (there is no os humeroscapulare in this species); the small belly inserts on the humerus proximal to the area of insertion of M. latissimus dorsi pars anterior.

The two heads of M. deltoideus major fuse, and there is a continuous insertion on the deltoid crest and the shaft of the humerus in many birds (e.g., *Goura, Otus, Upupa, Indicator*, Corvidae). In certain passerine birds (e.g., *Procnias, Fregilupus, Sturnus, Dendroica, Spizella*) the two parts of the muscle are independent throughout and, therefore, have separate areas of insertion, although they may be adjacent to each other. The most distal part of the insertion often is by means of an aponeurosis or a tendon; the proximal part of the insertion almost invariably (but not in *Chordeiles minor*) is by fleshy fibers. The insertion extends to the ectepicondylar process near the distal end of the humerus in passerine birds; in *Chen, Grus, Otus*, and *Aceros* the insertion is limited to approximately the proximal half of the humerus; in *Coracias* to the proximal three-fifths; in *Gavia* to the proximal third. According to Fürbringer (1902: p. 531), the major deltoid muscle inserts on the distal third of the humerus in *Chunga, Nothura, Opisthocomus, Harpactes*, most Fulicariae, Columbidae, *Corythaix, Atrichia, Apus (Cypselus)*, *Dendrochelidon, Rhamphastos, Collocalia, Colius*, and in most Pico-Passeres. In a specimen of *Apus*, Fürbringer found an extension of the insertion onto the antebrachial fascia covering the forearm muscles.

Fisher (1946) found only one head to M. deltoideus major in the Cathartidae, and Berger (1955b) found a single head in *Crax rubra*. Beddard (1898: pp. 86, 309) said that M. deltoideus major "appears to be absent" in *Psittacula* (Psittacidae) and in *Geophaps* (Columbidae). Lucas (1896) said that the muscle is absent in *Chaetura pelagica*, that it has a single head in *Collocalia, Cypseloides, Apus*, and *Tachornis*, and that it has two heads in *Hemiprocne* (Hemiprocnidae). Lowe (1939) reported that the muscle is "extremely reduced" in swifts and is "enormously reduced or absent" in hummingbirds. M. deltoideus major is, indeed, present in *Chaetura pelagica* and exhibits a similar development to that shown for *Hirund-apus giganteus* by Lowe (1939:

Plate 3). The muscle in *Chaetura* is a tiny fleshy band about 1 mm wide; it arises from the scapula posteroventral to the acromion process. The belly passes distad posterior to the tendon of M. supracoracoideus and inserts posterior and just distal to that tendon and anterior to the large ectepicondylar process at about the midlength of the humerus. I did not find the muscle in *Eugenes fulgens*.

21. M. Deltoideus Minor

a. Columba livia. The deltoid minor muscle is unusually well developed in the Rock Dove. It is a 7 mm-wide sheet of fleshy fibers, which has an extensive origin from the lateral surface of the apex of the coracoid, from the coracohumeral and coracoscapular ligaments, and from the inferior margin of the acromion process of the scapula. The muscle consists of more or less distinct superficial and deep layers, which are closely applied to the dorsal surface of the joint capsule. The muscle has a wide fleshy insertion on the anterodorsal surface of the humerus, just distal to the articular head.

b. Agelaius phoeniceus. M. deltoideus minor is composed of two independent parts. The *posterior* (deep) *belly* arises by fleshy fibers from the lateral surface of the acromion of the scapula. The flat belly (about 0.5 mm wide) passes outward and forward superficial to the tendon of insertion of M. supracoracoideus and inserts on the anteroproximal edge of the humerus at the margin of the articular head. The *anterior* (superficial) *belly* arises from the dorsolateral surface of the head of the coracoid. The flat belly (slightly wider than the deep belly) passes outward to insert on the humerus immediately anterior to the deep head. The tendon of M. supracoracoideus inserts proximal and between the areas of insertion of the two bellies of M. deltoideus minor.

c. Comparative data. Gadow and Selenka (1891: p. 234) state that most descriptions of M. deltoideus minor are so confused that only a small amount of the literature can be interpreted with certainty. This muscle has been described under several names: scapulohumeralis; deltoideus, deep brevis; deltoideus internus; deltoideus externus; supraspinatus; coracobrachialis internus (Fürbringer, 1902: pp. 535–538; Shufeldt, 1890; Howell, 1937).

Sullivan (1962: p. 467) commented that "the innervation of M. coracobrachialis anterior [=deltoideus minor] would suggest a relationship to M. deltoideus [major] if the Fürbringer hypothesis of unchangeable muscular nerve supply is accepted as the basis for assessing homology."[*] Sullivan adopted the name coracobrachialis anterior for this muscle be-

---

[*] See, however, the quotation from Straus, page 225.

cause, embryologically, it "is derived from the supracoracoid division of
the ventral premuscle mass. It has become innervated from the same
nerve trunk as M. deltoideus, which in young embryos terminates above
the foramen triosseum . . . but subsequently grows downwards to supply M. coracobrachialis anterior." He added that "if homologies and corresponding names are based on Romer's two-mass theory, then the name
deltoideus minor is inappropriate because M. deltoideus arises from
the dorsal mass and M. coracobrachialis anterior from the ventral mass."
(See comment under 14. M. coracobrachialis anterior earlier in this
section. See Figs. IX.35 and IX.36.)

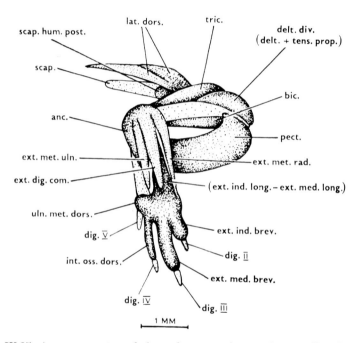

Fɪɢ. IX.35. A reconstruction of the right wing of an embryo *Gallus domesticus*
at stage 29–30 of Hamburger and Hamilton (1951). (By permission, Sullivan,
1962.) For Key to Abbreviations see legend to Fig. IX.26.

M. deltoideus minor typically has a single head (*pars dorsalis*), which
has been found in most birds. It arises from the lateral surface of the
acromion (e.g., *Geococcyx*, Corvidae, Fringillidae), from the lateral surface of the coracoid (*Eugenes, Coracias, Chloroceryle, Spizella*), or from
inside the triosseal canal from the scapula (*Chaetura, Pharomachrus,
Chordeiles, Upupa*), from the clavicle (*Chordeiles, Indicator, Procnias*),
or from the coracoid (*Chrysococcyx*). The muscle arises inside the trios-

seal canal from both the lateral surface of the clavicle and the coracoid in *Coua caerulea.*

Pars dorsalis overlaps and conceals the tendon of insertion of M. supracoracoideus in some genera (e.g., *Grus, Otus, Chaetura, Spizella*); it does not conceal the tendon in other genera (e.g., *Gallicolumba, Coracias, Upupa*).

Pars ventralis, a deep head, has been reported in a few birds. In *Grus canadensis tabida,* pars ventralis arises inside the triosseal canal from the procoracoid process and from the coracoclavicular membrane. Pars

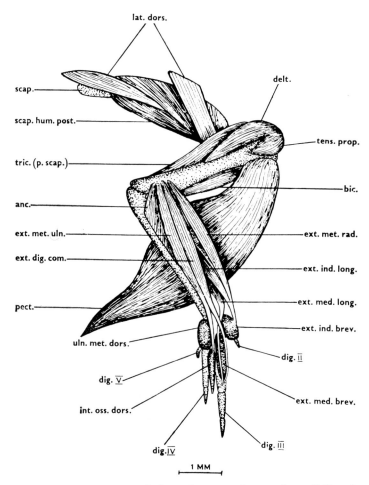

FIG. IX.36. A reconstruction of the right wing of an embryo *Gallus domesticus* at stage 36 of Hamburger and Hamilton (1951). (By permission, Sullivan, 1962.) For Key to Abbreviations see legend to Fig. IX.26.

dorsalis arises inside the triosseal canal from the ventral margin of the acromion process. The two heads fuse and insert as a single belly on the humerus distal and posterior to the insertion of M. supracoracoideus.

M. deltoideus minor is said to be absent in some hummingbirds (*Phaethornis, Amazilia = Agyrtria;* Buri, 1900), and, perhaps as an individual variation, in *Apus* (Fürbringer, 1902: p. 536). The muscle is well developed in *Chaetura pelagica.* The muscle is a minute band (about 0.3 mm in width) in *Eugenes fulgens;* it arises from the lateral surface of the apex of the coracoid and inserts on the anterodorsal edge of the humerus, just distal to its articular head. The minor deltoid muscle is absent in certain cuckoos (*Coccyzus, Pachycoccyx,* and *Centropus*).

22. M. Biceps Brachii

a. Columba livia. The biceps muscle has a double origin, and, unlike the condition in most other birds, the two heads can readily be separated throughout most of their length. The muscle arises by a strong, 3 mm-wide, flat tendon from the anterior surface of the apex of the coracoid; this tendon passes outward on the ventral surface of the fascia covering M. coracobrachialis anterior and gives rise to fleshy fibers at about the level of the distal end of the deltoid crest of the humerus; this coracoidal head is located primarily anterior and deep to the humeral head of the muscle. The second, or humeral, head of the biceps muscle arises by means of a much thinner, 4 mm-wide aponeurosis from the bicipital crest of the humerus; the aponeurosis is fused to the posterior border of the coracoidal tendon; the aponeurosis gives rise to the larger part of the fleshy belly, which lies posterior and superficial to the coracoidal head. The fleshy belly of the biceps brachii muscle (about 30 mm in maximum length) extends into the forearm between the flexor and extensor muscles. The two heads of the muscle fuse on a large common tendon, which inserts on the posterior surface of the proximal end of the radius. A much smaller, flat tendon arises from the distal end of the coracoidal head and inserts on the anterodorsal surface of the proximal end of the ulna. The manner of formation of these two tendons is unusual.

The *biceps slip* arises by a 5 mm-wide aponeurosis from about the midlength of the anteroventral margin of the coracoidal head of the biceps muscle. Arising from this relatively small attachment to the biceps muscle is a bulky, roughly quadrangular mass of muscle (9 mm in width and 8 mm in maximum length). The anterior edge of the biceps slip is fused with the proximal portion of the elastic tendon of M. tensor patagii longus. The muscle bundles of the biceps slip are arranged parallel to the tendon of M. tensor patagii longus. The distal border of the biceps slip gives rise to a well developed tendon, which runs distad in the propatagium, fuses with the anterior of the two tendons of M. tensor patagii longus, and inserts on a 5 mm-long sesamoid in the connective tissue and deep fascia covering the anterior surface of the wrist.

b. Agelaius phoeniceus. The primary origin of M. biceps brachii is by a strong, flat tendon attached to the anterolateral surface of the head of the coracoid, but, as in most birds, the tendon is strongly anchored to the bicipital crest of the humerus. The coracoidal tendon passes outward superficial to the coracohumeral ligament and deep to the belly of M. pectoralis pars thoracicus. Fleshy fibers of the biceps muscle begin at the level of the humeral attachment of the tendon of origin. The well developed belly extends to the distal end of the arm, where two tendons form. The tendons enter the forearm musculature by passing between M. extensor metacarpi radialis (anteriorly) and M. pronator superficialis (posteriorly). The larger tendon (about 1 mm wide) inserts on the proximal end of the ulna posterior to the area of insertion of M. brachialis. The much smaller tendon (about 0.2 mm wide) inserts on a tubercle on the posteroventral surface of the proximal end of the radius.

c. Comparative data. M. biceps brachii typically arises by a dense tendinous sheet (often L-shaped), which has one attachment to the lateral surface of the head of the coracoid and a second attachment to the bicipital crest of the humerus. The humeral attachment may be near the base of the internal tuberosity of the humerus (many birds) or it may extend along the entire length of the bicipital crest (Cathartidae; Fisher, 1946: p. 588). This double attachment of the tendon of origin is the only suggestion of two heads for the muscle in most birds, in which the biceps muscle has a single belly. There are two distinct and separate heads in *Pelecanus* and *Phalacrocorax;* the tendon of the humeral head also extends proximad to attach to the coracoid, either deep to or posterior to the origin of the typical coracoidal head (see Beddard, 1898: p. 405). The typical L-shaped tendon of origin in *Upupa epops* gives rise to two separate bellies. According to Beddard (1898: pp. 86, 499, 503), the biceps has only a coracoidal origin in *Rhea, Dromiceius,* the cassowary, loons, petrels, and some alcids. In *Rhea* and *Dromiceius* the biceps arises by a rounded tendon from the "coracoid spine" and by a tendon-sheet, edged with muscle, from the "whole of the coracoid and from just an adjacent bit of the sternum." The biceps has a single origin from the apex of the coracoid in *Eugenes fulgens.*

In most birds the tendon of insertion of M. biceps brachii bifurcates, sending one branch to insert on the proximal end of the ulna and one branch to insert on the proximal end of the radius. In the cassowary the tendon "ends without being definitely split into two tendons upon both radius and ulna"; in *Apteryx* it inserts on the radius only (Beddard, 1898: pp. 499, 504). Swinebroad (1954: p. 505) stated that the insertion is on the ulna only in *Passer domesticus, Richmondena cardinalis, Zonotrichia albicollis,* and *Melospiza melodia.* I found an insertion on both the radius and the ulna in *Spizella arborea,* although the tendon to the radius is much smaller than the ulnar tendon. In *Eugenes fulgens* the belly gives rise to a single tendon, which inserts on the ulna only. In *Upupa epops* the deep belly of the biceps brachii gives rise to a tendon which inserts on the proximal end of the ulna. The superficial belly gives rise to a single tendon, which then bifurcates: one branch inserts on the proximal end of the radius, just distal to the articular surface; the other branch inserts on the proximal end of the ulna, 1 mm distal to the insertion of the tendon derived from the deep belly. The biceps tendon has a high bifurcation in *Chordeiles minor;* the resulting branches insert on well developed tubercles on the facing surfaces of the proximal ends of the radius and ulna.

Beddard (1898: p. 371; Figure 180) described and illustrated an "accessory biceps" in *Rhinochetus;* the muscle arises from the humerus distal to the insertion of M. deltoideus major and inserts on the radius proximal to the insertion of the biceps tendon. Beddard (1898: p. 489) and Lowe (1942: p. 16) mentioned an accessory biceps muscle in the tinamous.

The biceps brachii muscle is said to be absent in penguins (Beddard, 1898: p. 397), swifts, and hummingbirds (Lowe, 1939). The muscle is absent in *Chaetura pelagica,* but it is present in *Eugenes fulgens.* The belly is weakly developed in the hummingbird, however, being about 2.5 mm in length; as pointed out above, the tendon inserts on the ulna only.

The *biceps slip* (Garrod, 1876: p. 195; 1881: p. 329) or *M. biceps propatagialis* (Gadow and Selenka, 1891: p. 255) is a muscular belly derived from the biceps brachii muscle (Fig. IX.37). The biceps slip passes outward in the propatagium and inserts by fleshy fibers and, sometimes, by a tendon on the tendon of insertion of M. tensor patagii longus. The biceps slip also has been called the "tensor accessorius" (Parker and Haswell, 1947: p. 441; Young, 1950: p. 427) and the "tensor patagii accessorius" (Shufeldt, 1887c).

The biceps slip is said to arise directly from the humerus (rather than from the biceps muscle) in *Jacana* (=*Parra*) *sinensis* and in *Porphyrula* (Beddard, 1898: pp. 324, 342). In loons, grebes, and ducks the biceps slip not only inserts on the tendon of M. tensor patagii longus but also sends a tendon toward the forearm, where it either ends in the connective tissue of the propatagium or inserts on the belly of M. extensor metacarpi radialis just distal to the area of insertion of M. tensor patagii brevis (Beddard, 1896b; Fürbringer, 1902: Fig. 206). In most of the Alcidae the biceps slip inserts on one of the tendons of the tensor patagii brevis muscle, occasionally also on the tensor patagii longus tendon (Beddard, 1898: p. 362).

The biceps slip has been widely used in the technical diagnoses of the families of birds. It has been found in the Gaviidae, Podicipedidae, Procellariiformes (except possibly *in Oceanites*), *Phaëthon, Phalacrocorax, Anhinga, Phoenicopterus,* Anatidae, Galliformes (except Cracidae,

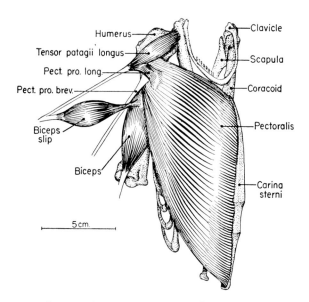

FIG. IX.37. Ventral view of proximal wing muscles to show the relations of the biceps slip in *Goura victoria* (Columbidae). (By permission, Berger, 1960b.)

Numididae, and Meleagrididae), Gruidae, Rallidae, Jacanidae, Charadriidae, Laridae, Alcidae, Columbidae, Caprimulgidae, and Coliidae (Fig. IX.38). The muscle undoubtedly is present in many other groups of nonpasserine birds.

23. M. Triceps Brachii

a. Columba livia. As in all birds, the triceps muscle in the Rock Dove is composed of two distinct parts.

M. scapulotriceps arises by fleshy fibers from the inferolateral surface of the scapula (posterior and ventral to the origin of the posterior head of M. deltoideus major) and by a tough aponeurosis from the inferior margin of the strongly developed posterior lip of the glenoid cavity. The aponeurosis has a strong tendinous connection with the posterodorsal scapulohumeral ligament. A 2 mm-wide aponeurotic anchor extends between the posterior surface of the humerus and the anterior and deep margin of the belly. The belly of M. scapulotriceps extends almost

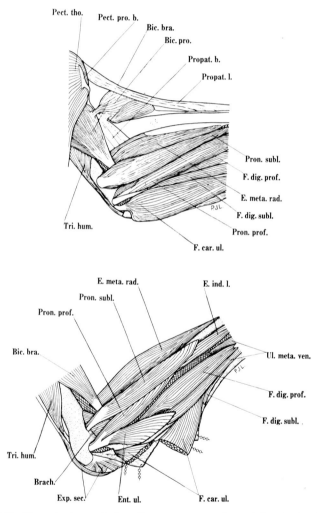

Fig. IX.38. Ventral views of the elbow region to show (above) the biceps slip (Bic. pro.) in the Band-tailed Pigeon (*Columba fasciata*) and (below) the relations of M. entepicondyloulnaris in the Blue Grouse (*Dendragapus obscurus*). (By permission, Hudson and Lanzillotti, 1955.) For Key to Abbreviations see legends to Fig. IX.26.

to the distal end of the humerus; the tendon of insertion passes around the distal end of the humerus in a groove lateral to the tendon of M. humerotriceps. The bellies of Mm. scapulotriceps and humerotriceps are independent throughout their length. There are minor fascial connections between the two muscles at the elbow, but the scapulotriceps has a separate insertion on the dorsal surface of the ulna near the base of the coronoid process.

M. humerotriceps arises from most of the posterior surface of the shaft of the humerus. The internal and external heads of the muscle are separable only in the pneumatic fossa and for a short distance distal to it. Both heads arise within the fossa and are separated only by a narrow interval. The internal head also has a tendinous origin from the bicipital crest, ventral to the area of insertion of M. dorsalis scapulae. The belly extends to the olecranon process of the ulna and inserts on it by short tendinous fibers.

b. Agelaius phoeniceus. M. scapulotriceps arises by two heads. The larger head arises by fleshy fibers from the lateral surface of the scapula just caudal to the acromion and superior to the glenoid cavity. The smaller head arises by fleshy fibers and by a large, flat tendon from the caudal face of the posterior rim of the glenoid cavity, ventral to the origin of the larger head. The two heads fuse at the level of insertion of M. latissimus dorsi pars anterior. The common belly passes down the posterior surface of the humerus deep to the posterior head of M. deltoideus major and inserts on the proximal face of a large sesamoid (*patella ulnaris*) posterior to the elbow. The sesamoid develops in the tendon of insertion of M. scapulotriceps; the tendon extends from the distal face of the sesamoid to its insertion on the dorsal surface of the base of the coronoid process of the ulna.

The external head of M. humerotriceps arises from the distal face of the bicipital crest of the humerus, from the ventral wall of the pneumatic fossa, and from slightly more than the proximal half of the shaft of the humerus. The internal head arises from the dorsal wall of the pneumatic fossa and from the posterodorsal surface of the shaft of the humerus throughout nearly its entire length. The external head is much larger than the internal head proximally. The two heads fuse about two-fifths of the way down the arm; the common belly extends to the distal end of the humerus. Some of the fibers of the internal head insert on the proximal end of the sesamoid in the tendon of M. scapulotriceps (deep to the insertion of that muscle), but most of the belly of M. humerotriceps passes distad in the external tricipital groove of the humerus and inserts on the well developed olecranon process of the ulna. The superficial part of the insertion is made by fleshy fibers but a tendon forms on the ventral border of the deep surface of the muscle and inserts on the olecranon.

c. Comparative data. The triceps muscle in birds is composed of two distinct parts: scapulotriceps and humerotriceps. This is the *triceps cubiti s. anconaeus* of Gadow and Selenka (1891: p. 263) and the *anconaeus* of Fürbringer (1902: p. 563).

M. scapulotriceps (triceps scapularis, anconaeus scapularis, anconaeus longus) arises by tendinous and/or fleshy fibers from the lateral surface of the scapula, usually just caudal to the glenoid cavity (fossa), frequently from the posterior glenoid lip; sometimes also it arises from the clavicle and the scapuloclavicular ligament (e.g., penguins, *Chen hyperborea*). In *Chen, Grus, Otus,* and *Aceros* the tendon of origin is Y-shaped, having an accessory attachment to the inferolateral edge of the scapula caudal to the glenoid cavity. M. scapulotriceps arises by two distinct heads in *Upupa epops.* The anterior head arises by a strong tendon from the posterolateral rim of the glenoid cavity; the posterior head has a typical origin from the lateral surface of the scapula. The two heads fuse about half way down the arm; the single tendon has an independent insertion on the coronoid process near the base of the olecranon; there are minor fascial connections with the belly and tendon of insertion of M. humerotriceps. M. scapulotriceps has an unusual origin in *Chloroceryle americana*, in which species the muscle arises not only from the lateral surface of the scapula, caudal and dorsal to the glenoid cavity, but also from the medial surface of the apex of the clavicle, dorsal to the origin of M. deltoideus major. In *Otus asio* the scapulotriceps arises primarily by a strong aponeurosis from the *ventral edge* of the scapula.

Beddard (1898) placed considerable emphasis on the presence of an accessory tendinous *humeral anchor* (*Ankerung*) between the anterior edge of M. scapulotriceps and the proximal end of the humerus. Beddard noted that the humeral anchor is characteristic of Garrod's Homalogonatae (birds possessing the ambiens muscle), but that there are exceptions: the anchor is present in some hornbills (*Buceros, Bucorvus*), absent in others (*Aceros, Tockus*); present in some parrots, absent in others (among parrots, the ambiens muscle, also, is present in some genera but lacking in other genera; Beddard, 1898: p. 268). The humeral anchor also has been reported in the Anhimidae, Anatidae, Falconiformes (it is especially broad in *Sagittarius*), *Grus, Rhinochetos*, Strigiformes, Caprimulgidae, and in *Upupa epops*. I have found the humeral anchor in *Gavia immer, Gallinula chloropus, Goura victoria, Columba livia, Otus asio, Pharomachrus mocino*, and *Chordeiles minor*. Beddard (1898: p. 276) reported the humeral anchor in *Saurothera, Coccyzus*, and *Centropus* (=*Pyrrhocentor*); but I failed to find it in these genera. The close relationship between the humeral anchor and the tendon of insertion of M. latissimus dorsi pars posterior, in *Otus, Chordeiles*, and *Pharomachrus* has been described earlier in this chapter.

In some birds (e.g., *Otus asio*) there also is an aponeurotic anchor between the posterior margin of M. scapulotriceps and the dorsolateral edge of the scapula, posterior to the main origin of the muscle.

The belly of M. scapulotriceps passes distad along the posterior surface of the humerus and inserts by a flat tendon on the dorsal surface of the coronoid process of the ulna or between the base of the olecranon and the coronoid process. The tendon may contain a sesamoid (the *patella ulnaris*) where it crosses the distal end of the humerus (e.g., *Eugenes fulgens, Chaetura pelagica, Procnias nudicollis, Dendroica kirtlandii, Spizella arborea*). The patella ulnaris is unusually large in *Eugenes;* it is capable of sliding back and forth and must operate in a similar manner to the patella of the knee joint in man. Judging from the examination of alcoholic specimens, one must conclude that some *rotation,* as well as flexion and extension, takes place at the elbow joint in the hummingbird. It is interesting to note that, although the scapulotriceps is a bulky muscle in the hummingbird, M. humerotriceps is larger. In the Chimney Swift, on the other hand, M. scapulotriceps is hypertrophied and is as large as both parts of M. humerotriceps.

Fibers of the internal head of M. humerotriceps insert on the tendon of M. scapulotriceps in many birds; in *Geococcyx* there is a continuous tendinous and fleshy insertion on the entire proximodorsal surface of the ulna. In other birds (e.g., *Columba livia, Pharomachrus mocino, Chordeiles minor, Upupa epops, Dendroica kirtlandii,* and *Spizella arborea*) the scapulotriceps is independent from origin to insertion and has no connection with M. humerotriceps.

M. humerotriceps (triceps humeralis, anconaeus humeralis) arises from nearly the entire posterior extent of the shaft of the humerus in most birds. The *internal* (*dorsal*) and *external* (*ventral*) heads of the muscle usually are separable only in the region of the pneumatic fossa of the humerus, where the heads form a V-shaped pattern, one head arising on either side of the area of insertion of M. proscapulohumeralis. When the latter muscle is absent or when it does not insert in the pneumatic fossa, there usually is little if any indication of two heads. The relationships of Mm. proscapulohumeralis and humerotriceps in the pneumatic fossa in *Corvus* and *Coccothraustes* have been illustrated by Bock (1962).

The external head usually arises from the anconal surface of the bicipital crest, the lateral crest of the pneumatic fossa, and from nearly the entire humeral shaft distal to these crests; in some birds (e.g., *Geococcyx,*

Corvidae) some fibers of the external head arise on either side of the tendon of insertion of M. dorsalis scapulae.

The internal head is more variable in origin than the external head: in *Crotophaga* and *Coccyzus* the internal head begins at the distal end of the capital groove; in *Geococcyx* it begins immediately proximal to the insertion of M. latissimus dorsi pars posterior; in the Cathartidae the internal head arises only from a small area in the "fourth fifth of the anconal surface" of the humerus (Fisher, 1946).

The two heads of M. humerotriceps fuse after a short independent course. The belly extends nearly to the elbow in most birds and inserts by a tendon or by semitendinous fibers on the olecranon process of the ulna. The olecranon is unusually small in *Chaetura pelagica*.

24. *M. Anconaeus Coracoideus*

a. Columba livia. This is a small band of striated muscle (about 15 mm long and 0.4 to 1.0 mm in width), which arises from the anterior surface of the long scapular tendon of M. expansor secundariorum at about the midlength of the humerus (Fig. IX.39). As it approaches the distal end of the humerus, the belly gives rise to a flat tendon, which

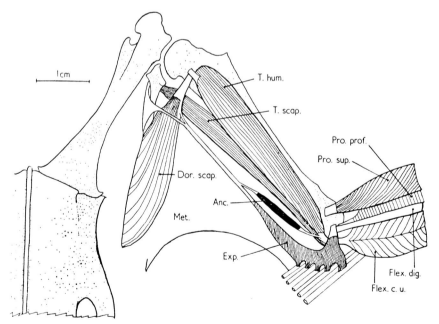

Fig. IX.39. Ventral view of the proximal region of the wing of *Columba livia* to show the relations of M. anconaeus coracoideus and M. expansor secundariorum. (By permission, Berger, 1956c.) For Key to Abbreviations see legend to Fig. IX.26.

passes deeply between the internal and external heads of M. humero-triceps and fuses with the aponeurotic raphe between the two heads.

b. Agelaius phoeniceus. Both the long tendon of M. expansor secundariorum and M. anconaeus coracoideus are absent in the Red-winged Blackbird.

c. Comparative data. M. anconaeus coracoideus apparently was first described by Fürbringer (1886: p. 124), who considered it to be a vestigial head (*caput coracoideum m. anconaei*) of M. triceps brachii, which he thought was homologous with the coracoidal head of the triceps muscle in certain reptiles. Fürbringer's studies led him to believe that the tendon of origin of M. anconaeus coracoideus had migrated to arise from the "sterno-coraco-scapulare internum" ligament; in some birds, however, this ligament is attached to the sternum and scapula only; and Gadow (in Newton and Gadow, 1896: p. 608), therefore, called it the sternoscapular ligament. According to Fürbringer (1902: p. 575), the tendon (*tendo m. anconaei coracoidei*; first mentioned by Carus, 1826; 1827: p. 359) gives rise to a vestigial striated muscle in the distal one-fifth to two-fifths of the arm in some birds: e.g., *Pelecanus*, Ardeidae, Ciconiidae, *Phoenicopterus*, most Anseriformes (including *Chauna*), *Cathartes* (=*Catharistes*), *Falco* (=*Tinnunculus*), *Grus*, *Aramus*. Fürbringer reported that the muscle is microscopic in size in *Podiceps*, *Phalacrocorax* (embryo), *Nyroca* (=*Fuligula*), *Eulabeornis* (Rallidae), and in *Eurypyga* and that the muscle consists of four to ten degenerate fibers in *Turnix* (=*Hemipodius*) and in *Gallirallus* (=*Ocydromus*).

M. anconaeus coracoideus apparently exhibits its best development in *Pelecanus*, in which genus the muscle inserts by a small tendon on the proximal end of the ulna adjacent to the insertion of M. humerotriceps (Fürbringer, 1902: Fig. 255). Berger (1956c) described and illustrated the muscle in *Grus canadensis tabida* and in *Columba livia* (Fig. IX.40). In these birds tendon m. anconaei coracoidei not only gives origin to M. anconaeus coracoideus but also serves as an accessory tendon of origin for M. expansor secundariorum, which is composed of smooth muscle fibers only. Fürbringer had concluded many years ago that M. anconaeus coracoideus had disappeared in most birds but that its tendon of origin had been retained in many birds in which a secondary fusion had taken place between the tendon and the belly of the expansor secundariorum muscle. Berger has also found M. anconaeus coracoideus in *Chen hyperborea atlantica*.

So little has been published on this interesting muscle that I have used Fürbringer's original name for it. If, indeed, it is derived from the triceps complex, it would be more logical to call it M. triceps coracoideus or M. coracotriceps.

25. M. Expansor Secundariorum

a. Columba livia. This muscle has a roughly triangular-shaped belly (about 2 cm long) composed entirely of smooth or nonstriated muscle fibers. It inserts on the fascia surrounding the bases of the five proximal secondary feathers. The belly arises from two separate tendons. The *distal* or *humeral tendon* arises from the medial epicondyle of the hu-

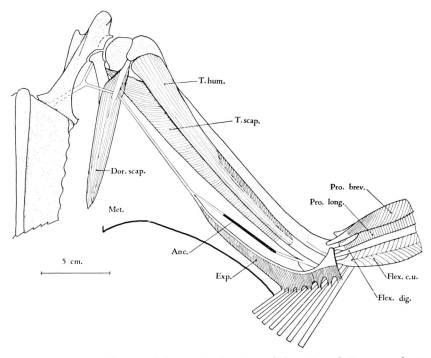

Fɪɢ. IX.40. Ventral view of the proximal region of the wing of *Grus canadensis tabida* to show the relations of Mm. anconaeus coracoideus and expansor secundariorum. (By permission, Berger, 1956c.) For Key to Abbreviations see legend to Fig. IX.26.

merus anterior to the origin of the tendon of M. flexor digitorum superficialis. The humeral tendon of M. expansor secundariorum passes posteriorly and distally superficial to all of the other tendons that arise from the medial epicondyle. Some of the most distal fibers of the muscle arise directly from the humeroulnar pulley, located deep to the humeral tendon. The *proximal* or *scapular tendon* arises from the dorsomedial edge of the scapula and is partly fused with the fascia covering the medial surface of M. subscapularis. As it descends through the axilla, the scapular tendon is intimately related with the axillary and vascular fascia. At the inferior margin of M. dorsalis scapulae a second, short tendon, arising from the fascial envelope surrounding the distal portion of the muscle, reinforces the main tendon. The proximal portion of the fleshy belly of M. expansor secundariorum arises from the scapular tendon near the junction of the middle and distal thirds of the humerus. The tendon continues distad, fans out on the deep surface of the belly of the muscle, and fuses with extensions of the humeral tendon.

b. *Agelaius phoeniceus.* M. expansor secundariorum is unusually well developed for a passerine bird. The muscle arises exclusively from the humeroulnar pulley. The flat, triangular-shaped belly passes posteriorly superficial to the tendon of origin of M. flexor carpi ulnaris, fans out to a width of 6 mm, and inserts on the ventral surface of the calami of the inner three secondary feathers.

c. *Comparative data.* This muscle apparently was first mentioned and illustrated (in *Gallus bankiva*) by Milne-Edwards (1867–1868), who considered it a part of M. coracobrachialis posterior. Garrod (1876: p. 193) named the expansor secundariorum muscle and suggested that its presence or absence might be of value in determining the affinities of birds. Fürbringer (1886: p. 124) reported that the muscle was composed of smooth muscle fibers and discussed its relationships to M. anconaeus coracoideus and to tendo m. anconaei coracoidei. Gadow and Selenka (1891: p. 259) described the expansor secundariorum muscle (after Garrod) as one of three components (two striated and one smooth) of their M. metapatagialis. Buri (1900) apparently was the first to report the presence of M. expansor secundariorum in passerine birds; he stated that the muscle is composed of elastic fibers in the Hirundinidae. Berger (1956c) confirmed Fürbringer's statement that M. expansor secundariorum is a smooth muscle, reported the presence of the muscle in representatives of 23 families of passerine birds, and commented that the muscle probably is present in most birds (Figs. IX.41–IX.43).

Two extremes of development of this muscle are illustrated above by the descriptions in the Rock Dove and the Red-winged Blackbird. The muscle arises from the distal end of the humerus and/or the humeroulnar pulley in passerine birds and in *Podilymbus, Otus, Caprimulgus, Chordeiles, Apus, Archilochus, Eugenes, Upupa, Aceros, Indicator,* and in all genera of the Picidae thus far investigated. I found no humeral origin in a single specimen of the Common Loon (*Gavia immer*); the belly (about 4.5 cm long and 4 mm wide) extends proximad from the proximal secondaries and their under coverts to end on the elastic tendon of M. serratus metapatagialis in the distal fourth of the arm. In

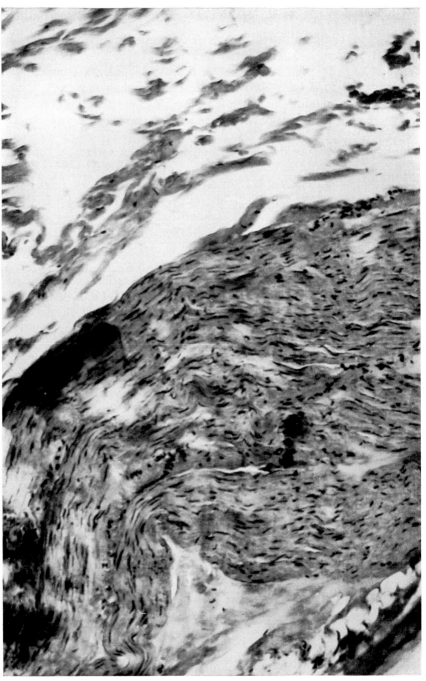

Fig. IX.41. Photomicrograph of the expansor secundariorum muscle of the Common Loon (*Gavia immer*).

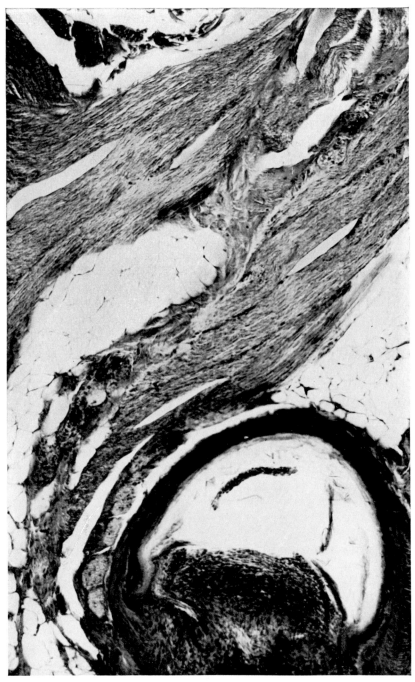

Fig. IX.42. Photomicrograph of the expansor secundariorum muscle of the Black Duck (*Anas rubripes*).

341

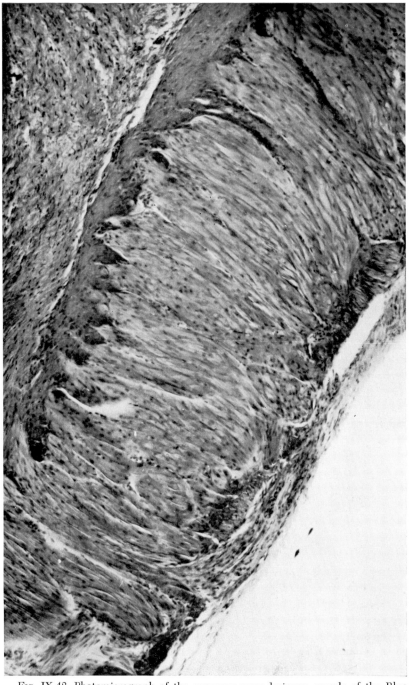

Fig. IX.43. Photomicrograph of the expansor secundariorum muscle of the Blue Jay (*Cyanocitta cristata*).

other nonpasserine genera there are two tendons of origin: one from the distal end of the humerus; the other from bones of the pectoral girdle and/or one or more of the following muscles—dorsalis scapulae, coraco-brachialis posterior, subcoracoideus, sternocoracoideus, pectoralis.

In the Sandhill Crane (*Grus canadensis tabida*) the triangular-shaped belly is about 10 cm in length and 3 cm in width at its insertion on the inner seven secondaries. The belly extends over a third the way up the arm, where some fasciculi are attached to the skin forming the dorsal layer of the metapatagium, before ending on a strong tendon. The tendon pierces the lowermost semitendinous fibers (which function as a pulley) of M. dorsalis scapulae, about 2 cm from the insertion of that muscle, and then bifurcates. The larger ventral branch of the tendon has its major attachment to the medial corner of the sternocoracoidal process of the sternum; the smaller, dorsal branch passes dorsomesiad to attach to the ventral edge of the scapula, near its articulation with the procoracoid. There also is a tendinous origin from the distal end of the humerus.

The origin of M. expansor secundariorum in the Common Gallinule or Moorhen (*Gallinula chloropus*) is similar to that in the Sandhill Crane. The over-all length of the fleshy belly is about 2 cm. From its insertion on the proximal secondaries the belly passes upward around the back of the elbow and ends on a strong, flat tendon. The tendon passes proximad in the metapatagium and through the lower margin of M. dorsalis scapulae. The tendon bifurcates in the axilla. The ventral branch descends to an attachment on the sternocoracoidal process of the sternum. The dorsal tendon passes upward between Mm. subscapularis (internal head) and subcoracoideus (scapular head) to attach to a tubercle on the dorsomedial edge of the scapula. Some of the fleshy fibers of the muscle insert into the skin forming the dorsal layer of the metapatagium. Located deep to the main belly at the elbow there is a second belly, which arises from the distal end of the humerus and from the humeroulnar pulley; the deep belly also inserts on the bases of the proximal secondaries.

M. expansor secundariorum is well developed in the Greater Snow Goose (*Chen hyperborea atlantica*), and its scapular tendon appears to have unusual relationships. The belly (about 6 cm long) has one origin by a flat tendon from the distal end of the humerus and from the humeroulnar pulley; it inserts on the inner four secondaries and their under coverts. The belly also extends upward posterior to the elbow to end on a tendon which continues proximad through the metapatagium, ventral to the belly of M. dorsalis scapulae, to reach the axilla. There the tendon fuses with a wide aponeurosis whose only bony attachment is to the dorsomedial surface of the acromion process of the scapula for a distance of about 5 mm. The aponeurosis, however, extends across the visceral compartment of the neck, between the trachea and esophagus, from one scapula to the other. The strongest part of the aponeurosis is a band that extends from one scapular attachment to the other. In effect, the tendons of the right and left expansor secundariorum muscles insert on this band about 2 cm from its scapular attachments.

M. expansor secundariorum in *Coracias abyssinica* has two discrete bellies, whose relationship is like that in *Colinus virginianus* (Berger, 1956c: Fig. 3). A deep, triangular-shaped belly arises by a flat tendon from the distal end of the humerus between the tendons of origin of Mm. pronator superficialis and pronator profundus. The fleshy belly inserts on the bases of the five innermost secondaries. A superficial belly inserts on the bases of the inner four secondaries; this belly passes upward in the metapatagium and tapers to insert on a flat tendon. Deep in the axilla the tendon becomes continuous with a vertically directed aponeurosis, which attaches inferiorly to the sternocoracoidal process of the coracoid (deep to the origin of M. coracobrachialis posterior) and attaches superiorly to the posterior edge of the apex of the clavicle, just below the scapuloclavicular articulation.

M. expansor secundariorum inserts on the calami of two or more of the proximal secondaries, occasionally also on distal tertials. The muscle apparently inserts on only two secondaries in *Dendroica* and in *Archilochus colubris* but on three secondaries in most passerine birds and in *Eugenes fulgens*. It inserts on five secondaries in *Columba*, on six in *Aceros undulatus*, and on seven in *Grus canadensis*.

26. M. Brachialis

a. Columba livia. This is a rectangular-shaped muscle, which arises from the brachial impression on the palmar surface of the distal end of the humerus and which inserts on the brachial impression (8 mm long) on the proximal end of the ulna.

b. Agelaius phoeniceus. M. brachialis arises by fleshy fibers in the brachial impression near the distal end of the shaft of the humerus. The belly passes across the elbow palmar to the tendons of insertion of M. biceps brachii and inserts by fleshy fibers along a 4 mm-long line on the posteroventral surface of the proximal end of the ulna.

c. Comparative data. This muscle also has been called M. brachialis inferior and M. brachialis anticus. M. brachialis exhibits relatively little variation among birds. It is an unusually large muscle, inserting on the radius, in penguins. Beddard (1898: p. 504) mentions a peculiar "accessory brachialis anticus" muscle in *Apteryx*.

27. *M. Pronator Superficialis (Pronator Brevis)*

a. Columba livia. The superficial pronator arises by a strong, flat (2 mm wide) tendon from a curved ridge near the distal end of the humerus. The well developed belly (about 41 mm long and 8 mm in maximum width) extends distad slightly over four-fifths the length of the forearm; it inserts primarily by fleshy fibers on the ventral surface of the radius, extending to within about 8 mm of the distal end of the bone.

b. Agelaius phoeniceus. The fleshy bellies of the flexor muscles of the forearm extend about two-thirds the way down the forearm. M. pronator superficialis has the most proximal origin of the muscles arising from the distomedial end of the humerus. The belly of the muscle (about 19 mm long) inserts on the posteroventral surface of the radius in its proximal two-thirds. Most of the insertion is by fleshy fibers, but, distally, the belly gives rise to an aponeurosis which fuses with the most distal part of the aponeurosis of insertion of M. pronator profundus. Mm. pronator superficialis and pronator profundus extend distad about the same distance.

c. Comparative data. Superficialis is a better name than brevis for this muscle because it is superficial to the second pronator in all birds; it is not, however, always shorter than M. pronator profundus (longus). This muscle is called the pronator sublimus by Gadow and Selenka (1891: p. 267) and Hudson and Lanzillotti (1955). The adjective "superficialis" replaces "sublimus" in human anatomy as being "more accurate" (Woerdeman *et al.*, 1961: p. 76).

M. pronator superficialis has the most proximal origin of the muscles that arise from the distomedial surface of the humerus. Fleshy fibers arise from the short tendon of origin, cross M. brachialis, and insert, primarily by fleshy fibers, on the anteroventral surface of the radius. The muscle extends almost to the distal end of the forearm in *Gallicolumba* and about three-fourths the length of the forearm in many cuckoos (e.g., *Coua, Geococcyx, Coccyzus, Crotophaga*). In *Polihiërax, Aceros, Chloroceryle,* and the Corvidae the belly is limited to about the proximal half of the forearm; in *Paradisaea rubra* and *Dendroica kirtlandii* to slightly more than the proximal half; in *Grus* to the proximal third; and in the Cathartidae the belly extends "distally two-fifths to one-half the way out the radius" (Fisher, 1946). In *Upupa epops* the fleshy belly tapers to a 7 mm-long tendon, which inserts at about midlength of the radius. In *Eugenes fulgens* the muscle arises by a tendon (shared with the accessory belly of M. pronator profundus) from about the midlength of the highly specialized hummingbird humerus.

28. M. Pronator Profundus (Pronator Longus)

a. Columba livia. The deep pronator arises by a strong, rounded tendon from the distal end of the humerus, deep to the tendon of origin of M. flexor digitorum superficialis. The tendon fans out as an aponeurosis on the ventral surface of the proximal part of the belly of the muscle. A small accessory fleshy belly arises from the distal end of the tendon of origin, passes anteriorly superficial to the aponeurosis, fuses with the anterior and proximal edge of the main belly, and inserts on the proximal end of the radius just distal to the course of the radial artery. The main belly (about 47 mm long) of M. pronator profundus extends the entire length of the forearm. It has a fleshy and tendinous insertion on the ventral surface of the radius posterior to the insertion of M. pronator superficialis. The two muscles are separated by a dense aponeurosis. The deep radial artery and the deep radial vein enter the forearm just proximal to the area where both the deep and superficial pronators begin their insertion on the proximal end of the radius.

b. Agelaius phoeniceus. M. pronator profundus has an unusual origin in the blackbird and other higher passerines studied. There is a typical tendinous origin from the distal end of the humerus (between the areas of origin of Mm. pronator superficialis and flexor digitorum superficialis). There is an additional, large fleshy origin from the humeroulnar pulley. There is some fusion between the belly arising from the humeral tendon and the belly arising from the humeroulnar pulley but most of the latter belly remains independent and inserts primarily by an aponeurosis on the posterior surface of the radius for a distance of about 6 mm, beginning 6 mm from the proximal end of the radius. The line of insertion of the aponeurosis lies posterior to the area of insertion of M. pronator superficialis. The main, "typical" belly (about 15 mm long) ends on a flat tendon, which inserts on a tubercle on the posterior surface of the radius about two-thirds the way out the bone at the distal end of the insertion of M. pronator superficialis.

c. Comparative data. The name "longus," as stated above, is applicable to this muscle in some birds only, whereas it is uniformly located deep to M. pronator superficialis. According to Beddard (1898: pp. 501, 504), the two pronators are fused in Ratites; but the profundus appears to be absent in *Rhea*.

M. pronator profundus typically arises by a strong tendon from the medial epicondyle of the humerus, adjacent to the origin of M. flexor digitorum superficialis and under cover of the humeral tendon (when present) of M. expansor secundariorum and distal to the origin of M. pronator superficialis. Fleshy fibers usually arise from the deep surface of the tendon near its origin. The insertion on the ulnar side of the radius is both fleshy and tendinous in most birds. The tendinous portion tends to be closely associated with the origin of M. extensor indicis longus.

In *Gallicolumba, Coua, Geococcyx, Crotophaga,* and *Eugenes,* M. pronator profundus extends nearly to the distal end of the radius, some distance beyond the end of M. pronator superficialis; in *Coccyzus, Otus, Chordeiles,* and *Upupa,* M. pronator profundus is considerably shorter, extending distad little further than M. pronator superficialis. The two muscles extend distad about the same distance in *Chaetura, Pharomachrus, Chloroceryle,* and *Spizella.* Hudson and Lanzillotti (1955) found that in "*Corvus* the pronator muscles are confined to about the proximal half of the forearm," whereas in other genera of the Corvidae they extend as much as two-thirds the length of the forearm. They also found that the profundus does not extend as far distally as the superficialis in *Cyanocorax* and *Cissa* (=*Kitta*). M. pronator profundus also is shorter than M. pronator superficialis in *Indicator variegatus*. Three patterns in the relative development of the two muscles are seen in the cuckoos: (1) the two muscles are about equal in length and both are relatively short in *Coccyzus, Dromococcyx, Chrysococcyx, Surniculus;* (2) they are about the same length, and they extend nearly to the distal end of the radius in *Morococcyx, Guira, Centropus, Ceuthmochares, Phaenicophaeus;* (3) both are long, but the profundus is longer than the superficialis in *Coua, Geococcyx, Crotophaga, Tapera, Piaya, Saurothera, Carpococcyx, Clamator, Cuculus*. In *Grus americana* and in *Grus canadensis* both muscles are restricted to about the proximal third of the forearm but the profundus reaches farther distad than does the superficialis (Fisher and Goodman, 1955; Berger, 1956e).

29. M. Pronator Quadratus

Beddard (1898: p. 501) mentioned such a muscle "running from the ulna to the radius" in *Struthio*.

30. M. Flexor Digitorum Superficialis

a. Columba livia. This muscle arises by a cordlike tendon from the medial epicondyle of the humerus, medial to the tendon of origin of M. flexor carpi ulnaris and proximal to the tendon of origin of M. pronator profundus. The tendon fans out to form a strong and extensive *humerocarpal band,* which not only conceals the bellies of Mm. flexor digitorum superficialis and flexor carpi ulnaris but which also sends an extension posteriorly between the bellies of the two muscles. Consequently, the belly of M. flexor carpi ulnaris is completely ensheathed by specializations of the humerocarpal band. The humerocarpal band extends the entire length of the forearm, attaches to the fascia surrounding the bases of the secondaries and their under wing coverts, and, at the distal end of the forearm, has a very strong tendinous attachment to the anterior edge of the os ulnare, where the band forms a vaginal sheath for the tendon of insertion of M. flexor digitorum superficialis. From its attachments to the os ulnare and the ligaments on the ventral surface of the wrist the humerocarpal band sends extensions into the hand, where it covers the ventral surface of M. ulnimetacarpalis dorsalis, passes posteriorly to end around the bases of the metacarpal primaries, and becomes indistinguishable from the deep fascia on the palmar surface of the hand.

The fleshy fibers of M. flexor digitorum superficialis arise from the deep surface of the humerocarpal band, beginning about 15 mm distal to its humeral origin. The belly of the muscle (about 31 mm in length) extends to the proximal face of the os ulnare, at which point a strong tendon of insertion is formed. The tendon passes through a groove on the anterior surface of the os ulnare and enters the hand. In the hand the tendon passes distad on the surface of M. abductor indicis and posterior to the tendon of insertion of M. flexor digitorum profundus. Near the distal end of the carpometacarpus the tendon of M. flexor digitorum superficialis passes anteriorly, deep to the tendon of M. flexor digitorum profundus, to insert, in part, on the base of the proximal phalanx of digit II; but most of the tendon continues distad, anterior to the tendon of M. flexor digitorum profundus, to insert on the anterior corner of the base of the distal phalanx of digit II adjacent to the insertion of M. flexor digitorum profundus. Tendinous fibers also attach to the anteroventral edge of much of the proximal phalanx of digit II.

b. Agelaius phoeniceus. M. flexor digitorum superficialis has a typical origin by a tendon from the medial epicondyle of the humerus. The tendon of origin fans out into a dense humerocarpal band which envelops (i.e., conceals) the belly of M. flexor digitorum superficialis and most of the belly and tendon of insertion of M. flexor carpi ulnaris. Posteriorly, the humerocarpal band fuses with the fascia surrounding the bases of all but the most proximal secondaries and their under coverts (i.e., those receiving the expansor secundariorum muscle). Distally, the humerocarpal band attaches to the palmar surface of the os ulnare and then continues around the wrist and into the hand, where the band ends on the bones and deep fascia forming a sheath over the tendon of M. flexor digitorum profundus.

The belly of M. flexor digitorum superficialis is about 14 mm long. The belly gives rise to a long, fine tendon which passes distad on the deep surface of the humerocarpal band, through a groove on the anterior surface of the os ulnare, and into the hand. The tendon then runs along the distal two-thirds of the carpometacarpus deep to the tendon of M. flexor digitorum profundus and inserts on the anteroventral corner of the base of the proximal phalanx of digit II.

c. Comparative data. This is the flexor digitorum sublimus of Gadow and Selenka (1891: p. 278) and Hudson and Lanzillotti (1955). The change to superficialis here is made in accordance with the *Nomina Anatomica.* Burt (1930) called this muscle the "flexor metacarpi ulnaris." Shufeldt (1890), Fisher (1946), Fisher and Goodman (1955), and Swinebroad (1954) incorrectly described this muscle as part of M. flexor carpi ulnaris. Hudson and Lanzillotti (1955) commented that Shufeldt's "description of the flexor digitorum sublimus makes it quite apparent that he did not find any such muscle." The confusion in the literature stems from the fact that the belly of this muscle is very small in some birds (absent in a few), and its aponeurotic specializations often completely envelop the belly and tendon of M. flexor carpi ulnaris. The areas of origin and insertion of the two muscles, however, are discrete and distinctive.

M. flexor digitorum superficialis arises by a cordlike tendon from the medial epicondyle of the humerus, distal to the origin of M. pronator profundus. A short distance after its origin from the humerus the tendon of origin of M. flexor digitorum superficialis fans out to become a dense aponeurosis, which Gadow and Selenka (1891: p. 279) called the *hu-merocarpal band,* a very useful designation for this extensive aponeurosis. When seen at its maximum development, the humerocarpal band conceals the belly of M. flexor digitorum superficialis, envelops the belly and tendon of insertion of M. flexor carpi ulnaris (passing posteriorly over both the superficial and deep surfaces of the muscle), sends tendinous slips to attach to the bases of most of the secondary feathers, attaches to the os ulnare, and extends into the hand to attach to muscles, bones, and the bases of proximal primaries. Lowe (1942) discussed these intimate relationships in several genera of birds (*Rhea, Nothoprocta, Opistho-comus, Lophoceros, Lagopus,* and *Corvus*), but his work seems to have gone unnoticed by most avian anatomists.

The belly of M. flexor digitorum superficialis arises directly from the humeral tendon or from either the anterior or the deep surface of the humerocarpal band. The tendon of insertion forms at the distal end of the belly, passes around the anterior surface of the os ulnare to enter the hand, and inserts on the proximal (e.g., *Gavia, Polihiërax, Aceros, Chaetura, Upupa, Indicator, Paradisaea, Spizella*) or distal (e.g., *Grus, Palamedea, Psittacus, Pharomachrus, Chordeiles, Coracias*) phalanx of digit II. The primary insertion in *Procnias nudicollis* is on the proximal phalanx of digit II; but, as it passes along the hand, extensions of the tendon conceal the tendon of M. flexor digitorum profundus and, distally, some of the fibers insert on the tendon of the profundus muscle. In *Chen hyperborea* and *Chen caerulescens*, where digit II has three phalanges, M. flexor digitorum superficialis inserts on the middle phalanx.

The fleshy belly is well developed in cuckoos, is poorly developed in most passerines thus far studied, and might be considered rudimentary in the Cathartidae, Gruidae, and Bucerotidae. A fleshy belly is absent in *Struthio* and *Rhea* (Gadow and Selenka, 1891: p. 279; Lowe, 1942). Beddard (1898: pp. 89, 501) says first that M. flexor digitorum superficialis is entirely absent in *Struthio* and later that Mm. flexor digitorum superficialis and flexor digitorum profundus "arise by a single head from the flexor condyle of the humerus." I know that the belly of M. flexor digitorum superficialis is absent in *Podilymbus podiceps* and in *Eugenes fulgens,* in which species the muscle is represented by the humerocarpal band extending from the humerus to the os ulnare.

Variation in the development and specialization of M. flexor digitorum superficialis can best be illustrated by describing the muscle in several species.

In the Sandhill Crane the strong tendon of origin arises from the distal end of the humerus posterior to the origin of M. pronator profundus, as described for the Whooping Crane by Fisher and Goodman (1955: p. 66). From the posterior edge of this tendon a thin but extensive aponeurosis (humerocarpal band) passes posteriad to attach to the ulna; distally, the tendon inserts, in part, on the anterobasal corner of the os ulnare but has several small slips, which pass into the manus to fuse with the deep fascia on the palmar surface. The rudimentary, bipennate, fleshy belly (about 10 cm long) of the flexor digitorum superficialis muscle arises from the anterior surface of the aponeurosis and from the deep surface of the main humeral tendon. The fleshy fibers begin about 4 cm distal to the humerus. The small ossified tendon of insertion of the superficialis muscle is entirely separate from the humerocarpal band. The superficialis tendon becomes fibrous as it passes around the anterior surface of the os ulnare (anterior to the insertion of the tendon of M. flexor carpi ulnaris) and into the manus, where the tendon becomes ossified again. The tendon passes distad along the anterior surface of the carpometacarpus and inserts primarily on the anterior edge, about midlength, of the distal phalanx of digit II; but there is a fascial continuation to the tip of that phalanx. In the crane the flexor digitorum superficialis tendon has a more distal insertion than the flexor digitorum profundus tendon.

The humerocarpal band is highly specialized in *Aceros undulatus.* In this hornbill the origin of M. flexor digitorum superficialis by a tendon from the distal end of the humerus is typical, but the tendon is concealed by the humeral tendon of origin of M. expansor secundariorum. The very small (6.5 cm long but only 2 mm in maximum width) fleshy belly lies in the middle portion of the forearm; the fleshy fibers begin 5 cm from the humeral origin of the tendon and end on the tendon of insertion about 4.5 cm from the distal end of the ulna. From the dorsal surface of the humeral tendon a 3 cm-wide aponeurotic sheet passes dorsad, deep to the belly of M. flexor carpi ulnaris, along the surface of the ulna to attach to the bases of secondaries numbers 9, 10, 11, and 12. Distal to these secondaries, individual tendinous slips pass dorsad to insert on the calami of the remaining secondaries except the first. The tendon of insertion has a typical course around the wrist and into the hand. Opposite the base of digit II the tendons of Mm. flexor digitorum superficialis and profundus are bound together by tough fascia, but the tendons do not fuse. The superficialis tendon inserts at about midlength on the basal phalanx of digit II; the profundus tendon inserts on the distal end of the proximal phalanx and on the base of the distal phalanx of digit II.

M. flexor digitorum superficialis exhibits certain unusual relationships in *Otus asio*, in that there are two tendons of origin and two bellies. There is a typical origin by a strong tendon from the distal end of the humerus. This tendon fans out as the humerocarpal band complex; it passes over the surface of M. flexor carpi ulnaris and conceals it and the belly of M. flexor digitorum superficialis; the band attaches to the os ulnare distally and continues into the hand to fuse with the deep fascia there. An accessory tendon arises from the humerus distal and anterior to the main tendon. The accessory tendon has a strong attachment on the proximal end of the ulna and then continues down the forearm deep to the belly of M. flexor carpi ulnaris, fanning out to form a very strong, wide aponeurosis; it has attachments to the ulna and to the fascia around the bases of the secondaries. M. flexor digitorum superficialis has two heads of origin: (1) a long rounded head arises from the deep surface of the main tendon (the humerocarpal band); (2) a shorter, but more bulky, head arises from the accessory tendon. The two heads fuse to form a common belly (23 mm in over-all length); the fleshy fibers begin 12 mm distal to the humeral origin of the tendons and extend to within 25 mm of the distal end of the os ulnare. The belly gives rise to a single tendon, which passes into the hand, where it is bound in the same vaginal sheath with the tendon of M. flexor digitorum profundus. The tendon of the flexor digitorum superficialis is anchored to the base of the proximal phalanx of digit II by fascia, but the tendon continues distad and inserts on the anteromedial corner near the distal end of the proximal phalanx of digit II.

31. M. Flexor Digitorum Profundus

a. *Columba livia.* M. flexor digitorum profundus, a deeply situated muscle, arises by fleshy fibers from the ventral surface of the ulna, beginning posterior to the distal half of the inserting fibers of M. brachialis. The belly (about 35 mm in length) passes distad superficial to the belly of M. ulnimetacarpalis ventralis and ends on a tendon at the level of the os ulnare. The tendon of insertion passes through a groove on the anterior surface of the os ulnare and then around the anterior surface of the pisiform process of the carpometacarpus. The tendon continues distad in a groove on the surface of M. abductor indicis; proximally, the tendon is almost completely concealed by the belly of the muscle. The tendon crosses superficial to the tendon of M. flexor digitorum superficialis near the distal end of the carpometacarpus and inserts on the anterior edge, near the base, of the distal phalanx of digit II.

b. *Agelaius phoeniceus.* M. flexor digitorum profundus arises from the ventral surface of the ulna, beginning at the proximal end of the bone and extending distad to the origin of M. ulnimetacarpalis ventralis. The origin is V-shaped proximally, where small heads arise on either side of the area of insertion of M. brachialis. The well developed belly (about 18 mm long) extends slightly less than two-thirds the way down the forearm. The tendon of insertion passes through a groove on the anterior surface of the os ulnare and then around the anterior surface of the pisiform process. The tendon continues distad in the manus, running superficial to the tendon of M. flexor digitorum superficialis in the distal two-thirds of the carpometacarpus, and inserts on the ventral surface of the basal half of the distal (second) phalanx of digit II.

c. *Comparative data.* Situated in the deep stratum of muscles on the ventral surface of the forearm, the general relations of this muscle are similar in most birds. The area on the ventral surface of the ulna from which the fleshy fibers arise is directly related to the length and area of origin of M. ulnimetacarpalis ventralis. In certain cuckoos (Berger, 1953, 1954, 1960a) and in *Indicator,* where the latter muscle is short and is limited to the distal end of the ulna, M. flexor digitorum profundus has a long origin. It has a relatively short origin in some cuckoos, in *Gavia, Grus, Chordeiles,* and *Sturnus,* in which genera M. ulnimetacarpalis ventralis is one-third or more the length of the forearm. The fleshy fibers of the profundus may arise as far proximally as the humeroulnar pulley (e.g., *Crotophaga, Pharomachrus, Coracias, Upupa*), but in most birds the belly arises near the area of insertion of M. brachialis. In *Grus, Galli-*

columba, Chrysococcyx, Otus, Chloroceryle, Indicator, Procnias, Sturnus, Fregilupus, Paradisaea, and *Corvus,* there are two small heads of origin, one arising on either side of the area of insertion of M. brachialis. The single head arises posterior to that muscle in *Goura, Aceros, Coccyzus, Crotophaga, Geococcyx,* and *Coracias.*

M. flexor digitorum profundus has two distinct bellies in *Eugenes fulgens* and in *Chaetura pelagica.* The typical belly in *Eugenes* arises by two small heads, one on either side of the insertion of M. brachialis. The larger, and most unusual, belly (5 mm long) arises by a tendon (shared with M. pronator superficialis) from the humerus and by a large mass of fleshy fibers from the humerus distal to the origin of the tendon. This belly gives rise to an aponeurosis which fuses with the distal end of the typical belly and contributes to the formation of its tendon of insertion. The tendon has a typical course around the pisiform process and along the surface of the small belly of M. abductor indicis; the tendon passes distad along the anterior or leading edge of the proximal phalanx of digit II and inserts on the base of the distal phalanx.

M. flexor digitorum profundus is unusual in *Chaetura* not only because it has two bellies but also because the muscle is superficial in position for the entire length of the belly (about 10 mm). The typical ulnar belly arises from the most proximal end of the ulna. The humeral belly has a very large semitendinous origin from the humerus, beginning just proximal to the origin of M. pronator superficialis and extending distad posterior to its origin. The two bellies fuse and give rise to a large tendon of insertion. Near the distal end of the proximal phalanx of digit II, the tendon swings around a bony pulley and passes *dorsad* to insert on a tubercle projecting downward from the anterodorsal corner of the base of the distal phalanx of digit II.

The tendon of insertion of M. flexor digitorum profundus passes through a groove on the anterior surface of the os ulnare and then around the pisiform process of the carpometacarpus. In the hand, the tendon passes distad in a groove on the surface of M. abductor indicis (when present), crosses superficial to the flexor digitorum superficialis tendon (often enclosed within a common sheath with it), and inserts on the distal phalanx (second in most birds; third in *Gavia* and *Chen*) of digit II. The area of insertion rarely (e.g., *Grus, Chordeiles*) is more proximal than the insertion of M. flexor digitorum superficialis.

The tendon of insertion is unusual in *Otus asio* in that a strong branch is sent to the pollex; this branch passes superficial to M. flexor pollicis and to the tendon of insertion of M. abductor pollicis. The main tendon of M. flexor digitorum profundus continues distad along the carpometacarpus and inserts on the base of the distal phalanx of digit II. The branch to the pollex was mentioned by Gadow and Selenka (1891: pp. 280–281).

32. M. Entepicondyloulnaris

Comparative data. This has been called the "gallinaceous" muscle. It is said to be found only in *Apteryx*, the Tinamiformes, and the Galliformes (except *Opisthocomus*). In *Crax rubra* (Berger, 1955b), it is a triangular-shaped muscle, arising tendinously from the humerus in common with M. flexor digitorum superficialis and M. pronator profundus. It inserts by fleshy fibers on the proximal end of the ulna, posterior to the insertion of M. brachialis and anterior to the humerocarpal band, which, in this species, represents most of M. flexor digitorum superficialis. Hudson and Lanzillotti (1955: Fig. 35) illustrated this muscle in *Dendragapus obscurus* (Fig. IX.38).

33. M. Flexor Carpi Ulnaris

a. Columba livia. This large muscle arises by a stout tendon from the distal end of the medial epicondyle (entepicondyle) of the humerus. The tendon passes through a strong ligamentous loop, the *humeroulnar pulley,* and then gives rise to a large fusiform belly, which extends the entire length of the forearm and inserts on the entire proximal face of the os ulnare. A posterior fleshy bundle splits off the posterior surface of the main belly, extends distad about one-third the way down the forearm, and inserts on the fascia surrounding the middle group of secondaries and their under coverts. Fleshy fibers pass posteriorly from the main belly and insert on the distal secondaries.

b. Agelaius phoeniceus. M. flexor carpi ulnaris arises by a strong tendon from the distal end of the medial epicondyle of the humerus. The tendon passes through a humeroulnar pulley and gives rise to a 19 mm-long belly, which extends two-thirds the way down the forearm before ending on a stout tendon. The tendon inserts on most of the proximal face of the os ulnare. Near its distal end, the belly gives rise to a small fleshy fasciculus, which ends on a flat tendon; this tendon inserts on the os ulnare dorsal to the insertion of the main tendon, but it also has fascial extensions which attach to the bases of the outer secondary feathers and their under coverts.

c. Comparative data. M. flexor carpi ulnaris is the largest muscle in the forearm in many birds. It arises by a short, stout tendon from the distal end of the medial epicondyle of the humerus. The tendon (sometimes containing a sesamoid bone) passes through a ligamentous loop, the *humeroulnar pulley,* which has attachments to the inner aspect of the medial epicondyle and to the posterior surface of the ulna, just distal to its proximal articular surface. The bulk of the fusiform belly of M. flexor carpi ulnaris may be limited to the proximal third of the forearm (e.g., *Grus*), to the proximal half (*Upupa*, passerines), or it may extend nearly the entire length of the forearm (Columbidae, many cuckoos, *Coracias, Indicator*). The relationships of the belly to the humerocarpal band have been described earlier in this chapter.

The main insertion of M. flexor carpi ulnaris is by means of a strong tendon on the proximal surface of the os ulnare; in *Tauraco leucotis* and some cuckoos this is the only insertion. In many birds (Anhimidae, Anatidae, Gruidae, Columbidae, Cuculidae, Caprimulgidae, *Chaetura, Colius, Pharomachrus, Chloroceryle*, Bucerotidae, *Indicator*, some passerines), a second, smaller fleshy belly arises from the deep surface of the tendon of origin and/or from the humeroulnar pulley. This belly sends fleshy fasciculi to the calami of a variable number of secondaries in the cuckoos (the eight distal secondaries in *Coua caerulea*). In *Paradisaea rubra*, the posterior belly inserts on the bases of the secondaries by fleshy fibers proximally and by an aponeurosis distally. In *Grus americana* the smaller posterior belly is present, but the attachments to the secondaries are entirely aponeurotic (Fisher and Goodman, 1955). Almost half of the belly is diverted to act on the secondaries in *Aceros undulatus;* a series of small fleshy fasciculi give rise to tendons which insert on the calami of secondaries two through eleven, and two separate tendons branch off the main tendon to insert on secondaries two and three.

M. flexor carpi ulnaris has a typical tendinous origin from the humerus in *Otus asio*. Fleshy fibers arise from the tendon as soon as it emerges through the humeroulnar pulley and form a wide belly, which, however, divides to form two bellies about one-third the way down the forearm. The ventral, typical, belly (about 35 mm long) ends on a very heavy, rounded tendon, which inserts on the ventral edge of the os ulnare. The slightly larger posterior belly also is about 35 mm long. Its tendon forms on the dorsal edge of the belly and inserts on the os ulnare dorsal, but adjacent, to the tendon of the anterior belly. The posterior belly and its tendon of insertion are closely associated by means of aponeurotic slips with the bases of the secondaries. Both bellies are intimately covered by the humerocarpal band complex of M. flexor digitorum superficialis.

Beddard (1898: p. 88) reports that M. flexor carpi ulnaris is represented by a tendon in penguins. Lowe (1942) described and illustrated M. flexor carpi ulnaris in *Rhea, Opisthocomus*, and *Lophoceros*, in which genera the posterior (postaxial) belly is much larger than the anterior (preaxial) belly.

34. M. Ulnimetacarpalis Ventralis (Flexor Carpi Ulnaris Brevis)

a. *Columba livia.* The belly of this muscle (about 28 mm long) is located in the distal half of the forearm deep to the belly and tendon of M. flexor digitorum profundus. M. ulnimetacarpalis ventralis arises by fleshy fibers from the ventral surface of the ulna, primarily distal to the origin of M. flexor digitorum profundus, but it also has a 14 mm-long head which arises posterior to that muscle. The belly ends on a very large, flat tendon, which passes dorsad in a groove on the os radiale and inserts on the anterodorsal corner of the external carpal trochlea.

b. *Agelaius phoeniceus.* M. ulnimetacarpalis ventralis arises by fleshy fibers from the ventral surface of the ulna in approximately its middle third. The belly is V-shaped proximally, where small heads arise on either side of the most distal origin of M. flexor digitorum profundus. The greatest length of the belly (posteriorly) of M. ulnimetacarpalis ventralis is 15 mm. The belly and tendon of insertion pass distad deep to the distal end of the belly of M. flexor digitorum profundus. The tendon makes a sharp turn distally at the end of the ulna, then winds around the distal surface of the os radiale, passing from its ventral to dorsal side, and inserts on the anterodorsal corner of the base of the carpometacarpus.

c. *Comparative data.* M. ulnimetacarpalis ventralis is the name given this muscle by Gadow and Selenka (1891: p. 272) and used by Hudson and Lanzillotti (1955). M. flexor carpi ulnaris brevis is the name used by Shufeldt (1890), Fisher (1946), Fisher and Goodman (1955), and by Berger (1960b). Sullivan (1962: p. 476) reports that embryological data reveal that this muscle is closely related to the development of M. flexor digitorum profundus and not to M. flexor carpi ulnaris.

M. ulnimetacarpalis ventralis is one of the deepest muscles on the flexor side of the forearm; it arises primarily from the ventral surface of the ulna. The muscle exhibits interesting differences in relative development in different birds. Its development appears to be correlated with locomotor habits in the cuckoos: the belly is very short, being limited to about the distal fourth of the ulna, in *Geococcyx, Morococcyx, Dromococcyx, Tapera, Crotophaga, Coua, Carpococcyx, Centropus, Phaenicophaeus,* and *Ceuthmochares;* it is relatively long in *Coccyzus, Piaya, Saurothera, Guira, Clamator, Cuculus, Chrysococcyx,* and *Surniculus* (Berger, 1960a). The muscle arises from about the middle third of the ventral and posterior surface of the ulna in the Corvidae (Hudson and Lanzillotti, 1955). The belly is limited to the distal fourth of the ulna in *Indicator;* to the distal third in *Goura;* to slightly more than the distal half in *Grus canadensis;* and to about the distal three-fourths in

Otus asio and *Sturnus vulgaris*. M. ulnimetacarpalis ventralis is much larger than M. flexor digitorum profundus in *Chordeiles minor* and arises from the ulna posterior, as well as distal, to the origin of the profundus muscle.

M. ulnimetacarpalis ventralis is unusually well developed in *Chaetura pelagica* and in *Eugenes fulgens*. In *Chaetura*, the belly (about 10 mm long) extends the entire length of the forearm; the fleshy fibers begin at the level of the base of the coronoid process. The insertion by a large flat tendon on the dorsal corner of the base of the carpometacarpus is typical. M. ulnimetacarpalis ventralis is unusual in *Eugenes fulgens* in that it arises by two separate heads. The typical head arises from the posterior surface of the ulna in most of its proximal four-fifths; the area of origin lies posterior to both the insertion of M. brachialis and the origin of M. flexor digitorum profundus. The accessory, but equally developed, head arises from the ventral and anterior surface of the ulna, beginning anterior to the insertion of M. brachialis and just distal to the insertion of M. biceps brachii; the accessory head also arises from approximately the proximal four-fifths of the ulna. The two heads fuse about one-third of the way down the forearm and give rise to a tendon near the distal end of the ulna. The wide, flat tendon of insertion has a typical course to the dorsal surface of the wrist to insert on the anterodorsal corner of the base of the carpometacarpus.

The strong tendon of insertion of M. ulnimetacarpalis ventralis passes through a groove on the os radiale, under cover of the tendons of Mm. extensor metacarpi radialis and extensor pollicis longus, to reach the dorsal surface of the manus, where the tendon inserts on the anterodorsal corner of the base of the carpometacarpus, in some birds adjacent to the area of origin of M. extensor pollicis brevis. Fibers of the latter muscle arise from the tendon of M. ulnimetacarpalis ventralis in some birds.

35. M. Extensor Metacarpi Radialis

a. Columba livia. This muscle has two distinct heads of origin in the Rock Dove. *Pars anconalis* has a semitendinous origin from the lateral epicondyle (ectepicondylar process) of the humerus. *Pars palmaris* has a large, primarily fleshy, origin from the epicondyle, both ventral and distal to the origin of pars anconalis. Pars palmaris fuses with the deep surface of pars anconalis, beginning just distal to the area of insertion of the tendon of M. tensor patagii brevis on the belly of pars anconalis. The fleshy belly of M. extensor metacarpi radialis extends about four-fifths the way down the forearm; it gives rise to a strong, flat tendon, which inserts on the extensor process of the carpometacarpus.

b. Agelaius phoeniceus. M. extensor metacarpi radialis is composed of a single belly extending about two-thirds the way down the forearm. The muscle has a strong fleshy and tendinous origin from the lateral epicondyle of the humerus. The belly ends on a strong, flat tendon, which passes through a wide groove on the dorsal surface of the distal end of the ulna and through a similar groove on the dorsal surface of the os radiale and then inserts on the extensor process of the carpometacarpus. The relations to the tendons of insertion of Mm. tensores patagii longus et brevis were described under those muscles. M. abductor pollicis arises from the tendon of M. extensor metacarpi radialis a short distance before its insertion.

c. Comparative data. Hudson and Lanzillotti (1955: p. 29) pointed out that the "M. extensor metacarpi ulnaris" of Gadow and Selenka (1891: p. 274) is a misprint; the name should read "M. extensor metacarpi radialis." Beddard (1898: p. 89) apparently was unaware of the typographical error in Gadow and Selenka and used the same name.

M. extensor metacarpi radialis arises by a strong tendon from the lateral epicondyle (*epicondylus lateralis humeri* of Hudson and Lanzillotti, 1955) of the humerus, and, in many birds, from the bone distal to the epicondyle. The origin may be by a tendon proximally and by fleshy fibers distally (e.g., *Coua, Eugenes, Chaetura,* Corvidae), or by fleshy fibers surrounded by a dense tendinous envelope (*Geococcyx, Crotophaga, Coccyzus, Paradisaea*). In some birds (e.g., *Grus, Rhinochetos, Goura, Columba, Aceros*), there are two distinct heads *pars anconalis* and *pars palmaris.* Pars anconalis arises by tendinous and fleshy fibers from the lateral epicondyle in *Aceros undulatus;* the smaller pars palmaris arises from the humerus by a 1 cm-wide tendon, which extends from the origin of pars anconalis distad to the origin of M. extensor digitorum communis. The fleshy belly of pars palmaris fuses with the belly of pars anconalis, from which a single tendon of insertion is formed. Both pars anconalis and pars palmaris give rise to separate tendons in *Grus americana* and *Grus canadensis;* the two tendons then fuse to form a single, ossified tendon of insertion. In addition to the typical insertion on the extensor process of the carpometacarpus, part of the tendon fuses with the tendon of M. extensor pollicis longus (= extensor longus digiti II); these relationships were illustrated for *Grus americana* by Fisher and Goodman (1955).

The fleshy belly of M. extensor metacarpi radialis may extend nearly the full length of the forearm (e.g., many cuckoos), about three-fourths the way down the forearm (*Gallicolumba*), about two-thirds (*Procnias*), or may be limited to the proximal half (*Chloroceryle*) or less than half the length of the forearm (*Goura*).

The belly of M. extensor metacarpi radialis is hypertrophied in *Eu-*

genes and *Chaetura*. The origin, development of the belly, and its relationships to the insertion of M. tensor patagii brevis in *Chaetura pelagica* are essentially the same as illustrated for *Hirund-apus giganteus* by Lowe (1939).

One of the characteristic features of M. extensor metacarpi radialis is that all or part of the tendon of insertion of M. tensor patagii brevis is anchored to, or inserts on, the belly or tendon of origin.

36. M. Extensor Metacarpi Ulnaris (*Extensor Carpi Ulnaris; Flexor Metacarpi Radialis*)

a. Columba livia. This muscle arises by a strong, flat tendon (shared with M. anconeus) from the lateral epicondyle (ectepicondyle) of the humerus. A strong aponeurosis passes posteriorly from the tendon to attach, in part, to the ulna (the *ulnar anchor*) about 12 mm distal to the tip of the olecranon, and, in part, to fuse with the fascia around the bases of the proximal secondaries and their upper coverts. The fleshy fibers of M. extensor metacarpi ulnaris arise from the tendon about 7 mm distal to its humeral origin. The belly (about 36 mm long) extends to within 6 mm of the distal end of the ulna, where it gives rise to a strong, round tendon. The tendon passes through a groove on the external ulnar condyle, posterior and deep to the tendon of M. extensor digitorum communis. As it crosses the dorsal surface of the wrist joint, the tendon of M. extensor metacarpi ulnaris is reinforced by a strong ligament, which splits off the dorsal ulnarcarpometacarpal ligament; the tendon inserts on the posterior surface of metacarpal II, at about the midlength of the carpometacarpus.

b. Agelaius phoeniceus. M. extensor metacarpi ulnaris arises by a flat tendon from the distal end of the humerus posterior to the origin of M. extensor digitorum communis. The 4 mm-long tendon gives rise to a tough, aponeurotic band which passes posteriorly and proximally to attach to the dorsal surface of the base of the ulna, thus forming an ulnar anchor. The fleshy belly of M. extensor metacarpi ulnaris takes its origin from the apex of the resulting V-shaped tendon of origin. The belly (20 mm long) extends a little more than two-thirds the way down the forearm before ending on a small tendon. The tendon passes along the anterodorsal surface of the ulna, expands, and makes a sharp turn posteriorly around a bony tubercle on the anterodorsal corner of the external condyle of the ulna. The tendon then passes posteriorly over the dorsal surface of the external condyle and the wrist to enter the hand. The tendon inserts on the posterior corner of metacarpal III a short distance beyond the proximal limit of the intermetacarpal space.

c. *Comparative data.* This muscle was called the flexor metacarpi radialis by Tiedemann as early as 1810. Other writers using this name are
Shufeldt (1890: p. 128), Beddard (1898: p. 90), Burt (1930: p. 493),
Fisher (1946: p. 593), Fisher and Goodman (1955: p. 61), Berger (1953–
1960,) and Swinebroad (1954: p. 507). Watson (1883: p. 95) and Hudson and Lanzillotti (1955: p. 32) called it the extensor carpi ulnaris.
Gadow and Selenka (1891: p. 276–277) called it M. extensor metacarpi
ulnaris and pointed out that the muscle belongs to the extensor group
but that it has secondarily assumed a flexor function owing to the modified structure of the wrist and hand in birds. There is no question but
that the muscle belongs to the extensor group of muscles; its origin,
position, and nerve supply would seem to be diagnostic.

The differences in terminology for this muscle are primarily a reflection
of the several schools of thought on how a muscle should be named: on
the basis of function, origin and insertion, or on embryology and homology. In the present instance, we are dealing with a muscle which flexes
the extended hand (metacarpals) and aids in flexing the forearm.
Whether one prefers to call this muscle a flexor or an extensor, I believe
that the term "metacarpi" should be included in the name.

In most birds, M. extensor metacarpi ulnaris arises by a roughly
L-shaped tendinous band, whose proximal (primary) attachment is to
the lateral epicondyle of the humerus or to the lateral supracondylar
ridge proximal to the epicondyle. The tendon arises proximal to the
origin of M. anconeus and passes distad superficial to Mm. anconeus
and extensor digitorum communis. The distal (secondary) attachment
is primarily on the proximal end of the anconal surface of the ulna. Functionally, this *ulnar anchor* serves as an accessory origin which improves
the muscle's angle of pull (thus considered by Hudson and Lanzillotti,
1955), but, phylogenetically, it probably represents a secondary area of
insertion (thus considered by Fisher, 1946; Fisher and Goodman, 1955).
The distal attachment may also extend to the bases of several of the
proximal secondaries (e.g., *Polihiërax, Aceros*) or it may attach exclusively to the secondaries (many cuckoos). The ulnar anchor exhibits an
especially peculiar development in *Eugenes fulgens.* In this hummingbird, the ulnar anchor curves around the posterior border of the ulna
(just distal to the base of the olecranon) and fuses with the humeroulnar
pulley on the palmar (ventral) side of the forearm. The anchor contains
within it an enormous (for the size of the bird) sesamoid bone, which
extends from the posterior border of the tendon of origin and belly of
M. extensor metacarpi ulnaris on the dorsal side of the forearm almost
to the attachment of the anchor to the humeroulnar pulley on the ventral
surface of the forearm. One assumes that this sesamoid is related to ro-

tatory movements of the proximal end of the ulna at the elbow joint. In *Otus asio* M. extensor metacarpi ulnaris arises from the superficial surface of a common tendon shared with M. anconeus.

The fleshy fibers of M. extensor metacarpi ulnaris begin at the level of, or distal to, the ulnar attachment of the tendon of origin. The belly extends nearly to the distal end of the forearm in *Chaetura, Pharomachrus,* and *Indicator;* it extends about three-fourths the length of the forearm in *Geococcyx* and about one-half its length in *Grus, Chloroceryle,* and *Corvus.*

The tendon of insertion of M. extensor metacarpi ulnaris passes around the lateral surface of the external ulnar condyle in a fibro-osseous canal and inserts on the carpometacarpus. The tendon inserts at the proximal limit of the intermetacarpal space in *Grus,* in *Tauraco,* and in cuckoos; it inserts distal to the proximal limit of the intermetacarpal space in *Gallicolumba* and *Chordeiles.* The tendon may insert on metacarpal II (Cathartidae, *Goura, Chaetura, Pharomachrus*) or on metacarpal III (*Aceros, Upupa, Indicator, Procnias, Paradisaea, Spizella,* Corvidae). In *Cathartes* there is a secondary attachment to fascia of the hand; in *Sarcoramphus* "the inserting tendon, besides attaching to metacarpal II, is continuous with the central tendon of M. interosseous dorsalis" (Fisher, 1946: p. 593). Some of the fleshy fibers of M. interosseous dorsalis arise from the tendon of insertion of M. extensor metacarpi ulnaris in *Gallicolumba.*

37. M. Extensor Digitorum Communis

a. Columba livia. This muscle arises by a common tendon (shared with M. supinator) from the lateral epicondyle of the humerus. The relatively small belly (30 mm long) tapers to a tendon about 11 mm from the distal end of the ulna. The tendon passes through a groove on the external ulnar condyle and into the hand, where the tendon bifurcates. A short branch inserts on a tubercle on the posterior edge of the pollex, about 3 mm from its base. The long tendon passes distad in a shallow groove on the dorsal surface of metacarpal II, anterior to the tendon of M. extensor indicis longus, until it reaches the middle of the carpometacarpus, beyond which the tendon turns posteriorly and passes deep to the tendon of M. extensor indicis longus. The long tendon of M. extensor digitorum communis passes through a deep groove near the distal end of the carpometacarpus, makes a diagonal turn anteriorly, and inserts deep to the tendon of M. extensor indicis longus on the anterodorsal corner of the base of the proximal phalanx of digit II.

b. Agelaius phoeniceus. M. extensor digitorum communis arises by a tendon from the distal surface of the base of the ectepicondylar process

of the humerus just distal to the insertion of the humeral tendon of
M. tensor patagii brevis. The belly of M. extensor digitorum communis
(about 19 mm long) passes down the forearm superficial to M. supinator
and gives rise to a tendon about two-thirds the way down the forearm.
The tendon passes through a fibrous covered groove on the distal end of
the ulna and then runs diagonally forward to the base of the pollex,
where the tendon bifurcates. A short fibrous branch inserts on the posteroproximal corner of the pollex. The main tendon makes a right-angle
turn around a bony process on metacarpal II and runs distad on the
anterodorsal surface of that bone. About two-thirds the way out the
carpometacarpus, the tendon passes deep to the tendon of M. extensor
indicis longus, continues distad in a groove on the dorsal surface of the
carpometacarpus, makes a sharp turn around a bony flange near the distal end of metacarpal II, and inserts on the anterodorsal corner of the
base of the proximal phalanx of digit II.

   c. *Comparative data.* In most birds, M. extensor digitorum communis
arises from the lateral epicondyle of the humerus, deep to the tendon
of origin of M. extensor metacarpi ulnaris. M. extensor digitorum communis shares a common tendinous origin with M. supinator in *Otus* and
Columba. Fisher and Goodman (1955: p. 60) appear to be the only authors who have described an accessory fleshy origin from the radius, as
well as a tendinous origin from the humerus. They pointed out that it
is the origin from the proximal third of the radius in the Whooping
Crane that "makes the muscle bipennate on its deep side." I found a
similar bipennate pattern in the Quetzal (*Pharomachrus mocino*), in
which M. extensor digitorum communis arises not only by a tendon
from the humerus but also by fleshy fibers for a distance of 25 mm on
the proximal end of the radius.

   The belly of M. extensor digitorum communis lies in the proximal
half to three-fourths of the forearm in most birds. The belly is poorly
developed in *Goura* and occupies less than the proximal half of the forearm in *Coracias abyssinica.*

   The tendon of insertion of M. extensor digitorum communis passes
through a fibrous-covered groove on the external ulnar condyle and into
the hand, where the tendon bifurcates near the base of the pollex in
most birds. The shorter, and in most birds the weaker, branch inserts on
or near the base of the pollex; in *Gavia immer,* this branch is the
stronger of the two. The longer branch runs distad along the anterodorsal surface of the carpometacarpus to about its midlength, at which
point, the tendon turns posteriorly, passing deep to the tendon of M. extensor indicis longus. The tendon of M. extensor digitorum communis
typically passes through a groove near the distal end of the carpo-

metacarpus, takes a sharp turn anteriorly at the distal end of that bone, then passes deep to the tendon of M. extensor indicis longus a second time, and inserts on or near the anterodorsal corner of the base of the proximal phalanx of digit II; in some birds (e.g., cuckoos), the tendon inserts on the posterodorsal corner of the proximal phalanx. In the Tree Sparrow (*Spizella arborea*), the tendon passes through a bony canal on the anterior edge of the carpometacarpus opposite the base of the pollex. According to Beddard (1898: p. 88), no tendon is sent to the pollex in *Struthio*, and the entire muscle is absent in *Rhea*, and is represented by a tendon in penguins.

M. extensor digitorum communis is hypertrophied in *Eugenes fulgens*. The muscle arises largely by fleshy fibers from the expanded portion of the humerus distal to the ectepicondyle. The tendon of insertion passes around a large bony tubercle on the distal end of the ulna and enters the hand. The tendon does not bifurcate; no branch is sent to the pollex. The tendon passes diagonally forward to about the midlength of the carpometacarpus, where the tendon turns around a bony ridge on the anterior edge of that bone. The tendon then passes diagonally posteriorly and distally in a deep groove on the dorsal surface of the carpometa-carpus. At the distal end of that bone, the tendon turns anteriorly around the posterior surface of a large bony tubercle and inserts on the base of the proximal phalanx of digit II. There is a large sesamoid in the tendon where it crosses the carpometacarpophalangeal joint.

38. M. Anconeus (Ectepicondyloulnaris)

a. Columba livia. This deeply situated muscle arises from the deep surface of a common tendon (shared with M. extensor metacarpi ulnaris) from the lateral epicondyle of the humerus. The fleshy belly (about 30 mm long) inserts on the anterodorsal surface of the ulna, beginning about 12 mm distal to the tip of the olecranon and extending distad about three-fifths the length of the ulna.

b. Agelaius phoeniceus. M. anconeus has the most distal origin of the extensor muscles arising from the humerus. It arises by a tendon distal to the origin of M. extensor metacarpi ulnaris. The flat tendon crosses the elbow and gives rise to a fleshy belly 15 mm long, which inserts primarily by fleshy fibers on the anterodorsal surface of the ulna in approximately its proximal half.

c. Comparative data. It should be understood that this muscle is in no way related to the muscle which Fürbringer (1902: p. 563) called M. anconaeus (=M. triceps brachii) or which Beddard (1898: p. 84) called M. anconaeus longus (=M. scapulotriceps). M. anconeus is M. ectepicondylo-ulnaris of Gadow and Selenka (1891: p. 268).

Arising by a tendon from the lateral epicondyle or the lateral supra-condylar ridge of the humerus, the fleshy fibers of M. anconeus pass distad deep to the tendon and belly of M. extensor metacarpi ulnaris to insert on the ulna. In many birds (e.g., *Chen, Chaetura, Gallicolumba, Otus, Chloroceryle*), M. anconeus arises from the deep surface of a common tendon shared with M. extensor metacarpi ulnaris. In *Aceros undulatus* there are two tendons of origin and two bellies, which fuse before inserting on the ulna.

Gadow and Selenka (1891: p. 269) report that M. anconeus exhibits its best development in the Galliformes, Turnicidae, Columbidae, and Tinamidae, in which groups it extends nearly the entire length of the ulna; the muscle is small in *Uria, Phalacrocorax* (=*Carbo*), and *Podiceps*. The belly of M. anconeus extends less than half the length of the forearm in *Chordeiles minor;* about one-half the length of the ulna in *Grus, Goura,* the Cathartidae, and the Corvidae; about two-thirds its length in *Paradisaea;* and about three-fourths its length in many cuckoos. Watson (1883: p.92) did not find this muscle in the penguins.

39. M. Supinator

a. Columba livia. The supinator muscle arises from the anterior and deep surfaces of a common tendon (shared with M. extensor digitorum communis) from the distal end of the humerus, just proximal to the origin of M. extensor metacarpi ulnaris. The relatively bulky belly (31 mm long) of M. supinator inserts on the anterior surface of the radius in slightly more than the proximal two-thirds of the bone; the belly extends to within about 14 mm of the distal end of the radius.

b. Agelaius phoeniceus. M. supinator is a relatively long (10 mm), thin muscle in the blackbird. The muscle arises by a fine tendon from the humerus distal to the origin of M. extensor digitorum communis. The muscle inserts by fleshy fibers on the anterodorsal surface of the radius in approximately its proximal one-third.

c. Comparative data. Some authors have called this muscle M. supinator brevis, but, inasmuch as there is no supinator longus, Hudson and Lanzillotti (1955) and Berger (1960a,b) dropped "brevis" from the name. This is M. ectepicondyloradialis of Gadow and Selenka (1891: p. 269).

M. supinator is, in most birds, a long thin muscle closely applied to the anterior surface of the proximal end of the radius. The muscle arises tendinously from the lateral epicondyle of the humerus, between the origins of M. anconeus and M. extensor digitorum communis. M. supinator arises from the deep side of a common tendon shared with M. extensor digitorum communis in *Otus asio*. M. supinator is especially weakly developed in *Fregilupus, Dendroica,* and *Spizella;* it is relatively weakly developed in *Chordeiles* and *Upupa.* The muscle is, relative to the size of the bird, strongly developed in *Eugenes fulgens;* the belly (about 4 mm long) arises by a strong tendon (1.5 mm long) from a tubercle on the distal end of the humerus. M. supinator inserts by fleshy fibers on the anterior surface of the radius in its proximal quarter in *Sturnus vulgaris,* the proximal half in *Goura victoria,* the proximal two-thirds in *Crotophaga sulcirostris,* and the proximal three-fourths in *Gallicolumba luzonica.*

40. *M. Extensor Indicis Longus (Extensor Longus Digiti III)*

a. Columba livia. M. extensor indicis longus is a long (30 mm), relatively thin muscle, arising solely from the posterior surface of the radius, beginning about 12 mm from the proximal end of the bone. The belly gives rise to a flat tendon, which curves around the anterior surface of the external ulnar condyle and into the hand. A strong ligament extends from the distal end of the ulna to the base of digit II; this ligament passes superficial to the tendon of M. extensor indicis longus and acts as a vaginal sheath, which holds the tendon close to the bone. The ligament splits near the distal end of the carpometacarpus, sending one branch anteriorly to attach to ligaments and fascia covering the anterior corner of the base of the proximal phalanx of digit II, and sending a second branch posteriorly (superficial to the tendon of M. extensor indicis longus) to attach to the fascia around the bases of the primaries along the proximal phalanx of digit II. The tendon of M. extensor indicis longus is anchored to ligaments at the distal end of the carpometacarpus but the tendon continues distad to insert on the base of the distal phalanx of digit II; the tendon contains a large sesamoid at the distal end of the carpometacarpus and a small sesamoid just proximal to the insertion on digit II.

A distal head (=M. flexor metacarpi brevis) of M. extensor indicis longus arises from the portion of the joint capsule spanning the interval between the distal end of the os ulnare and the anteroproximal corner of the carpometacarpus. The triangular-shaped belly (about 8 mm long) tapers to a short tendon, which inserts on the anteroventral edge of the tendon of M. extensor indicis longus.

b. Agelaius phoeniceus. The belly (about 20 mm long) of M. extensor indicis longus is unusually long and well developed for the size of the bird. The muscle arises by fleshy fibers from the posterior surface of the radius in its proximal two-thirds. The tendon of insertion passes through a groove on the distal end of the external ulnar condyle to the base of the manus, where the tendon takes a diagonal course out the manus under

cover of the deep fascia and superficial to the tendon of M. flexor digitorum profundus. The tendon of M. extensor indicis longus crosses the
dorsal surface of the carpometacarpophalangeal joint superficial to the
tendon of insertion of the flexor digitorum profundus, then passes to the
anterior surface of the proximal phalanx of digit II, and inserts on a
tubercle on the anterior surface near the base of the distal (second)
phalanx of digit II.

    c. Comparative data. This is the extensor indicis proprius of Buri
(1900: p. 499); it is the extensor indicis longus plus the flexor metacarpi brevis muscles of Fisher (1946) and Berger (1953–1960); it is the
extensor longus digiti III of Fisher and Goodman (1955); it is the extensor medius longus of Sullivan (1962).

    M. extensor indicis longus arises from the ulnar surface of the radius in
most birds. Hudson and Lanzillotti (1955) reported an anomolous origin
from the ulna in single specimens of *Cyanocorax* (unilateral) and *Aphe-
locoma* (bilateral). There is much variation in the length of the belly of
the muscle and in its area of origin from the radius among birds. The
belly arises by fleshy fibers from the proximal four-fifths of the radius in
Paradisaea rubra; from the proximal three-fifths to two-thirds in the
Corvidae; from the middle third in *Geococcyx, Crotophaga,* and *Coccyzus;* from the third quarter in *Chen;* from approximately the distal two-
thirds in *Coua caerulea;* from the distal half in *Goura victoria;* from the
distal third in *Gavia immer.*

    M. extensor indicis longus is said to be absent in *Rhea* (Beddard,
1898: p. 503). The muscle is almost rudimentary in the cranes and hornbills. In a bird the size of the Sandhill Crane, for example, the very small,
spindle-shaped belly is 12 cm in length but it has a maximum width of
only 3 mm; it arises from the posterior surface of about the distal half of
the radius. The similarly small belly in the Whooping Crane arises from
the middle third of the radius (Fisher and Goodman, 1955). In *Aceros
undulatus,* the spindle-shaped belly is 4.5 cm long but only about 2 mm
in maximum width; the muscle arises from the midportion of the radius,
beginning 5 cm from the proximal end of that bone, at the distal end
of the area of insertion of M. pronator profundus. M. extensor indicis
longus is strongly developed in *Chaetura pelagica* and in *Eugenes fulgens.*
In *Eugenes* the belly extends the entire length of the forearm and increases in size distally. A very strong dorsal radioulnar ligament holds
the distal end of the belly and the tendon of insertion in place at the
distal end of the forearm. The tendon inserts on the anterior edge of the
base of the distal phalanx of digit II. The tendon contains small sesamoids
where it crosses the joint between the carpometacarpus and the proximal

phalanx of digit II and also where the tendon crosses the interphalangeal joint. Similar sesamoids occur in the tendon at the distal end of the carpometacarpus in *Chordeiles* and *Chloroceryle*.

M. extensor indicis longus typically inserts on the base of the distal phalanx of digit II, between the areas of insertion of Mm. interosseous dorsalis and flexor digitorum profundus; in *Apteryx australis*, however, the tendon inserts on the carpometacarpus (Beddard, 1898: p. 503). In *Aceros undulatus*, the primary insertion is on the anterodorsal corner of the base of phalanx 2, but posterior extensions of the tendon insert on the bases of the digital primaries. In *Geococcyx californianus*, the tendon inserts adjacent to the tendon of M. interosseous dorsalis, from which area of common insertion there are fascial extensions to the distal end of digit II. In *Sarcoramphus* the tendon inserts "a third of the way out phalanx 2" of digit II (Fisher, 1946). In *Gavia immer* and *Chen hyperboreal*, in which digit II has three phalanges, M. extensor indicis longus inserts on the anterodorsal corner of the middle phalanx.

The distal head of M. extensor indicis longus (M. flexor metacarpi brevis). In some birds (e.g., *Rhea, Chen, Polihiërax, Goura, Podargus, Caprimulgus, Colius,* and some genera of cuckoos), there is a distal head to M. extensor indicis longus, which arises from various structures near the wrist: e.g., the distal end of the radius, the os radiale, the base of the carpometacarpus and associated ligaments. The small fleshy head gives rise to a tendon which inserts on the tendon of the *proximal* or *radial head* of M. extensor indicis longus.

Fisher (1946: p. 601) and Berger (1953–1960) refer to the distal head of M. extensor indicis longus as M. flexor metacarpi brevis. Hudson and Lanzillotti (1955) object to the use of this name because they, following Gadow and Selenka (1891: p. 285), consider it to be a short distal head of M. extensor indicis longus. They also "deplore the coining of names simply because the muscles have not been properly identified," and they suggest that the name flexor metacarpi brevis be dropped from the literature. Sullivan (1962, p. 502) reports that his embryological data support the interpretation of Hudson and Lanzillotti, but Sullivan does not present any details on the matter. Until such details are available, it might be equally reasonable to assume that two different muscles are involved and that the insertion of the brevis tendon on the tendon of M. extensor indicis longus represents a secondary condition. Such secondary, phylogenetic fusion of two unrelated muscles on a common tendon of insertion occurs in other vertebrate animals. Although they were unusually astute, Fürbringer and Gadow were not infallible in their analysis and interpretation of the myology and neurology of birds. Moreover, nothing new is added to our knowledge by quoting the nerve supply of muscles from Fürbinger (1888, 1902) or Gadow and Selenka (1891). It would seem to be scientifically naive *to assume* that the nerve supply of a muscle in one genus is the same in all other genera and families of birds.

Berger (1960a,b) continued to use the name flexor metacarpi brevis because of the potential taxonomic value of the muscle. We have very little information on the distribution of this muscle throughout the orders and families of birds. If one does object to the name flexor metacarpi brevis for this small muscle, one should make it clear in describing M. extensor indicis longus whether or not this accessory head is present. One of the best arguments for not using the name flexor metacarpi brevis is that Shufeldt (1890: p. 151) applied this name to an entirely different muscle (M. flexor metacarpi posterior =M. ulnimetacarpalis dorsalis). Sullivan (1962) called it M. extensor medius brevis.

M. flexor metacarpi brevis arises from the os radiale in the Cathartidae, in *Gallicolumba*, and in *Crotophaga sulcirostris;* from the base of the carpometacarpus in *Chrysococcyx cupreus* and *Coccyzus erythropthalmus;* from the capsule of the dorsal ulnare-carpometacarpal joint in *Polihiërax semitorquatus* and *Goura victoria.* M. flexor metacarpi brevis has a well developed fleshy belly (7mm long and 2 mm wide) in *Coracias abyssinica.* The muscle arises on the dorsal surface of the proximal end of the carpometacarpus posterior to the origin of M. extensor pollicis brevis. The belly tapers to a flat tendon, which inserts on the tendon of M. extensor indicis longus about half way out the carpometacarpus. In *Rhea*, M. extensor indicis longus is represented only by "the belly arising from the wrist" (Beddard, 1898: p. 503).

Buri (1900: p. 501; Plate 21) described M. flexor metacarpi brevis (*caput carpi*) in *Podargus, Caprimulgus*, and *Colius.* Berger can verify the presence of this muscle in *Chen hyperborea, Chen caerulescens, Polihiërax semitorquatus, Columba livia, Goura victoria, Gallicolumba luzonica, Otus asio, Chordeiles minor, Coracias abyssinica*, and some genera of cuckoos. Among cuckoos, M. flexor metacarpi brevis is absent in *Coua, Geococcyx, Morococcyx* and *Carpococcyx;* it is present in all other genera examined (Berger, 1960a). Berger can verify the absence of this muscle in *Gavia immer, Crax rubra, Grus canadensis, Tauraco leucotis, Aceros undulatus, Pharomachrus mocino, Chaetura pelagica, Eugenes fulgens, Upupa epops, Chloroceryle americana, Indicator variegatus, Procnias nudicollis, Paradisaea rubra, Sturnus vulgaris, Aplonis tabuensis, Artamella viridis, Fregilupus varius, Dendroica kirtlandii, Agelaius phoeniceus*, and *Spizella arborea.* Hudson and Lanzillotti (1955) did not find the muscle in the Corvidae.

41. M. *Extensor Pollicis Longus* (*Extensor Longus Digiti II*)

a. Columba livia. This well developed muscle (over-all length 40 mm) extends the entire length of the forearm; it is visible superficially in its distal half. The muscle has two fleshy heads of origin. The larger head arises for a distance of about 9 mm from the anterior surfaceof the proximal end of the ulna; the smaller head arises for a distance of 20 mm from the radius, beginning about 10 mm from the proximal end of the bone. The two heads fuse to form a single belly. Its tendon inserts on the proximodorsal surface of the extensor process deep to the insertion of M. extensor metacarpi radialis.

b. Agelaius phoeniceus. M. extensor pollicis longus is scarcely visible to the naked eye. The belly is about 9 mm long and 1 mm in maximum width near its origin from a small area 4 mm long on the anterior surface of the proximal end of the ulna, ventral to the radioulnar interosseous membrane. The thin, flat belly tapers to a minute tendon, which passes diagonally down the forearm dorsal to the belly of M. extensor indicis longus to reach the posterodorsal surface of the distal end of the radius, where the hairlike tendon fuses with the posterior edge of the tendon of insertion of M. extensor metacarpi radialis.

c. Comparative data. This is the "extensor ossis metacarpi pollicis" of Shufeldt (1890). Adopting the evidence on the numbering of the hand digits presented by Montagna (1945), Fisher and Goodman (1955: p. 39) accordingly changed the names of certain muscles that insert on the digits. They proposed that the present muscle be called M. extensor longus digiti II. While not accepting Montagna's evidence, Hudson and Lanzillotti (1955: p. 43), on the other hand, proposed that if there were name changes, M. extensor pollicis longus should be called "M. extensor indicis longus." This would be an unfortunate mistake for the obvious reason that one would then have two entirely different muscles known by the same name (see Sullivan, 1962: Table 1).

Typically, M. extensor pollicis longus is said to arise by two heads from the facing surfaces of the radius and ulna. The muscle lies in contact with the interosseous membrane and, when well developed (as in *Coua caerulea, Tauraco leucotis*), fills most of the interval between the radius and ulna in their proximal two-thirds. The belly occupies approximately the proximal half of the forearm in the Cathartidae. In most birds in which there are two heads, the ulnar head is larger than the radial head (e.g., Cathartidae, *Geococcyx, Crotophaga, Coccyzus, Tauraco*). In *Polihiërax semitorquatus* the longer radial head arises from the second quarter of the radius; the ulnar head arises from a small area on the proximal end of the ulna. Each head gives rise to a tendon; the two tendons fuse near the distal end of the forearm. In *Otus asio*, also, the primary origin is from the radius.

In a few genera for which specific data are available, there is but a single head to M. extensor pollicis longus. In *Paradisaea rubra*, for example, the single head arises from the radius and is limited to the distal third of the forearm. The muscle arises from the radius only in *Chen hyperborea*, in *Aceros undulatus*, and in *Paradisaea rubra*. The single head arises only from the ulna in *Pharomachrus mocino*, *Chloroceryle americana*, *Indicator variegatus*, *Procnias nudicollis*, *Fregilupus varius*, *Sturnus vulgaris*, the Corvidae, and, according to Swinebroad (1954), in *Passer domesticus*, *Richmonena cardinalis*, *Zonotrichia albicollis*, and *Melospiza melodia*.

M. extensor pollicis longus is rudimentary in *Eugenes fulgens*. The muscle is represented by a very long, thin, bandlike belly, arising from a small area on the proximal end of the ulna. The belly is composed primarily of aponeurotic fibers. The fine tendon of insertion ends on the tendon of M. extensor metacarpi radialis at the level of the os radiale, which is almost 3 mm proximal to the insertion on the extensor process of the carpometacarpus. The pollex in this hummingbird is completely embedded under the skin, so that there are no true alula quills.

The tendon of insertion of M. extensor pollicis longus passes through a fibrous-covered tendinal groove on the radius and the os radiale to insert on the extensor process of the carpometacarpus in most birds. The area of insertion usually is adjacent to the insertion of the tendon of M. extensor metacarpi radialis. In *Grus americana*, *Grus canadensis*, *Agelaius phoeniceus*, and in certain fringillids, the tendon of the extensor pollicis longus inserts on the distal end of the tendon of the extensor metacarpi radialis muscle for a common insertion on the extensor process. The insertion is peculiar in *Paradisaea rubra* in that the tendon ends on the posteroproximal corner of the os radiale; no trace of a tendon extending to the extensor process could be found (Berger, 1956b). In *Coccyzus erythropthalmus* fleshy fibers of M. extensor pollicis brevis arise from the distal end of the tendon of insertion of M. extensor pollicis longus.

42. *M. Ulnimetacarpalis Dorsalis* (*Flexor Metacarpi Posterior*)

a. Columba livia. This is a very strongly developed muscle, arising by a flat tendon (2.5 mm wide) from the dorsal surface of the distal end of the ulna just proximal to the lateral condyle. The large fleshy belly splits into three main bundles. These insert: (1) on the posterior surface of metacarpal III in its proximal half and on a fibrous septum between this muscle and fibers of origin of M. interosseus palmaris; (2) on the fascia around the bases of the proximal primaries; (3) by means of a long fleshy fasciculus which passes along the posterior edge of the hand to end by semitendinous fibers in the fascia along the posterior margin of digit III.

b. Agelaius phoeniceus. M. ulnimetacarpalis dorsalis is absent, being represented by a ligament only.

c. Comparative data. M. ulnimetacarpalis dorsalis is the name used by Gadow and Selenka (1891: p. 273) and Hudson and Lanzillotti (1955). It is the flexor metacarpi posterior of Fisher (1946), Fisher and Goodman (1955), and Berger (1960b). M. ulnimetacarpalis dorsalis is the preferred name, as pointed out by Sullivan (1962), if one names the muscles in accordance with their embryological origin rather than on the basis of function. The change also is made here, in the interest of standardization of the names for avian muscles.

M. ulnimetacarpalis dorsalis arises by a strong, flat tendon from a ridge or a tubercle on the anconal surface of the distal end of the ulna. Fleshy fibers cross the wrist joint to insert on the posterior surface of metacarpal III and on the bases of a variable number of metacarpal primaries. The muscle arises by a strong tendon from the distal end of the ulna and by a large bundle of fleshy fibers from the posterior surface of the os ulnare in *Chaetura pelagica.* The tendon gives rise to two bellies: (1) one belly inserts on the proximal 3 mm of the posterior surface of metacarpal III; (2) the other belly fuses with the fleshy bundle arising from the os ulnare. The common belly thus formed also gives rise to two fleshy fasciculi: (1) the posterior fasciculus inserts on the bases of the proximal primaries; (2) the anterior fasciculus inserts on some of the proximal primaries, but, in addition, gives rise to a well developed tendon, which continues to the end of the carpometacarpus, sending slips to the bases of the primaries.

The fleshy belly of M. ulnimetacarpalis dorsalis is exceptionally large in *Goura, Columba, Gallicolumba, Tauraco,* and in certain cuckoos; it is small in *Gavia, Chen, Aceros, Otus, Pharomachrus, Coracias, Chloroceryle,* and *Indicator.* When well developed, the muscle inserts by fleshy fibers on the posterior surface of metacarpal III throughout most of its length. The muscle is poorly developed or absent in most passerine birds; it is rudimentary in *Procnias nudicollis.* M. ulnimetacarpalis dorsalis is absent in *Eugenes fulgens, Dendroica kirtlandii, Agelaius phoeniceus,* and *Spizella arborea.*

43. M. Extensor Pollicis Brevis (*Extensor Brevis Digiti II*)

a. Columba livia. This relatively well developed muscle arises by fleshy fibers by two incompletely separated heads from the dorsal surface of the extensor process and from the anterodorsal surface of the base of the carpometacarpus. A few fibers arise from the tendon of insertion of M. ulnimetacarpalis ventralis. The two heads fuse on a short tendon, which inserts on a tubercle on the anterodorsal corner of the pollex.

b. *Agelaius phoeniceus.* This muscle is absent in the Red-winged Blackbird.

c. *Comparative data.* Fisher and Goodman (1955) called this muscle the extensor brevis digiti II. Hudson and Lanzillotti (1955) proposed that it be called "M. extensor indicis brevis."

This muscle arises from the anterodorsal surface of the base of the carpometacarpus, from the extensor process, and, occasionally, from the tendon of insertion of M. extensor pollicis longus. The muscle inserts either by fleshy fibers or by a tendon on the anterobasal corner of the pollex.

M. extensor pollicis brevis is a long, thin sheet of tendinous and fleshy fibers in *Gavia immer;* it is a large fleshy mass in *Chen hyperborea.* In *Geococcyx californianus* there is a second belly, which arises from the radialecarpometacarpal ligament; the two bellies fuse to insert together. The belly of this muscle is hypertrophied in *Chaetura pelagica;* the belly is 2.5 mm wide at its origin on the extensor process and the base of metacarpal II; the muscle is fleshy throughout most of its course but it has a semitendinous insertion on the pollex.

M. extensor pollicis brevis is absent in all passerine birds thus far investigated: *Procnias nudicollis, Fregilupus varius, Sturnus vulgaris, Aplonis tabuensis, Artamella viridis, Paradisaea rubra, Dendroica kirtlandii, Agelaius phoeniceus, Passer domesticus, Richmondena cardinalis, Spizella arborea, Zonotrichia albicollis, Melospiza melodia,* and the Corvidae.

44. M. Abductor Pollicis (Abductor Alae Digiti II)

a. *Columba livia.* This is a well developed complex composed of two intimately related bellies with an over-all fleshy length of about 13 mm. The superficial belly (9 mm long) arises by fleshy fibers from the ventral edge of the tendon of insertion of M. extensor metacarpi radialis. The belly gives rise to an aponeurosis which fuses with the superficial surface of the deep belly. The deep belly arises by a flat aponeurotic band (6 mm long) from the deep surface of the tendon of M. extensor metacarpi radialis. The common belly inserts by fleshy and tendinous fibers on approximately the basal half of the anteroventral surface of the pollex.

b. *Agelaius phoeniceus.* M. abductor pollicis is a small muscle (4.5 mm long) arising by tendinous fibers from the ventral edge of the tendon of insertion of M. extensor metacarpi radialis a short distance proximal to its attachment to the extensor process of the carpometacarpus. The belly of M. abductor pollicis passes outward ventral to the extensor process and inserts by tendinous fibers on the anteroventral surface of the pollex about a third the way out the bone.

c. Comparative data. This is the extensor proprius pollicis of Shufeldt (1890) and the abductor alae digiti II of Fisher and Goodman (1955). Hudson and Lanzillotti (1955) proposed the name of "M. abductor indicis," with which we heartily disagree for the same reason mentioned under M. extensor pollicis longus.

M. abductor pollicis arises from the tendon of insertion of M. extensor metacarpi radialis. In *Grus, Columba, Coua, Geococcyx, Crotophaga, Otus, Chaetura,* and *Chloroceryle,* there are two heads, one superficial and one deep. In *Coua caerulea,* for example, the larger superficial head arises by fleshy fibers from the tendon of insertion of M. extensor metacarpi radialis; a strong tendinous aponeurosis forms near the anterior edge of the superficial head; this aponeurosis inserts on somewhat more than half of the palmar surface of the pollex, forming a sheath over the deep belly. The smaller, deep, head of M. abductor pollicis arises by a tendon (5 mm long) from the deep surface of the tendon of M. extensor metacarpi radialis; the tendon gives rise to a fusiform belly about 5 mm long, which inserts by fleshy fibers on the basal half of the palmar surface of the pollex. In *Grus canadensis* one head arises from the tendon of M. extensor metacarpi radialis; the other head arises from the extensor process. M. abductor pollicis is well developed in *Eugenes fulgens,* even though the pollex lies deep to the skin.

M. abductor pollicis inserts by a tendon, by fleshy fibers, or by both. The muscle inserts on the base of the pollex (*Gavia, Paradisaea*), near the middle of the bone (*Chordeiles,* Corvidae), or on the proximal half or more of the palmar surface of the pollex (*Geococcyx, Coracias*).

45. M. Adductor Pollicis (*Adductor Alae Digiti II*)

a. Columba livia. This muscle arises from the anterior surface of metacarpal II, opposite the base of the pollex. The well developed fleshy belly passes outward to a semitendinous insertion on the distal 3 mm of the posterior surface of the pollex.

b. Agelaius phoeniceus. M. adductor pollicis is a very small muscle with a belly about 3 mm in length. It arises by a tendon from the anteroventral surface of the carpometacarpus opposite the articular facet for the pollex and just distal and anterior to the base of the pisiform process. The belly passes outward and inserts by fleshy fibers on most of the posterior surface of the pollex.

c. Comparative data. This is the "flexor brevis pollicis" of Shufeldt (1890); it is the adductor alae digiti II of Fisher and Goodman (1955). Hudson and Lanzillotti (1955) proposed the name "adductor indicis."

This small muscle arises by tendinous or fleshy fibers from the anterior surface of the carpometacarpus, near the base of the extensor process. The belly passes forward and outward to insert on a small (*Coua, Coracias*) or large (*Chen, Chaetura, Chloroceryle, Procnias, Paradisaea*) area on the posterior surface of the pollex. The fleshy fibers insert on the distal half of the pollex in *Chaetura*, on the basal two-thirds in *Chloroceryle*, and on most of the posterior surface in *Chen*. In *Chordeiles minor*, the muscle arises by fleshy fibers from the *palmar* surface of the carpometacarpus. The belly wraps around the anterior surface of that bone, passes outward and forward toward the pollex, and appears to insert entirely on the fascia surrounding the outermost alula quill; there is no direct insertion on bone. According to Beddard (1898: p. 89), M. adductor pollicis "ends in the ala spuria and not on the thumb bone" in *Palamedea*. I found no evidence of this muscle in a single specimen of *Aceros undulatus*.

46. M. Flexor Pollicis (*Flexor Digiti II*)

a. Columba livia. This well developed muscle arises by two separate heads, which fuse and have a large fleshy and tendinous insertion on the posteroventral corner of the pollex. The shorter, posterior head arises from the ligaments which form a vaginal sheath around the tendon of M. flexor digitorum profundus as it passes around the anterior surface of the pisiform process. The larger and longer anterior head arises from a fossa near the base of the carpometacarpus, proximal and anterior to the pisiform process.

b. Agelaius phoeniceus. M. flexor pollicis is absent in the blackbird.

c. Comparative data. This is the flexor digiti II of Fisher and Goodman (1955). Hudson and Lanzillotti (1955) proposed that the muscle be called "M. flexor indicis."

This short fleshy muscle arises from the ventral surface of the carpometacarpus, anterior to the pisiform process. The tendon of M. flexor digitorum profundus typically passes between the bellies of Mm. abductor indicis and flexor pollicis. Some fleshy fibers of the flexor pollicis muscle arise from the vaginal sheath covering the surface of M. flexor digitorum profundus in *Otus asio*. The belly may take origin from ligaments on the palmar surface of the wrist joint as well as from the carpometacarpus (e.g., *Chaetura pelagica*).

M. flexor pollicis inserts by either fleshy or tendinous fibers on or near the base of the pollex. M. flexor pollicis is absent in all passerine genera thus far investigated; it was "clearly observed in only one crow wing" out of a total of 28 wings of the crow and raven dissected by Hudson and Lanzillotti (1955). I did not find M. flexor pollicis in *Eugenes fulgens, Chloroceryle americana, Upupa epops,* or *Indicator variegatus.*

47. M. Abductor Indicis (Abductor Major Digiti III)

a. Columba livia. Relative to its development in many birds, M. abductor indicis in the Rock Dove may be described as hypertrophied. The fleshy belly (about 30 mm long) extends the entire length of the carpometacarpus; it arises by fleshy fibers from the posterior and distal surfaces of the pisiform process, from the ligaments of the wrist joint proximal to the process, and from nearly the entire ventral surface of metacarpal II. The proximal portion of the belly is grooved so deeply by the tendon of M. flexor digitorum profundus that only a small portion of the tendon is visible in the undisturbed condition. M. abductor indicis gives rise to a strong, short tendon near the distal end of the carpometacarpus; it inserts on the anterior corner of the base of the proximal phalanx of digit II, adjacent, but ventral, to the insertion of the proximal tendon of M. flexor digitorum superficialis.

b. Agelaius phoeniceus. M. abductor indicis is absent in the blackbird.

c. Comparative data. This is M. abductor major digiti III of Fisher and Goodman (1955). Hudson and Lanzillotti (1955) proposed that the muscle be called M. abductor medius.

M. abductor indicis is one of the deep intrinsic hand muscles, lying deep to the tendons of the long flexors to digit II. The muscle arises primarily from the base of the carpometacarpus, beginning at the level of the pisiform proesss in most birds. The belly may arise also from the distal face of the pisiform process (e.g., *Otus asio, Pharomachrus mocino*). The belly is well developed, extending the entire length of the carpometacarpus in *Goura victoria, Coracias abyssinica, Indicator variegatus,* and the cuckoos; it is weakly developed in *Chen hyperborea, Eugenes fulgens, Chloroceryle americana,* and *Aceros undulatus.* The fleshy belly of M. abductor indicis is short (9 mm long) and weakly developed in *Pharomachrus mocino;* it ends on a 12 mm-long, thin tendon, which inserts on the base of the proximal phalanx of digit II.

M. abductor indicis is vestigial or absent in many passerine birds. It is relatively weakly developed in *Procnias nudicollis;* the fleshy origin begins about 3 mm distal to the pisiform process; the insertion is typical. The belly of M. abductor indicis might be considered vestigial in *Paradisaea rubra, Fregilupus varius, Sturnus vulgaris, Aplonis tabuensis,* and

Artamella viridis. In *Paradisaea,* for example, the muscle is represented by a fascial band containing a few fleshy fasciculi, which extends from the base of the pisiform process to the base of the proximal phalanx of digit II. In *Fregilupus* the small belly (3 mm long and 0.4 mm in maximum width) arises from the anteroventral edge of the carpometacarpus in the second third of the bone; the fine tendon of insertion fuses with the deep surface of the tendon of M. flexor digitorum superficialis, just before that tendon inserts on the anterior edge of the base of phalanx 1, digit II (Berger, 1957). Hudson and Lanzillotti (1955) reported the presence of this muscle in all genera of the Corvidae they examined. M. abductor indicis is absent in *Dendroica kirtlandii, Agelaius phoeniceus, Spizella arborea,* and, according to Swinebroad (1954), in *Passer domesticus, Richmondena cardinalis, Zonotrichia albicollis,* and *Melospiza melodia.*

M. abductor indicis inserts on, or near, the anterobasal corner of the proximal phalanx of digit II. In some birds (e.g., *Chen,* Cathartidae), there is a small, deep distal head ("M. abductor indicis brevis" of Fisher, 1946), whose tendon fuses with the tendon of the main head.

48. *M. Interosseus Dorsalis*

a. Columba livia. This is a well developed muscle, which arises not only from the facing surfaces of the bones bounding the intermetacarpal space but also from the bones and ligaments proximal to the space; a small bundle of fibers also arises from the tendon of insertion of M. extensor metacarpi ulnaris. The unusually large tendon of insertion forms as a midline raphe in the belly, passes distad along the anterodorsal edge of the proximal phalanx of digit II, and inserts on the base of the distal phalanx. There is a large sesamoid bone in the tendon just proximal to its insertion, where the tendon crosses the interphalangeal joint.

b. Agelaius phoeniceus. M. interosseus dorsalis has a small (4.5 mm long), fleshy belly arising from the facing surfaces of the metacarpals in the proximal third of the intermetacarpal space. The tendon forms as a midline raphe, passes through a shallow groove on the dorsal surface of the distal end of the carpometacarpus, then runs diagonally across the dorsal surface of the proximal phalanx of digit II, and inserts on the anterodorsal corner of the base of the second phalanx of digit II. As it crosses the dorsal surface of the interphalangeal joint of digit II, the tendon expands and encloses a well developed sesamoid.

c. Comparative data. As is true of most of the muscles of the forearm and hand, there is little published information on the interosseus muscles. The bellies of Mm. interosseus dorsalis and interosseus palmaris are about the same size in some birds (e.g., Columbidae, Cuculidae, Corvidae), but the belly of M. interosseus dorsalis is much smaller than M. interosseus palmaris in many birds (e.g., *Otus, Chaetura, Pharomachrus, Chloroceryle, Coracias, Procnias, Dendroica*).

M. interosseus dorsalis lies in the intermetacarpal space and arises from the facing surfaces of metacarpals II and III. The tendon of insertion forms as a midline raphe, turns dorsal at the distal end of the intermetacarpal space, passes distad along the anterodorsal surface of the proximal phalanx of digit II, and inserts on the distal (second in most birds) phalanx of digit II. In *Gavia immer* and *Chen hyperborea*, in which digit II has three phalanges, the tendon inserts on the third (distal) phalanx. The most common site of insertion appears to be on the anterodorsal corner of the base of the distal phalanx, but the tendon inserts on the posterodorsal corner in *Chaetura pelagica;* the tendon inserts on a spine near the base of the posterior surface of the distal phalanx in *Indicator variegatus*. Extensions of the tendon of insertion fuse with the fascia surrounding the base of the first primary in *Otus asio*. In *Pharomachrus mocino* there is a large sesamoid in the tendon where it crosses the distal end of the proximal phalanx of digit II. The tendon of insertion passes through a bony canal on the dorsal surface of the distal end of the carpometacarpus in *Eugenes fulgens*.

49. M. Interosseus Palmaris

a. Columba livia. This strongly developed muscle arises from the facing surfaces of the bones delimiting the intermetacarpal space, from a fibrous septum separating the interosseus muscle from the inserting fibers of M. ulnimetacarpalis dorsalis, from the carpometacarpus, the carpometacarpo-ulnare ligament, and from the os ulnare proximal to the intermetacarpal space. Consequently, there is a large bundle of fleshy fibers that extends ventral to the intermetacarpal space and occupies the interval between the bellies of M. abductor indicis (anteriorly) and M. ulnimetacarpalis dorsalis (posteriorly). The belly passes dorsad at the distal end of the intermetacarpal space to the dorsal surface of the hand; fleshy fibers extend distad along the proximal half of the proximal phalanx of digit II. The tendon of insertion passes along the posterodorsal edge of the proximal phalanx and fans out to insert for a distance of about 5 mm on the posterior surface of the distal phalanx of digit II, beginning at the midlength of the phalanx.

b. Agelaius phoeniceus. M. interosseus palmaris is much larger than the dorsal interosseus muscle, having a length of about 9 mm. In addition to its origin from the bones bounding the intermetacarpal space, M. interosseus palmaris arises from the ventral surface of metacarpal II proximal to the intermetacarpal space, beginning just distal to the base of the pisiform process. The tendon forms as a midline raphe, passes to the dorsal surface of the hand at the distal end of the intermetacarpal space, runs distad along the dorsal surface of the carpometacarpus posterior to the tendon of M. interosseus dorsalis, and then takes a diagonal course across the dorsal surface of digit III and the proximal phalanx of digit II. The tendon inserts on the posterior surface of the distal phalanx of digit II about half way out the bone.

c. *Comparative data.* This muscle also has been called M. interosseus volaris and M. interosseus ventralis. Gadow and Selenka (1891: p. 290), Fisher (1946), and Berger (1953–1960) call it M. interosseus palmaris. Palmaris is the preferred name in human anatomy (Woerdeman *et al.,* 1961).

M. interosseus palmaris lies in the intermetacarpal space and arises from the facing surfaces of the metacarpals that bound that space. The tendon forms as a midline raphe, passes dorsad at the distal limit of the intermetacarpal space, runs distad along the posterodorsal surface of the proximal phalanx of digit II, and inserts on the distal (second in most birds) phalanx. In *Gavia immer* and in *Chen hyperborea,* in which digit II has three phalanges, M. interosseus palmaris inserts on the third (distal) phalanx. The tendon inserts on the posterior corner of the base of the distal phalanx in *Chloroceryle, Procnias,* and *Spizella;* on a tubercle on the posterior surface, near the tip, of the distal phalanx in *Gallicolumba* and *Chordeiles;* inserts beyond midlength and on the *posteroventral* edge of the phalanx in *Otus asio;* and on the distal half of the phalanx in *Goura victoria.*

M. interosseus palmaris is twice the bulk of M. interosseus dorsalis in *Chaetura pelagica.* The tendon of the interosseus palmaris passes through a pulley at the distal end of the carpometacarpus, then passes diagonally posteriorly, fanning out and inserting on the fascia surrounding the base of the outermost primary; there appears to be no direct insertion on bone.

Both of the interosseus muscles are relatively small in *Eugenes fulgens* but M. interosseus palmaris is the larger of the two. It arises from the ventral surface of the carpometacarpus proximal to the limit of the intermetacarpal space, between the pisiform process and the os ulnare. The tendon of insertion (which is smaller than the tendon of M. interosseus dorsalis) passes through its own bony canal on the dorsal surface near the distal end of the carpometacarpus, runs distad along the posterodorsal surface of the proximal phalanx of digit II, continues distad in the fascia surrounding the bases of the outer two primaries, and inserts on a spine on the posterior surface of the distal phalanx of digit II, about 3 mm from the tip, of the phalanx. The tendon has a similar insertion in *Chordeiles minor.*

50. M. Flexor Digiti III (Flexor Digiti IV)

a. Columba livia. This is a weakly developed muscle, arising by fleshy fibers from the posterior surface of metacarpal III in slightly less than its distal half. The muscle has a relatively wide (2 mm) insertion, primarily by fleshy fibers, on the proximal surface of the posterior spine of digit III.

b. Agelaius phoeniceus. The fleshy belly (13 mm long) of M. flexor digiti III arises from the posterior surface of metacarpal III in its basal half. The belly tapers to a tiny tendon about 0.1 mm wide, which inserts on a tubercle on the posterior edge of digit III about a third the way out the bone. A tiny deep head arises from metacarpal III just distal to the origin of the superficial head; it ends on a minute tendon which fuses with the anterior edge of the main tendon.

c. Comparative data. This is M. flexor digiti IV of Fisher and Goodman (1955) and M. flexor digiti quarti of Sullivan (1962).

The development of M. flexor digiti III varies considerably among different birds. The muscle is weakly developed in *Chen, Otus, Pharomachrus, Chordeiles, Chloroceryle, Procnias,* and *Paradisaea.* The belly is strongly developed in *Coracias* and *Indicator,* in which genera the belly extends the entire length of the carpometacarpus. The muscle is well developed in cuckoos, as well, but the belly is limited to about the distal third of the carpometacarpus and the bulk of the fibers arise from the distal end of metacarpal III, completely filling the interval between it and digit III; this is the portion of the muscle which Fisher (1946) called "M. flexor brevis digiti III." There is a small distal head in *Pharomachrus.*

M. flexor digiti III is a long, thin muscle in *Chaetura pelagica,* arising from nearly the entire length of metacarpal III, including an area proximal to the insertion of M. ulnimetacarpalis dorsalis on the dorsal surface of the base of the metacarpal. M. flexor digiti III has a very small, spindle-shaped belly in *Eugenes fulgens;* it arises from approximately the distal half of metacarpal III; it inserts by a tendon on about the basal half of digit III.

M. flexor digiti III inserts primarily by fleshy fibers on the postero-proximal portion of the posterior spine and shaft of digit III in many birds, often sending a tendon to the tip of the posterior spine. The muscle inserts by fleshy fibers distal to the spine in some cuckoos. The muscle inserts solely by a tendon on the posterior spine in passerine birds.

VI. Muscles of the Leg

1. M. Sartorius (Extensor Iliotibialis Anterior)

a. Columba livia. M. sartorius is a long straplike muscle extending down the anterior border of the thigh to the level of the patella. The muscle arises by an aponeurosis (shared with M. rhomboideus superficialis) from the anterior 5 mm of the anterior iliac crest, from the median dorsal ridge of the synsacrum, and from the anterior iliac process (Fig. IX.44). A small, deep head arises from the tip of the anterior iliac process and from the dense fascia covering M. iliotrochantericus posterior. The deep head fuses with the medial border of the superficial head. M. sartorius inserts by short tendinous fibers on the anteromedial surface of the patellar ligament.

b. Agelaius phoeniceus. M. sartorius arises from the posterior portion of an aponeurosis shared with M. rhomboideus profundus attached to the neural spine of the last dorsal vertebra and the anterior edge of the median dorsal ridge of the synsacrum, and by fleshy fibers from the anterior iliac process and the lateral edge of the ilium posterior to the anterior iliac process. The straplike belly of M. sartorius passes down the anterior surface of the thigh, crosses superficial to the patellar ligament at the knee, and inserts by fleshy and tendinous fibers on the anterior edge of the tibiotarsus at the base of the inner cnemial crest and just proximal to the origin of M. gastrocnemius pars interna. M. latissimus dorsi dorsocutaneous passes cephalad superficial to the most proximal part of the belly of M. sartorius.

c. Comparative data. This is M. iliotibialis internus s. sartorius of Gadow and Selenka; it is M. sartorius of Shufeldt, Hudson, Berger, and many others; it is M. extensor iliotibialis anterior of Fisher.

M. sartorius is the most anterior muscle in the thigh. The typically flat, straplike fleshy belly passes downward and backward (often fused with the anterior edge of M. iliotibialis) and inserts on the patellar ligament and the medial surface of the proximal end of the tibiotarsus; on the rotular (procnemial) process of the tibiotarsus in the Common Loon. Part of the tendinous insertion often is intimately related to the fascia covering the muscles on the anterior and medial surfaces of the proximal end of the crus.

The origin of M. sartorius (by an aponeurosis and/or by fleshy fibers) varies among different groups of birds: the neural spine of the last one or two dorsal vertebrae, the median dorsal ridge of the synsacrum, the anterior iliac process of the ilium, or the anteroventral edge of the ilium. The aponeurotic origin may be shared with Mm. latissimus dorsi

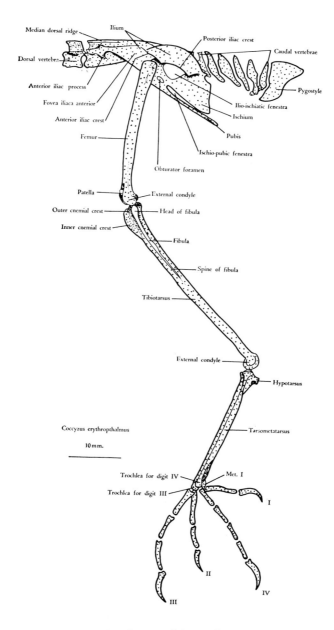

FIG. IX.44. Lateral view of pelvis, caudal vertebrae, and left leg of *Coccyzus erythropthalmus* (Cuculidae) to show major bony landmarks. (By permission, Berger, 1952.)

pars posterior, rhomboideus superficialis, or rhomboideus profundus, and often is continuous posteriorly with the aponeurosis of origin of M. iliotibialis (Fig. IX.45).

In *Gavia immer* M. sartorius arises by fleshy fibers from the neural spines of the "second and third from the last dorsal vertebrae (anterior by one to the fused sacral vertebrae)" and from the anterior half of the ventrolateral margin of the preacetabular ilium (Wilcox, 1952). According to Hudson (1937), M. sartorius arises only from the median dorsal ridge of the synsacrum in *Sula brewsteri;* only from the anterior edge of the ilium in *Fregata magnificens, Pedioecetes phasianellus, Colinus virginianus,* and several species of *Buteo* and *Falco;* and exclusively from the ventral edge of the ilium in *Bubo virginianus* and *Otus asio.* In the Sandhill Crane (*Grus canadensis*), M. sartorius arises primarily by an aponeurosis, shared with M. latissimus dorsi pars posterior, from the neural spine of the last dorsal vertebra, and from the anterior 5 cm of the median dorsal ridge of the synsacrum (Berger, 1956e). In *Coua caerulea* and many other cuckoos, the muscle arises by a short aponeurosis from the median dorsal ridge of the synsacrum and from the tendons of M. spinalis thoracis (longissimus dorsi); there is no direct origin from the neural spines of dorsal vertebrae. M. sartorius arises from the anterodorsal end of the ilium only in *Tauraco leucotis* (Berger, 1960a).

M. sartorius has two heads of origin in *Paradisaea rubra* and *Fregilupus varius* (Berger, 1956b, 1957). In *Paradisaea* the anterior, more superficial, head arises by an aponeurosis from the neural spines of the last two dorsal vertebrae and from a small area on the anterior edge of the ilium. The posterior, deeper, head arises by an aponeurosis from an area 15 mm long on the ventral edge of the ilium, beginning at the anteriormost end of the bone and extending caudad to the area of origin of M. iliotrochantericus medius. The superficial and deep heads fuse along their line of contact a short distance inferior to the ilium. The anterior part of the muscle inserts by an aponeurosis primarily on the anteromedial edge of the head of the tibiotarsus. The posterior part of the belly inserts by fleshy fibers on the distal end of the belly and tendon of insertion of M. femorotibialis internus.

The superficial head of M. sartorius arises from the neural spine of the last dorsal vertebra and from the anterior end of the ilium in *Fregilupus.* The deep head arises primarily by fleshy fibers from the ventrolateral edge of the ilium anterior to the origin of M. iliotrochantericus anterior. The two heads fuse to form a single belly, which inserts by fleshy fibers on the medial surface of the head of the tibiotarsus at the base of the inner cnemial crest. The insertion is intimately fused with the origin of pars interna of M. gastrocnemius. Just proximal to its insertion, M. sar-

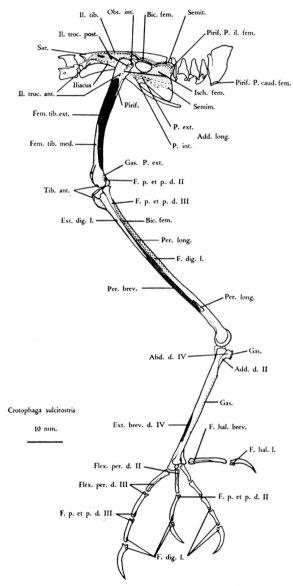

FIG. IX.45. Lateral view of pelvis, caudal vertebrae, and left leg of *Crotophaga sulcirostris* (Cuculidae) showing muscle attachments. (By permission, Berger, 1952.)

torius is closely applied to the anterior surface of the patellar ligament.

M. sartorius has a single head in *Sturnus vulgaris, Aplonis tabuensis, Artamella viridis,* and all other passerine birds thus far investigated. Gadow and Selenka (1891: p. 150) report that M. sartorius is composed of three separate parts in *Phoenicopterus.* They also say that the muscle arises from the last dorsal vertebra and its rib, from the ilium, and from the spina pubica (pectineal process) in *Rhea.*

2. M. Iliotibialis (*Extensor Iliotibialis Lateralis*)

a. Columba livia. This muscle exhibits a moderate development in the Rock Dove. M. sartorius lies anterior to M. iliotibialis; the posterior and distal parts of M. biceps femoris and Mm. semitendinosus and piriformis pars caudofemoralis are visible posterior to M. iliotibialis. M. iliotibialis arises primarily by a thin, but dense, aponeurosis from the anterior iliac crest and from the lateral surface of the postacetabular ilium. The central portion of the sheetlike belly of M. iliotibialis is entirely aponeurotic in the distal three-fourths of the thigh and is fused with the subjacent M. femorotibialis externus; the anterior and posterior segments of the muscle are fleshy. The three portions of M. iliotibialis converge on a dense aponeurosis, which forms the superficial lamina of the patellar ligament.

The *patellar ligament* (or *patellar tendon*) encloses the patella, covers the anterior surface of the knee joint, and inserts primarily on the rotular crest of the tibiotarsus. The patellar ligament is formed by the conjoined tendons of Mm. iliotibialis, femorotibialis externus, and femorotibialis medius. The tendon of the ambiens muscle passes diagonally (from medial to lateral) through a compartment in the patellar ligament.

b. Agelaius phoeniceus. M. iliotibialis is an expansive muscle lying immediately posterior to M. sartorius and concealing Mm. femorotibialis externus et medius as well as the origin and the proximal portion of the belly of M. biceps femoris. M. semitendinosus and the most distal part of the belly of M. semimembranosus are visible posterior to Mm. iliotibialis and biceps femoris.

M. iliotibialis arises from an extensive aponeurosis attached to the median dorsal ridge, the anterior iliac crest, and the anterior two-thirds of the posterior iliac crest of the ilium. The most posterior part of the muscle arises by fleshy fibers. The belly of M. iliotrochantericus posterior is visible through the anterior part of the aponeurosis of origin. The anterior and posterior parts of M. iliotibialis are fleshy to within a few millimeters of the patella. The central part of the muscle is aponeurotic in the distal two-thirds of the thigh. The aponeurotic portion is fused with the underlying femorotibialis externus muscle, and considerable care must be exercised in removing M. iliotibialis. M. iliotibialis ends on a dense aponeurosis which forms the most superficial layer of the patellar ligament. The aponeurosis then inserts on the proximal end of the tibiotarsus. The most anterior and medial part of the belly of M. iliotibialis passes inward to insert by short tendinous fibers on the posteromedial edge of the tibiotarsus, medial to the area of insertion of M. sartorius.

c. Comparative data. Gadow and Selenka (1891: p. 151) divide this complex into three parts because of presumed homologies with human thigh muscles: iliotibialis anterior; iliotibialis medius or tensor fasciae; iliotibialis posterior or gluteus posterior. Hudson and Berger refer to the entire complex as M. iliotibialis. Fisher calls it M. extensor iliotibialis lateralis. Shufeldt named it M. gluteus primus.

M. iliotibialis is the most superficial muscle on the lateral surface of the thigh (Figs. IX.46 and IX.47). When fully developed, the muscle arises (primarily by an aponeurosis in most birds) from most of the anterior and posterior iliac crests of the ilium, and conceals Mm. iliotrochanterici, femorotibiales externus et medius, and biceps femoris. The belly of M. iliotrochantericus posterior typically is visible through the aponeurotic origin from the anterior iliac crest. M. iliotibialis arises primarily by fleshy fibers from the ilium and the last two dorsal vertebrae in *Gavia immer*. The muscle also arises from the anteroventral edge of the ilium in some hawks and owls.

In most birds, the fleshy fibers of the middle portion of the muscle are limited to the proximal one-fourth to one-half of the thigh; the muscle is aponeurotic in the distal one-half to three-fourths of the thigh and is intimately fused with the underlying M. femorotibialis externus: e.g., *Ardea herodias, Butorides virescens, Chen hyperborea, Crax rubra, Pedioecetes phasianellus, Colinus virginianus, Grus americana, Grus canadensis, Fulica americana, Totanus melanoleucus, Larus pipixcan, Columba livia, Tauraco leucotis, Cuculus canorus, Chrysococcyx cupreus, Crotophaga sulcirostris, Coua caerulea, Procnias nudicollis, Corvus brachyrhynchos, Paradisaea rubra, Pipilo erythrophthalmus*. The middle portion of the muscle is entirely aponeurotic (from origin to insertion) in *Coccyzus erythropthalmus, Chrysococcyx (Lampromorpha) caprius, Coracias abyssinica, Indicator variegatus, Colaptes auratus*, and *Dendrocopos villosus*.

The preacetabular and acetabular portions of the muscle are present but the postacetabular portion is absent in the Accipitridae, Falconidae, Strigidae, *Podargus, Chaetura pelagica, Buceros*, Tyrannidae, and Hirundinidae (see Gadow and Selenka, 1891: p. 154; Hudson, 1937; Berger, 1956a) (Fig. IX.48). The postacetabular portion of M. iliotibialis has been found in all other passerine species thus far examined, including

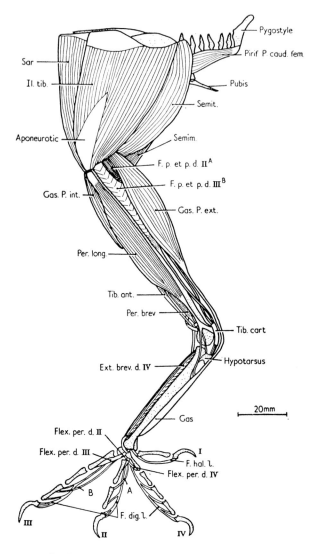

FIG. IX.46. Superficial muscles of the left leg of *Coua caerulea*. Modified from
Berger (1953). Superscripts refer to the tendons of the muscles concerned.

Abbreviations used in leg muscle drawings: Abd. d. IV—M. abductor digiti IV;
Acc.—M. accessorius semitendinosi; Add. long. p. ext.—M. adductor longus et brevis
pars externa; Auto ext.—automatic extensor; Bic. fem.—M. biceps femoris; Bic.
loop—biceps loop; Ext. brev. d. IV—M. extensor brevis digiti IV; Ext. dig. 1.—M.
extensor digitorum longus; Ext. hal. 1.—M. extensor hallucis longus; F. dig. 1.—M.
flexor digitorum longus; F. hal. brev.—M. flexor hallucis brevis; F. hal. 1.—M.
flexor hallucis longus; F. p. et p. d. II—M. flexor perforans et perforatus digiti
II; F. p. et p. d. III—M. flexor perforans et perforatus digiti III; Flex. per. d. II—

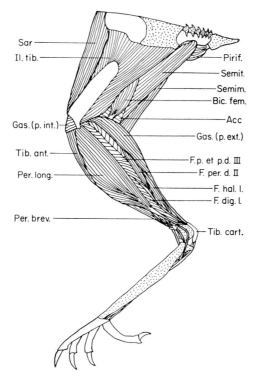

Sar
Il. tib.
Gas. (p. int.)
Tib. ant.
Per. long.
Per. brev.

Pirif.
Semit.
Semim.
Bic. fem.
Acc
Gas. (p. ext.)
F.p. et p.d. III
F. per. d. II
F. hal. I.
F. dig. I.
Tib. cart.

Fig. IX.47. Lateral view of the superficial muscles of the left leg of the Rufous-sided Towhee (*Pipilo erythrophthalmus*). (By permission, Stallcup, 1954.) For Key to Abbreviations see legend to Fig. IX.46.

Procnias nudicollis(Cotingidae). Only the preacetabular portion of the muscle is present in *Eugenes fulgens, Pharomachrus mocino,* and *Chloroceryle americana.* In these species, Mm. femorotibialis externus, iliotrochantericus posterior, and biceps femoris are visible after the skin and subcutaneous connective tissue are removed. M. iliotibialis is inseparably fused with the posterior border of M. sartorius in *Eugenes fulgens.*

M. flexor perforatus digiti II; Flex. per. d. III—M. flexor perforatus digiti III; Flex. per. d. IV—M. flexor perforatus digiti IV; Gas. p. ext.—M. gastrocnemius pars externa; Gas. p. int.—M. gastrocnemius pars interna; Il. tib.—M. iliotibialis; Il. troc. ant.—M. iliotrochantericus anterior; Isch. fem.—M. ischiofemoralis; Ligament—ligamentum transversum; Per. brev.—M. peroneus brevis; Per. long.—M. peroneus longus; Pirif. p. caud. fem.—M. piriformis pars caudofemoralis; Pirif. p. il. fem.— M. piriformis pars iliofemoralis; Sar.—M. sartorius; Semim.—M. semimembranosus; Semit.—M. semitendinosus; Tib. ant.—M. tibialis anterior; Tib. cart.—tibial cartilage; Vin.—vinculum.

Only the postacetabular portion of M. iliotibialis is present in *Chordeiles minor.* The muscle arises primarily by fleshy fibers from most of the posterior iliac crest but it has a small aponeurotic origin from the ilium dorsal to the acetabulum. The thin straplike belly passes down the posterior surface of the thigh, fuses, in part, with the posterior border of M. femorotibialis externus in its distal half, and inserts on the most posterior part of the patellar ligament.

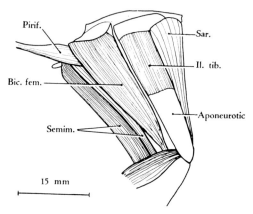

Fɪɢ. IX.48. Lateral view of the superficial muscles of right thigh of *Polihiërax semitorquatus.* (By permission, Berger, 1956a.) For Key to Abbreviations see legend to Fig. IX.46.

M. iliotibialis is vestigial in *Fregata magnificens,* in which species the very narrow belly arises only from the acetabular portion of the ilium and inserts by fleshy fibers on the belly of M. femorotibialis externus about the midlength of the thigh (Hudson, 1937) (Fig. IX.49). M. iliotibialis is completely lacking in *Upupa epops* and *Aceros undulatus.*

At the knee the aponeurosis of insertion of M. iliotibialis contributes to the formation of the patellar ligament, which encloses the patella and inserts on the rotular crest of the head of the tibiotarsus. Extensions of the patellar ligament commonly end in the fascia covering the muscles on the anterior and lateral surfaces of the proximal end of the crus.

3. M. Iliotrochantericus Posterior (Gluteus Profundus)

a. Columba livia. This large muscle lies in the anterior iliac fossa and is exposed after the aponeurosis of origin of M. iliotibialis is removed. M. iliotrochantericus posterior arises by fleshy fibers from the bone of the entire anterior iliac fossa and from all but the posterior

5 mm of the anterior iliac crest. The most posterior fibers of the muscle arise dorsal to the acetabulum. The bulky belly converges on a strong, flat (about 4 mm wide) tendon, which inserts on a curved ridge on the lateral surface of the femur just distal to the trochanter.

b. Agelaius phoeniceus. M. iliotrochantericus posterior arises by fleshy fibers from the bone of the entire anterior iliac fossa and from the anterior iliac crest to a point dorsal to the acetabulum. The bulky belly ends on a wide (3 mm), flat tendon, which inserts on a curved ridge on the lateral surface of the femur just distal to the trochanter.

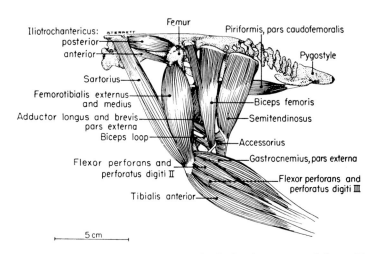

FIG. IX.49. Superficial muscles of the left thigh of *Aceros undulatus.* Note the absence of M. iliotibialis in this hornbill. (By permission, Berger, 1960b.) For Key to Abbreviations see legend to Fig. IX.46.

c. Comparative data. This is M. iliotrochantericus posterior of Gadow and Selenka, Hudson, and Berger. It is the gluteus profundus of Fisher and the gluteus medius of Shufeldt.

M. iliotrochantericus posterior, lying deep to Mm. sartorius and iliotibialis, arises primarily by fleshy fibers from the bone of the entire anterior iliac fossa (gluteal fossa of Fisher); the origin extends laterally on the anterior iliac process of the ilium in some species. The fleshy fibers pass caudolaterad and end on a wide and dense tendon, which inserts on the lateral surface (on the anterior border in *Gavia immer*) of the femur just distal to the trochanter. The shape of M. iliotrochantericus posterior, which has been found in all birds dissected, is directly related to the shape of the preacetabular ilium. M. iliotrochantericus posterior is much larger than M. iliotrochantericus anterior in nearly all birds. The latter muscle, however, is the larger of the two in *Podiceps* ("*Colymbus*") *caspicus* (Hudson, 1937). The two muscles are equal in size in *Gavia immer*.

4. M. Iliotrochantericus Anterior

a. Columba livia. This muscle arises by tendinous and fleshy fibers from the ventrolateral edge of the ilium for a distance of about 7 mm beginning at the tip of the anterior iliac process. The belly passes backward and outward, tapers to a flat tendon (2.5 mm wide), and inserts on the anterolateral surface of the femur, beginning 8 mm distal to the trochanter. The belly is partly concealed by M. iliotrochantericus posterior. The distal part of the belly and the tendon of insertion of M. iliotrochantericus anterior pass between the proximal portions of Mm. femorotibialis externus and femorotibialis medius.

b. Agelaius phoeniceus. M. iliotrochantericus anterior arises primarily by fleshy fibers from the tip of the anterior iliac process and from the lateral edge of the ilium for a distance of about 4 mm. The origin from the anterior iliac process is partly aponeurotic and is shared with M. iliotrochantericus posterior. Most of the belly of M. iliotrochantericus anterior lies just lateral and ventral to the belly of M. iliotrochantericus posterior but the deepest part of the belly is covered by the latter muscle. The flat belly of M. iliotrochantericus anterior passes backward and outward to insert between Mm. femorotibialis externus and femorotibialis medius on the posterolateral surface of the shaft of the femur for a distance of 2 mm, beginning about 3 mm from the proximal end of the bone.

c. Comparative data. This is M. iliotrochantericus anterior of Gadow and Selenka, Hudson, and Berger. It is "M. iliacus" of Fisher and M. gluteus minimus of Shufeldt.

M. iliotrochantericus anterior arises primarily by fleshy fibers from the ventral margin of the ilium (ventral to the origin of M. iliotrochantericus posterior), and, in some birds, from the anterior iliac process of the ilium (Fig. IX.50). The medial border of the muscle is concealed by M. iliotrochantericus posterior in many birds. The belly of M. iliotrochantericus anterior passes backward and outward and inserts by a flat tendon (usually) on the lateral surface of the femur a short distance distal and anterior to the area of insertion of M. iliotrochantericus posterior. The tendon passes between the proximal portions of Mm. femorotibialis externus and femorotibialis medius. M. iliotrochantericus anterior has been found in all birds except the genus *Sula* (Hudson, 1937).

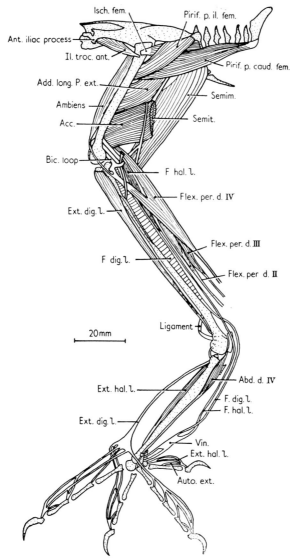

Fig. IX.50. Lateral view of left leg of *Coua caerulea* to show a deep layer of muscles. Modified from Berger (1953). For Key to Abbreviations see legend to Fig. IX.46.

5. M. Iliotrochantericus Medius ("C" in Leg-Muscle Formulas)

a. Columba livia. This small muscle lies deep to M. iliotrochantericus posterior and posterior to M. iliotrochantericus anterior. The large nerve to M. iliotrochantericus posterior passes dorsad between Mm.

iliotrochantericus anterior and medius. Medius is a small band of fleshy
fibers 4 mm wide at its origin from the ventrolateral edge of the ilium,
beginning a short distance posterior to the origin of M. iliotrochantericus
anterior. The belly of medius tapers to a 2 mm-wide, flat tendon which
inserts on the anterolateral surface of the femur midway between the
tendons of insertion of Mm. iliotrochantericus anterior et posterior.

b. *Agelaius phoeniceus.* M. iliotrochantericus medius is a small muscle
about 6 mm long and 2 mm wide at its origin from the ventrolateral
edge of the ilium posterior to the origin of M. iliotrochantericus anterior. The belly of M. iliotrochantericus medius tapers to a thin aponeurosis which inserts on the lateral surface of the femur just proximal
to the area of insertion of M. iliotrochantericus anterior.

c. *Comparative data.* Hudson (1937) proposed that this muscle
be designated by the letter "C" in leg-muscle formulas.

M. iliotrochantericus medius is a small muscle arising from the ventral edge of the ilium just anterior to the acetabulum and posterior
to the origin of M. iliotrochantericus anterior. The belly passes outward
to insert on the femur, between the areas of insertion of the other
two iliotrochanterici muscles.

M. iliotrochantericus medius has been found in *Struthio, Rhea, Casu-
arius, Gavia, Podiceps,* the Cathartidae, *Chauna,* Galliformes (except
Opisthocomus), *Grus, Larus, Columba, Zenaidura, Goura, Gallicolumba,
Eugenes, Pharomachrus, Chloroceryle, Coracias, Upupa, Aceros, Indi-
cator, Colaptes, Dendrocopos, Procnias,* and all other passerine birds
examined. The muscle is known to be absent in *Sula, Fregata, Ardea,
Butorides, Sagittarius, Accipiter, Buteo, Aquila, Circus, Pandion, Falco,
Polihiërax, Fulica, Totanus, Uria, Tauraco,* the Cuculidae, *Otus, Bubo,
Chordeiles,* and *Chaetura.*

Gadow and Selenka (1891:p. 142) and Hudson (1937) did not
find this muscle in the genus *Grus,* but Fisher and Goodman (1955)
found it in *Grus americana* and Berger (1956e) found the muscle bi-
laterally in two specimens and unilaterally in a third specimen of
G. canadensis tabida. In the Sandhill Crane, Mm. iliotrochantericus
anterior et medius are separate at their origins only; the bellies fuse
distally and insert by a common wide (1.5 cm) aponeurosis. In the
right hip of one specimen, the two muscles were completely fused,
so that the complex was represented by a single muscle-mass, arising
from the same area occupied by both muscles in the other dissections.
The fusion of these two muscles is an example of the tendency toward fusion of muscles which arise from contiguous areas and whose
fibers are essentially parallel. Some specimens of *Chen* and *Anas*

have M. iliotrochantericus medius partially separated from M. iliotro-chantericus anterior.

6. *M. Gluteus Medius et Minimus ("D" in Leg-Muscle Formulas)*

a. Columba livia. M. gluteus medius et minimus is absent in the Rock Dove.

b. Agelaius phoeniceus. This muscle is absent in the blackbird.

c. Comparative data. Hudson and Berger call this muscle the gluteus medius et minimus. It is the iliofemoralis externus of Gadow and Selenka, and the "piriformis" of Fisher. Hudson (1937) proposed that this muscle be designated by the letter "D" in leg-muscle formulas.

M. gluteus medius et minimus is a deeply situated muscle arising by fleshy fibers from the iliac crest dorsal to the acetabulum. Its fibers pass over the trochanter to insert by a small tendon on the femur, just proximal to the insertion of M. ischiofemoralis. We agree with Hudson (1937: p. 14) that "it is very difficult in the case of small birds to determine whether this little muscle is absent or simply rudi-mentary. Gadow (1891: p. 144) indicates that in some cases it is completely fused with the posterior margin of the Il. troc. post. How-ever, as has already been pointed out in connection with the Il. troc. med., such a completely fused muscle is for all practical considera-tions absent, especially if the innervation fails to provide a definite basis for determination as Gadow indicates is the case with the Glut. med. et. min."

M. gluteus medius et minimus has been found in *Gavia, Sula, Phala-crocorax, Fregata, Ardea, Butorides, Ciconia, Phoenicopterus,* the Ana-tidae, the Falconiformes (Fisher, 1946; Hudson, 1948; Berger, 1956a), the Galliformes (Hudson *et al.,* 1959), *Grus, Fulica, Totanus, Larus, Uria, Alca, Tauraco, Otus,* and *Bubo.*

M. gluteus medius et minimus is known to be absent in the follow-ing: *Spheniscus, Podiceps, Columba, Zenaidura, Goura, Gallicolumba, Didunculus,* Cuculidae, *Chordeiles, Chaetura, Apus, Eugenes, Pharo-machrus, Chloroceryle, Momotus, Coracias, Eurystomus, Upupa, Aceros, Indicator, Colaptes, Dendrocopos, Procnias,* and all other passerine birds examined. Passerine species studied by Hudson, Berger, and Stallcup include *Procnias nudicollis, Tyrannus tyrannus,* Corvidae, *Paradisaea rubra, Artamella viridis, Sturnus vulgaris, Aplonis tabuensis, Fregilupus varius, Vireo olivaceus, Dendroica kirtlandii, Seiurus motacilla, Age-laius phoeniceus, Icterus galbula, Molothrus ater, Piranga rubra, Passer domesticus, Estrilda amandava, Poephila guttata, Spizella arborea,* and many other genera of the Fringillidae (see Stallcup, 1954).

7. *M.* Femorotibialis Externus (Vastus Lateralis)

a. Columba livia. This deep muscle on the lateral surface of the femur has both a proximal and a distal head. The *proximal head* arises from a long area on the lateral and anterolateral surfaces of the femur, beginning just proximal to the level of insertion of M. iliotrochantericus anterior. The proximal head is fused with the underlying M. femorotibialis medius. The *distal head* of M. femorotibialis externus arises primarily from the posterolateral surface of the femur in its distal two-thirds, but, near the distal end of the femur, the muscle arises from the lateral surface of the bone. Both heads give rise to dense aponeuroses which contribute to the formation of the patellar ligament.

b. Agelaius phoeniceus. M. femorotibialis externus arises from the lateral and posterolateral surfaces of the femur, beginning about 2.5 mm from the proximal end of the bone and extending distad for most of the length of the shaft of the femur. The fleshy fibers of the *proximal head* begin between the areas of insertion of M. ischiofemoralis (posteriorly) and Mm. iliotrochantericus anterior and iliotrochantericus medius (anteriorly). The distal part of the belly of M. iliotrochantericus anterior passes between the proximal portions of Mm. femorotibialis externus and femorotibialis medius. Distal to this area, the anteromedial border of M. femorotibialis externus is inextricably fused with M. femorotibialis medius. As it approaches the knee, the belly of M. femorotibialis externus gives rise to a dense aponeurosis, which forms the lateral part of the patellar ligament. A roughly triangular-shaped *distal head* lies deep to the proximal head and arises from the posterolateral surface of the distal third of the shaft of the femur. The distal head also ends on an aponeurosis; it forms the deep layer of the most lateral part of the patellar ligament.

c. Comparative data. M. femorotibialis externus is M. femoritibialis externus of Gadow and Selenka, Hudson, and Wilcox (1952); it is M. vastus lateralis of Howell (1938) and Fisher (1946); it is the vastus externus component of M. extensor femoris of Shufeldt.

Lying deep to M. sartorius and M. iliotibialis, M. femorotibialis externus arises from and covers most of the lateral, anterolateral, and posterolateral surfaces of the femur. The muscle exhibits very little variation among the orders of birds. The chief variations pertain to the proximal area of origin (just distal to the trochanter, between the tendons of insertion of Mm. iliotrochantericus anterior and ischiofemoralis, or distal to the insertion of those tendons) and the presence or absence of a discrete distal head. A deep, distal head has been found, for example, in many gruiform birds, in *Goura victoria, Gallicolumba luzonica, Coua caerulea, Indicator variegatus, Fregilupus varius, Dendroica kirtlandii,* and *Agelaius phoeniceus* (Mitchell, 1901b; Fisher and Goodman, 1955; Berger, 1953, 1957).

In the Sandhill Crane, the distal head arises from the posterior and lateral surfaces of the distal half of the femur. The tendon of the distal head fuses, in part, with the patellar ligament, but the strongest portion of the tendon passes distad and inserts on the outer cnemial crest of the tibiotarsus.

The *proximal head* of M. femorotibialis externus in *Fregilupus varius* arises from the lateral surface of the femur, beginning at the level of insertion of the tendon of M. iliotrochantericus medius and between that tendon and the tendon of M. ischiofemoralis. Throughout most of its extent, this head is fused with the lateral border of M. femorotibialis medius. Proximally the two muscles are separated by the tendons of insertion of Mm. iliotrochanterici anterior et medius. The *distal head* of M. femorotibialis externus lies deep to and posterior to the proximal head; it arises by tendinous and fleshy fibers from the posterolateral surface of the distal half (15 mm) of the femur. Both heads, but especially the proximal head, become tendinous near the knee and contribute to the formation of the patellar ligament.

Hudson (1937) used what we believe to be the proper interpretation of the femorotibialis complex; he did not, however, describe a deep, distal head in any of the genera he examined (including *Grus*). In his 1959 paper he considered the distal head only to represent M. femorotibialis externus; the proximal head he described as a lateral head of M. femorotibialis medius (Hudson *et al.*, 1959: Fig. 2). We see no justification for this second interpretation of the femorotibialis muscle complex.

8. M. *Femorotibialis Medius* (*Vastus Medialis*)

a. Columba livia. This muscle arises by tendinous and fleshy fibers from the trochanteric ridge and from the anterior surface of the femur throughout nearly its entire length. Mm. femorotibialis externus et medius are intimately fused except proximally, where the two muscles are separated by the tendon of insertion of M. iliotrochantericus anterior. The fleshy fibers of M. femorotibialis medius insert on the entire proximal surface of the patella; the tendon contributes to the patellar ligament. M. ambiens passes distad on the medial surface of M. femorotibialis medius.

b. Agelaius phoeniceus. M. femorotibialis medius is the largest of the three parts of this complex; it arises primarily by fleshy fibers from the trochanteric ridge and the anterior surface of the shaft of the femur throughout nearly its entire length. The proximal part of the muscle lies deep to the distal (outer) ends of Mm. iliotrochantericus anterior and iliotrochantericus medius. The fleshy fibers of M. femorotibialis medius insert on the proximal surface of the patella. The lateral portion of the muscle gives rise to aponeurotic fibers which aid in the formation of the patellar ligament.

c. *Comparative data.* M. femorotibialis medius is M. vastus medialis of Howell (1938) and Fisher (1946), and it is the cruraeus part of M. extensor femoris of Shufeldt.

M. femorotibialis medius arises by tendinous and fleshy fibers from the trochanteric ridge and by fleshy fibers from the anterior surface of the shaft of the femur throughout nearly its entire length (Fig. IX.51). M. femorotibialis medius lies anteromedial to M. femorotibialis externus. The two muscles are fused along their contiguous borders except proxi-

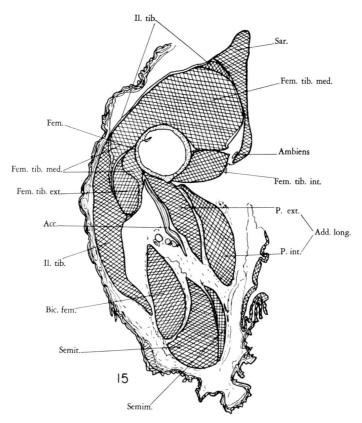

Fig. IX.51. Cross section made a little below the middle of the thigh; Blue Grouse. (By permission, Hudson *et al.,* 1959.) For Key to Abbreviations see legend to Fig. IX.46.

mally, where the belly and tendon of M. iliotrochantericus anterior passes between the origins of the two muscles. The dense aponeuroses of insertion of both muscles contribute to the formation of the patellar ligament but the fleshy belly of M. femorotibialis medius characteristically inserts on the proximal border of the patella.

9. M. Femorotibialis Internus

a. Columba livia. This muscle lies on the medial surface of the thigh between Mm. femorotibialis medius and adductor longus et brevis pars interna. M. femorotibialis internus arises by fleshy fibers from the medial surface of the shaft of the femur, beginning about 11 mm distal to the trochanter; fleshy fibers arise on either side of the area of insertion of M. iliacus proximally. The belly of M. femorotibialis internus increases in size as it passes distally, crosses the medial surface of the knee joint, and inserts by a flat tendon on the anteromedial corner of the head of the tibiotarsus.

b. Agelaius phoeniceus. M. femorotibialis internus is composed of two independent bellies. The *proximal* or "typical" *belly* is a long, spindle-shaped muscle that arises from the medial surface of the femur, beginning just distal to the insertion of M. iliacus about 3 mm from the neck of the femur. The proximal belly ends on a flat aponeurosis, which inserts on the anteromedial corner of the head of the tibiotarsus. The deep *distal head* (about 10 mm long) arises by aponeurotic and fleshy fibers from the medial surface of the femur just proximal to the internal condyle. The belly ends on a flat tendon which inserts on the tibiotarsus posterior and adjacent to the insertion of the tendon of the proximal belly.

c. Comparative data. All modern authors use the name femorotibialis (femoritibialis) internus for this muscle. It is M. vastus internus of Shufeldt.

M. femorotibialis internus arises from the medial surface of the femur, lying between the femorotibialis medius and adductor longus et brevis muscles. The fleshy fibers begin either at the level of, or proximal to, the insertion of M. iliacus (in most birds studied), or distal to that muscle (e.g., *Fregata, Falco, Polihiërax, Coccyzus, Geococcyx, Pharomachrus, Chloroceryle, Upupa Aceros*).

Hudson (1937) points out that this muscle "shows a very definite longitudinal division into two parts in *Buteo*," and that "many other forms show a slight division as in *Corvus*." Similarly, Stallcup (1954) reports that M. femorotibialis internus "is divided, especially near the distal end, into two parts, lateral and medial." Berger (1957) described two independent bellies and tendons of insertion in *Fregilupus*, similar to those described here for *Agelaius phoeniceus*. Berger also has found two independent bellies in *Dendroica kirtlandii*. Gadow and Selenka (1891: p. 156) described a half-tendinous head of M. femorotibialis internus arising from the spina pubica in *Lanius*. They postulated that this head represented a vestige of the ambiens muscle, which is lacking in passerine birds.

Gadow and Selenka also describe two or three parts to the muscle in ratite birds. Variation in the pattern of development of M. femorotibialis internus was found in three specimens of the Sandhill Crane dissected by Berger (1956e). The muscle was indistinctly divided into two heads in one right leg. In another right leg, one long and two short heads were present: each gave rise to a tendon and the three tendons fused for a common insertion. In the other dissections, there were two distinct heads. The posterior or long head arose from the postero-medial surface of the femur, beginning a short distance proximal to the area of insertion of M. iliacus; the origin was fleshy as far as the internal condyle. The short or distal head arose from a small area (about 2 cm long) on the anteromedial surface of the femur, just superior to the internal condyle. The small tendon from the latter head fused, in part, with the patellar ligament and, in part, with the tendon of the long head. The combined tendon inserted on the medial corner of the tibio-tarsus at the base of the inner cnemial crest. Berger (1953, 1956b) also described two tendons of insertion in *Coua caerulea* and *Paradisaea rubra*. Hudson (1937) notes that *Fregata* "is peculiar in having the tendon of insertion bifurcated, one branch connecting with the patellar tendon, the other with the tibia."

10. M. Biceps Femoris (*Extensor Iliofibularis*)

a. Columba livia. M. biceps femoris arises by a thin aponeurosis from the anterior iliac crest dorsal to the acetabulum and by fleshy and tendinous fibers from the anterior two-thirds of the posterior iliac crest. The well developed belly passes down the posterior surface of the thigh deep and posterior to M. iliotibialis and superficial to M. piriformis and M. accessorius semitendinosi. Near the distal end of the femur, the belly gives rise to a strong tendon which passes through the ligamentous *biceps loop* and inserts on a tubercle on the posterior surface of the fibula, beginning 10 mm from the proximal end of the bone. M. biceps femoris enters the leg musculature by passing between pars externa and pars media of M. gastrocnemius.

The biceps loop is composed of three arms: two femoral and one fibular. The proximal femoral arm (about 1.5 mm wide) is attached to a ridge on the anterolateral surface of the femur 7 mm from the distal end of the bone. The narrower distal arm is attached to the postero-lateral surface of the femur at the proximal end of the external condyle. The two arms form a ligamentous loop behind the knee which acts as a pulley for the tendon of insertion of M. biceps femoris. An extension from the bottom of the loop passes forward around the lateral surface of the fibula and attaches to its anterior border. A downward extension from this fibular arm fuses with the tendon of M. ambiens. Upward extensions of the fibular arm fuse with the patellar ligament and with the aponeurosis of origin of M. flexor perforans et perforatus digiti II.

b. Agelaius phoeniceus. M. biceps femoris arises by tendinous and fleshy fibers from the ventral surface of the posterior iliac crest in its anterior 5.5 mm. A small portion of the belly of M. ischiofemoralis is visible proximally between the posterior border of M. biceps femoris and the anterior border of M. semitendinosus. The belly of the biceps muscle passes down the back of the thigh, tapers to a small tendon, descends through the biceps loop, and inserts on a tubercle on the posterior face of the shaft of the fibula about 8 mm from the proximal end of the bone. The tendon of the biceps muscle enters the leg musculature by passing between pars externa and pars media of M. gastrocnemius.

The ligamentous biceps loop is composed of three arms: two femoral and one fibular. The proximal femoral arm (less than 1 mm wide) is attached to the anterolateral surface of the femur about 4 mm from the distal end of the bone. The distal femoral arm is attached to a tubercle on the proximal end of the external femoral condyle. The fibular arm passes distad from the bottom of the biceps loop deep to the origin of Mm. flexor perforans et perforati digiti II et III, and attaches to the shaft of the fibula a short distance inferior to the neck of the bone.

c. Comparative data. M. biceps femoris of Hudson, Berger, and Stallcup is M. iliofibularis of Gadow and Selenka, M. extensor iliofibularis of Howell and Fisher, and M. biceps flexor cruris of Shufeldt.

The biceps muscle arises by an aponeurosis and by fleshy fibers from the posterior part of the anterior iliac crest (e.g., *Columba, Goura, Coua, Crotophaga, Geococcyx, Corvus, Pipilo*) and/or from a variable length of the posterior iliac crest (most birds). There are two heads in hummingbirds (all?) and in *Aceros undulatus* and *Ceratogymna elata*. The anterior head in *Aceros undulatus* arises by a flat tendon from the dorsal surface of the antitrochanter of the ilium. The posterior head arises by fleshy fibers from the lateral surface of the posterior iliac crest for a distance of about 2 cm, at which point the posterior iliac crest curves sharply mediad and gives origin to M. semitendinosus. The two heads fuse at about the junction of the proximal and middle thirds of the thigh.

M. biceps femoris passes down the posterior surface of the thigh an-

terior to M. semitendinosus and superficial to the piriformis, ischiofemoralis, and accessory semitendinosus muscles. The major arteries and
nerves descend on the deep surface of the belly of the biceps muscle.
From its relatively wide origin, the belly of the biceps muscle tapers
to a stout tendon behind the knee, where the tendon, blood vessels, and
nerves pass through the ligamentous biceps loop. Beddard (1898: pp.
325, 363, 462) says that the tendon has three points of insertion in
Podica, and that in *Struthio*, the Anatidae, and some of the Rallidae and
Alcidae a separate slip of the biceps tendon inserts on the fascial covering of M. gastrocnemius. There is a single insertion on the posterior
surface of the fibula in most birds.

The biceps loop in most birds is similar to that found in *Columba
livia* and *Agelaius phoeniceus*. Minor variations in the relations of the
fibular arm occur. Beddard (1898: p. 226) says that the biceps loop is
absent in *Phaëthon* and in some swifts.

11. *Mm. Semitendinosus and Accesorius Semitendinosi ("X" and
    "Y" in Leg-Muscle Formulas)*

a. Columba livia. M. semitendinosus ("X") arises by fleshy and tendinous fibers from the posterior third of the posterior iliac crest and
by an aponeurosis from the dorsolateral edge of the ilium and from the
transverse process of the first free caudal vertebra. The bulky belly
passes downward and forward posterior to M. biceps femoris and superficial to M. piriformis pars caudofemoralis and M. semimembranosus.

A ligamentous raphe separates the belly of M. semitendinosus from a
second belly (M. accessorius semitendinosi; "Y") about 10 mm posterior
to the knee. The accessory semitendinosus muscle extends forward from
the raphe and attaches by fleshy fibers for a distance of about 4 mm
on the posterolateral surface of the distal end of the femur and extending
medially into the popliteal fossa. The area of insertion lies medial to the
distal head of M. femorotibialis externus and lies distal to the insertion
of M. adductor longus et brevis. The accessory semitendinosus muscle
lies deep to the inferior portion of the belly of M. biceps femoris.

The ligamentous raphe shared by the semitendinosus and the accessory semitendinosus muscles fans out into a broad aponeurosis at
the inferior margin of the muscles and then splits into two parts. The
smaller part fuses with the aponeurosis of insertion of M. gastrocnemius
pars media; the larger part of the aponeurosis fuses with the lateral surface of the tendon of insertion of M. semimembranosus.

b. Agelaius phoeniceus. M. semitendinosus arises primarily by tendinous fibers from the ventrolateral surface of the posterior iliac crest in
its caudal 2 mm and by an aponeurosis which extends medially posterior
to the ilium and superficial to the dorsal muscles of the tail to attach

primarily to the transverse processes of the first three free caudal vertebrae. The well developed belly passes downward and forward superficial to the belly of M. piriformis pars caudofemoralis and ends on a ligamentous raphe shared with the accessory semitendinosus part of the muscle complex. Part of the small raphe fans out into a flat aponeurosis inferior to the bellies of the two muscles. The aponeurosis fuses with the superior border of the aponeurosis of insertion of M. semimembranosus and inserts on the tibiotarsus with it. The remainder of the raphe fuses with the belly of M. gastrocnemius pars media.

The accessory semitendinosus muscle is a small band of fleshy fibers (about 7 mm long and 3.5 mm wide), extending between the common raphe and the distal end of the femur. The accessory semitendinosus muscle inserts on the posterior surface of the femur, beginning just proximal to the proximal arm of the biceps loop and extending medially into the popliteal fossa and to the inner surface of the internal femoral condyle and the origin of M. gastrocnemius pars media.

c. Comparative data. Garrod (1881), Forbes (1885), Beddard (1898), Shufeldt (1890), Hudson, and Berger use the names semitendinosus and accessory semitendinosus for this complex. It is M. caudilioflexorius of Gadow and Selenka, and M. flexor cruris lateralis of Howell (1938) and Fisher (1946). Garrod (1881: p. 208) proposed that the semitendinosus muscle be designated by the letter "X" and the accessory semitendinosus muscle by "Y" in leg-muscle formulas.

The posterior border of the thigh is formed by two muscles: the semitendinosus laterally and the semimembranosus medially. M. semitendinosus lies on the same plane as M. biceps femoris proximally, but, distally, the semitendinosus muscle passes medial to the biceps.

M. semitendinosus arises from the caudal part of the posterior iliac crest or from the dorsolateral edge of the ilium, sometimes also (by means of an aponeurosis) from free caudal vertebrae, and in some genera (e.g., *Gavia, Sula, Uria, Cathartes*) the origin extends downward onto the ischium or even to the pubis (*Chauna, Cathartes;* see Fisher, 1946: p. 663). When the muscle arises by an aponeurosis caudal to the pelvis, the aponeurosis typically passes between the dorsal and ventral muscles of the tail. The precise limits of the aponeurosis are, as Hudson (1937: p. 23) points out, difficult to determine because the aponeurosis fuses with the muscular fascia of the region. M. semitendinosus arises solely from the ilium in some birds (e.g., *Gavia, Podiceps, Opisthocomus, Grus, Fulica, Goura, Tauraco, Geococcyz, Coua, Aceros.*)

The belly of M. semitendinosus passes downward and forward superficial to Mm. piriformis pars caudofemoralis and semimembranosus. At a variable point posterior to the knee, the belly is divided by a tendinous raphe, which is very large in some birds but indistinct in others. Anterior to the raphe, the fleshy fibers (the *accessory semitendinosus muscle*) continue forward to an insertion on the femur, on or just superior to the condyles and the popliteal fossa. The most medial part of the insertion of the accessory semitendinosus muscle (on the posterior surface of the internal femoral condyle) typically is intimately related to the origin of pars media of M. gastrocnemius. Gadow and Selenka (1891: p. 163) discuss reasons for considering the accessory semitendinosus muscle as a femoral insertion of M. semitendinosus rather than as an accessory origin of the muscle.

The relative development of the accessory semitendinosus muscle varies considerably among different birds. An example of this variability is Hudson's description of this muscle in galliform birds (Hudson *et al.*, 1959): "The insertion of the accessorius is most extensive in *Pedioecetes*, reaching far above the middle of the femoral shaft; extends up to middle of femoral shaft or a little above in *Crax, Ortalis, Numida* and *Opisthocomus*. In all others the insertion is usually confined to much less than the distal half of the femoral shaft." In many birds, however, the accessory semitendinosus muscle inserts on a relatively small area in the popliteal fossa and a small area proximal to it (see description for *Agelaius*).

The accessory semitendinosus muscle has two heads in *Grus americana* and *Grus canadensis* (Fisher and Goodman, 1955; Berger, 1956e). In the latter species, the more proximal head inserts by fleshy fibers on the posterior surface of the internal condyle and the popliteal (intercondylar) fossa of the femur, immediately proximal to the common origin of Mm. flexor hallucis longus, flexor perforatus digiti III, and flexor perforatus digiti IV, and the tendon of origin of M. gastrocnemius pars media. The attachment to the femur is nearly transverse in direction, rather than vertical, as in many birds. The distal head of the accessorius muscle passes lateral to the tendon of insertion of M. semimembranosus and does not insert on the belly of M. gastrocnemius pars media, as it does in the Whooping Crane. Fisher (1946: pp. 662–665) describes two heads in the Cathartidae.

At the inferior border of the fleshy bellies of Mm. semitendinosus and accessorius semitendinosi, the raphe which separates the two muscles continues distad to the crus, where it inserts in a wide variety of patterns among different birds: solely on the tibiotarsus; on the tibiotarsus and on the tendon or belly of M. gastrocnemius pars media (e.g., *Coua, Geococcyx, Fregilupus, Corvus, Pipilo*), or pars interna (*Crotophaga*), or on both pars media and pars interna (*Coccyzus*); or part of the raphe fuses with the superior border of the tendon of insertion of M. semimembranosus (*Goura, Coracias, Aceros, Procnias, Paradisaea, Fregilupus, Pipilo*). In *Grus canadensis* the raphe continues downward between pars media and pars interna of M. gastrocnemius to become continuous with the common tendon of that muscle; the raphe is calcified about the middle of the belly of the gastrocnemius. In its course between the two heads of that muscle, the raphe is accompanied by a small fleshy belly, the "distal accessory" head of Fisher and Goodman. The raphe separating the two parts of the complex in *Aceros undulatus* takes a straight course distad from the deep surface of the belly of M. semitendinosus and fuses with the upper margin of the tendon of insertion of M. semimembranosus. The common tendon of insertion attaches to a ridge on the medial surface of the tibiotarsus, beginning 1.2 cm distal to the proximal articular surface of the bone and at the distal margin of the attachment of the medial femorotibial ligament. The raphe is not apparent on the superficial or lateral surface of the semitendinosus muscle.

When the accessory semitendinosus muscle is absent, M. semitendinosus gives rise to a tendon or a flat aponeurosis which usually fuses with the proximal border of the tendon of M. semimembranosus for a common insertion on the proximal end of the tibiotarsus.

Both the semitendinosus and accessory semitendinosus muscles have been reported in the following birds:

Struthionidae	Turnicidae	Meropidae
Rheidae	*Grus*	*Coracias*
Casuariidae	*Fulica*	*Upupa*
Dromiceiidae	Otididae	*Aceros*
Apterygidae	*Totanus*	*Galbula*
Tinamidae	*Larus*	*Indicator*
Oceanites	Columbidae	*Colaptes*
Phaëthon	Psittacidae	*Dryocopus*
Ardea	(one exception;	*Centurus*
Butorides	Beddard, 1898: 261)	*Asyndesmus*
Phoenicopterus	*Tauraco*	*Melanerpes*
Anhima cornuta	Cuculidae	Passeriformes
Cathartidae	*Steatornis*	(except *Dicrurus*;
Sagittarius	*Chordeiles*	Garrod, 1881: p. 222;
Galliformes	Coliidae	accessory absent)
	Momotidae	

The semitendinosus muscle is present but the accessory semitendinosus muscle is absent in the following:

Spheniscidae	*Phalacrocorax*	*Alca*
Gaviidae	*Anhinga*	Trogonidae
Podiceps	*Chauna torquata*	*Chloroceryle*
Procellariidae	Anatidae	*Sphyrapicus*
Pelecanus	*Podica*	*Dendrocopos*
Sula	*Heliornis*	*Picoïdes*
	Uria	

Both parts of the muscle are absent in *Fregata*, Accipitridae, Pandionidae, Falconidae, Strigidae, and Apodiformes.

12. *M. Piriformis* (*Caudofemoralis;* "A" *and* "B" *in Leg-Muscle Formulas*)

a. Columba livia. M. piriformis is composed of two separate bellies in the Rock Dove: pars caudofemoralis and pars iliofemoralis. The two parts lie deep to Mm. biceps femoris and semitendinosus and superficial to Mm. ischiofemoralis, adductor longus et brevis, and semimembranosus.

(1) *Pars caudofemoralis* ("A" in leg-muscle formulas) arises by tendinous and fleshy fibers from the ventral surface of the pygostyle but primarily from the dense aponeurosis which extends forward from the under tail coverts to the pelvis ventral to all of the tail muscles. The large, straplike belly (about 40 mm long) passes forward between Mm. semitendinosus (superficially) and semimembranosus (deeply), and gives rise to a 2.5 mm-wide tendon, which fuses with the deep surface of the distal half of the tendon of insertion of pars iliofemoralis.

(2) *Pars iliofemoralis* ("B") arises primarily by fleshy fibers from the ventral surface of the posterior iliac crest ventral to the origin of the posterior part of M. biceps femoris. The flat belly of pars iliofemoralis passes downward and forward superficial to pars caudofemoralis to insert on the femur by fleshy fibers and by a 4 mm-wide tendon, beginning about 15 mm from the proximal end of the femur (i.e., at about the junction of the proximal and middle thirds of the femur). Pars iliofemoralis inserts medial to the origin of the most proximal part of the distal head of M. femorotibialis externus.

b. Agelaius phoeniceus. Only one part of this complex is present in the blackbird.

(1) *Pars caudofemoralis* arises by a strong, but short (1.5 mm) tendon from the ventrolateral corner of the base of the pygostyle. From its flat tendon of origin, the well developed belly (about 23 mm long) expands to a maximum width of about 5 mm. The belly tapers again and inserts by a narrow (less than 1 mm wide), thin aponeurosis on the posterior surface of the femur, beginning about 7.5 mm from the proximal end of the bone. The belly of pars caudofemoralis passes forward deep to M. semitendinosus and superficial to M. ischiofemoralis.

(2) *Pars iliofemoralis* is absent in the blackbird.

c. Comparative data. Garrod (1881), Forbes (1885), and Beddard (1898) use the names femorocaudal and accessory femorocaudal for this complex. Fisher (1946) and Fisher and Goodman (1955) call it M. caudofemoralis, which consists of pars caudifemoralis and pars iliofemoralis; Gadow and Selenka (1891: p. 158) call it M. caudiliofemoralis. Hudson (1937) calls it M. piriformis because of Gadow's statement that the muscle is homologous with the piriformis muscle of mammals; Berger and Stallcup follow Hudson (Fig. IX.52).

In many birds, M. piriformis (femorocaudal) is composed of two independent parts: pars caudofemoralis and pars iliofemoralis. Gar-

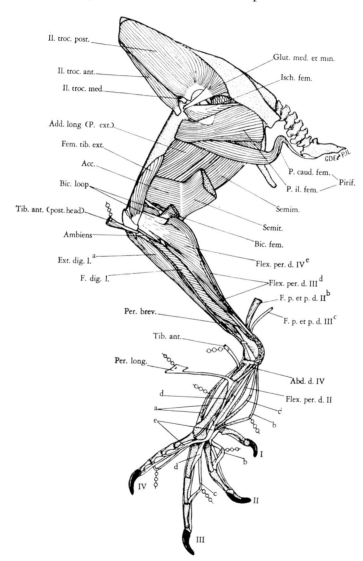

Il. troc. post.

Glut. med. et min.

Il. troc. ant.

Isch. fem.

Il. troc. med.

Add. long (P. ext.)

Fem. tib. ext.

Acc.

GDE PIL

Bic. loop

P. caud. fem.

Pirif.

P. il. fem.

Tib. ant. (post. head)

Semim.

Ambiens

Semit.

Ext. dig. l. ª

Bic. fem.

F. dig. I.

Flex. per. d. IV ᵉ

Flex. per. d. III ᵈ

F. p. et p. d. II ᵇ

Per. brev.

F. p. et p. d. III ᶜ

Tib. ant.

Per. long.

Abd. d. IV

d

Flex. per. d. II

a

c

e

b

b

I

IV

d

c

II

III

FIG. IX.52. Lateral view of a deep layer of muscles of the Blue Grouse. (By permission, Hudson *et al.*, 1959.) Superscripts refer to the tendons of the muscles concerned. For Key to Abbreviations see legend to Fig. IX.46.

rod (1881: p. 208) proposed that pars caudofemoralis be designated by the letter "A" and pars iliofemoralis (=accessory femorocaudal) be designated by the letter "B" in leg-muscle formulas. Fisher and Goodman use the name piriformis for the muscle which Hudson and others call M. gluteus medius et minimus.

(1) *Pars caudofemoralis* typically arises by a tendon or by an aponeurosis from the base of the pygostyle; it arises by tendinous and fleshy fibers in *Colinus, Zenaidura,* and *Tauraco.* The muscle arises primarily from the dense fascia covering the ventral surface of the tail muscles in a few birds (e.g., *Crax rubra, Grus canadensis, Columba livia*). Pars caudofemoralis arises by a small tendon (3 cm long, but only 0.5 mm in diameter) from the fascia covering the depressor muscles of the tail in *Grus canadensis tabida;* Berger (1956e) found no direct attachment to the pygostyle. In this crane the tendon of origin passes through a bony notch at the most caudal end of the projecting posterior iliac crest; the tendon is held in the notch by a ligament, which forms a fibro-osseous canal. Pars caudofemoralis arises by fleshy fibers from the "ventrolateral aspect of the transverse processes of the coccygeal vertebrae" in *Gavia immer* (Wilcox, 1952). Hudson *et al.,* (1959) discuss variations in the origin among genera of galliform birds.

The thin, straplike belly of pars caudofemoralis passes forward between M. semitendinosus and M. semimembranosus posteriorly, continues anteriad deep to M. biceps femoris and superficial to M. adductor longus et brevis, tapers to a tendon or an aponeurosis, and inserts on the posterolateral surface of the femur, medial (deep) to the area of insertion of pars iliofemoralis. The aponeurosis of insertion of pars caudofemoralis is said to fuse with the deep surface of pars iliofemoralis in some birds (Hudson, 1937; Hudson *et al.,* 1959), but the aponeurosis of pars caudofemoralis often can be teased away from pars iliofemoralis; in many birds, the two parts of the muscle insert independently. The area of insertion of pars caudofemoralis on the femur is near the proximal end of the bone (at the level of insertion of M. iliotrochantericus anterior) in *Pedioecetes,* about a third the way down the femur in many birds, at about its midlength in *Fregata, Bubo, Uria,* and *Chaetura,* and on the distal half of the bone in *Chen.*

Pars caudofemoralis is present in most birds but it is said to be absent in *Rhea, Dromiceius, Podiceps, Leptoptilos, Phoenicopterus, Gymnogyps, Sarcoramphus, Vultur, Sagittarius, Meleagris, Cariama cristata, Chunga burmeisteri, Psophia, Otis, Burhinus* (=*Oedicnemus*), *Balearica,* and *Grus leucogeranus* [But not in other species of the genus; see Gadow and Selenka (1891: p. 161), Beddard (1898: p. 367), Fisher and Goodman (1955), and Berger (1956e)]

(2) *Pars iliofemoralis* arises primarily by fleshy fibers from the lateral surface of the posterior iliac crest of the ilium in most birds. The posterior part of the origin is aponeurotic in *Grus americana* (Fisher and Goodman, 1955). The origin lies deep to the area of origin of Mm. biceps femoris and semitendinosus. In birds which have a projecting posterior iliac crest (e.g., *Crax rubra, Goura victoria, Geococcyx californianus, Coua caerulea*), the muscle arises from the ventral surface of the crest. The origin begins at the posterior border of the ilioischiatic fenestra (ischiadic foramen of Hudson, 1937: p. 27) in cuckoos. The origin extends downward onto the dorsal part of the ischium in some birds (e.g., *Gavia immer, Dendragapus*, Anatidae). The origin is limited to the ischium in *Uria*.

The belly of pars iliofemoralis passes downward and forward superficial to pars caudofemoralis and M. ischiofemoralis and inserts by fleshy fibers on the posterolateral surface of the femur. Although more bulky than pars caudofemoralis in most birds, pars iliofemoralis is a thin sheet of fibers in *Crax, Grus,* and *Goura*.

Pars iliofemoralis has been reported in the Spheniscidae, Struthionidae, Rheidae, Casuariidae, Dromiceiidae, *Apteryx*, Tinamidae, Gaviidae, Podicipedidae, some of the Procellariiformes, *Phalacrocorax* (variable), Threskiornithidae, Phoenicopteridae, some Anhimidae, Anatidae, *Sagittarius*, Galliformes, most of the Gruiformes (only one species of Turnicidae and not in *Rhinochetus, Grus leucogeranus,* or some species of *Balearica*), some of the Charadriiformes, the Pteroclidae, the Columbidae (except *Lopholaemus;* Beddard, 1898: p. 310), *Tauraco leucotis* (Musophagidae), and some cuckoos. A "peculiar extra accessory femoro-caudal which is pierced by the sciatic artery and nerve" has been described for *Struthio, Rhea, Casuarius, Dromiceius, Apteryx,* and the tinamous by Garrod (1881: pp. 206–207), Beddard (1898: pp. 490, 493), and Lowe (1942: p. 14). Beddard called it a "suprasciatic" slip of the accessory femorocaudal muscle.

Pars iliofemoralis is known to be absent in the following birds: *Pelecanoides, Phaëthon, Pelecanus, Sula, Phalacrocorax lugubris, Phalacrocorax brasiliensis, Anhinga, Fregata, Ardea,* most Ciconiidae, *Phoenicopterus,* all falconiform birds except *Sagittarius* (Hudson, 1948), *Turnix, Grus leucogeranus, Balearica regulorum* (Beddard, 1898: p. 367), *Totanus, Stercorarius, Larus,* some Alcidae, parrots, some cuckoos, owls, and representatives of all remaining orders that have been studied (e.g., *Chordeiles minor, Chaetura pelagica, Eugenes fulgens, Colius striatus, Pharomachrus mocino, Chloroceryle americana, Coracias abyssinica, Upupa epops, Aceros undulatus, Indicator variegatus,* all woodpeckers and passerine birds).

Both pars caudofemoralis and pars iliofemoralis occur in the following: Spheniscidae, *Struthio, Casuarius, Apteryx,* Tinamidae, Gaviidae, Procellariidae, *Phalacrocorax carbo* (?; Beddard, 1898: p. 405), Threskiornithidae, Anhimidae, Anatidae, Galliformes (except *Meleagris*), Mesoenatidae, Pedionomidae, some Gruidae, Rallidae, Heliornithidae, Eurypygidae, Jacanidae, Haematopodidae, Recurvirostridae, Dromadidae, Glareolidae, Thinocoridae, Chionididae, some terns, Rynchopidae, *Uria,* Pteroclidae, Columbidae (except *Lopholaemus;* Beddard, 1898: p. 310), *Tauraco leucotis,* some cuckoos.

Both parts of M. piriformis are absent in the following: *Leptoptilus,* some Cathartidae (*Gymnogyps, Sarcoramphus, Vultur;* Fisher, 1946), *Grus leucogeranus, Balearica regulorum* (Beddard, 1898: p. 367), *Chunga* ("*Dicholophus*") *burmeisteri* (Gadow and Selenka, 1891: p. 161), and *Steatornis* (Beddard, 1898: p. 237).

A notable example of the presence or absence of pars iliofemoralis within a family is found in the Cuculidae. Both parts of the muscle are present (formula AB) in *Coua, Carpococcyx, Geococcyx, Morococcyx, Dromococcyx, Centropus, Crotophaga, Guira, Ceuthmochares,* and *Phaenicophaeus.* Pars iliofemoralis is absent (formula A) in *Cuculus, Chrysococcyx, Clamator, Surniculus, Saurothera, Piaya, Coccyzus,* and *Tapera* (Berger, 1960a).

Intraspecific variation in the presence or absence of either part of M. piriformis has not been observed in the family Cuculidae but has been reported in the Gruidae. Some of the variation reported may represent anomalous variation in a given specimen. Pars caudofemoralis is very small in some birds (e.g., *Coragyps atratus;* Fisher, 1946: p. 667, Fig. 20), however, and may be in the process of "dropping-out" phylogenetically. In a bird the size of the Sandhill Crane, the belly of pars caudofemoralis is only 8 to 9 cm long and about 6 mm in maximum width; the tendon of origin is but 0.5 mm in diameter (Berger, 1956e). Similarly, the muscle is about 9 cm long and 7 mm in maximum width in the Great Curassow (*Crax rubra;* Berger, 1955b). Hudson *et al.* (1959) report that pars caudofemoralis is very weak in *Pavo* and has no connection with the pygostyle but arises from the fascia posterior to the ischium.

Fisher (1957c) studied the function of pars caudofemoralis in pigeons by removing sections of the muscle. He concluded that "any function the caudofemoralis muscles have in moving the tail, when a bird lands, is relatively so minor that it is easily and largely compensated for by other muscles."

13. M. Ischiofemoralis

a. Columba livia. This bulky, deeply situated muscle arises from nearly the entire lateral surface of the ischium beginning at the posterior margin of the obturator foramen and extending to the caudal end of the bone. The upper margin of the belly parallels the origin of M. piriformis pars iliofemoralis and lies deep to that muscle; the lower margin of the belly extends inferiorly to the origins of Mm. semimembranosus and adductor longus et brevis. The belly of M. ischiofemoralis passes forward and inserts by a strong, 2 mm-wide tendon on a ridge on the lateral surface of the femur, beginning 6.5 mm distal to the trochanter; the area of insertion lies posterior to, and between, the areas of insertion of Mm. iliotrochanterici anterior et medius.

b. Agelaius phoeniceus. M. ischiofemoralis arises by fleshy fibers from most of the lateral surface of the ischium and from the ventral surface of the projecting posterior iliac crest. A small area on the posteroventral surface of the ischium between M. ischiofemoralis (anteriorly and superiorly) and M. semimembranosus (posteriorly and inferiorly) is devoid of any muscle attachment. The tendon of insertion of M. ischiofemoralis forms on the superficial surface of the belly, tapers to a width of 1.5 mm, and inserts on a ridge on the lateral surface of the femur, beginning 2.5 mm from the proximal end of the bone.

c. Comparative data. This is M. flexor ischiofemoralis of Fisher (1946) and "M. obturator externus" of Shufeldt (1890: p. 186).

M. ischiofemoralis is the deepest of the muscles arising from the lateral surface of the ischium, dorsal to the areas of origin of Mm. adductor longus et brevis and semimembranosus. The origin of M. ischiofemoralis typically begins at the posterior margin of the obturator foramen. The muscle arises from the anterior half of the ischium in *Gavia* and *Chen*, from the anterior two-thirds in *Goura*, from the anterior two-thirds to three-fourths in *Ortalis, Penelope, Crax, Tympanuchus, Pedioecetes,* and *Meleagris,* and from nearly the entire surface of the ischium caudal to the obturator foramen in many birds. The typically well developed, fleshy belly converges on a strong, flat tendon, which inserts on the femur just proximal to the insertion of M. iliotrochantericus anterior.

14. M. Semimembranosus (Flexor Cruris Medialis)

a. Columba livia. This is a flattened band of fleshy fibers about 8 mm wide at its origin from a small area on the posteroinferior surface of the ischium dorsal to the ischiopubic fenestra and the most caudal origin of M. adductor longus et brevis. The belly passes distad medial to M. semitendinosus and posterior to M. adductor longus et brevis. As it reaches the leg, the belly of M. semimembranosus gives way to a thin, flat aponeurosis, which enters the leg musculature by passing between pars media and pars interna of M. gastrocnemius. The 6 mm-wide, bandlike aponeurosis inserts on the medial surface of the tibiotarsus, beginning 7 mm from the proximal end of the bone.

b. Agelaius phoeniceus. M. semimembranosus arises by semitendinous fibers on a line 5 mm long on the ventrolateral surface of the caudal half of the ischium about 1 mm dorsal to the ischiopubic fenestra. The wide, flat fleshy belly passes distad as the most caudal of the muscles on the posterior surface of the thigh. The belly ends on a dense aponeurosis (4.5 mm wide), which enters the leg musculature by passing between pars interna and pars media of M. gastrocnemius, and inserts on the posteromedial surface of the tibiotarsus, beginning about 5 mm from the proximal end of the bone.

c. Comparative data. This is M. ischioflexorius of Gadow and Selenka (1891: p. 166); M. flexor cruris medialis of Howell (1938) and Fisher (1946); M. semimembranosus of Shufeldt (1890), Hudson (1937), and Berger (1960b).

M. semimembranosus is the most medial of the muscles in the posterior part of the thigh (Fig. IX. 53). The thin, bandlike muscle arises by an aponeurosis or by fleshy fibers from the posteroventral edge of the ischium (primarily) and the pubis. The belly is wider in the male than in the female in *Phasianus* (Hudson *et al.,* 1959).

The belly gives rise to a thin, flat tendon or aponeurosis, which enters the crus by passing between pars interna and pars media of M. gastrocnemius and then inserts on a ridge on the anteromedial edge of the tibiotarsus near its proximal end. In most birds there is some connection between the tendon of M. semimembranosus and the raphe of M. semitendinosus as well as with some part of the gastrocnemius complex. In some birds (e.g., *Chen, Coracias, Aceros, Procnias, Paradisaea, Fregilupus*), part of the raphe of the semitendinosus muscle fuses with and forms the proximal portion of a common aponeurosis of insertion of Mm. semitendinosus and semimembranosus. There is no connection between the tendons of the two muscles in *Tauraco leucotis* and *Coccyzus erythropthalmus.*

Hudson (1937: p. 24) did not find M. semimembranosus in one specimen of *Podiceps caspicus.* The muscle has two heads in penguins and in *Phoenicopterus.* The second head has an unusual origin from the "aponeurosis of the abdominal muscles" in the penguins (Beddard, 1898: p. 397). There are two distinct bellies in the Falconidae (Beddard, 1898: p. 94; Hudson, 1948; Berger, 1956a). The two bellies insert together in *Falco.* The two bellies are independent throughout in *Polihiërax semitorquatus.* In this species, the two bellies arise adjacent to each other on the posteroventral edge of the ischium and pass downward and forward toward the crus. The posterior belly has a typical insertion for M. semimembranosus: by an aponeurosis (5 mm long and 1 mm wide) on the tibiotarsus, beginning about 4.5 mm inferior to the proximal end of the bone. The anterior belly arises anterior and dorsal to the posterior belly; it inserts by a flat tendon (3 mm long and 1 mm wide) on the postero-medial surface of the tibiotarsus deep to the medial femorotibial ligament and beginning 1.5 mm inferior to the proximal end of the bone. This is

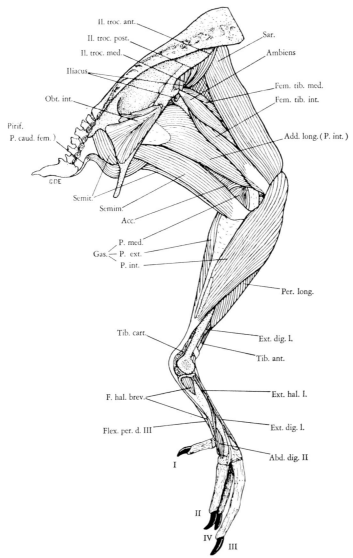

Fig. IX.53. Medial view of the superficial muscles of the left leg of the Blue Grouse. (By permission, Hudson *et al.*, 1959.) For Key to Abbreviations see legend to Fig. IX.46.

a typical area of attachment for the upper arm of the ligamentous raphe which separates Mm. semitendinosus and accessorius semitendinosi when those muscles are present; both of these muscles are absent in *Polihiërax.*

15. *M. Adductor Longus et Brevis* (*Adductor Superficialis et Profundus*)

a. Columba livia. This is a large rectangular muscle composed of two intimately related parts (pars externa and pars interna) in many birds and in some specimens of the Rock Dove. In some Rock Doves, however the two parts appear to be completely fused so that there is a single mass of muscle. The following descriptions apply when two more or less independent bellies are present.

(1) *Pars externa* arises by an aponeurosis (shared in common with pars interna) from the ventral margin of the ischium for a distance of about 14 mm, beginning just caudal to the obturator foramen. The line of attachment of the aponeurosis lies immediately dorsal to the ischiopubic fenestra. The fleshy fibers of pars externa arise from the outer surface of the aponeurosis a short distance from its attachment to the ischium. The belly passes distad medial to M. piriformis and inserts by fleshy fibers primarily on the posterolateral surface of the femur in slightly less than its distal half. The area of insertion lies just distal to the insertion of M. piriformis, medial to the origin of M. femorotibialis externus, and medial and proximal to the insertion of the accessory semitendinosus muscle. As it reaches the distal end of the femur, the posterior part of pars externa passes medially and fuses with the belly of pars interna to insert by fleshy fibers in the popliteal fossa of the femur and, by tendinous fibers, on the belly of M. gastrocnemius pars media.

(2) *Pars interna* arises from the ventral margin of the ischium by a common aponeurosis shared with pars externa. Anteriorly, pars interna arises by a small bundle of tendinous and fleshy fibers from the bone ventral and caudal to the obturator foramen. The muscle is fleshy from origin to insertion in its anterior 3 mm; posteriorly, the aponeurosis of origin extends distad a short distance (maximum of 6 mm) before the fleshy fibers arise in a modified V-shaped pattern. Pars interna inserts medial to the insertion of pars externa on the posterior surface of the shaft of the femur in slightly more than its distal third. Pars interna also inserts on the posteromedial face of the internal femoral condyle and, after fusing with the posterior part of pars externa, it inserts by fleshy and tendinous fibers on the belly of pars media of M. gastrocnemius.

b. Agelaius phoeniceus. M. adductor longus et brevis consists of two independent bellies, which, in passerine birds, are called pars anterior and pars posterior (Fig. IX.54).

(1) *Pars anterior* arises by tendinous and fleshy fibers on a 5 mm-long line from the ventrolateral surface of the ischium along the dorsal border of the ischiopubic fenestra, beginning at the caudal border of the obturator foramen. The flattened belly passes downward and forward

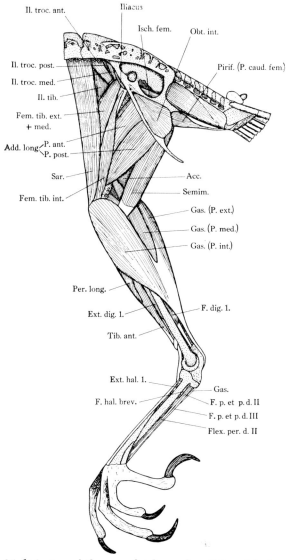

Fig. IX.54. Medial view of the superficial muscles of the right leg of the Common Crow. (By permission, Hudson, 1937.) For Key to Abbreviations see legend to Fig. IX.46.

to insert by fleshy fibers on the posterior surface of the femur in approximately its distal two-thirds.

(2) *Pars posterior* arises by a long, relatively wide (about 4 mm) and thin aponeurosis from the dorsal margin of the ischiopubic fenestra primarily posterior to the origin of pars anterior, but the posterior aponeurotic origin of pars anterior lies dorsal and superficial to the origin of pars posterior. The flat belly of pars posterior passes downward posterior and medial to pars anterior and inserts on a small area on the posteromedial surface of the distal end of the femur and the posteroproximal end of the internal femoral condyle, where the insertion is intimately fused with the origin of M. gastrocnemius pars media.

c. Comparative data. This is M. pubischiofemoralis of Gadow and Selenka (1891: p. 174); M. adductor superficialis et profundus of Howell (1938) and Fisher (1946); M. adductor longus et magnus of Shufeldt (1890); M. adductor longus et brevis of Hudson (1937) and Berger (1960b).

In most nonpasserine birds this complex consists of a superficial (pars externa) and a deep (pars interna) belly, but in passerines of an anterior (pars anterior) and a posterior (pars posterior) belly. There appears to be a single muscle mass in the following: *Gavia, Larus, Uria, Goura, Gallicolumba, Zenaidura, Chaetura, Eugenes, Chloroceryle, Colaptes,* and *Dendrocopos.* There is a suggestion of two bellies only at the insertion in *Indicator* and *Pharomachrus.*

Hudson (1937) has pointed out that both parts of this complex may be entirely fleshy or both parts may be partly tendinous at their origins. Pars externa (or pars anterior) almost always inserts by fleshy fibers, whereas pars interna (or pars posterior) may insert by an aponeurosis. Both parts of the muscle arise from the ventral margin of the ischium in most birds; the origin extends downward onto the ischiopubic membrane and pubis in some (Gadow and Selenka, 1891: p. 175; Stallcup, 1954); the muscle arises only from the ventral edge of the pubis in *Chaetura* (Hudson, 1937). The area of origin lies ventral to the origin of M. ischiofemoralis and either anterior or ventral to the origin of M. semimembranosus.

Pars externa of M. adductor longus et brevis arises dorsal to the origin of pars interna. Both parts insert on the posterior surface of the femur, and pars interna frequently has a connection with pars media of M. gastrocnemius. Pars externa inserts on the distal fifth of the femoral shaft in *Anas,* on the distal half in *Goura,* the distal two-thirds in *Crotophaga,* and on nearly the entire length of the bone in *Uria.* Pars externa is usually larger than pars interna, but it is smaller in some birds (e.g., *Fre-*

gata, Pedioecetes, Tympanuchus). Hudson *et al.* (1959) describe the relative proportions of the two parts in galliform birds.

Two bellies and tendons of insertion form from the common origin of pars interna in *Aceros undulatus*. One tendon inserts on a tubercle on the posteromedial edge of the femur medial to the most distal fibers of insertion of pars externa; the more posterior tendon passes distad to insert primarily on the posteromedial corner of the tibiotarsus, but it also fuses with the tendon of origin of M. gastrocnemius pars media. Beddard (1898: Fig. 101) shows three points of insertion in *Aceros nipalensis*.

16. M. Obturator Externus

a. Columba livia. This muscle consists of a single, fusiform belly about 8 mm long. It arises by fleshy fibers from the bone forming the ventral margin of the obturator foramen. The belly passes dorsolaterad superficial to the tendon of M. obturator internus and ends on a tendon, which fuses with the lateral margin of the tendon of M. obturator internus near its insertion on the proximal end of the femur.

b. Agelaius phoeniceus. M. obturator externus is composed of two independent bellies in the Red-winged Blackbird. The *dorsal belly* arises by fleshy fibers from the ischium along the posterodorsal border of the obturator foramen. The small fleshy belly (about 4 mm long and less than 1 mm in width) passes outward and forward, gives rise to a delicate aponeurosis, and inserts partly on the tendon of insertion of M. obturator internus and partly on the femur anterior to that tendon.

The larger *ventral belly* arises from the ischium along the ventral margin of the obturator foramen. The rectangular-shaped belly (about 2 mm wide) passes outward to insert primarily by fleshy fibers on a ridge on the lateral surface of the femur distal to the insertion of the obturator internus tendon; a few fibers insert on the obturator internus tendon.

c. Comparative data. M. obturator externus is M. gemellus of Shufeldt (1890).

M. obturator externus arises by fleshy fibers from the bone around the obturator (ischiadic) foramen. The muscle arises by a single head from the ventral, anterior, or (rarely) dorsal margin of the obturator foramen in the Anatidae, most galliform birds, *Columba, Goura, Gallicolumba, Tauraco, Eugenes, Upupa, Aceros, Indicator*, the Picidae, and certain passerine birds (*Passer, Estrilda, Poephila, Hesperiphona, Carpodacus, Pinicola, Leucosticte, Spinus*, and *Loxia;* Stallcup, 1954).

M. obturator externus is composed of two independent, primarily dorsal and ventral, heads in *Fulica, Larus, Uria, Pharomachrus, Chloroceryle, Coracias, Procnias*, and many other passerine birds (*Tyrannus, Corvus,*

Paradisaea, Artamella, Fregilupus, Sturnus, Aplonis, Vireo, Seiurus, Dendroica kirtlandii, Icterus, Molothrus, Piranga, Richmondena, Guiraca, Passerina, Spiza, Chlorura, Pipilo, Calamospiza, Chondestes, Junco, Spizella, Zonotrichia, Passerella, and *Calcarius;* Hudson, 1937; Berger, 1956b, 1957; Stallcup, 1954).

The fleshy fibers of both heads of M. obturator externus pass outward and insert, usually by fleshy fibers, on the femur just distal and/or posterior to the tendon of insertion of M. obturator internus. The dorsal head often inserts on the tendon of the latter muscle. In some birds (e.g., *Coracias*), the two heads of the obturator externus insert on, and almost completely conceal, the tendon of the obturator internus muscle. Both the dorsal and ventral heads are very large in *Procnias nudicollis*. The ventral head inserts by fleshy fibers on the femur distal to the insertion of the tendon of the obturator internus muscle; the dorsal head inserts by tendinous and fleshy fibers on the femur both proximal and posterior to the tendon of M. obturator internus.

M. obturator externus may be a single mass or may be partially separated into two heads in the Sandhill Crane. The muscle is a broad band of fleshy fibers with a nearly continuous origin from the anterodorsal to the anteroventral margin of the obturator foramen. The belly conceals much of the tendon of insertion of M. obturator internus and has a broad (1 cm wide), fleshy insertion both proximal and distal to the tendon of the obturator internus muscle.

17. *M. Obturator Internus*

a. Columba livia. This is a long, roughly oval-shaped muscle arising by fleshy fibers from the medial surface of the pubis, the ischiopubic membrane, and the ischium, beginning at the posterior border of the obturator foramen and extending caudally to the posterior end of the ischium and to within about 9 mm of the caudal end of the pubis. The belly tapers to a broad, thick tendon, which forms on the deep surface of the belly in the obturator foramen. The tendon passes through the foramen and inserts in a pit on the posterolateral surface of the femur just distal to the trochanter. A small band of fleshy fibers emerges from the obturator foramen and inserts on the deep and medial surfaces of the tendon as it curves around the posterior surface of the head of the femur.

b. Agelaius phoeniceus. M. obturator internus is a roughly triangular-shaped muscle arising by fleshy fibers from the medial surface of the ischium, the ischiopubic membrane, and the pubis. Two tendons form on the deep surface of the anterior part of the muscle. The two tendons fuse at the obturator foramen. The large single tendon thus formed passes through the obturator foramen and inserts on the posteroproximal end of the femur about 1 mm from the proximal articular surface of the bone.

c. Comparative data. Garrod (1881: p. 325) pointed out that M. obturator internus is almost invariably either distinctly oval or triangular in shape when observed in the undisturbed condition. This point deserves further investigation although it seems likely that the shape of the muscle is determined in large part by the shape of the pelvis. Garrod noted that the muscle is oval-shaped in grebes, shearwaters, pelicaniform birds, bustards, plovers, gulls, auks, pigeons, and a few other birds. The muscle is oval-shaped in *Goura, Gallicolumba, Pharomachrus, Chloroceryle, Coracias, Upupa,* and *Indicator.* Hudson (1937: p. 27) describes the muscle as being "long and slender" (=oval-shaped) in *Gavia, Podiceps, Fregata, Sula, Larus, Totanus, Uria, Zenaidura, Chordeiles,* and *Chaetura.*

M. obturator internus arises from the medial surfaces of the ischium and pubis; in some birds (e.g., *Gavia, Crotophaga, Geococcyx*), it also arises from the medial surface of the ischiopubic membrane. In some genera (*Fulica, Porzana, Megapodius, Crax, Lophortyx, Colinus, Tauraco, Coua, Geococcyx, Coccyzus*), a second head arises inside the pelvis from the ventral surface of the ilium (the posteroventral wall of the renal depression). This part of the muscle is visible through the ilioischiatic fenestra. There is no origin from the pubis in *Coragyps* (Fisher, 1946).

The fleshy belly of M. obturator internus typically converges on a stout tendon, which passes outward through the obturator foramen and inserts on the posterolateral edge of the trochanter of the femur. Two tendons form in certain American vultures (Fisher, 1946), and in *Fulica* and *Porzana* (Hudson, 1937); three tendons form in certain cuckoos (e.g., *Coua, Geococcyx, Crotophaga, Coccyzus;* Berger, 1952, 1953). These multiple tendons fuse to form a single tendon of insertion. Fleshy fibers pass out through the obturator foramen with the tendon of insertion in some birds (e.g., *Sula, Colinus, Dendragapus, Totanus, Geococcyx, Coccyzus*).

When present, the tendon of insertion of M. gluteus medius et minimus passes distad superficial to the areas of insertion of Mm. obturator internus and obturator externus.

18. M. Iliacus (*Psoas; "E" in Leg-Muscle Formulas*)

a. Columba livia. This is a flat, bandlike muscle 17 mm long and 2 mm in width throughout most of its length. M. iliacus arises by fleshy fibers from the ventral edge of the ilium just medial to the origin of M. iliotrochantericus medius. The belly passes backward and outward to insert by fleshy fibers on the medial surface of the shaft of the femur for a distance of about 5 mm, beginning 5 mm from the proximal end of the bone and extending distad between the two arms of origin of M. femorotibialis internus.

b. Agelaius phoeniceus. M. iliacus is a tiny band of fleshy fibers about 4 mm long and 0.5 mm in width. The muscle arises by fleshy fibers from the ventral edge of the ilium immediately posterior to the origin of M. iliotrochantericus medius. M. iliacus passes backward and outward, fans out to a width of about 1 mm, and inserts on the medial surface of the femur about 1.5 mm inferior to the neck of the femur.

c. Comparative data. This is M. iliofemoralis internus of Gadow and Selenka (1891: p. 144); M. psoas of Howell (1938) and Fisher (1946); and M. iliacus of Hudson (1937) and Berger (1960b). "M. iliacus" of Fisher equals M. iliotrochantericus anterior of Hudson and Berger.

Hudson (1937) reported that among American genera of birds M. iliacus is "present in all forms examined and is one of the most uniformly developed thigh muscles in birds." Berger, however, did not find M. iliacus in *Tauraco leucotis* (Musophagidae), certain genera of Old World cuckoos (*Coua, Carpococcyx, Centropus, Chrysococcyx, Cuculus*), *Upupa epops, Indicator variegatus,* or *Eugenes fulgens. Berger* (1959a, 1960a) proposed that M. iliacus be added to muscle formulas and that it be designated by the letter "E."

M. iliacus is the smallest of all the thigh muscles. It arises by fleshy fibers from the ventral margin of the ilium, anterior to the acetabulum and inferior to the origin of M. iliotrochantericus medius. The belly passes outward to insert by fleshy fibers on the medial surface of the femur a short distance inferior to its neck. The muscle is unusually large in *Chordeiles minor;* Hudson says that the muscle also is strongly developed in *Gavia, Podiceps,* and *Fulica.* M. iliacus is very small in many birds (about 1 mm in maximum width in many cuckoos) and might well be considered vestigial, with a weak action. In a bird the size of the Wreathed Hornbill (*Aceros undulatus*), M. iliacus has a fleshy origin from the ventral edge of the ilium for a distance of 8 mm anterior to the pubic tubercle. The belly rapidly tapers to a width of 1 mm, passes outward and backward, and inserts on the posteromedial surface of the femur about 1 cm distal to the neck of the bone. Gadow and Selenka (1891: p. 145) reported M. iliacus absent as an individual variation in *Bucorvus* and *Platycercus.*

19. M. Ambiens

a. Columba livia. The ambiens muscle ("Am" in leg-muscle formulas) is the most medial muscle of the thigh. The muscle arises by a short (3 mm long) bandlike aponeurosis from the ventral edge of the anterior portion of the pubis ventral to the acetabulum. The fleshy belly is about 20 mm long and 3.5 mm in maximum width. The belly tapers to a small tendon (about 0.3 mm wide), which increases in size as it reaches the distal end of the femur. The tendon then passes along the medial surface of the patella, takes a diagonal course (from medial to lateral) within a compartment in the patellar ligament, reaches the lateral surface of the knee, and then continues downward anterior to the head and neck of the fibula. The ambiens tendon crosses the lateral surface of the shaft of the fibula and continues downward deep to the tendon of M. biceps femoris. Deep to the biceps tendon, the tendon of M. ambiens fans out and gives rise to the distal heads of Mm. flexores perforati digiti II, III, and IV. A short distance inferior to the neck of the fibula, the ambiens tendon is reinforced by a ligamentous band that extends downward from the fibular attachment of the third arm of the biceps loop.

b. Agelaius phoeniceus. M. ambiens is absent in the blackbird.

c. Comparative data. Garrod (1881: pp. 212–214) divided birds into two groups according to the presence or absence of M. ambiens: Homalogonatae ("typically kneed, because the ambiens runs in the tendon of the knee") and Anomalogonatae (the "abnormally kneed," in which the ambiens muscle is absent). These terms are obsolete (except for use on doctoral examinations!), but further information is needed on the occurrence of the ambiens muscle among the families and genera of birds. Garrod used a plus or minus sign in his muscle formulas to indicate the presence or absence of the ambiens muscle. Hudson (1937) proposed that the muscle be represented by the symbol "Am."

M. ambiens is the most medial muscle in the anterior part of the thigh. It arises by a tendon and/or by fleshy fibers from the pectineal process (spina pubica), and, rarely (*Gavia*), the origin extends backward onto the body of the pubis. The flat, straplike belly extends distad toward the knee and terminates in a flat tendon, which passes diagonally downward and laterad through or deep to the patellar ligament (through the patella in a few forms) to the front of the knee. In the upper part of the crus, the tendon gives origin to at least part of one or more of the long flexors to digits II, III, and IV in most birds. In *Rhea* (variable), *Casuarius, Uria, Strigops, Burhinus, Opisthocomus, Phaëthon,* and some of the Procellariiformes, the tendon ends in the capsule of the knee joint, and, therefore, has no connection with the flexors of the toes.

Fisher and Goodman (1955) called attention to the differences in termination of the ambiens tendon in *Grus americana* and *G. c. canadensis.* In the former, the ambiens tendon serves as the "principal, if not sole, origin for M. flex. perf. dig. II, although there is strong fascial inter-connection between the origins of Mm. flex. perf. dig. II, III, and IV, and in one instance there is actually a branch of the main ambiens tendon that goes to the tibiotarsus." In the Little Brown Crane, "M. ambiens connected distally to the small lateral head of M. flex. perf. dig. III. It had little connection with M. flex. perf. dig. II and none with M. flex. perf. dig. IV."

Berger (1956e) found that the ambiens muscle arises primarily by a flat tendon from the pectineal process in the Sandhill Crane. The small, spindle-shaped belly (6 to 8 cm long and less than 1 cm in maximum width) gives rise to a very small tendon (1 mm wide). The tendon passes through the patellar ligament, passes distad medial to the biceps tendon, and serves as the primary origin for the lateral head of M. flexor perforatus digiti III; the ambiens tendon does not give rise to any other muscle.

Hudson (1948) reported that *Falco* "is apparently unique" among birds in that the ambiens tendon passes distad *lateral* to the tendon of insertion of M. biceps femoris. In *Polihiërax semitorquatus* (another member of the Falconidae), Berger (1956a) found that the ambiens tendon passes distad *medial* to the tendon of insertion of M. biceps femoris, as in all other birds thus far examined.

Hudson *et al.* (1959) described differences in origin, length of belly, and mode of termination of the ambiens muscle in a large number of galliform birds. Berger (1952, 1953) reported on variation in the termination of the ambiens tendon among genera of cuckoos. In *Crotophaga sulcirostris* the thin ambiens tendon forms a short distance above the femoral condyles. The tendon, concealed by M. sartorius, then passes through the patellar ligament along the distal surface of the patella to the lateral side of the knee. The tendon continues distad diagonally across the head of the fibula superficial to the third arm of the biceps loop, with which it is intimately fused. The ambiens tendon is further reinforced by a tendon arising from the posterolateral surface of the external femoral condyle. This combined tendon serves for a part of the origins of Mm. flexores perforati digiti II, III, and IV. In *Coccyzus erythropthalmus* the ambiens tendon serves as the sole origin for M. flexor perforatus digiti II, the primary origin for M. flexor perforatus digiti IV, and part of the origin of M. flexor perforatus digiti III. In *Coua caerulea* the ambiens tendon fuses with a broad tendinous band formed as a ventral prolongation of the proximal and third arms of the biceps loop. The resulting complex runs distad for a distance of 35 mm and serves as the sole origin for the anterior head of M. flexor perforatus digiti IV and serves as a tendon of origin for fleshy fibers of Mm. flexores perforati digiti II and III.

M. ambiens has been found in the following birds:

Spheniscidae	Anhimidae
Struthio	Anatidae
Rhea	Falconiformes
Casuarius	Galliformes
Apteryx	Gruiformes
Tinamidae	Charadriiformes (except *Rynchops*
Gavia	and most Alcidae; present in
Most Procellariiformes	*Uria* and *Cerorhinca*)
Sula	Pteroclidae
Phalacrocorax	Most Columbidae
Anhinga	Some Psittacidae (Beddard, 1898:
Fregata	pp. 268–269)
Most Ciconiidae	Musophagidae
Threskiornithidae	Cuculidae
Phoenicopteridae	

M. ambiens has been reported absent in the following:

Dromiceius	Most Psittacidae
Podiceps	Strigiformes
Phaëthon (?)	Caprimulgiformes
Pelecanidae	Apodiformes
Ardeidae	Coliiformes
Scopidae (?)	Trogoniformes
Some Ciconiidae	Coraciiformes
Rynchops	Piciformes
Most Alcidae	Passeriformes
Some Columbidae	
(e.g. *Goura, Treron,*	
Geopelia)	

It may be noted that the Ciconiidae, Alcidae, Columbidae, and Psittacidae have some genera that possess the ambiens muscle and other genera in which the muscle is absent.

20. M. Gastrocnemius

a. Columba livia. This complex is composed of three independent heads, each of which gives rise to an aponeurosis of insertion. The three aponeuroses fuse to form a common Tendo Achillis.

(1) *Pars externa* has a strong tendinous origin on a tubercle located on the posterolaetral surface of the femur just proximal to the external (fibular) condyle of the femur. The tendon of origin lies posterior and proximal to the femoral attachment of the distal femoral arm of the biceps loop and is partially fused with it. The belly of pars externa passes distad superficial to the biceps loop and the tendon of insertion

of M. biceps femoris. The belly extends about two-thirds the way down the crus and ends on a tendon which forms the most lateral part of the Tendo Achillis. Pars externa is separated from pars media by the distal end of the belly and tendon of insertion of M. biceps femoris.

(2) *Pars media* is separated from pars interna by the aponeurosis of insertion of M. semimembranosus. Pars media is the smallest of the three parts of M. gastrocnemius; its belly is about 20 mm long and 6 mm in maximum width. Pars media arises by tendinous fibers in the intercondyloid region of the femur and from the posterior surface of the internal femoral condyle. The area of origin lies just distal to the insertion of the accessory semitendinosus muscle. The most distal fibers of M. adductor longus et brevis insert on the belly of pars media a short distance beyond its origin. Rounded at its origin, pars media quickly becomes a flat band of muscle which ends on an aponeurosis. The aponeurosis passes distad between the bellies of pars externa and pars interna, fuses with them, and forms the central (posterior) part of the Tendo Achillis.

(3) *Pars interna* is the largest of the three parts of M. gastrocnemius. The belly extends a little more than two-thirds the way down the crus, concealing the muscles on the medial surface of the leg. Pars interna arises from the entire medial surface of the inner cnemial crest, from a small area on the head of the tibiotarsus, from the shaft of the bone for a short distance distal to the head, and from a plane of fascia lying between pars interna and M. tibialis anterior. The belly of pars interna ends in a tough tendon, which forms the medial part of the Tendo Achillis.

The conjoined Tendo Achillis passes over the posterior surface of the tibial cartilage, inserts on the posterior surface of the hypotarsus, and continues distad inserting on the posterolateral ridge of the tarsometatarsus throughout most of its length. By fusing with the deep fascia on the back of the tarsometatarsus, the distal portion of the Tendo Achillis completes a fibro-osseous compartment for the flexor tendons to the toes.

b. Agelaius phoeniceus. M. gastrocnemius is composed of the three typical heads in the Red-winged Blackbird.

(1) *Pars externa* has a well developed belly (about 23 mm long) extending slightly more than half way down the crus. Pars externa arises by a tendon from a tubercle on the posterolateral surface of the femur just proximal to the lateral condyle. The tendon of origin fans out on the deep surface of the muscle and is fused with the superficial surface of the distal femoral arm of the biceps loop. The belly of pars externa passes distad superficial to the tendon of insertion of M. biceps femoris and ends on an aponeurosis which forms the most lateral part of the Tendo Achillis.

(2) *Pars media* is a small muscle (13 mm long and 4 mm in maximum width) arising from a prominent tubercle on the posteroproximal surface of the internal femoral condyle. The origin is shared with the insertion of M. adductor longus et brevis pars posterior and lies adjacent to the insertion of the most medial and inferior fibers of the accessory semitendinosus muscle. The belly of pars media ends on a thin aponeurosis which passes downward between the bellies of pars externa and pars interna to form the central part of the Tendo Achillis.

(3) *Pars interna* is the most superficial muscle of the anteromedial surface of the proximal end of the crus. The muscle arises by fleshy fibers from the medial surface of the inner cnemial crest and the head of the tibiotarsus. The fleshy belly of pars interna ends on an aponeurosis a short distance beyond the midlength of the crus; the aponeurosis forms the most medial portion of the Tendo Achillis.

The common tendon of insertion of the three parts of the gastrocnemius muscle passes distad over the posterior surface of the tibial cartilage, inserts on the posterior surface of the hypotarsus, and continues distad to insert on the posterolateral ridge of the tarsometatarsus. Extensions of the Tendo Achillis fuse with the deep fascia on the back of the tarsometatarsus and form a sheath superficial to the tendons of the flexor muscles of the toes.

c. Comparative data. M. gastrocnemius is the largest and most superficial muscle on the back of the crus. The muscle is composed of three separate heads in most birds. *Pars externa* and *pars media* arise from the femur; *pars interna* arises from the medial surface of the inner cnemial crest of the tibiotarsus, sometimes also from the patellar ligament. The tendons or aponeuroses of the three heads fuse to form a common Tendo Achillis, which passes posteriorly over the tibial cartilage to insert on the hypotarsus (perforated process of Hudson) and the shaft of the tarsometatarsus. Sesamoids occur in the tendon in some birds, especially galliform birds.

At its origin, pars media is intimately related to the insertion of the accessory semitendinosus muscle. The tendon of insertion of M. semimembranosus *passes between pars interna and pars media*, except in *Aceros undulatus.* In some birds (e.g., *Chen, Cathartes, Pedioecetes, Colinus, Grus, Fulica, Totanus, Larus, Uria, Coua, Leucosticte*), pars interna covers not only the deeper muscles on the anteromedial aspect of the proximal end of the crus but also winds around to the anterolateral surface to conceal part of M. peroneus longus and/or M. tibialis anterior.

Pars externa has an unusual origin in *Gavia immer,* in which species the muscle arises from a long line on the lateral surface of the *distal half* of the shaft of the femur (Hudson, 1937).

Pars interna has a unique (?) origin in *Aceros undulatus* in that the muscle does not arise from the medial surface of the inner cnemial crest of the tibiotarsus but arises by fleshy fibers along a line (4 cm long) on the posteromedial surface of the shaft of the tibiotarsus, beginning just distal to the inner articular surface of the bone. Because of this origin, the tendon of insertion of M. semimembranosus does not pass between pars interna and pars media.

Pars externa consists of two separate bellies in the cuckoos (Berger, 1952); pars media is double in *Grus canadensis* and *Aceros undulatus* (Berger, 1956e). According to Hudson (1937), pars interna is double in *Gavia, Podiceps, Uria,* and *Chaetura,* "the semimembranosus inserting between the two heads." The tendon of M. semimembranosus, however, typically passes between pars interna and pars media of M. gastrocnemius, and one wonders, therefore, if it is not pars media that is double in the genera listed by Hudson. Stallcup (1954) described a bipartite configuration of pars interna in several passerine birds.

The intimate relationships between the insertion of the accessory semitendinosus muscle and the origin of pars media makes it difficult to interpret the second head of pars media in some birds. Beddard (1898: p. 217) considered the extra muscle to be a second head of the accessory semitendinosus muscle rather than an accessory head of pars media in the hornbills (see also Gadow and Selenka, 1891: p. 184). The accessory head in *Aceros* arises by fleshy fibers from the intercondyloid region of the femur just distal to the insertion of M. adductor longus et brevis and proximal and lateral to the femoral origin of pars media of the gastrocnemius complex. The origin of the accessory head of pars media is separated by an interval of 3 mm from the fleshy insertion of the accessory semitendinosus muscle. The accessory head of pars media passes distad lateral to a tendinous extension of the raphe separating the semitendinosus and accessory semitendinosus muscles and is reinforced by slips of the semitendinosus tendon.

Hudson *et al.* (1959) discuss intergeneric variation in the structure of the gastrocnemius complex among galliform birds. They describe a "narrow bridge of bone," extending between the hypotarsus and the posteromedial edge of the tarsometatarsus, which "apparently represents an ossified portion" of the gastrocnemius muscle.

21. M. Tibialis Anterior

a. Columba livia. This muscle arises by two typical heads. The *superficial* or *tibial head* arises from the anterior edge of the inner cnemial crest, the rotular crest, and the medial surface of the outer cnemial crest of the tibiotarsus. The *deep* or *femoral head* arises by a stout tendon (5 mm long) from a tubercle on the anterodistal end of the external femoral condyle. The spindle-shaped belly of the deep head fuses with the deep surface of the tibial head a short distance before the tendon of insertion is formed. The well developed belly (40 mm long) of M. tibialis anterior extends to within 15 mm of the distal end of the tibiotarsus, where the belly tapers to a large, flat tendon. The tendon is held close to the anterior surface of the tibiotarsus by a strong *ligamentum transversum* near the distal end of the bone. The tendon crosses the anterior surface of the tibiotarsal-tarsometatarsal joint and inserts on the anterior surface of the tarsometatarsus about 4 mm from the proximal end of the bone. Nearly the entire tibial head and the common belly of M. tibialis anterior are visible anterior to the belly of M. peroneus longus.

b. Agelaius phoeniceus. All but the most distal end of the tibial head and the common belly of M. tibialis anterior lies deep to the relatively large belly of M. peroneus longus. The *tibial head* of M. tibialis anterior arises under cover of M. peroneus longus from a small area on the lateral surface of the inner cnemial crest, from the rotular crest, and from a relatively large area on the medial surface of the outer cnemial crest of the tibiotarsus. The long (about 20 mm), rounded *femoral head* arises by a short, stout tendon from a pit on the apex of the external femoral condyle. The fleshy belly passes downward in the interval between the heads of the fibula and the tibiotarsus and then down the anterior surface of the tibiotarsus deep to the tibial head of the muscle. The two heads fuse about half way down the crus, a short distance proximal to the formation of the tendon of insertion. The over-all length of the tibial head and the common belly is about 30 mm, extending about three-fourths the way down the crus.

The single, large tendon of insertion passes distad deep to the ligamentum transversum, but superficial to the tendon of M. extensor digitorum longus, and inserts on the anterior surface of the tarsometatarsus about 3 mm from the proximal end of the bone.

c. Comparative data. M. tibialis anterior exhibits very little variation among different groups of birds except for the length of the fleshy belly. The muscle has two heads of origin, one by a tendon (often calcified) from the external condyle of the femur, the other by tendinous and fleshy fibers from the inner and outer cnemial crests and the rotular crest of the tibiotarsus. The femoral head is usually smaller than the tibial head, but the two heads are equal in size in *Grus* and *Uria*. The stout tendon of insertion passes under the ligamentum transversum near the distal end of the tibiotarsus. M. tibialis anterior typically inserts by a single tendon on a tubercle on the anterior surface of the proximal end of the tarsometatarsus. Small accessory tendons were mentioned by Hudson (1937), but these appear to be "subject to great individual variation" (Hudson *et al.*, 1959), and Berger did not find them in certain genera mentioned by Hudson. The muscle does insert by two separate tendons, one inserting anterior to the other, in *Bubo* and *Otus* (Hudson, 1937). The tendon of insertion contains a sesamoid bone in some galliform genera (Hudson *et al.*, 1959).

22. M. Extensor Digitorum Longus

a. Columba livia. The long extensor of the digits lies deep to M. tibialis anterior. M. extensor digitorum longus arises primarily by fleshy fibers from the rotular crest, the inner surfaces of the inner and outer cnemial crests, and from a long narrow line on the anterolateral surface of the tibiotarsus in a little more than its proximal half; there is a minor origin from the distal end of the patellar ligament. The belly (about 40 mm long) tapers to a tendon, which passes under the ligamentum transversum deep to the tendon of M. tibialis anterior and then through a bony canal at the level of the distal attachment of the ligamentum transversum just proximal to the tibial condyles. The tendon continues distad across the joint between the tibiotarsus and the tarsometatarsus and is held in place by a ligament on the proximomedial surface of the tarsometatarsus, after which the tendon passes distad medial to the tendon of M. tibialis anterior and lateral to M. extensor hallucis longus. The tendon continues its course along the anterior surface of the tarsometatarsus superficial in position to the intrinsic muscles in that region and immediately under the deep fascia of the anterior compartment of the tarsometatarsus. The tendon of M. extensor digitorum longus fans out in the distal half of the tarsometatarsus and then gives rise to four separate tendons: one each to digits II and IV, and two tendons to digit III. The tendons to digits II and IV end on the dorsal surface of the base of the terminal phalanx of those digits, but the tendons also have attachments to the proximal ends of the intermediate phalanges. The medial tendon to digit III ends primarily on the base of the second phalanx; the lateral tendon inserts on the terminal phalanx but also has attachments to the bases of the other phalanges of digit III. All of the tendons are intimately related to the deep fascia covering the dorsal surface of the digits.

b. Agelaius phoeniceus. Most of the small belly of M. extensor digitorum longus is limited to the proximal third of the crus although fleshy fibers insert on the tendon of insertion beyond the midlength of the crus. The muscle has a relatively large origin from most of the lateral surface of the inner cnemial crest, from the base of the outer cnemial crest, and from the anterior surface of the head and the proximal end of the shaft of the tibiotarsus. The belly passes downward medial to the femoral head of M. tibialis anterior and rapidly tapers to a large tendon. The tendon passes under the ligamentum transversum deep to the tendon of M. tibialis anterior and then passes through a bony canal just proximal to the condyles of the tibiotarsus. The tendon passes through a second bony canal on the proximal end of the tarsometatarsus and then continues distad medial to the tendon of insertion of M. tibialis anterior and lateral to the belly of M. extensor hallucis longus.

The tendon of M. extensor digitorum longus trifurcates near the distal end of the tarsometatarsus. Small tendons pass along the dorsal surfaces of digits II and IV, held close to the bones by dense fascial sheaths. The primary insertion of each tendon is on the dorsal surface of the base of the terminal (ungual) phalanx, but small branches of each main tendon insert on the bases of all but the proximal phalanx of each digit. The tendon to digit III is larger than the other two tendons combined. The tendon passes along the dorsal surface of the proximal phalanx of digit III and bifurcates near the distal end of the phalanx. The resulting medial and lateral branch-tendons insert on the dorsal surface of the base of the terminal phalanx and also send slips to the bases of the second and third phalanges of the digit.

c. Comparative data.   This is M. extensor digitorum communis of Gadow and Selenka (1891: p. 178)

M. extensor digitorum longus lies deep to M. tibialis anterior; it arises primarily by fleshy fibers from the anterior surface of the head and shaft of the tibiotarsus. The muscle exhibits very little variation among birds except for the length of the fleshy belly. The tendon of insertion passes under the ligamentum transversum near the distal end of the tibiotarsus and then under a bony bridge (the *supratendinal bridge* of Stallcup, 1954; the *inter-malleolar loop* of Hudson *et al.*, 1959), except in *Bubo* and *Otus*, in which genera the tendon is held in place by a ligament. In a single specimen of *Aceros undulatus*, Berger found a bony bridge on the tibiotarsus in one leg but a ligament in the other leg.

The tendon is held in place by a ligament on the proximal end of the tarsometatarsus in most birds, but the tendon passes through a bony canal in *Fulica, Zenaidura, Chaetura, Bubo, Otus*, the Picidae, and in some passerine birds (e.g., *Procnias, Tyrannus, Corvus, Paradisaea, Artamella, Dendroica kirtlandii*, and *Agelaius*). In addition to the genera reported on by Hudson (1937), Berger can state that the tendon of M. extensor digitorum longus is held in place by a ligament on the proximal end of the tarsometatarsus in *Grus, Gallicolumba, Tauraco,* cuckoos, *Pharomachrus, Chloroceryle, Coracias, Aceros, Upupa, Indicator, Fregilupus, Sturnus,* and *Aplonis.*

The tendon trifurcates near the distal end of the tarsometatarsus, sending branches along the dorsal surfaces of digits II, III, and IV. The primary insertion is on the base of the claw of each digit, but many accessory attachments are found in most genera. The minute details of insertion have been described by Hudson (1937), Hudson *et al.* (1959), Fisher (1946), Fisher and Goodman (1955), Berger (1952, 1953, 1957), and Stallcup (1954).

23. M. Peroneus Longus (Peroneus Superficialis)

a. Columba livia. This is a relatively weakly developed muscle on the anterolateral aspect of the crus. M. peroneus longus arises from a small, 8 mm-long aponeurosis (shared with M. flexor perforans et perforatus digiti III) attached to the anterior edge of the outer cnemial crest of the tibiotarsus; from a raphe shared with the underlying M. peroneus brevis in the distal part of the crus; and from the lateral surface of the fibula. The fleshy belly of M. peroneus longus (38 mm long) begins about 10 mm from the proximal end of the tibiotarsus and ends on a wide flat tendon about 10 mm from the distal end of that bone. The tendon is anchored to the lateral surface of the tibial cartilage by a large band of tendinous fibers. The configuration of this attachment in most birds is such that it is appropriate to describe it as the short branch of the tendon of insertion of M. peroneus longus. The main tendon crosses the lateral surface of the joint between the tibiotarsus and the tarsometatarsus and fuses with the tendon of M. flexor perforatus digiti III about 7 mm distal to the proximal end of the tarsometatarsus.

b. Agelaius phoeniceus. M. peroneus longus conceals all but the most distal part of the belly of M. tibialis anterior. The fleshy belly (about 28 mm long) of M. peroneus longus extends almost three-fourths the way down the crus. The belly arises primarily by fleshy fibers along a narrow line on the anterior edge of the inner cnemial crest, the rotular crest, and the outer cnemial crest of the head of the tibiotarsus. The origin is intimately related to the origin of the underlying tibialis anterior muscle. The belly of M. peroneus longus tapers to a medium-sized tendon, which bifurcates about 3 mm superior to the tibial cartilage. The larger branch continues distad in the direction of the common tendon and inserts on the proximolateral corner of the tibial cartilage. The smaller branch passes downward and forward over the lateral condyle, passes superficial to the tendon of insertion of M. peroneus brevis, and inserts on the tendon of M. flexor perforatus digiti III about 5 mm inferior to the proximal end of the hypotarsus.

c. Comparative data. This is M. peroneus superficialis of Gadow and Selenka (1891: p. 180). Hudson (1937) called it M. peroneus longus because of Gadow's statement that the muscle is homologous with M. peroneus longus of mammals. Moreover, the muscle is not always superficial in position.

The long peroneal muscle exhibits considerable variation in structure among birds and is absent in *Pandion*, the Strigidae, *Steatornis, Aegotheles*, Apodiformes, *Upupa*, and the Bucerotidae. Lowe (1946: p. 117) said that M. peroneus longus was absent in *Indicator indicator;* Berger found the muscle in *Indicator variegatus*. Lowe also reported the muscle to be absent or "much degenerated" in the Picidae; Burt (1930) and Hudson (1937) did not find this to be true.

M. peroneus longus may have a superficial (primarily tendinous) origin from the proximal end of the tibiotarsus and/or it may have a deep (primarily fleshy) origin from the fibula and the shaft of the tibiotarsus. The belly may be very large, covering the deeper muscles on the anterolateral surface of the crus, or it may be small, leaving M. tibialis anterior completely exposed (Hudson, 1937: Fig. 1; Berger, 1952: Plates II, XIV; Stallcup, 1954: Fig. 1). Mitchell (1913) discussed and illustrated Mm. peroneus longus and brevis in a large number of birds.

The tendon of insertion bifurcates in most birds. The short branch inserts on the tibial cartilage. The long branch (absent in *Gavia, Podiceps, Chloroceryle, Indicator variegatus*, and woodpeckers) crosses the intertarsal joint and inserts on the tendon of insertion of M. flexor perforatus digiti III a short distance inferior to the hypotarsus. Fisher (1946) found an accessory tendon attaching to the hypotarsus in *Vultur* and *Sarcoramphus.*

Despite the wide variation in relative development of Mm. peroneus longus and peroneus brevis among birds, neither Hudson (1937) nor Berger (1959a) felt that these muscles could be used profitably in muscle formulas. Intergeneric variation in the development of M. peroneus longus has been discussed in the Cathartidae (Fisher, 1946), Psittacidae (Beddard, 1898: p. 261), and the Cuculidae (Berger, 1960a). The muscle exhibits two extremes of development among the cuckoos. At its highest development, M. peroneus longus arises from the proximal end of the tibiotarsus, and its belly (or aponeurosis of origin) conceals all but the most distal parts of Mm. tibialis anterior and peroneus brevis. This situation is found, in general, in terrestrial cuckoos (*Geococcyx, Morococcyx, Centropus, Coua, Carpococcyx, Crotophaga, Guira*, and *Tapera*). In a second group of primarily arboreal cuckoos, M. peroneus longus is a long, thin, and deeply situated muscle, concealing no part of M. tibialis anterior (*Coccyzus, Piaya, Saurothera, Ceuthmochares, Clamator, Chrysococcyx, Cuculus, Surniculus*, and *Phaenicophaeus*). Because of this intergeneric variation in the development of M. peroneus longus among cuckoos, the relative development of the muscle is of no value in determining the relationship between the cuckoos and the tauracos, as proposed by Lowe (1943: p. 514).

24. M. Peroneus Brevis (*Peroneus Profundus*)

a. *Columba livia*. This is a relatively weakly developed muscle with a belly about 29 mm long. The muscle arises from the lateral surface of the tibiotarsus and the anterior surface of the fibula, beginning just distal to the insertion of the tendon of M. biceps femoris. The fusiform belly is very small at its origin but increases in size distally before tapering to a stout tendon, which is held in place by a ligament just proximal to the lateral tibial condyle. The tendon inserts on the lateral surface of the proximal end of the tarsometatarsus just anterior to the course of the long tendon of M. peroneus longus.

b. *Agelaius phoeniceus*. M. peroneus brevis has a small, spindle-shaped belly (about 22 mm long) arising from the anterior surface of the shaft of the fibula, beginning at the level of insertion of M. biceps femoris. The tendon of insertion is held in place by a ligament on the anterolateral surface of the tibiotarsus at the level of the ligamentum transversum. The tendon then passes deep to the long tendon of M. peroneus longus and inserts on a tubercle on the lateral surface of the proximal end of the tarsometatarsus.

c. *Comparative data*. This is M. peroneus profundus of Gadow and Selenka (1891: p. 182); "M. tibialis posticus" of Shufeldt (1890).

M. peroneus brevis arises by tendinous and fleshy fibers from the anterolateral surface of the fibula and the tibiotarsus. The origin may begin at the level of insertion of M. biceps femoris, or shortly distal to it; rarely more proximally. The origin is limited to about the distal fourth of the crus in *Goura*, to the distal third in *Fregata*, and the distal half in *Aceros*. The tendon of insertion is held in place by a ligament just above the tibiotarsal condyles, crosses the intertarsal joint, and inserts on the proximal end of the tarsometatarsus. The tendon typically passes deep to the long tendon of M. peroneus longus.

M. peroneus brevis has been reported absent in Ratites (except *Apteryx*), *Podiceps*, *Sula*, some of the Ciconiidae, *Scopus*, *Phoenicopterus*, *Aramus*, the Otididae, *Burhinus*, *Pterocles*, *Nyctidromus*, *Caprimulgus*, and *Chordeiles*; it is very much reduced or absent in *Recurvirostra*, *Haematopus*, and *Vanellus*. Although usually the smaller of the two peronei, M. peroneus brevis is larger than M. peroneus longus in the Procellariidae, Cathartidae, Falconidae, some Psittacidae, *Podargus*, and in some coraciiform and piciform genera.

25. *M. Flexor Perforans et Perforatus Digiti III*

a. Columba livia. This muscle and M. flexor perforans et perforatus digiti II are the most superficial muscles on the lateral surface of the proximal end of the crus. The bellies of the two muscles are flanked posteriorly by M. gastrocnemius pars externa and anteriorly by Mm. tibialis anterior and peroneus longus. M. flexor perforans et perforatus digiti III lies anterior to M. flexor perforans et perforatus digiti II. The two muscles conceal the femoral head of M. tibialis anterior, the ambiens tendon, the biceps loop, and the tendon of insertion of M. biceps femoris.

M. flexor perforans et perforatus digiti III has a tendinous origin (shared with M. peroneus longus) from the anterior edge of the outer cnemial crest of the tibiotarsus and a fleshy origin from the lateral surface of the outer cnemial crest and the patellar ligament. The posterior edge of the proximal end of the belly is fused with the anterior edge of M. flexor perforans et perforatus digiti II for a distance of about 10 mm; the bellies of the two muscles arise in a pennate manner from a raphe between the two muscles.

The 37 mm-long belly of M. flexor perforans et perforatus digiti III tapers to a small, flat tendon, which passes through a fibrous canal in the lateral part of the posterior surface of the tibial cartilage medial to the tendon of M. flexor perforatus digiti IV and superficial to the wide tendon of M. flexor perforatus digiti III. The tendon of M. flexor perforans et perforatus digiti III then descends along the posterior surface of the tarsometatarsus with the other flexor tendons to the toes. The tendon of M. flexor perforans et perforatus digiti III is connected to the tendon of M. flexor perforatus digiti III by a *vinculum* near the distal end of the tarsometatarsus. The tendon of M. flexor perforans et perforatus digiti III then expands and passes deep to the tendon of M. flexor perforatus digiti III, perforating the latter tendon at about the midlength of the proximal phalanx of digit III.The tendon of M. flexor perforans et perforatus digiti III bifurcates to permit the passage of the tendon of M. flexor digitorum longus; the resulting two branches insert, respectively, on the medial and lateral corners of the proximal end of the third phalanx of digit III.

b. Agelaius phoeniceus. M. flexor perforans et perforatus digiti III is the most superficial muscle on the lateral surface of the crus, lying anterior to M. gastrocnemius pars externa and M. flexor perforans et perforatus digiti II and posterior to M. peroneus longus. M. flexor perforans et perforatus digiti III arises by two heads, although the posterior head is very tiny. The *anterior head* arises primarily by fleshy fibers from the lateral surface of the outer cnemial crest of the tibiotarsus and the head of the fibula; there is some aponeurotic origin shared with M. peroneus longus. The *posterior head* arises by an aponeurosis from the lateral femoral condyle just distal to the origin of M. flexor perforans et perforatus digiti II. The belly of M. flexor perforans et perforatus digiti III (with an over-all length of about 25 mm) rapidly tapers to a fair-sized tendon, which passes down the posterior surface of the crus under cover of the gastrocnemius muscle and tendon, through a fibrous canal in the medial half of the tibial cartilage, and then through the most superficial bony canal in the medial half of the hypotarsus. The tendon expands near the distal end of the tarsometatarsus, passes deep to (and is ensheathed by) the tendon of M. flexor perforatus digiti III, and then ensheathes the tendon of M. flexor digitorum longus. The tendon of M. flexor perforans et perforatus digiti III splits to permit the passage of the tendon of M. flexor digitorum longus near the middle of the second phalanx of digit III and then inserts on the base of the third phalanx of the digit.

c. Comparative data. This is "M. flexor perforatus medius secundus pedis" of Shufeldt (1890).

This and the following muscle are the two perforating and perforated flexor muscles of digits II and III. The proximal portions of the bellies of both muscles are visible on the lateral surface of the crus after the skin and sucutaneous connective tissue have been removed in most birds (as described for *Columba* and *Agelaius*), and both muscles are completely exposed after Mm. peroneus longus and gastrocnemius pars externa have been reflected. Hudson (1937) says that M. flexor perforans et perforatus digiti II overlaps and completely conceals the proximal part of M. flexor perforans et perforatus digiti III in *Larus;* this is an unusual pattern.

M. flexor perforans et perforatus digiti III has a complex origin from the patellar ligament, the femur, tibiotarsus, and fibula (from the fibula only in *Chaetura*) among different birds. The tendon of insertion passes through a fibrous canal in the tibial cartilage and through a bony canal in the hypotarsus in many birds. The tendon perforates the tendon of M. flexor perforatus digiti III at the level of the proximal phalanx of digit III and, more distally, is perforated by the tendon to digit III from M. flexor digitorum longus; the tendon inserts on one or more of the phalanges of digit III. Detailed descriptions of the origin of the muscle and the mode of insertion are given in the papers by Hudson (1937), Hudson *et al.* (1959), Fisher (1946), Fisher and Goodman (1955), Berger (1952, 1953, 1957), and Stallcup (1954). These authors also described the intricate relations of the flexor tendons in their course through the tibial cartilage and the hypotarsus. There is wide variation in pattern of the tendons among different groups of birds, but the pattern appears to be relatively uniform in a closely related group, especially within the tibial cartilage.

The *hypotarsus* (*perforated process* of Hudson) exhibits much variation in structure. It may be a well developed bony process containing from one to five bony canals, or it may take the form of two or more parallel vertical ridges and grooves and a single or no bony canal. All seven of the flexor tendons pass through bony canals in the hypotarsus in *Gavia*, the Picidae, and the Passeriformes. All of the tendons except that of M. flexor hallucis longus pass through bony canals in *Indicator variegatus*. Only the tendon of Mm. flexor digitorum longus and flexor hallucis longus pass through bony canals in *Fregata, Sula, Ardea, Pandion,* the Cuculidae, and *Aceros*. Only the tendon of M. flexor digitorum longus traverses a bony canal in *Butorides, Chen, Grus, Totanus, Larus, Tauraco, Chordeiles, Chloroceryle, Coracias,* and *Upupa*. None of the flexor tendons pass through bony canals in the Falconiformes (except *Pandion*), *Uria, Chaetura, Bubo,* and *Otus*. Other patterns are described by Hudson (1937) and Hudson *et al.* (1959).

In their course down the posterior sulcus of the hypotarsus, the tendons of Mm. flexor perforatus digiti III and flexor perforans et perforatus digiti III are connected by a tendinous band or *vinculum* in some birds. Hudson (1937) proposed that this vinculum be represented by the letter "V" in muscle formulas. Our knowledge of the occurrence of this vinculum is limited almost entirely to information obtained since Hudson's 1937 paper. The vinculum has been found in the following: *Gavia, Sula,* Anatidae, Cathartidae, *Sagittarius,* Galliformes (except *Opisthocomus*), *Grus, Fulica, Totanus, Larus, Pterocles, Columba, Zenaidura, Goura, Gallicolumba,* and *Tauraco*.

The vinculum has not been found in *Podiceps, Fregata, Ardea, Buteo, Falco, Polihiërax, Uria,* the Cuculidae, *Bubo, Otus, Chordeiles, Chaetura, Pharomachrus, Chloroceryle, Coracias, Upupa, Aceros, Indicator, Colaptes, Dendrocopos,* and all passerine birds thus far studied (including *Procnias nudicollis*).

Hudson (1937) and Fisher and Goodman (1955) found a vinculum in *Grus c. canadensis,* and Berger (1956e) found a vinculum in *Grus canadensis tabida*. Fisher and Goodman, however, did not find a vinculum in *Grus americana,* although they added "V" to the muscle formula for this species.

26. M. Flexor Perforans et Perforatus Digiti II

a. Columba livia. This superficial muscle arises by fleshy fibers from the lateral surface of the external femoral condyle (distal to the femoral attachment of the distal arm of the biceps loop, and just lateral to, and partly fused with, M. flexor hallucis longus), and by an aponeurosis, which is fused with the underlying fibular arm of the biceps loops and the lateral femorofibular ligaments of the knee joint. The proximal part of the belly is fused with the belly of M. flexor perforans et perforatus digiti III.

The belly (24 mm long) of M. flexor perforans et perforatus digiti II tapers to a flat, bandlike tendon, which forms on the superficial surface of the belly. The tendon rapidly tapers in width, passes through the most medial of the fibrous canals on the back of the tibial cartilage, and then passes through a bony canal in the hypotarsus. The tendon lies posterior to the tendon of M. flexor perforatus digiti II within the bony canal. At the distal end of the tarsometatarus, the tendon of M. flexor perforans et perforatus digiti II passes deep to the tendon of M. flexor perforatus digiti II and then is completely ensheathed by the greatly expanded tendon of that muscle. The tendon of M. flexor perforans et perforatus digiti II also expands into a thick fibrous mass, which ensheathes the tendon of M. flexor digitorum longus, and then gives rise (after being perforated by the flexor digitorum longus tendon) to a single, strong tendon; it inserts on the medial corner of the base of the second (middle) phalanx of digit II.

b. Agelaius phoeniceus. M. flexor perforans et perforatus digiti II is a small muscle with a belly 10 mm long and 2 mm in maximum width. Proximally, the belly is visible anterior to M. gastrocnemius pars externa but most of the belly and the tendon of insertion are concealed by pars externa. M. flexor perforans et perforatus digiti II arises from a small area on the posteroproximal face of the lateral femoral condyle just distal to the origin of M. gastrocnemius pars externa. The aponeurosis of origin is shared with the more deeply situated Mm. flexor perforatus digiti II and flexor hallucis longus; fleshy fibers on the anterior and deep surface of M. flexor perforans et perforatus digiti II arise from a raphe shared with M. flexor perforans et perforatus digiti III.

The belly of M. flexor perforans et perforatus digiti II ends on a flat aponeurosis, which tapers to a small tendon. The tendon passes distad deep to the belly and tendon of M. gastrocnemius, through the posterior surface of the tibial cartilage, and then traverses a bony canal on the medial surface of the hypotarsus. The tendon continues down the posterior surface of the tarsometatarsus and through the lateral surface of a large fibrocartilaginous pulley at the base of digit II to reach the plantar surface of that digit. The tendon then expands and forms a sheath for the tendon of M. flexor digitorum longus near the middle of the proximal phalanx of digit II, splits to permit the passage of the longus tendon, and inserts on the medial side of the base of the second phalanx of digit II.

c. Comparative data. This is "M. flexor perforatus indicis secundus pedis" of Shufeldt.

The single head (two in some galliform birds; three in *Gavia*) of M. flexor perforans et perforatus digiti II usually arises from the external femoral condyle and the patellar ligament, but it has a tibial origin also in *Ardea, Falco, Fulica,* and *Larus;* the origin is primarily from the fibula in *Fregata.* The belly typically is much smaller than that of M. flexor perforans et perforatus digiti III, but M. flexor perforans et perforatus digiti II is relatively large in *Gavia, Podiceps,* many galliform birds, *Fulica, Bubo,* and *Otus.* The discrepancy in size between the bellies of the two muscles is especially marked in *Indicator variegatus.* The belly of M. flexor perforans et perforatus digiti III is, relatively, very large in *Indicator* (23 mm long and 5 mm in maximum width), and extends almost three-fourths the way down the crus. By contrast, the belly of M. flexor perforans et perforatus digiti II is only 10 mm long and 2 mm in maximum width; it gives rise to the smallest of the long flexor tendons to the toes.

Before the tendon of M. flexor perforans et perforatus digiti II inserts on one or more of the phalanges of digit II, the tendon perforates the tendon of M. flexor perforatus digiti II (in most birds), and shortly thereafter is perforated by the tendon of M. flexor digitorum longus. The tendon of M. flexor perforatus digiti II is not perforated by the tendon of M. flexor perforans et perforatus digiti II in *Pharomachrus, Aceros, Upupa, Paradisaea, Fregilupus, Sturnus, Aplonis, Artamella, Agelaius,* and *Dendroica.* The tendon of M. flexor perforans et perforatus digiti II is not perforated by the tendon of M. flexor digitorum longus in *Coccyzus, Chaetura,* and woodpeckers.

27. *M. Flexor Perforatus Digiti IV*

a. Columba livia. This muscle lies deep to Mm. flexores perforantes et perforati digiti II et III and superficial to M. flexor perforatus digiti III. M. flexor perforatus digiti IV is fused to the superficial surface of M. flexor perforatus digiti III for a distance of about 30 mm.

M. flexor perforatus digiti IV arises by two heads. A *proximal* or *femoral head* arises in common with M. flexor perforatus digiti III from the lateral part of the intercondyloid region of the femur. The femoral head arises just distal to the insertion of the accessory semitendinosus muscle, lateral to the origin of M. gastrocnemius pars media, medial to the origin of M. gastrocnemius pars externa, and just proximal to the origin of M. flexor hallucis longus.

The *distal head* of M. flexor perforatus digiti IV arises as a direct continuation of the ambiens tendon, in common with, but superficial to, the distal heads of Mm. flexores perforati digiti II et III.

The tendon of insertion of M. flexor perforatus digiti IV forms along the posterior edge of the tapering belly of the muscle. The tendon passes down the posterolateral surface of the crus and through a fibrous canal on the lateral half of the tibial cartilage. Within the canal, the tendon lies lateral to the tendon of M. flexor perforans et perforatus digiti III, and both tendons descend on the surface of the greatly expanded tendon of M. flexor perforatus digiti III. The tendon of M. flexor perforatus digiti IV fans out into a large fibrous mass at the distal end of the tarsometatarsus and then splits to permit the passage of the tendon of M. flexor digitorum longus opposite the head of the proximal phalanx of digit IV. A large slip from the deep surface of the tendon of M. flexor perforatus digiti IV inserts on most of the plantar surface of the base of the second phalanx of the digit; the main tendon splits into two terminal branches; these have attachments on the medial and lateral surfaces of the bases of the third and fourth phalanges of digit IV.

b. Agelaius phoeniceus. M. flexor perforatus digiti IV has a large tendinous and fleshy origin (shared with Mm. flexor perforatus digiti III and flexor hallucis longus) from the intercondyloid region of the femur, extending medially onto the posterior face of the internal femoral condyle. The area of origin lies immediately distal to the area of insertion of the accessory semitendinosus muscle. M. flexor perforatus digiti IV is the most posterior of the three muscles sharing the common origin. The fleshy belly of M. flexor perforatus digiti IV (about 28 mm long) extends about three-fourths the way down the crus and ends on a flat tendon. The tendon passes through a fibrous canal in the lateral half of the tibial cartilage and through the most superficial of the bony canals in the lateral half of the hypotarsus. In its course through the tibial cartilage and the bony canal in the hypotarsus, and throughout most of its descent along the posterolateral surface of the tarsometatarsus, the tendon of M. flexor perforatus digiti IV lies superficial to the tendon of M. flexor perforatus digiti III. The tendon of M. flexor perforatus digiti IV expands as it crosses the distal end of the tarsometatarsus, forms a sheath around the tendon of M. flexor digitorum longus, gives rise to a wide branch which inserts on the fibrous joint pad between the first and second phalanges of digit IV, and then splits to permit the passage of the tendon of M. flexor digitorum longus. The tendon of M. flexor perforatus digiti IV then inserts on the plantar joint pad between the second and third phalanges of digit IV.

c. Comparative data. This is "M. flexor perforatus annularis primus pedis" of Shufeldt (1890).

M. flexor perforatus digiti IV arises from the intercondyloid region of the femur in *Podiceps, Fregata, Sula, Uria,* and most passerines (*Tyrannus* is an exception; Hudson, 1937). The origin by fleshy fibers from the posterior surface of the femur proximal to the intercondyloid region in *Gavia* is unusual. The single head in *Falco* and *Polihiërax* arises from the lateral femoral condyle and the head of the fibula; the single head arises from the external femoral condyle only in *Chaetura pelagica*.

M. flexor perforatus digiti IV has two heads of origin in many birds. The medial head arises from the intercondyloid region of the femur. The lateral head arises from the lateral femoral condyle, from the head and/or shaft of the fibula, from the ambiens tendon (e.g., *Columba, Tauraco,* cuckoos), or from other flexor muscles. The tendon of insertion of the biceps femoris muscle may pass between the two heads or pass lateral to both of them (see Hudson, 1937: p. 43). In *Aceros undulatus,* the two heads arise, respectively, from the posterior surface of the shaft of the fibula and from the deep surface of M. flexor perforans et perforatus digiti II.

The tendon of insertion of M. flexor perforatus digiti IV forms a sheath around the tendon of M. flexor digitorum longus in most birds: that is, the tendon is perforated by the longus tendon. The tendon of M. flexor perforatus digiti IV is not perforated by the tendon of M. flexor digitorum longus in 16 genera of cuckoos studied by Berger (1960a), but it is perforated by the longus tendon in *Dromococcyx* and *Phaenicophaeus. Phaenicophaeus* presents an intermediate condition in that about 95% of the tendon inserts on the lateral side of the basal phalanx of digit IV, whereas the remainder of the tendon inserts on the medial side of the same phalanx. Hudson (1937) reported that the longus tendon does not perforate the tendon of M. flexor perforatus digiti IV in the Picidae.

28. M. Flexor Perforatus Digiti III

a. Columbia livia. This muscle arises by two heads, both of which are shared with M. flexor perforatus digiti IV. Fleshy fibers of the *femoral head* arise from the superficial surface of an aponeurosis attached to the medial part of the intercondyloid region of the femur. The *distal head* arises in common with, but deep to, the distal head of M. flexor perforatus digiti IV as a continuation of the ambiens tendon. The two heads fuse at the level of insertion of the biceps tendon. The deep surface of the common belly is intimately fused with the belly of M. flexor perforatus digiti II. An *accessory belly* (14 mm long; two specimens) arises as a continuation of the ambiens tendon, although the accessory belly appears to split off the anterolateral surface of the main belly at about the midlength of the crus. The accessory belly gives rise to an independent tendon, which fuses with the tendon of the main belly a short distance proximal to the tibial cartilage.

The large tendon of insertion (over 1 mm wide) of M. flexor perforatus digiti III descends through the superficial fibrous compartment in the lateral half of the tibial cartilage. The tendons of Mm. flexor perforatus digiti IV and flexor perforans et perforatus digiti III descend on the superficial surface of the tendon of M. flexor perforatus digiti III.

The long tendon of M. peroneus longus inserts on the tendon of M. flexor perforatus digiti III about 3 mm inferior to the hypotarsus. At the level of the first metatarsal bone, a *vinculum* passes downward from the tendon of M. flexor perforatus digiti III and fuses with the tendon of M. flexor perforans et perforatus digiti III. The tendon of M. flexor perforatus digiti III then expands and passes distad to about the middle of the proximal phalanx of digit III, where the tendon bifurcates to permit the passage of the tendons of Mm. flexor perforans et perforatus digiti III and flexor digitorum longus. The two branches of the tendon of M. flexor perforatus digiti III then insert on the medial and lateral corners of the base of the second phalanx of digit III and on the fibrocartilaginous pad on the plantar surface of the joint between the proximal and second phalanges of the digit.

b. Agelaius phoeniceus. M. flexor perforatus digiti III arises in the intercondyloid region of the femur from the most medial portion of the common tendinous and fleshy origin shared with Mm. flexor perforatus digiti IV and flexor hallucis longus. The small belly (about 23 mm long) of M. flexor perforatus digiti III extends a little over half way down the crus. The belly ends on a flat tendon, which expands as it nears the tibial cartilage. The tendon of M. flexor perforatus digiti III passes through the tibial cartilage and a bony canal in the hypotarsus immediately deep to the tendon of M. flexor perforatus digiti IV. The long tendon of M. peroneus longus inserts on the tendon of M. flexor perforatus digiti III about 5 mm inferior to the proximal end of the hypotarsus. The tendons of M. flexor perforatus digiti III and M. flexor perforans et perforatus digiti III are not interconnected by a vinculum.

The tendon of M. flexor perforatus digiti III splits opposite the base of the proximal phalanx of digit III and is thus perforated by the tendons of Mm. flexor perforans et perforatus digiti III and flexor digitorum longus. The two branches of the tendon of M. flexor perforatus digiti III insert on the plantar joint pad between the first and second phalanges of digit III.

c. Comparative data. This is "M. flexor perforatus medius primus pedis" of Shufeldt (1890).

The chief origin of M. flexor perforatus digiti III is in the intercondyloid region of the femur; this is the only origin in *Fregata, Cathartes, Sagittarius,* and passerines. In most birds, however, there is a second (distal) head arising from a variety of structures in different birds: the external femoral condyle (*Chaetura, Colaptes, Dendrocopos*); from the ambiens tendon and M. flexor perforatus digiti IV (*Columba*); from the ambiens tendon and the head of the fibula (*Gavia, Colinus, Grus, Fulica, Totanus, Larus, Zenaidura, Coccyzus*); from the head of the fibula (*Chordeiles*); from the shaft of the fibula (*Podiceps, Uria*); primarily from other flexor muscles (*Chen, Buteo, Falco, Pedioecetes, Bubo, Otus*). Two tendons are formed in a few birds (e.g., *Colinus, Fulica, Uria, Colaptes*), but these fuse before reaching the tibial cartilage.

The tendon of M. flexor perforatus digiti III passes through a fibrous compartment in the tibial cartilage and through a bony or fibro-osseous compartment in the hypotarsus, and is joined by the long tendon of M. peroneous longus in the proximal third of the tarsometatarsus in most birds, but near the distal end of the bone in *Fregata*. The tendon of M. flexor perforatus digiti III is perforated by the tendons of M. flexor perforans et perforatus digiti III and M. flexor digitorum longus in nearly all birds (*Pandion* is an exception) and inserts on the basal one or two phalanges of digit III.

29. M. Flexor Perforatus Digiti II

a. Columba livia. This muscle arises by two heads. A *femoral head* arises from the deep surface of a common aponeurosis shared with M. flexor perforatus digiti III from the intercondyloid region of the femur. The *distal head* arises from the ambiens tendon. Both heads are intimately fused with the heads of M. flexor perforatus digiti III; and M. flexor perforatus digiti II exists as an independent muscle only in its distal 11 mm, before giving rise to its tendon of insertion a short distance (7 mm) superior to the tibial cartilage. The tendon passes through a separate fibrous canal in the tibial cartilage deep (anterior) to the canal for the tendon of M. flexor perforatus digiti III. The tendon then passes through a bony canal in the hypotarsus, where the tendon lies deep to the tendon of M. flexor perforans et perforatus digiti II. The tendon of M. flexor perforatus digiti II expands as it reaches the distal end of the tarsometatarsus, conceals the tendons of M. flexor perforans et perforatus digiti II and flexor digitorum longus, and then splits to insert on the medial and lateral corners of the base of the proximal phalanx of digit II.

b. *Agelaius phoeniceus*. This muscle arises just distal to the origin of M. gastrocnemius pars externa and the femoral attachment of the distal arm of the biceps loop. M. flexor perforatus digiti II arises from the posterodistal surface of the external femoral condyle by a tendon shared with M. flexor hallucis longus. The common head of the two muscles and the short independent belly of M. flexor perforatus digiti II extend about half way down the crus, but the latter muscle exists as an independent muscle only in its distal third.

The tendon of M. flexor perforatus digiti II passes through a fibrous canal near the lateral border of the tibial cartilage, passes deep to the tendons of Mm. flexor perforatus digiti III et IV, takes a diagonal course from lateral to medial through the intertarsal space, and descends through a bony canal in the medial half of the hypotarsus. The tendon continues down the medial side of the tarsometatarsus, through a fibrous canal on the lateral surface of metatarsal I, and then curves around a large fibrocartilaginous pulley at the base of digit II. The tendon inserts on the medial corner of the base of the proximal phalanx of digit II without ensheathing the tendons of M. flexor perforans et perforatus digiti II or M. flexor digitorum longus.

c. *Comparative data*. This is "M. flexor perforatus indicis primus pedis" of Shufeldt (1890).

M. flexor perforatus digiti II is deeply situated among the muscles on the posterolateral border of the crus except in passerine birds, in which the muscle occupies a more superficial position. The muscle arises tendinously from the intercondyloid region of the femur in common with other long flexors of the digits. In passerine birds the muscle arises by a tendon shared with M. flexor hallucis longus from the external femoral condyle (*Paradisaea, Fregilupus, Pipilo*), or from a tendon shared with Mm. flexores perforans et perforati digiti II et III (*Tyrannus, Corvus*); the tendon of origin also is fused with the capsule of the knee joint and one or more of the arms of the biceps loop. There is an additional (many families) or exclusive (*Tauraco leucotis*) origin from the ambiens tendon and the deep surface of M. flexor perforatus digiti III, rarely from the fibula also (*Ardea, Uria*). The second head arises from the external femoral condyle in owls. In some cranes (*Grus*), one head arises indirectly from the ambiens tendon; a second head, from the patellar ligament. In *Aceros undulatus*, the belly arises only from the deep surface of M. flexor perforatus digiti III in the distal third of the crus. M. flexor perforatus digiti II is said to be absent in *Struthio, Podiceps,* and *Chaetura.*

The tendon of insertion of M. flexor perforatus digiti II passes through a fibrous canal in the tibial cartilage and through a bony or fibro-osseous canal in the hypotarsus in most birds. Hudson (1937) has pointed out that the flexor tendons do not pass through bony canals in those birds in which the hypotarsus takes the form of a wide groove between two bony ridges: e.g., *Cathartes,* Accipitridae, *Falco, Polihiërax, Sagittarius, Uria, Chaetura, Bubo, Otus.* The tendon of M. flexor perforans et perforatus digiti II fuses with the tendon of M. flexor perforatus digiti II at the level of the tibial cartilage in *Pandion* (Gadow and Selenka, 1891: p. 192; Hudson, 1948).

Just proximal to its insertion on the proximal phalanx of digit II, the tendon of M. flexor perforatus digiti II typically expands into a broad sheet or a fibrous pad and is perforated by the tendons of Mm. flexor perforans et perforatus digiti II and flexor digitorum longus. The tendon is not perforated by either of the deep flexor tendons in the Anatidae, *Buteo, Falco, Polihiërax, Uria, Aceros,* and *Paradisaea.* In comparing his results with those of Hudson, Fisher (1946: p. 680) said: "I assume that the differences in origin and in perforation of the tendon in *Cathartes* show that these features are variable within a genus."

In *Fregata* a strong branch of the tendon of M. flexor perforatus digiti II arises below the hypotarsus and inserts on the base of the proximal phalanx of the hallux (Hudson, 1937).

30. M. Plantaris ("F" in Leg-Muscle Formulas)

a. Columba livia. This muscle arises from the posteromedial surface of the shaft of the tibiotarsus for a distance of about 17 mm, beginning just below the proximal articular surface. The belly (24 mm long) extends almost half way down the crus, tapers to a flattened tendon, and inserts on the proximal end of the medial half of the tibial cartilage.

b. Agelaius phoeniceus. M. plantaris is a tiny muscle with a belly about 6 mm long and 1 mm in maximum width. The muscle arises by fleshy fibers from the posteromedial surface of the head of the tibiotarsus. The belly tapers to a hairlike tendon, which passes down the medial surface of the crus and inserts on the proximomedial corner of the tibial cartilage.

c. Comparative data. This is "M. soleus" of Shufeldt (1890). Berger (1959a) proposed that M. plantaris be designated by the letter "F" in muscle formulas.

M. plantaris arises by fleshy fibers from the posteromedial face of the tibiotarsus, just inferior to the proximal articular surface. The origin is

"divided into two parts by the proximal end of the insertion of M. popliteus" in *Gavia* (Wilcox, 1952). According to Gadow and Selenka (1891:
p. 186), the muscle arises from the femur in *Corythaix* (=*Tauraco*);
it does not do so in *Tauraco leucotis*, in which species there is a typical
origin from the tibiotarsus.

The typically small belly of M. plantaris extends less than half the
length of the tibiotarsus in most birds: one-sixth in *Pipilo;* one-fourth in
Pharomachrus; one-third in *Anas, Gallicolumba,* and *Upupa;* two-fifths
in many galliform birds. Hudson *et al.* (1959) reported individual variation in the length of belly in some galliform birds (e.g., *Dendragapus,
Tympanuchus, Pedioecetes, Gallus, Opisthocomus*). The belly extends
from one-half to two-thirds the length of the crus in *Coccyzus.* M. plantaris exhibits its strongest development in *Falco* and *Polihiërax,* in which
the belly extends three-fourths or more the way down the tibiotarsus
(Hudson, 1937; Berger, 1956a).

The belly of M. plantaris ends on a fine tendon in most birds (e.g., less
than 1 mm wide in *Chen hyperborea*) and inserts on the proximomedial
corner of the tibial cartilage. The tendon expands and inserts on the entire proximal surface of the tibial cartilage in *Falco* and *Polihiërax;* on
most of the proximal surface in *Tauraco leucotis.* The tendon inserts
on the deep surface of the tibial cartilage in *Coua caerulea;* only the
tendons of Mm. flexor digitorum longus and flexor hallucis longus lie deep
to the plantaris tendon at that level. The tendon is ossified in some
galliform birds.

M. plantaris has been reported in the following:

Gavia	*Grus*	*Podargus* (Gadow)
Podiceps	*Fulica*	*Chordeiles*
Sula	*Totanus*	*Pharomachrus*
Fregata	*Larus*	*Chloroceryle*
Ardea	*Uria*	*Momotus* (Gadow)
Butorides	*Columba*	*Coracias*
Chauna torquata	*Zenaidura*	*Upupa*
Anatidae	*Goura*	*Indicator*
Cathartidae	*Gallicolumba*	*Ramphastos* (Gadow)
Falconidae	*Tauraco*	Picidae
Galliformes	Cuculidae	Passeriformes

M. plantaris is known to be absent in *Sagittarius,* Accipitridae, *Pandion,* Pteroclidae, Psittacidae, *Bubo, Otus, Chaetura, Eugenes,* and *Aceros.*

31. M. Flexor Hallucis Longus

a. Columba livia. The major portion of this muscle arises by fleshy
and tendinous fibers from the lateral part of the popliteal fossa, lateral
to the femoral origin of Mm. flexores perforati digiti II et III. The small

belly (about 15 mm long) of M. flexor hallucis longus tapers to a flat tendon a short distance inferior to the insertion of the tendon of M. biceps femoris on the fibula. Beginning at the distal end of the belly of M. flexor hallucis longus, a series of fleshy fasciculi derived from the deep side of the common belly of Mm. flexores perforati digiti II et III insert in a unipennate pattern on the tendon of M. flexor hallucis longus for a distance of 30 mm (i.e., to within about 16 mm of the distal end of the tibiotarsus). Contraction of these fleshy fibers reinforces the pull of the small belly of M. flexor hallucis longus.

The tendon of insertion of M. flexor hallucis longus passes through its own fibrous canal on the posterolateral edge of the tibial cartilage and then through the most lateral of the bony canals in the hypotarsus. After emerging from their respective bony canals in the hypotarsus, the tendon of M. flexor hallucis longus takes a diagonal course from lateral to medial, passing superficial to the tendon of M. flexor digitorum longus. The two tendons are connected by a weak vinculum about 10 mm from the distal end of the tarsometatarsus. The primary insertion of M. flexor hallucis longus is on the plantar surface of the base of the distal phalanx of the hallux, but a branch, given off the deep surface of the tendon, inserts on the fibrocartilaginous pad at the joint between the proximal and distal phalanges of the hallux.

b. Agelaius phoeniceus. M. flexor hallucis longus is peculiar in that it arises by three separate, though small, heads. The most *medial head* arises in common with Mm. flexor perforatus digiti IV and flexor perforatus digiti III from the intercondyloid region of the femur. The *intermediate head* arises by a short tendon from the posterolateral surface of the femur, proximal to the external condyle and distal to the origin of M. gastrocnemius pars externa, and medial to the origin of M. flexor perforatus digiti II. The short tendon of the intermediate head gives rise to a fleshy belly which passes distad medial to the biceps loop and the tendon of M. biceps femoris. The *lateral head* arises in common with M. flexor perforatus digiti II from the distal end of the femur adjacent to the attachment of the intermediate head and deep to the aponeurosis of origin of M. flexor perforans et perforatus digiti II. The lateral head passes distad lateral to the fibular arm of the biceps loop and is fused with its outer surface. The medial and intermediate heads fuse behind the knee. The lateral head fuses with the main belly at the level of insertion of M. biceps femoris about 8 mm distal to the proximal end of the fibula. The over-all length of the fleshy muscle is about 29 mm, extending almost three-fourths the way down the crus.

The large tendon of insertion of M. flexor hallucis longus descends through a fibrous canal in the lateral half of the tibial cartilage and through the deepest (most anterior) bony canal in the lateral half of the hypotarsus. As it descends through the posterior compartment of the tarsometatarsus, the tendon of M. flexor hallucis longus crosses superficial to the tendon of M. flexor digitorum longus; the two tendons are not connected by a vinculum. The tendon then curves around the lateral surface and the distal end of metatarsal I in a well developed fibrous sheath and reaches the plantar surface of the hallux. The tendon passes distad along the plantar surface of the proximal phalanx of the hallux held close to the bone by a tough vaginal sheath and inserts on the base of the terminal phalanx. A large vinculum derived from the deep surface of the tendon, inserts on the medial surface of the distal end of the proximal phalanx of the hallux.

c. *Comparative data.* M. flexor hallucis longus has a single head in most nonpasserine genera and is exceptionally large in hawks and owls; it arises by a tendon (sometimes calcified or ossified) from the intercondyloid area of the femur. The tendon is shared with other flexor muscles. In hawks, owls, and woodpeckers, and most of the passerines thus far examined, a second head arises from the external femoral condyle and associated ligaments and tendons, or from the fibula (woodpeckers). The biceps tendon passes between the two heads in passerine birds, but lateral to M. flexor hallucis longus in other birds. M. flexor hallucis longus consists of a single head, arising from the intercondyloid region, in *Vireo olivaceus* (Stallcup, 1954); this is the only passerine bird known to have a single head for this muscle. *Agelaius phoeniceus* and *Dendroica kirtlandii* are the only passerine species known to have a flexor hallucis longus muscle that arises by three heads.

The tendon of insertion of M. flexor hallucis longus passes through a bony canal on the distal end of the *tibiotarsus* in *Aceros undulatus;* this pattern apparently has not previously been described for any other bird.

The tendon usually lies lateral to the tendon of M. flexor digitorum longus in a fibrous canal within the tibial cartilage, but the hallucis tendon is superficial to the digitorum tendon in *Fregata, Sagittarius, Falco, Polihiërax,* Accipitridae, *Chaetura, Bubo,* and *Otus.* In *Polihiërax* the tendon of the flexor hallucis longus muscle expands into a thick mass (1.5 mm wide, 7 mm long, and 0.5 mm thick) at the distal end of the crus; this expanded tendon passes over the posterior surface of the tibial cartilage (rather than through a fibrous canal) and is completely separate from it. The tendon of M. flexor hallucis longus may or may not pass through a bony canal in the hypotarsus.

In most birds, the flexor hallucis longus tendon is completely ensheathed by the greatly expanded tendon of M. flexor hallucis brevis opposite the base of the proximal phalanx of the hallux. The longus tendon does not perforate the tendon of the flexor hallucis brevis in *Sagittarius, Pandion, Falco, Polihiërax,* Accipitridae, *Grus americana, Grus canadensis,* or *Centropus,* however.

The primary insertion of the flexor hallucis longus tendon is on the base of the distal phalanx of the hallux, but, in many birds, one or more vinculae pass from the deep surface of the main tendon and attach to the distal end of the proximal phalanx or to the fibrocartilaginous joint pad between the proximal and distal phalanges.

Berger (1952: pp. 554, 580; 1953: p. 75) described an *automatic flexor* of the hallux in several cuckoos; it is present in other birds, as well. The automatic flexor in *Coccyzus erythropthalmus* is a strong ligament which arises from the wing of the trochlea for digit IV and the fibrocartilaginous mass filling the external intertrochlear notch. This ligament passes mesiad across the intertrochlear space to the plantar surface of the hallux superficial to the tendons of Mm. flexor hallucis longus and flexor hallucis brevis. Near the distal end of the proximal phalanx of the hallux, the ligament passes to the mesial side of the tendon of the flexor hallucis longus and attaches to the joint pad between the proximal and terminal phalanges.

Gadow (1882) reported that M. flexor hallucis longus is absent in *Pterocles,* but that M. flexor hallucis brevis is present. Beddard wrote that W. A. Forbes found the flexor hallucis longus muscle to be "totally absent" in *Centropus,* but Berger (1960a) found the muscle in *Centropus bengalensis* and *C. superciliosus.* Beddard (1898: p. 276) further stated that the deep plantar tendons of *Centropus* are peculiar in that "no branch is sent to the hallux," and Berger found this to be true. M. flexor digitorum longus in *Centropus* is at least twice as bulky as M. flexor hallucis longus, although the latter muscle extends distad about half the length of the crus. The tendons of both muscles traverse bony canals in the hypotarsus, below which the tendon of M. flexor hallucis longus fuses completely with the tendon of M. flexor digitorum longus. The resulting common tendon trifurcates and sends branches to insert on digits II, III, and IV; *no branch is sent to the hallux.* There exists, however, a most unusual condition that apparently has not been found in any other genus. From its attachment to the trochlea and the fibrocartilaginous pulley for digit IV, a very large automatic flexor of the hallux passes mesiad to the base of the hallux and then runs distad (held close to the bone by a fibrous vaginal sheath) to attach to the entire plantar surface of the base of the distal phalanx of the hallux. The relationship of the automatic flexor to the phalanges in *Centropus* is identical to that of the flexor hallucis longus tendon when it is present, as in all other cuckoos. The absence of the tendon of M. flexor hallucis longus to the hallux in

Centropus is compensated for, in part, because M. extensor hallucis longus not only has a typical insertion on the dorsal surface of the distal phalanx but it also sends a strong branch to insert on the medial and plantar edge of the proximal phalanx of the hallux (for other examples of this double insertion, see Hudson, 1937: p. 52).

In those tridactyl birds (hallux absent) thus far studied (e.g., *Uria, Picoïdes*), M. flexor hallucis longus is present but its tendon fuses with the tendon of M. flexor digitorum longus. The hallucis tendon also fuses with the digitorum longus tendon in *Casuarius, Dromiceius, Rhea, Gavia, Podiceps,* Procellariiformes, some Anhimidae, *Phoenicopterus, Turnix, Hydrophasianus, Cariama,* and *Larus* (Newton and Gadow, 1893: p. 616; Hudson, 1937); no branch is sent to the small hallux in these birds.

The tendon of M. flexor hallucis longus crosses superficial to the tendon of M. flexor digitorum longus as the two muscles descend along the posterior sulcus of the tarsometatarsus. The two tendons (referred to as the *deep plantar tendons*) remain independent (that is, unconnected by a vinculum) in the Passeriformes (except the Eurylaimidae; Garrod, 1881: p. 368; Forbes, 1885: pp. 139–140; Lowe, 1931), in two genera of the Ardeidae (*Botaurus* and *Ixobrychus* = "*Ardetta*"; Beddard, 1898: p. 431), in *Upupa* (Upupidae), and in *Rhinopomastus* and *Phoeniculus* (Phoeniculidae; see Garrod, 1881: p. 298; Forbes, 1885: p. 282; Beddard, 1898: pp. 222–223; Lowe, 1946: p. 121). Newton and Gadow (1893: p. 618), however, state that a vinculum interconnects the tendons of the two muscles in *Upupa* and in *Phoeniculus* (="*Irrisor*"). Nevertheless, Berger failed to find a vinculum between the two tendons in a single specimen of *Upupa epops,* but he did find an unusual fibroelastic branch of the flexor hallucis longus tendon. This branch arose from the main tendon in the distal third of the tarsometatarsus, followed a straight course distad, and inserted on the proximal end of the trochlea for digit II. This branch could serve only as an anchor for the main tendon, which curved medially to reach the plantar surface of the hallux.

The deep plantar tendons (either or both may be ossified) are connected by a fibrous vinculum in all other birds thus far examined. Variation in the pattern of the vinculum and in the pattern of insertion of the deep plantar tendons was noted as early as 1831 by C. J. Sundevall, a Swedish ornithologist. A. H. Garrod called attention to Sundevall's work and reported his own findings on the deep plantar tendons in a paper read before the Zoological Society of London in 1875. Gadow and Selenka (1891: p. 195) described seven patterns in the configuration of the deep plantar tendons; in Newton's *Dictionary of Birds* 1896 (pp. 615–618), Gadow listed eight major types (most of which are "connected by intermediate stages") and illustrated fifteen patterns.

Mitchell (1901b) illustrated the considerable intergeneric variation in the pattern of the two deep plantar tendons in several gruiform birds. Berger (1956e) described variation in three specimens of the Sandhill Crane. In one specimen, most of the tendon of M. flexor hallucis longus fused with the tendon of M. flexor digitorum longus in the distal fourth of the tarsometatarsus; only a very small branch of the hallucis tendon continued directly to the hallux. In a second specimen of Sandhill Crane, the tendon of flexor hallucis did not fuse with the tendon of flexor digitorum, but they were connected by a strong vinculum (representing over half of the hallucis tendon) 4 cm proximal to the distal end of the tarsometatarsus; the remainder of the hallucis tendon inserted on the hallux. In a third specimen, the two tendons were connected by a weak vinculum (2.5 cm long), but the hallucis tendon retained its integrity throughout.

Following are descriptions of Gadow's eight major patterns of the deep plantar tendons among birds:

Type I. The flexor hallucis longus tendon inserts on the hallux; the flexor digitorum longus tendon trifurcates, sending branches to digits II, III, and IV. The vinculum passes downward from the hallucis tendon and fuses with the flexor digitorum tendon; hence, the flexor hallucis longus muscle aids in flexing all of the toes. This pattern is found in many birds: for example, *Columba,* Ardeidae, Ciconiidae, Galliformes, many Gruiformes and Charadriiformes, Psittacidae, Musophagidae, Cuculidae, and Eurylaimidae. Hudson *et al.* (1959) reported considerable variation in the development of the vinculum among genera of galliform birds.

Type II. This type is like Type I except that most of the flexor hallucis longus tendon becomes the vinculum and fuses with the tendon of M. flexor digitorum longus. Only a small part of the hallucis tendon continues distad to insert on the hallux. This pattern is found in the Spheniscidae, *Apteryx,* Tinamidae, Pelicaniformes, Anhimidae, Anatidae (Gadow).

Type III. The two deep plantar tendons are "more or less fused throughout the greater extent" of the tarsometatarsus but the vinculum passes from the distal portion of the hallucis tendon to the branch of flexor digitorum longus which goes to digit II only. This pattern is found in *Sagittarius,* the Accipitridae, *Falco,* and *Polihiërax* (Hudson, 1948; Berger, 1956a).

Type IV. The entire tendon of M. flexor hallucis longus fuses with the tendon of M. flexor digitorum longus. The combined tendon trifurcates and sends branches to digits II, III, and IV; no branch is sent to the hallux. This pattern is found in tridactyl birds and those in which the hallux is small: for example, *Rhea, Casuarius, Dromiceius, Gavia, Podiceps,* Procellariiformes, *Phoenicopterus,* some Anhimidae, *Turnix,* and *Pterocles* (mostly after Gadow).

Type V. The entire tendon of M. flexor hallucis longus fuses with the tendon of M. flexor digitorum longus. The common tendon then gives rise to four branches, which supply all four toes (e.g., *Fregata,* Cathartidae, *Pandion, Chordeiles, Chaetura, Apus, Colius, Buceros, Aceros*). Neither Fisher (1946) nor Hudson (1948) found the elaborate branching to the toes in the Cathartidae described by Gadow. In *Coracias abyssinica* the tendon of flexor hallucis fuses with the lateral margin of the tendon of flexor digitorum in the distal fourth of the tarsometatarsus. The combined tendon then sends branches to all four toes, but there is no crossover of the tendons visible grossly; the tendon of M. flexor hallucis longus contributes to that part of the combined tendon that supplies digit IV and the hallux.

An "exaggerated condition" of this type is found in todies, motmots, bee-eaters, and some kingfishers, in which the tendon to the hallux arises a short distance superior to the fusion of the two deep plantar tendons (Gadow). Hudson (1937) describes a similar pattern in *Chen* and *Mergus.*

Gadow describes a third modification in the Trochilidae, in which the tendon of flexor hallucis longus supplies digits I and IV and the tendon of the flexor digitorum longus supplies digits II and III.

An apparently previously unrecorded pattern is found in *Chloroceryle americana.* The tendon of M. flexor digitorum longus supplies all four digits; the tendon bifurcates just inferior to the hypotarsus. The medial branch supplies the hallux; the larger lateral branch trifurcates at the level of metatarsal I and supplies digits II, III, and IV. M. flexor hallucis longus *does not send a branch to the hallux.* The tendon bifurcates and sends branches, which join similar branches of the digitorum tendon, to digits III and IV only.

Type VI. The tendon of M. flexor digitorum longus is reinforced by a vinculum and inserts on digit III only. The tendon of M. flexor hallucis longus sends a vinculum to the digitorum tendon and also sends branches to insert on the hallux and on digits II and IV. By means of the vinculum, therefore, the hallucis tendon acts on all four toes. This pattern is found in the Piciformes (Galbulidae, Bucconidae, Capitonidae, Indicatoridae, Ramphastidae, Picidae, Jyngidae). Berger found this configuration of tendons in *Indicator variegatus.*

Type VII. The deep plantar tendons are independent throughout; a vinculum is absent. The flexor hallucis tendon inserts on the hallux only. The flexor digitorum tendon trifurcates and inserts on digits II, III, and

IV. This pattern is characteristic of the Passeriformes (except the Eurylaimidae). Berger found this pattern in the cotinga, *Procnias nudicollis*.

Type VIII. The tendon of the flexor digitorum longus, reinforced by a large vinculum from the hallucis tendon, inserts on digits III and IV only. The flexor hallucis tendon bifurcates to supply digits I and II; the vinculum goes to that part of the flexor digitorum tendon that inserts on digit III. This pattern is found only in the heterodactyl Trogonidae. Berger can verify this pattern in *Pharomachrus mocino*.

32. M. Flexor Digitorum Longus

a. Columba livia. The primary origin of the largest of the flexor muscles of the toes is on the fibula and the tibiotarsus, but, in one specimen, there were two small, almost vestigial, *femoral heads*. Each of the femoral heads is a thin band of fleshy fibers about 1 mm wide. The lateral femoral head arises from the posterolateral portion of the capsule of the knee joint; the medial femoral head arises in the intercondylar region of the femur lateral to the aponeurosis of M. flexor perforatus digiti III. The two small femoral heads descend into the crus superficial to the belly of M. popliteus and then fuse with the superficial surface of the main fibular head of the muscle.

The *fibular head* of M. flexor digitorum longus arises from the posterior surface of the head, neck, and shaft of the fibula for a distance of about 36 mm. The *tibiotarsal* head arises from the posterior surface of the shaft of the tibiotarsus in slightly more than its proximal two-thirds. The belly of the muscle extends to within 10 mm of the distal end of the tibiotarsus. M. popliteus is visible in the V-shaped interval between the fibular and tibiotarsal heads at the proximal end of the crus.

The tendon of insertion of M. flexor digitorum longus enters a fibrous canal in the center of the tibial cartilage, medial to, but on the same plane as, the fibrous canal for the tendon of M. flexor hallucis longus. The tendon then passes through the deepest (most anterior) of the bony canals in the hypotarsus. A short distance beyond the point where the vinculum from the tendon of M. flexor hallucis longus joins the tendon of M. flexor digitorum longus, the latter tendon trifurcates, sending single tendons to digits II, III, and IV. In addition to their main insertion on the plantar surface of the base of the distal phalanx of the respective digits, vinculae are given off the deep surface of the main tendon; these insert on the fibrous pads on the plantar surface between the articulations of the two distal joints of the digit.

b. Agelaius phoeniceus. M. flexor digitorum longus arises by two typical heads, one from the posterior surface of the fibula, the other from the posterior surface of the tibiotarsus. The belly (about 30 mm long) extends about three-fourths the way down the crus, lying deep to M. flexor hallucis longus and the bellies of the flexor muscles to digits II, III, and IV. The large tendon of insertion of M. flexor digitorum longus passes through the deep stratum of the medial half of the tibial cartilage and then through the deepest bony canal in the medial half of the hypotarsus. Inferior to the hypotarsus, the tendon (which may be calcified) of M. flexor digitorum longus passes deep to the tendon of M. flexor hallucis longus and then lateral to it. The tendon of M. flexor digitorum longus trifurcates at the level of metatarsal I.

1. The tendon to digit II passes through fibrous tissue at the base of the proximal phalanx of digit II and along the plantar surface of the digit to insert on the base of the distal phalanx. A vinculum from the deep surface of the tendon inserts on the fibrous plantar joint pad at the distal end of the penultimate phalanx of the digit. The tendon does not perforate the tendon of M. flexor perforatus digiti II but it does perforate the tendon of M. flexor perforans et perforatus digiti II.

2. The tendon to digit III passes between the two limbs of the tendon of insertion of M. flexor perforatus digiti III near the base of the proximal phalanx, perforates the tendon of M. flexor perforans et perforatus digiti III near the distal end of the second phalanx, and inserts on the base of the distal phalanx. A small vinculum inserts on the fibrous pad at the distal end of the third phalanx.

3. The branch to digit IV is ensheathed by the tendon of M. flexor perforatus digiti IV at the level of the proximal phalanx of that digit, perforates that tendon near the distal end of the proximal phalanx, and inserts on the base of the distal phalanx. A vinculum inserts on the fibrous pad between the distal and penultimate phalanges of digit IV.

c. Comparative data. This is M. flexor perforans digitorum profundus of Shufeldt (1890) and Burt (1930); it is M. flexor profundus s. perforans of Gadow and Selenka (1891: p. 193).

M. flexor digitorum longus is one of the deepest muscles on the posterior surface of the crus, typically lying deep to M. flexor hallucis longus. The muscle remains deeply situated in most birds, but the distal part of the belly is visible superficially on the lateral surface of the crus in *Pandion* and the Accipitridae (Hudson, 1948).

M. flexor digitorum longus has a V-shaped origin by two fleshy heads from the posterior surfaces of the fibula and the tibiotarsus in most birds. The popliteus muscle is visible between the two heads in some birds. Hudson (1937) stated that *Tyrannus* and *Corvus* "are unique" in having an origin from the external condyle of the femur as well as the

origin from the fibula and the tibiotarsus; Berger (1956b) found a similar origin in *Paradisaea rubra*. Hudson added that this condition is "apparently peculiar to the Passeriformes." This proves not to be the case
because there is no femoral origin in the passerine birds studied by
Stallcup (1954) and Berger (1957), nor in *Agelaius phoeniceus* or
Dendroica kirtlandii.

According to Hudson (1937), the muscle has no origin from the fibula
or the femur in *Colaptes* and *Dendrocopos*, but Burt (1930) described
an origin from the internal condyle of the femur in several woodpeckers.
Wilcox (1952) describes an origin from the femur in *Gavia immer*. Two
small femoral heads in one specimen of *Columba livia* are described
above.

The tendon of insertion of M. flexor digitorum longus passes through
a fibrous canal in the medial half of the tibial cartilage in most birds.
The tendon then usually passes through a bony canal in the hypotarsus.
The relation of the tendon to that of M. flexor hallucis longus has been
described earlier in this chapter.

The tendon of M. flexor digitorum longus trifurcates in most birds and
inserts on the base of the plantar surface of the terminal phalanx of
digits II, III, and IV. (Exceptions were cited earlier in this chapter.)
Accessory insertions on subterminal phalanges are common. Typically the
three branches of M. flexor digitorum longus perforate the tendons of the
other muscles that insert on digits II, III, and IV, but there are some
exceptions.

33. M. Popliteus ("G" in Leg-Muscle Formulas)

a. Columba livia. This is a roughly rectangular-shaped muscle about
5.5 mm long and 2.0 mm wide. The muscle arises from the posteromedial
surface of the head of the fibula. The belly passes downward and mesiad
to insert on a ridge on the posterior surface of the tibiotarsus, beginning
2 mm inferior to the head of the bone. The belly of M. popliteus is visible
between the V-shaped origin of M. flexor digitorum longus.

b. Agelaius phoeniceus. M. popliteus is absent in the blackbird.

c. Comparative date. Berger (1959a) proposed that M. popliteus be
designated by the letter "G" in muscle formulas.

M. popliteus is the deepest muscle on the posterior surface of the
tibiotarsus, where it lies deep to and between the fibular and tibial
heads of M. flexor digitorum longus (Fig. IX. 55). M. popliteus is a small
muscle, rectangular in shape, in nearly all birds. It arises by fleshy fibers
from the posteromedial surface of the head and neck (rarely from the
shaft) of the fibula. The belly passes distomesiad and inserts on the

popliteal ridge of the tibiotarsus, opposite or just distal to the origin of the muscle. Little is known about the presence of M. popliteus in most families.

M. popliteus is known to be present in the following birds: *Gavia, Podiceps, Sula, Fregata, Ardea, Butorides, Chauna torquata,* Anatidae, Falconiformes, Galliformes, *Grus americana, Grus canadensis, Fulica americana, Totanus melanoleucus, Totanus flaviceps, Larus pipixcan, Uria aalge, Columba livia, Zenaidura macroura, Gallicolumba luzonica, Goura victoria, Tauraco leucotis,* Cuculidae, *Otus asio, Bubo virginianus, Chordeiles minor,* and *Coracias abyssinica.*

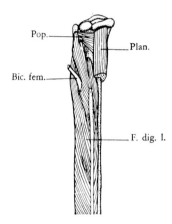

Fig. IX.55. Posterior view of the proximal end of the tibiotarsus to show the relations of Mm. popliteus and plantaris in the Blue Grouse. (By permission, Hudson *et al.*, 1959.) For Key to Abbreviations see legend to Fig. IX.46.

M. popliteus is absent in *Psittacus* (Gadow), *Chaetura pelagica, Eugenes fulgens, Pharomachrus mocino* (Trogonidae), *Chloroceryle americana, Upupa epops, Aceros undulatus, Indicator variegatus,* the Picidae, and in all Passeriformes thus far investigated (including *Procnias nudicollis,* Berger).

34. M. Flexor Hallucis Brevis

a. Columba livia. This muscle has a bipennate origin from the medial surface of the hypotarsus, from the posterior surface of the shaft of the tarsometatarsus, and from the medial surface of an intermuscular septum that extends distad from the inferomedial border of the hypotarsus. The belly (about 20 mm long) extends two-thirds the way down the tarsus. The tendon of insertion fans out, completely ensheathes the tendon of M. flexor hallucis longus at the distal end of the tarsometatarsus, and inserts over an extensive area on the plantar surface of the base of the proximal phalanx of the hallux.

b. Agelaius phoeniceus. The short toe muscles in the Red-winged Blackbird approach the minimum size for description by means of gross dissection, even with 20× magnification. It is quite possible that fleshy fibers, vestiges of muscles not described here, occur in the deep fascia of the tarsus, but these fleshy fibers would have to be demonstrated with certainty by using histological techniques.

M. flexor hallucis brevis has a belly about 4 mm long and 0.5 mm in maximum width at its origin from the anteromedial corner of the base of the hypotarsus. The minute tendon passes down the back of the tarsometatarsus medial to the tendons of all of the deep flexor muscles, then follows a curved path around the lateral surface of metatarsal I, and inserts on a large fibrous pad, which is attached to the base of the plantar surface of the proximal phalanx of the hallux.

c. Comparative date. M. flexor hallucis brevis arises from the hypotarsus (or hypotarsal ridge) and the posterior surface of the tarsometatarsus. The area of origin is very small in woodpeckers and passerines, extensive in *Fregata, Sula, Ardea, Opisthocomus, Dendragapus, Zenaidura, Goura, Aceros, Chordeiles, Chaetura*, etc. (Fig. IX. 56). The mus-

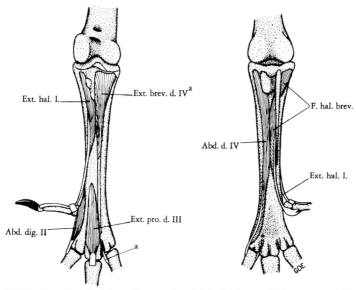

FIG. IX.56. Anterior (left) and posterior (right) views of the tarsometatarsus to show the intrinsic muscles in the Blue Grouse. (By permission, Hudson *et al.*, 1959.) Superscripts refer to the tendons of the muscles concerned. For Key to Abbreviations see legend to Fig. IX.46.

cle arises from the tibial cartilage and the greatly expanded medial hypotarsal ridge in *Polihiërax semitorquatus* (Berger, 1956a). Except at its proximal end, M. flexor hallucis brevis consists of two well developed (4 cm long) bellies (one superficial, the other deep) in *Aceros undulatus*. Each belly gives rise to a large tendon. The two tendons expand near the distal end of the tarsus and then fuse to form a wide (almost 1 cm) fibrous mass, which inserts on the medial and lateral sides of the plantar surface of the basal phalanx of the hallux; the fibrous pad is perforated by the tendon of M. flexor hallucis longus. There are two independent bellies (one superficial, the other deep) in *Coracias abyssinica*. Both fleshy bellies extend almost to the distal end of the tarsometatarsus and end on independent tendons, which fuse at the base of the proximal phalanx of the hallux and form a strong sheath around the tendon of M. flexor hallucis longus. Two independent tendons are formed in *Fulica, Totanus, Larus, Bubo*, and *Otus;* the tendons do not fuse but have separate areas of insertion (Hudson, 1937). The single belly in the Accipitridae gives rise to two tendons, which fuse at the insertion (Hudson, 1948).

The main insertion of the tendon of M. flexor hallucis brevis is on the base of the proximal phalanx of the hallux. The tendon completely ensheathes the tendon of M. flexor hallucis longus in many birds, but not in the Falconiformes (except the Cathartidae), *Grus, Fulica, Totanus, Larus, Bubo, Otus, Chordeiles*, and *Chaetura*.

M. flexor hallucis brevis is absent in *Gavia, Cygnus, Uria*, and some passerines (e.g., *Fregilupus, Sturnus, Aplonis;* Berger, 1957).

35. M. Extensor Hallucis Longus

a. Columba livia. This muscle arises from the anteromedial surface of the proximal half of the tarsometatarsus. The belly (20 mm long) extends about two-thirds the way down the tarsus, tapers to a tendon which passes along the dorsal surface of the proximal phalanx of the hallux and inserts on the base of the distal phalanx. The tendon of insertion is held close to the bone by tough fascia on the dorsal surface of the digit.

An *accessory extensor of the hallux* is present in the form of a short (12 mm long), fleshy belly arising by an aponeurosis, partly from the lateral surface of the distal end of the belly of M. extensor hallucis longus, but primarly from a small ridge on the posteromedial surface of the tarsometatarsus. The belly gives rise to a small tendon which inserts on the dorsolateral surface of the proximal phalanx of the hallux a short distance from its proximal articular surface.

b. Agelaius phoeniceus. M. extensor hallucis longus is a minute muscle about 10 mm long and less than 0.1 mm in width. The muscle arises from a small area near the anteromedial surface of the proximal end of the tarsometatarsus. The belly and tendon pass distad medial to the tendon of M. extensor digitorum longus and through a fascial sheath on metatarsal I to the dorsal surface of the hallux. The tendon ends on a large fibroelastic ligament, which extends from the distal end of the proximal phalanx to the base of the terminal phalanx of the hallux. The belly of M. extensor hallucis longus is so small that it can have very little action in extending the hallux.

c. Comparative data. This is M. extensor hallucis brevis of Gadow and Selenka (1891: p. 197).

M. extensor hallucis longus is one of the more variable of the short toe muscles (Fig. IX.57). It arises from the anteromedial surface of the tarsometatarsus, for most of its length in some birds (e.g., *Fregata, Sula, Ardea, Grus, Chordeiles*), but from only the distal half in *Chen* and *Totanus*. There are two heads in *Pandion, Falco, Polihiërax*, the Accipitridae, *Larus, Sterna, Aceros, Bubo*, and *Otus*. In the last two genera, the larger head arises from the medial malleolus of the tibiotarsus. Hudson *et al.* (1959) found a "distinct, short distal head" in *Crax, Penelope, Ortalis, Pipile*, and *Opisthocomus*. There are two heads and two separate tendons of insertion in *Columba, Gallicolumba*, and *Zenaidura*, but not in *Goura victoria*. M. extensor hallucis longus has a V-shaped origin by two fleshy heads (one on each side of the tendon of insertion of M. tibialis anterior) in *Tauraco leucotis* (Berger, 1960a).

The main insertion is on the base of the ungual phalanx of the hallux in most birds but accessory insertions on the proximal phalanx are common. The strongest part of the insertion is on the base of the proximal phalanx in *Fregata, Sula, Fulica, Totanus*, and *Larus*. Berger (1952, 1953, 1957) described an automatic extensor ligament of the claw of the hallux, lying deep to the tendon of M. extensor hallucis longus, in several cuckoos and in *Fregilupus*. M. extensor hallucis longus has a poorly developed belly about 20 mm long but less than 0.5 mm in maximum width in *Fregilupus*. The belly arises from the anteromedial surface of the tarsometatarsus, medial to the tendon of M. extensor digitorum longus, and beginning at the proximal end of the bone. The elastic automatic extensor of the claw is unusually large. It arises from the dorsal surface, near the distal end, of the proximal phalanx of the hallux; it attaches on the base of the terminal phalanx. The minute, hairlike tendon of M. extensor hallucis longus inserts on the automatic extensor at the base of the terminal phalanx. A strong ligament extends from the wing of the trochlea for digit IV to the terminal phalanx of the hallux. This ligament occupies the position of an automatic flexor of the hallux, but in *Fregilupus* it attaches distally to the automatic extensor. Hence it may aid in compensating for the weak extensor hallucis longus muscle and for the large flexor hallucis longus muscle.

Similar automatic extensors of the hallux have been described by Hudson (1937) and Richardson (1942). Hudson remarked that the "structure of this elastic tissue is such that it functions as an extensor of the

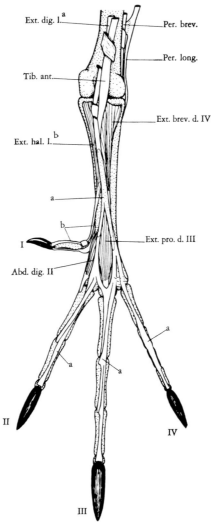

Fig. IX.57. Anterior view of the left foot of the Blue Grouse to show the relations of the tendons of Mm. tibialis anterior and extensor digitorum longus to the intrinsic foot muscles. (By permission, Hudson *et al.*, 1959.) Superscripts refer to the tendons of the muscles concerned. For Key to Abbreviations see legend to Fig. IX.46.

claw and, therefore, as an antagonist of the F. hal. 1. When the tension on the big flexor tendon is relaxed this elastic ligament automatically elevates the claw. It appears that this spring-like device serves the purpose of compensating for the lack of a strong hallucial extensor muscle."

M. extensor hallucis longus is absent in *Gavia, Podiceps,* and *Uria* (Hudson, 1937).

36. *M. Abductor Digiti II*

a. Columba livia. This is a relatively long (15 mm) muscle located in slightly more than the distal half of the tarsometatarsus. The belly lies medial to the belly and tendon of M. extensor hallucis longus and lateral to the belly of M. extensor proprius digiti III. The belly increases in size distally, gives rise to a small tendon, and inserts on the dorsomedial surface of the proximal phalanx of digit II a short distance beyond its proximal articular surface.

b. Agelaius phoeniceus. M. abductor digiti II is absent.

c. Comparative data. M. abductor digit II arises primarily from the dorsomedial surface of the tarsometatarsus, throughout most of its extent in *Buteo;* from the distal half in *Fregata, Uria, Zenaidura,* and *Coccyzus;* from the distal fourth in *Bubo* and *Geococcyx.* The origin frequently encroaches on metatarsal I; the origin is almost exclusively from that bone in *Falco* and *Polihiërax.* The tendon inserts on the basomedial side of the proximal phalanx of digit II.

M. abductor digiti II is known to be present in *Gavia, Podiceps, Sula, Fregata, Ardea, Butorides,* Anatidae, Falconiformes, Galliformes, *Grus, Fulica, Totanus, Larus, Uria, Columba, Goura, Gallicolumba, Zenaidura, Tauraco,* Cuculidae, *Otus, Bubo, Chordeiles, Chaetura, Pharomachrus, Coracias, Upupa,* and *Aceros.* Hudson *et al.* (1959) discuss intergeneric differences in development of the muscle among galliform birds.

Gadow and Selenka (1891: p. 201) did not find this muscle in *Procellaria, Psittacus, Ramphastos,* or *Picus.* Berger did not find it in *Indicator.* The muscle is absent in all woodpeckers and passerine birds thus far studied (Hudson, 1937; Stallcup, 1954; Berger, 1956b, 1957). The muscle was not found in a single specimen of *Procnias nudicollis* dissected by Berger.

37. *M. Adductor Digiti II*

a. Columba livia. This is a long (21 mm), thin muscle, whose fleshy belly extends from the lateral surface of the hypotarsus to the plane of metatarsal I. The belly ends on a tiny tendon, which passes distad between the trochleae for digits II and III, fans out, and inserts on the lateral surface of the base of the proximal phalanx of digit II.

b. Agelaius phoeniceus. M. adductor digiti II is absent.

c. Comparative data. M. adductor digiti II is a deeply situated muscle on the posterior surface of the tarsometatarsus (Fig. IX.58). The muscle arises by fleshy fibers from the ventral surface of the hypotarsus and/or from the bone of the posterior sulcus of the tarsometatarsus. In *Aceros undulatus* the muscle arises from the posterolateral surface of the tarsometatarsus, beginning at the proximal end of the bone; proximally, the muscle preempts the usual area of origin of M. extensor brevis digiti IV. M. adductor digiti II arises from the lateral surface of the lateral

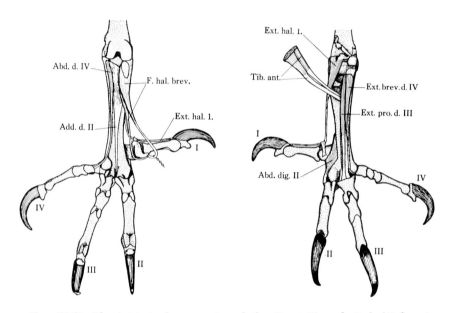

Fig. IX.58. The intrinsic foot muscles of the Great Horned Owl (*Bubo virginianus*). Left: posterior view. Right: anterior view. (By permission, Hudson, 1937.) For Key to Abbreviations see legend to Fig. IX.46.

ridge of the hypotarsus in *Coracias abyssinica*. The belly extends nearly the entire length of the tarsometatarsus in *Fregata, Sula, Fulica, Zenaidura, Columba, Chordeiles,* and *Chaetura;* the belly is confined to the distal half or less in *Ardea, Chen, Colinus, Phasianus, Alectoris,* and *Meleagris* (Hudson *et al.,* 1959). The tendon of insertion is, of course, very long in those birds in which the belly is limited to the proximal end of the tarsus: for example, *Gavia, Podiceps, Opisthocomus, Bubo,* and certain cuckoos. The belly of the muscle is 4 cm long and 4 mm in maximum width in the Sandhill Crane; it arises at the proximal end of the tarsometatarsus, immediately inferior to the hypotarsal area; the hairlike tendon is about 0.3 mm wide. In *Geococcyx californianus*, the minute muscle is about 1 mm in width at its origin from the ventral midline of the hypotarsus and the tarsometatarsus directly below it for a distance of about 8 mm; a hairlike tendon passes diagonally down the bone, through the intertrochlear notch, and inserts laterally on the base of the proximal phalanx of digit II.

Gadow and Selenka (1891: p. 203) report the presence of M. adductor digiti II in *Phoenicopterus, Pandion, Bubo,* and *Bucorvus.* The muscle also is known to be present in *Gavia, Podiceps, Sula, Fregata, Ardea, Butorides, Chauna torquata,* Anatidae, Falconiformes, Galliformes (except Tetraonidae; Hudson *et al.,* 1959), *Grus, Fulica, Totanus, Larus, Uria, Columba, Gallicolumba, Goura, Zenaidura,* many cuckoos, *Otus, Bubo, Chordeiles, Chaetura, Coracias,* and *Aceros* (Hudson, 1937, 1948; Berger, 1960a).

Gadow and Selenka reported this muscle to be rudimentary (presumably meaning absent) in *Psittacus, Tauraco* ("*Corythaix*"), *Cuculus, Ramphastos, Picus,* and passerines. Hudson *et al.* (1959) report the absence of M. adductor digiti II in the Tetraonidae. The muscle is present in some genera of cuckoos, absent in others (including *Cuculus*) and in *Tauraco* (Berger, 1960a). Berger did not find the muscle in *Upupa* or *Indicator.* Hudson (1937) reported its absence in woodpeckers and in *Tyrannus* and *Corvus.* M. adductor digiti II has not been found in any passerine bird (Hudson; Stallcup, 1954; Berger, 1956b, 1957).

38. M. Extensor Proprius Digiti III

a. Columba livia. This muscle arises from the anterior surface of the tarsometatarsus in approximately its distal four-fifths; fleshy fibers begin a short distance inferior to the insertion of M. tibialis anterior and arise almost to the distal end of the tarsometatarsus. The muscle lies between M. extensor brevis digiti IV (medially) and Mm. extensor hallucis longus and abductor digiti II (laterally). The tendon of M. extensor proprius digiti III fans out at the distal end of the tarsometatarsus, fuses with the fascia forming a capsule over the tarsometatarsophalangeal joint, and inserts on nearly the entire dorsal surface of the base of the proximal phalanx of digit III. The tendon contains a small sesamoid just proximal to its insertion.

b. Agelaius phoeniceus. This muscle is absent in the blackbird.

c. Comparative data. Gadow and Selenka (1891: pp. 199–200) describe two extensor muscles to the third toe in a very few birds: extensor proprius digiti III (=extensor longus digiti III) and extensor brevis digiti III. The descriptions of these muscles by Gadow and Selenka are confused, misleading, and, in some respects, undoubtedly in error. This would be irrelevant were it not for the note by Holmes (1962), in which he called attention to Hudson's (1937) apparent misinterpretation of the nomenclature for the two muscles. Holmes suggested that Hudson's terminology be reversed, presumably to agree with Gadow, whose own descriptions are ambiguous. This would serve only to add confusion to the literature, inasmuch as all recent American anatomists have followed Hudson's terminology. Moreover, except for some of the work of Gadow (primarily on ratite birds; 1880), there is almost no reliable information on the short toe muscles of birds prior to the publication of Hudson's first paper (1937). Were it not for the illustration of the two short muscles to the third toe in *Anser domesticus* in Gadow and Selenka (1891; Plate XXIVa, mislabeled XXIIIa), one would be hard put to know what the authors were talking about. We propose, therefore, that until more comparative data are available, the single (in the majority of birds) extensor muscle to the third toe be called M. extensor proprius digiti III. It may be pointed out that Gadow's description of M. extensor proprius digiti III fits the configuration of the single extensor muscle to the third toe in many carinate birds.

A second extensor to the third toe occurs in Ratites (Gadow), tinamous (Gadow; Holmes, 1962), and in *Pandion* (Hudson, 1948). The more medial of the two muscles in these birds is appropriately called M. extensor brevis digiti III in accordance with Gadow's illustrations and Holmes' figure of the two muscles in *Crypturellus cinnamomeus*.

As defined here (and by Hudson), M. extensor proprius digiti III arises by fleshy fibers from the anterior surface of the tarsometatarsus. The origin may begin near the proximal end of the bone (or near the level of insertion of M. tibialis anterior) and the belly may extend throughout most of the length of the tarsometatarsus (e.g., *Aquila, Buteo, Pandion, Opisthocomus, Ardea, Butorides, Zenaidura, Coccyzus, Bubo, Otus, Coracias, Aceros,* woodpeckers). The belly is limited to the distal half (or somewhat less) of the tarsometatarsus in *Dendragapus, Goura, Chordeiles, Pharomachrus,* and some cuckoos; to the distal two-thirds in *Gallicolumba*. The belly is weakly developed and is limited to the distal end of the tarsometatarsus in *Sula, Chen, Alectoris, Phasianus, Fulica, Totanus, Uria,* and *Geococcyx*. Hudson *et al.* (1959) describe intergeneric differences in development of the belly in galliform birds.

M. extensor proprius digiti III is vestigial in *Gavia, Podiceps, Cathartes, Coragyps, Falco, Polihiërax, Grus,* and *Chaetura*. Fisher and Goodman (1955) found a few fleshy fibers in *Grus americana;* Berger (1956e) found a few fleshy fibers on the anterior surface of the distal half of the tarsometatarsus in *Grus canadensis,* but Hudson (1937) did not find the muscle in this species. The muscle is represented by a fleshy belly 4 mm long and only 0.5 mm wide in *Polihiërax semitorquatus* (Berger, 1956a). The muscle is absent in *Fregata,* in *Sagittarius,* and in all passerine birds thus far examined.

M. extensor proprius digiti III inserts by a wide tendon (often containing a sesamoid) on the dorsal surface of the base of the proximal phalanx of digit III in most birds. The single tendon inserts on the *dorsomedial* corner of the proximal phalanx in *Crotophaga sulcirostris, Indicator variegatus,* and woodpeckers, all birds with zygodactyl feet; the tendon inserts on the entire dorsal surface of the proximal phalanx in some other birds with zygodactyl feet, however (e.g., *Coua, Geococcyx*). Two tendons, interconnected by dense fascia, insert on the proximal end of a large sesamoid on the dorsal surface of the base of digit III in *Coracias abyssinica.*

Berger (1960a) concluded that the relative development of M. extensor proprius digiti III seems to be correlated with locomotor habits in the Cuculidae. In the more arboreal cuckoos, the muscle arises just distal to the insertion of M. tibialis anterior, and the belly extends to the distal end of the tarsometatarsus (e.g., *Coccyzus, Piaya, Saurothera, Ceuthmochares, Clamator, Chrysococcyx, Cuculus*). In a second group of primarily cursorial birds, the entire muscle is limited to the distal half or less of the tarsometatarsus (e.g., *Geococcyx, Morococcyx, Dromococcyx, Tapera, Carpococcyx, Coua,* and *Centropus*).

39. M. Extensor Brevis Digiti III

a. Columba livia. M. extensor brevis digiti III is absent in the Rock Dove.

b. Agelaius phoeniceus. This muscle is absent in the Red-winged Blackbird.

c. Comparative data. The known occurrence and the relations of this muscle were discussed under the preceding muscle. It may be pointed out that Gadow and Selenka (1891: p. 200) state that M. extensor brevis digiti III arises from the distal ninth or twelfth, respectively, of the tarsometatarsus in *Ciconia* and *Sagittarius* (=“Serpentarius”), but that Hudson (1948) found “no trace” of a short extensor to the third digit in *Sagittarius.*

40. M. Extensor Brevis Digiti IV

a. Columba livia. This is a long (20 mm), thin muscle arising from the anterolateral surface of the tarsometatarsus, beginning just distal to the plane of insertion of M. tibialis anterior. The tendon of insertion passes through a bony canal between the trochleae for digits III and IV and inserts on the medial surface of the base of the proximal phalanx of digit IV.

b. Agelaius phoeniceus. This muscle is absent in the blackbird.

c. Comparative data. M. extensor brevis digiti IV arises from the anterolateral surface of the tarsometatarsus, extending most of the length of the bone in many birds (e.g., *Pandion,* Cathartidae, many galliform birds, *Tauraco,* many cuckoos, *Pharomachrus, Coracias*). The fleshy belly is limited to the proximal half of the tarsus in *Polihiërax, Lagopus, Canachites,* and *Bonasa;* to the distal third in *Sagittarius* and *Grus.* There are two heads (medial and lateral) but a single tendon of insertion in *Fregata* (Hudson, 1937).

The tendon of insertion passes through a bony canal (or under a bony bridge) between the trochlea for digits III and IV at the distal end of the tarsometatarsus in most birds, but not in *Tauraco,* cuckoos, *Bubo,* or *Aceros.* The tendon inserts on the medial side of the base of the proximal phalanx of digit IV. The tendon fans out and inserts on the entire medial surface of the phalanx in *Coua caerulea,* on the ventromedial (plantar) corner in *Geococcyx* and *Coracias.*

M. extensor brevis digiti IV is "reduced to a thin sheet of connective tissue" in *Podiceps* (Hudson, 1937). The muscle is absent in woodpeckers and most passerines (Hudson, 1937; Stallcup, 1954; Berger, 1956a, 1957), but Berger found the muscle in a specimen of *Procnias nudicollis.* Berger did not find the muscle in specimens of *Upupa* and *Indicator.*

41. M. Abductor Digiti IV

a. Columba livia. This is a relatively weakly developed muscle, which, however, arises from the posterolateral surface of the tarsometatarsus in its proximal two-thirds. The tendon of insertion passes through a fibrous-covered groove on the lateral surface of the trochlea for digit IV and inserts on the ventrolateral corner of the base of the proximal phalanx of digit IV.

b. Agelaius phoeniceus. M. abductor digiti IV is absent in the blackbird.

c. Comparative data. M. abductor digiti IV arises by fleshy fibers from the hypotarsus, the posterolateral ridge of the tarsometatarsus, and, in cuckoos (e.g., *Coccyzus, Crotophaga, Geococcyx, Coua*) from the tibial cartilage. The belly is strongly developed in *Fregata, Sula, Pandion,* the Cathartidae, *Aquila, Dendragapus, Megapodius,* and *Opisthocomus.* The belly is limited to the proximal half of the tarsometatarsus in *Buteo* and *Falco,* to less than the proximal third in *Polihiërax* and *Pharomachrus,* to the distal two-fifths in *Chordeiles,* and the distal fourth in *Sagittarius.*

Fisher (1946: pp. 687, 692) described and illustrated a proximal and a distal belly in *Coragyps*. The tendon inserts on the lateral side of the proximal phalanx of digit IV in most birds, but on the lateral side of the second phalanx in *Pandion* and *Falco* (Hudson, 1948).

M. abductor digiti IV is so small in passerine birds that Stallcup (1954) commented that it is "extremely small, delicate and difficult to demonstrate." Hudson (1937) noted that the muscle "is very weakly developed" in *Gavia, Podiceps, Colaptes, Dendrocopos, Tyrannus,* and *Corvus*. Berger (1956b) did not find the muscle in a specimen of *Paradisaea rubra*. M. abductor digiti IV in *Fregilupus varius* is a vestigial muscle, consisting of a thin layer of striated fibers in a sheet of fascia about 2 mm long, lying at the distal end of the tarsometatarsus (Berger, 1957). In order to demonstrate that muscle fibers were present, however, it was necessary to use the staining technique described by Berger (1956c); no tendon of insertion was found.

42. *M. Adductor Digiti IV*

a. Columba livia. M. adductor digiti IV is absent in the Rock Dove.

b. Agelaius phoeniceus. This muscle is absent in the Red-winged Blackbird.

c. Comparative data. Gadow and Selenka (1891: p. 204) described this muscle in *Rhea* (but not in other ratites) as lying between Mm. adductor digiti II and abductor digiti IV on the posterior surface of the tarsus; its tendon was said to insert on the medial side of the base of the proximal phalanx of digit IV. These authors also said that the muscle was present in *Ramphastos* and *Bucorvus;* Berger did not find the muscle in *Aceros undulatus*. Wilcox (1952) described M. adductor digiti IV in *Gavia immer.* Hudson (1937) described such a muscle in *Phasianus colchicus,* but Hudson et al. (1959) stated that they "failed to find it in any of the Galliform birds examined."

43. *M. Lumbricalis*

a. Columba livia. This is a weakly developed bundle of fleshy fibers about 12 mm long and 0.6 mm wide. The muscle arises solely from the lateral margin of the tendon of M. flexor digitorum longus in the distal half of the tarsometatarsus. M. lumbricalis inserts by fleshy fibers on the proximal end of a fibrous pad located on the medial surface of the trochlea for digit IV.

b. Agelaius phoeniceus. M. lumbricalis appears to be absent in the blackbird.

c. Comparative data. Gadow and Selenka (1891: p. 204) called this M. flexor brevis digiti III, presumably because they believed the usual insertion to be exclusively on the base of digit III. This appears not to be true.

M. lumbricalis exhibits considerable variation among different groups of birds. It is, as Hudson (1937) pointed out, often very small and/or ligamentous and vestigial, so that it may not be possible to determine the presence of fleshy fibers without resorting to histological techniques. For all practical purposes, the muscle appears to be absent in the majority of birds.

M. lumbricalis is well developed in *Ardea, Butorides, Pandion, Opisthocomus, Columba, Zenaidura, Goura, Gallicolumba,* many cuckoos, *Chordeiles, Chaetura,* and *Aceros.* The muscle arises by fleshy fibers (a variable distance inferior to the hypotarsus) solely from the tendon of insertion of M. flexor digitorum longus in *Dendragapus, Columba, Goura, Geococcyx, Indicator,* and *Pipilo;* it arises from the tendons of Mm. flexor digitorum longus and flexor hallucis longus in *Butorides, Gallicolumba, Coccyzus, Crotophaga, Chordeiles,* and *Aceros.* In *Gallicolumba luzonica,* M. lumbricalis is a large mass of fleshy fibers arising primarily from the lateral surface of both of the deep plantar tendons, proximal to their interconnecting vinculum. The fleshy belly arising from the tendon of M. flexor hallucis longus inserts on the base of digit IV; the belly arising from M. flexor digitorum longus inserts primarily on the base of digit III but also sends a small slip to digit IV. M. lumbricalis also consists of two bellies in *Opisthocomus* (Hudson *et al.,* 1959). A posterolateral belly arises from the lateral surface of the tendon of M. flexor hallucis longus and inserts on the joint pulley for digit IV. An anteromedial belly arises from the anterior surface of the tendon of M. flexor digitorum longus and inserts primarily on the joint pulley for digit III.

M. lumbricalis inserts only on the joint pulley for digit III in the Cathartidae and *Dendragapus;* only on the pulley for digit IV in *Bucorvus* (Gadow), *Coua,* and *Aceros;* on both digits III and IV in the Anatidae, *Grus,* and *Goura;* and on digits II, III, and IV in *Coccyzus* and *Geococcyx.*

Hudson (1937) did not mention M. lumbricalis in his discussion of *Corvus* and *Tyrannus.* Berger (1956b, 1957) did not find the muscle in several passerine species, nor did he find it in *Procnias nudicollis.* Stallcup (1954), however, described the muscle in *Pipilo erythrophthalmus.* Hudson *et al.* (1959) did not find the muscle in *Pavo;* Berger did not find it in *Upupa* or *Coracias.*

REFERENCES

Arvey, M. D. (1951). Phylogeny of the waxwings and allied birds. *Univ. Kansas Publ., Museum Nat. Hist.* 3: 473–530.

Barnikol, A. (1953a). Zur Morphologie des Nervus trigeminus der Vögel unter besonderer Berücksichtigung der Accipitres, Cathartidae, Striges und Anseriformes. *Z. Wiss. Zool.* **157**: 285–332.

Barnikol, A. (1953b). Vergleichend anatomische und taxonomischphylogenetische Studien am Kopf der Opisthocomiformes, Musophagidae, Galli, Columbae und Cuculi. *Zool. Jahrb., Abt. Anat. Ontog. Tiere* **81**: 487–526.

Baumel, J. J. (1958). Variation in the brachial plexus of Progne subis. *Acta Anat.* **34**: 1–34.

Beddard, F. E. (1891). Contributions to the anatomy of the Kagu (*Rhinochetus jubatus*). *Proc. Zool. Soc. London* **1891**: 9–21.

Beddard, F. E. (1896a). A contribution to the knowledge of the anatomy of *Rhynchops*. *Proc. Zool. Soc. London* **1896**: 299–303.

Beddard, F. E. (1896b). On the anatomy of a grebe (*Aechmophorus major*), with remarks upon the classification of some of the schizognathous birds *Proc. Zool. Soc. London* **1896**: 538–547.

Beddard, F. E. (1896c). Contributions to the anatomy of Picarian birds. Part III. On some points in the anatomy of the kingfishers. *Proc. Zool. Soc. London* **1896**: 603–606.

Beddard, F. E. (1898). "The Structure and Classification of Birds." Longmans, Green, New York.

Beddard, F. E., and Mitchell, P. C. (1894). On the anatomy of *Palamedea cornuta*. *Proc. Zool. Soc. London* **1894**: 536–557.

Beecher, W. J. (1950). Convergent evolution in the American orioles. *Wilson Bull.* **62**: 51–86.

Beecher, W. J. (1951a). Adaptations for food-getting in the American blackbirds. *Auk* **68**: 411–440.

Beecher, W. J. (1951b). Convergence in the Coerebidae. *Wilson Bull.* **63**: 274–287.

Beecher, W. J. (1953). A phylogeny of the oscines. *Auk* **70**: 270–333.

Beecher, W. J. (1962). The bio-mechanics of the bird skull. *Bull. Chicago Acad. Sci.* **11**: 10–33.

Berger, A. J. (1952). The comparative functional morphology of the pelvic appendage in three genera of Cuculidae. *Am. Midland Naturalist* **47**: 513–605.

Berger, A. J. (1953). On the locomotor anatomy of the Blue Coua, *Coua caerulea*. *Auk* **70**: 49–83.

Berger, A. J. (1954). The myology of the pectoral appendage of three genera of American cuckoos. *Misc. Publ. Museum Zool., Univ. Mich.* **85**.

Berger, A. J. (1955a). On the anatomy and relationships of Glossy Cuckoos of the genera *Chrysococcyx, Lampromorpha*, and *Chalcites*. *Proc. U.S. Natl. Museum*, **103**, No. 3335: 585–597.

Berger, A. J. (1955b). Notes on the myology of the Great Curassow. *Wilson Bull.* **67**: 136–138.

Berger, A. J. (1955c). Suggestions regarding alcoholic specimens and skeletons of birds. *Auk* **72**: 300–303.

Berger, A. J. (1956a). The appendicular myology of the Pygmy Falcon. (*Polihiërax semitorquatus*). *Am. Midland Naturalist* **55**: 326–333.

Berger, A. J. (1956b). On the anatomy of the Red Bird of Paradise, with comparative remarks on the Corvidae. *Auk* **73**: 427–446.

Berger, A. J. (1956c). The expansor secundariorum muscle, with special reference to passerine birds. *J. Morphol.* **99**: 137–168.

Berger, A. J. (1956d). Anatomical variation and avian anatomy. *Condor* **58**: 433–441.

Berger, A. J. (1956e). The appendicular myology of the Sandhill Crane, with comparative remarks on the Whooping Crane. *Wilson Bull.* **68**: 282–304.

Berger, A. J. (1957). On the anatomy and relationships of *Fregilupus varius*, an extinct starling from the Mascarene Islands. *Bull. Am. Museum Nat. Hist.* **113**: 225–272

Berger, A. J. (1959a). Leg-muscle formulae and systematics. *Wilson Bull.* **71**: 93–94.

Berger, A. J. (1959b). The serratus muscles in cuckoos, a correction. *Auk* **76**: 242–244.

Berger, A. J. (1960a). Some anatomical characters of the Cuculidae and the Musophagidae. *Wilson Bull.* **72**: 60–104

Berger, A. J. (1960b). The musculature. *In* "Biology and Comparative Physiology of Birds." (A. J. Marshall, ed.), Vol. 1 Academic Press, New York.

Berger, A. J. (1961). "Bird Study." Wiley, New York.

Boas, J. E. V. (1929). Biologisch-anatomische Studien über den Hals der Vögel. *Kgl. Danske Videnskab. Selskab, Skrifter, Naturvidenskab. Math. Afdel.* [9] **1**: 102–222.

Bock, W. J. (1960a). Secondary articulation of the avian mandible. *Auk* **77**: 19–55.

Bock, W. J. (1960b). The palatine process of the premaxilla in the Passeres. *Bull. Museum Comp. Zool.* **122**: 361–488.

Bock, W. J. (1962). The pneumatic fossa of the humerus in the passeres. *Auk* **79**: 425–443.

Bock, W. J., and Miller, W. DeW. (1959). The scansorial foot of the woodpeckers, with comments on the evolution of perching and climbing feet in birds. *Am. Museum Novitates* **1931**: 45 pp.

Buri, R. O. (1900). Zur Anatomie des Flügels von Micropus melba und einigen anderen Coracornithes, zugleich Beitrag zur Kenntnis der systematischen Stellung der Cypselidae. *Jena. Z. Natu..v.* **23**: 361–610.

Burt, W. H. (1930). Adaptive modifications in the woodpeckers. *Univ. Calif. (Berkeley) Publ. Zool.* **32**: 455–524.

Carus, C. G. (1826). "Erläuterungstafeln zur vergleichenden Anatomie." No. 1, Leipzig.

Carus, C. G. (1827). "An Introduction to the Comparative Anatomy of Animals," Vol. 1. Longman, Rees, Orme, Brown, Green, London.

Conrad, R. (1915). Untersuchungen über den unteren Kehlkopf der Vögel. I. Zur Kenntnis der Innervierung. *Z. Wiss. Zool.* **114**: 532–576.

Coues, E. (1903). "Key to North American Birds," 5th ed. Dana Estes & Co., Boston, Massachusetts.

Davids, J. A. G. (1952). Étude sur les attaches au crâne des muscles de la tête et du cou chez *Anas p. platyrhyncha* (L.). II. *Koninkl. Ned. Akad. Wetenschap. Proc. Ser. C* **55**: 525–540.

Edgeworth, F. H. (1935). "The Cranial Muscles of Vertebrates." Cambridge Univ. Press, London and New York.

Engels, W. L. (1938). Tongue musculature of passerine birds. *Auk* **55**: 642–650.

Engels, W. L. (1940). Structural adaptations in thrashers (Mimidae: Genus Toxostoma) with comments on interspecific relationships. *Univ. Calif. (Berkeley) Publ. Zool.* **42**: 341–400.

Fiedler, W. (1951). Beiträge zur Morphologie der Kiefermuskulatur des Oscines. *Zool. Jahrb., Abt. Anat. Ontog. Tiere* **71**: 235–288.

Fisher, H. I. (1945). Flying ability and the anterior intermuscular line on the coracoid. *Auk* **62**: 125–129.

Fisher, H. I. (1946). Adaptations and comparative anatomy of the locomotor apparatus of New World vultures. *Am. Midland Naturalist* **35**: 545–727.

Fisher, H. I. (1955a). Some aspects of the kinetics in the jaws of birds. *Wilson Bull.* **67**: 175–188.

Fisher, H. I. (1955b). Avian anatomy, 1925–1950, and some suggested problems. *In* "Recent Studies in Avian Biology" (A. Wolfson, ed.) Univ. Illinois Press, Urbana, Illinois. pp. 57–104.

Fisher, H. I. (1957a). Bony mechanism of automatic flexion and extension in the pigeon's wing. *Science* **126**: 446.

Fisher, H. I. (1957b). Footedness in domestic pigeons. *Wilson Bull.* **69**: 170–177.

Fisher, H. I. (1957c). The function of M. depressor caudae and M. caudofemoralis in pigeons. *Auk* **74**: 479–486.

Fisher, H. I. (1958). The "hatching muscle" in the chick. *Auk* **75**: 391–399.

Fisher, H. I. (1959). Some functions of the rectrices and their coverts in the landing of pigeons. *Wilson Bull.* **71**: 267–273.

Fisher, H. I. (1961). The hatching muscle in North American grebes. *Condor* **63**: 227–233.

Fisher, H. I. (1962). The hatching muscle in Franklin's Gull. *Wilson Bull.* **74**: 166–172.

Fisher, H. I., and Goodman, D. C. (1955). The myology of the Whooping Crane, *Grus americana*. *Illinois Biol. Monographs* **24**, No. 2: 127 pp.

Fisher, J. R. (1962). The hatching muscle in the American Coot. *Trans. Illinois State Acad. Sci.* **55**: 71–77.

Forbes, W. A. (1885). "The Collected Scientific Papers of the late William Alexander Forbes" (F. E. Beddard, ed.). R. H. Porter, London.

Friant, M. (1946). La morphologie du muscle releveur de l'aile chez les oiseux. *Compt. Rend.* **222**: 1516–1518.

Fürbringer, M. (1886). Über Deutung und Nomenklatur der Muskulatur des Vogelflügels. *Morphol. Jahrb.* **11**: 121–125.

Fürbringer, M. (1888). "Untersuchungen zur Morphologie und Systematik der Vögel, zugleich ein Beitrag zur Anatomie der Stütz- und Bewegungsorgane," 2 vols. Van Holkema, Amsterdam.

Fürbringer, M. (1902). Zur vergleichenden Anatomie des Brustschulterapparates und der Schultermuskeln. *Jena. Z. Naturw.* **36**: 289–736.

Gadow, H. (1880). "Zur vergleichenden Anatomie der Muskulatur des Beckens und der hinteren Gliedmassen der Ratiten," 56 pp. Fischer, Jena.

Gadow, H. (1882). On some points in the anatomy of *Pterocles*, with remarks on its systematic position. *Proc. Zool. Soc. London* **1882**: 312–332.

Gadow, H., and Selenka, E. (1891). Aves. *In* Bronn's "Klassen und Ordnungen des Thier-Reichs, in Wort und Bild," 2 Vols., Anatomischer Theil, 1891, Systematischer Theil, 1893. Leipzig.

Garrod, A. H. (1876). On the anatomy of *Chauna derbiana*, and on the systematic position of the screamers (Palamedeidae). *Proc. Zool. Soc. London* **1876**: 189–200.

Garrod, A. H. (1881). "The Collected Scientific Papers of the Late Alfred Henry Garrod" (W. A. Forbes, ed.). R. H. Porter, London.

George, W. G. (1962). The classification of the Olive Warbler, *Peucedramus taeniatus*. *Am. Museum Novitates* **2103**: 1–41.

Gladkov, N. A. (1937a). The weight of pectoral muscles and wings of birds in connection with the character of their flight. *Zool. Zh.* **16**: 677–687.

Gladkov, N. A. (1937b). The importance of length of wing for the bird's flight. *Arch. Museum Zool. Univ. Moscow* **4**: 35–47.

Goodge, W. R. (1960). Adaptations for amphibious vision in the Dipper (*Cinclus mexicanus*). *J. Morphol.* **107**: 79–92.

Goodman, D. C., and Fisher, H. I. (1962). "Functional Anatomy of the Feeding Apparatus in Waterfowl. Aves: Anatidae." Southern Illinois Univ. Press, Carbondale, Illinois.

Gregory, W. K., and Camp, C. L. (1918). Studies in comparative myology and osteology. No. III. *Bull. Am. Museum Nat. Hist.* **38**: 447–563.

Haecker, V. (1924). Über die Innervierung der Vogelsyrinx. Phänogenetische Betrachtungen über Parallelbildungen. *Z. Morphol. Anthropol.* **24**: 47–58.

Hamburger, V., and Hamilton, H. L. (1951). A series of normal stages in the development of the chick embryo. *J. Morphol.* **88**: 49–92.

Helm, F. (1884). Über die Hautmuskeln der Vögel, ihre Beziehungen zu den *Federfluren* und ihre Functionen. *J. Ornithol.* **32**: 321–379.

Hofer, H. (1945). Untersuchungen über den Bau des Vogelschädels, besonders über den der Spechte und Steisshühner. *Zool. Jahrb., Abt. Anat. Ontog. Tiere* **69**: 1–158.

Hofer, H. (1950). Zur Morphologie der Kiefermuskulatur der Vögel. *Zool. Jahrb., Abt. Anat. Ontog. Tiere* **70**: 427–556.

Hofer, H. (1954). Neure Untersuchungen zur Kopfmorphologie der Vögel. *Acta 11th Congr. Intern. Ornithol., 1954*, pp. 104–137. Birkhäuser, Basel.

Holmes, E. B. (1962). The terminology of the short extensor muscles of the third toe in birds. *Auk* **79**: 485–488.

Holmgren, N. (1955). Studies on the phylogeny of birds. *Acta Zool. (Stockholm)* **36**: 243–328.

Howell, A. B. (1937). Morphogenesis of the shoulder architecture: Aves. *Auk* **54**: 363–375.

Howell, A. B. (1938). The muscles of the avian hip and thigh. *Auk* **55**: 71–81.

Huber, J. F. (1936). Nerve roots and nuclear groups in the spinal cord of the pigeon. *J. Comp. Neurol.* **65**: 43–91.

Hudson, G. E. (1937). Studies on the muscles of the pelvic appendage in birds. *Am. Midland Naturalist* **18**: 1–108.

Hudson, G. E. (1948). Studies on the muscles of the pelvic appendage in birds II: the heterogeneous order Falconiformes. *Am. Midland Naturalist* **39**: 102–127.

Hudson, G. E., and Lanzillotti, P. J. (1955). Gross anatomy of the wing muscles in the family Corvidae. *Am. Midland Naturalist* **53**: 1–44.

Hudson, G. E., Lanzillotti, P. J., and Edwards, G. D. (1959). Muscles of the pelvic limb in galliform birds. *Am. Midland Naturalist* **61**: 1–67.

Jenkin, P. M. (1957). The filter-feeding and food of flamingoes (Phoenicopteri). *Phil. Trans. Roy. Soc.* **B240**: 401–493.

Köditz, W. (1925). Uber die Syrinx einiger Clamatores und aüslandischer Oscines. *Z. Wiss. Zool.* **126**: 70–144.

Kuroda, N. (1960). On the pectoral muscles of birds. *Misc. Rept., Yamashina's Inst. Ornithol. Zool.* **2**: 50–59.

Kuroda, N. (1961a). A note on the pectoral muscles of birds. *Auk* **78**: 261–263.

Kuroda, N. (1961b). Analysis of three adaptive body forms in the Steganopodes, with note on pectoral muscles. *Misc. Rept., Yamashina's Inst. Ornithol. Zool.* 3: 54–66.

Kuroda, N. (1962). On the cervical muscles of birds. *Ibid.,* 3: 189–211.

Lakjer, T. (1926). "Studien über die trigeminus-versorgte Kaumuskulatur der Sauropsiden." C. A. Reitzel, Copenhagen.

Langley, J. N. (1903). On the sympathetic system of birds and on the muscles which move the feathers. *J. Physiol. (London)* 30: 221–252.

Leiber, A. (1907). Vergleichende Anatomie der Spechtzunge. *Zoologica (Stuttgart)* No. 51.

Lord, R. D., Jr. (1956). A comparative study of the eyes of some falconiform and passeriform birds. *Am. Midland Naturalist* 56: 325–344.

Lowe, P. R. (1928). Studies and observations bearing on the phylogeny of the ostrich and its allies. *Proc. Zool. Soc. London* 1928: 185–247.

Lowe, P. R. (1931). On the anatomy of *Pseudocalyptomena* and the occurrence of broadbills (Eurylaemidae) in Africa. *Proc. Zool. Soc. London* 1931: 445–461.

Lowe, P. R. (1938). Some anatomical and other notes on the systematic position of the genus *Picathartes,* together with some remarks on the families Sturnidae and Eulabetidae. *Ibis* 1938: 254–269.

Lowe, P. R. (1939). On the systematic position of the swifts (Suborder Cypseli) and humming-birds (Suborder Trochili), with special reference to their relation to the Order Passeriformes. *Trans. Zool. Soc. London* 24: 307–348.

Lowe, P. R. (1942). Some additional anatomical factors bearing on the phylogeny of the Struthiones. *Proc. Zool. Soc. London* B112: 1–20.

Lowe, P. R. (1943). Some notes on the anatomical differences obtaining between the Cuculidae and the Musophagidae. *Ibis* 1943: 490–515.

Lowe, P. R. (1946). On the systematic position of the woodpeckers (Pici), honey-guides (Indicator), hoopoes and others. *Ibis* 1946: 103–127.

Lucas, F. A. (1896). The deltoid muscle in the swifts. *Auk* 13: 82–83.

Magnan, A. (1913a). Rapport de la surface alaire avec le poids du corps chez les oiseaux. *Bull. Museum Hist. Nat., Paris* 19: 45–52.

Magnan, A. (1913b). Les muscles releveurs de l'aile chez les oiseaux. *Bull. Museum Hist. Nat., Paris* 19: 125–128.

Magnan, A. (1913c). Le poids des muscles pectoraux et le poids du coeur chez les oiseaux. *Compt. Rend. Assoc. Franc. Avan. Sci.* 41: 457–459.

Mayr, E. (1931). Die Syrinx einiger Singvögel aus Neu-Guinea. *J. Ornithol.* 79: 333–337.

Mayr, E. (1955). Comments on some recent studies of song bird phylogeny. *Wilson Bull.* 67: 33–44.

Miller, A. H. (1934). The vocal apparatus of some North American Owls, *Condor* 36: 204–213.

Miller, A. H. (1937). Structural modifications in the Hawaiian Goose (*Nesochen sandvicensis*). . . . *Univ. Calif. (Berkeley) Publ. Zool.* 42: 1–80.

Milne-Edwards, A. (1867–1871). "Recherches anatomiques et paleontologiques pour servir à l'histoire des oiseaux fossiles," Vol. 1, 1867–1868; Vol. 2, 1869–1871. Masson, Paris.

Miskimen, M. (1951). Sound production in passerine birds. *Auk* 68: 493–504.

Miskimen, M. (1963). The syrinx in certain Tyrant Flycatchers. *Auk* 80: 156–165.

Mitchell, P. C. (1894). On the perforated flexor muscles in some birds. *Proc. Zool. Soc. London* 1894: 495–498.

Mitchell, P. C. (1901a). On the anatomy of the kingfishers, with special reference to the conditions in the wing known as eutaxy and diastataxy. *Ibis* 1901: 97–123.

Mitchell, P. C. (1901b). On the anatomy of gruiform birds, with special reference to the correlation of modifications. *Proc. Zool. Soc. London* 1901: 629–655.

Mitchell, P. C. (1913). The peroneal muscles in birds. *Proc. Zool. Soc. London* 1913: 1039–1072.

Mitchell, P. C. (1915). Anatomical notes on the gruiform birds *Aramus giganteus* Bonap., and *Rhinochetus kagu*. *Proc. Zool. Soc. London* 1915: 413–423.

Moller, W. (1930). Über die Schnabel- und Zungenmechanik blütenbesuchender Vögel. I. Ein Beitrag zur Biologie des Blumenvogels. *Biol. Generalis* 6: 651–726.

Moller, W. (1931). Über die Schnabel- und Zungenmechanik blütenbesuchender Vögel. II. Ein Beitrag zur Biologie des Blumenvogels. *Biol. Generalis* 7: 99–154.

Mollier, G. (1937). Beziehungen zwischen Form und Funktion der Sehnen im Muskel-Sehnen-Knochen-System. *Morphol. Jahrb.* 79: 161–199.

Montagna, W. (1945). A re-investigation of the development of the wing of the fowl. *J. Morphol.* 76: 87–113.

Mudge, G. P. (1903). On the myology of the tongue of parrots, with a classification of the order, based upon the structure of the tongue. *Trans. Zool. Soc. London* 16: 211–278.

Müller, J. (1878). "On Certain Variations in the Vocal Organs of the Passeres that Have Hitherto Escaped Notice." Oxford Univ. Press (Clarendon), London and New York.

Myers, J. A. (1917). Studie on the syrinx of *Gallus domesticus*. *J. Morphol.* 29: 165–215.

Nair, K. K. (1954a). A comparison of the muscles in the forearm of a flapping and a soaring bird. *J. Animal Morphol. Physiol.* 1: 26–34.

Nair, K. K. (1954b). The bearing of the weight of the pectoral muscles on the flight of some common Indian birds. *J. Animal Morphol. Physiol.* 1: 71–76.

Nel, J. T. (1940). Histologische und anatomische Untersuchungen an der Hinterextremität einiger Vögel. *Verhandl. Naturhist.-Med. Vereins, Heidelberg* 18: 223–244.

Nelson, O. E. (1953). "Comparative Embryology of the Vertebrates." McGraw-Hill (Blakiston), New York.

Newton, A., and Gadow, H. (1893–1896). "A Dictionary of Birds." Adam & Charles Black, London.

Nishida, T. (1960). Comparative and topographical anatomy of the fowl. II. On the blood vascular system of the thoracic limb in the fowl. *Japan. J. Vet. Sci.* 22: 229–231.

Palmgren, P. (1949). Zur biologischen Anatomie der Halsmuskulatur der Singvögel. *In* "Ornithologie als Biologische Wissenschaft. . . . Erwin Streseman." pp. 190–203. Carl Winter, Heidelberg.

Parker, W. K. (1875a). On the morphology of the skull in the woodpeckers (Picidae) and wrynecks (Yungidae). *Trans. Linnean Soc. London (Zool.)* 1: 1–22.

Parker, W. K. (1875b). On Aegithognathous birds (Part I). *Trans. Zool. Soc. London* 9: 289–352.

Parker, W. K. (1890). On the morphology of the duck tribe (*Anatidae*) and the auk tribe (*Alcidae*). *Roy. Irish Acad.* "Cunningham Mem." 6: 1–132.

Parker, T. J., and Haswell, W. A. (1947). "A Text-book of Zoology," 6th ed., Vol. 2. Macmillan, New York.

Portmann, A., and Stingelin, W. (1961). The central nervous system. *In* "Biology and Comparative Physiology of Birds." (A. J. Marshall, ed.), Vol. 2, pp. 1–36. Academic Press, New York.

Prins, F. X. (1951). Die "Musculus orbitoquadratus." *Ann. Univ. Stellenbosch* **A27**: 101–130.

Richardson, F. (1942). Adaptive modifications for tree-trunk foraging in birds. *Univ. Calif. (Berkeley) Publ. Zool.* **46**: 317–368.

Romer, A. S. (1927). The development of the thigh musculature of the chick. *J. Morphol. Physiol.* **43**: 347–385.

Rüppell, W. (1933). Physiologie und Akustik der Vogelstimme. *J. Ornithol.* **81**: 433–542.

Scharnke, H. (1931). Beiträge zur Morphologie und Entwicklungsgeschichte der Zunge der Trochilidae, Meliphagidae und Picidae. *J. Ornithol.* **79**: 425–491.

Scharnke, H. (1932). Über den Bau der Zunge der Nectariniidae, Promeropidae und Drepanididae nebst Bemerkungen zur Systematik der blütenbesuchenden Passeres. *J. Ornithol.* **80**: 114–123.

Setterwall, C. G. (1901). Studier öfver Syrinx hos Polymyoda Passeres. 128 pp., 7 plates. Akademisk Afhandling, Gleerupska, Universitetsbokhandeln, Lund.

Seuffert, L. (1862). Über das Vorkommen und Verhalten glatter Muskeln in der Haut der Säugethiere und Vögel. *Würzberger Naturw. Z.* **3**: 111–158.

Shufeldt, R. W. (1887a). Another muscle in birds of taxonomic value. *Science 9,* No. 229: 623–624; **10,** No. 234: 57.

Shufeldt, R. W. (1887b). The dermo-tensor patagii muscle. *Auk* **4**: 353–356.

Shufeldt, R. W. (1887c). A review of the muscles used in the classification of birds. *J. Comp. Med. Surg.* **8**: 321–344.

Shufeldt, R. W. (1888). On the skeleton in the genus *Sturnella,* with osteological notes upon other North-American Icteridae, and the Corvidae. *J. Anat. (London),* **22**: 309–348.

Shufeldt, R. W. (1890). "The Myology of the Raven (*Corvus corax sinuatus*)." Macmillan, New York.

Sims, R. W. (1955). The morphology of the Hawfinch (*Coccothraustes coccothraustes*). *Bull. Brit. Museum Zool.,* **13**: 371–393.

Slonaker, J. R. (1918). A physiological study of the anatomy of the eye and its accessory parts of the English Sparrow (*Passer domesticus*). *J. Morphol.* **31**: 351–459.

Stallcup, W. B. (1954). Myology and serology of the avian family Fringillidae, a taxonomic study. *Publ. Museum Nat. Hist., Univ. Kansas* **8**: 157–211.

Starck, D. (1959). Neure Ergebnisse der vergleichenden Anatomie und ihre Bedeutung für die Taxonomie, erläutert an der Trigeminus-Muskulatur der Vögel. *J. Ornithol.* **100**: 47–59.

Starck, D., and Barnikol, A. (1954). Beiträge zur Morphologie der Trigeminus-Muskulatur der Vögel. *Morphol. Jahrb.* **94**: 1–64.

Steinbacher, G. (1935). Funktionell-anatomische Untersuchungen an Vogelfüssen mit Wendzehen und Ruckzehen. *J. Ornithol.* **83**: 214–282.

Steinbacher, J. (1934). Untersuchungen über den Zungenapparat indischer Spechte. *J. Ornithol.* **82**: 399–408.

Steinbacher, J. (1957). Über den Zungenapparat einiger neotropischer Spechte. *Senckenbergiana Biol.* **38**: 259–270.

Stejneger, L. H. (1887). Pars propatagialis musculi cucullaris. *Science* **10,** No. 235: 70–71.

Stejneger, L. H. (1888). Propatagialis cucullaris. *Auk* **5:** 120–123.

Stejneger, L. H. (1889). Cucullaris propatagialis in oscinine birds. *Science* **13,** No. 309: 16.

Stolpe, M. (1932). Physiologisch-anatomische Untersuchungen über die hintere Extremität der Vögel. *J. Ornithol.* **80:** 161–247.

Storer, R. W. (1945). Structural modifications in the hind limb in the Alcidae. *Ibis* **87:** 433–456.

Storer, R. W. (1960). Adaptive radiation in birds. *In* "Biology and Comparative Physiology of Birds" (A. J. Marshall, ed.), Vol. 1, p. 15. Academic Press, New York.

Straus, W. L., Jr. (1946). The concept of nerve-muscle specificity. *Biol. Rev. Cambridge Phil. Soc.* **21:** 75–91.

Sullivan, G. E. (1962). Anatomy and embryology of the wing musculature of the domestic fowl (*Gallus*). *Australian J. Zool.* **10:** 458–518.

Swinebroad, J. (1954). A comparative study of the wing myology of certain passerines. *Am. Midland Naturalist* **51:** 488–514.

Sy, M. (1936). Funktionell-anatomische Untersuchungen am Vogelflügel. *J. Ornithol.* **84:** 199–296.

Teresa, S. (1933). Beitrag zur Frage der Entstehung der Tracheal- und Syringialmuskulatur der Vögel. *Zool. Zh.* **12:** 150–169.

Tordoff, H. B. (1954a). A systematic study of the avian family Fringillidae based on the structure of the skull. *Misc. Publ. Museum Zool., Univ. Mich.* **81.**

Tordoff, H. B. (1954b). Relationships of the New World nine-primaried oscines. *Auk* **71:** 273–284.

Van Tyne, J., and Berger, A. J. (1959). "Fundamentals of Ornithology." Wiley, New York.

Verheyen, R. (1961). Tendances evolutives et ornithosystématique. *Inst. Roy. Sci. Nat. Belg., Bull.* **37:** 1–27.

Waddington, C. H. (1952). "The Epigenetics of Birds." Cambridge Univ. Press, London and New York.

Watson, M. (1883). Report on the anatomy of the Spheniscidae collected during the voyage of H.M.S. Challenger, during the years 1873–1876. *In* "Zoology of the Voyage of the Challenger," Vol. 7.

Webb, M. (1957). The ontogeny of the cranial bones, cranial peripheral and cranial parasympathetic nerves, together with a study of the visceral muscles of *Struthio*. *Acta Zool.* (*Stockholm*) **38:** 81–203.

Wedin, B. (1953). The development of the eye muscles in *Ardea cinerea* L. *Acta Anat.* **18:** 30–48.

Wetmore, A. (1960). A classification for the birds of the world. *Smithsonian Inst. Misc. Collections* **139.**

Weymouth, R. D., Lasiewski, R. C., and Berger, A. J. (1964). The tongue apparatus in hummingbirds. *Acta Anat.* **58:** 252–270.

Wilcox, H. H. (1952). The pelvic musculature of the loon, *Gavia immer*. *Am. Midland Naturalist* **48:** 513–573.

Woerdeman, M. W., *et al.* (1961). "Nomina Anatomica," 2nd ed. Excerpta Medica Foundation, Amsterdam.

Wunderlich, L. (1886). Beiträge zur vergleichenden Anatomie und Entwicklungsgeschichte des unteren Kehlkopfes der Vögel. *Nova Acta Kaiserl. Leopoldin.-Carolin. Deut. Akad. Naturforsch.* **48:** 1–80.

Yasuda, M. (1960). Comparative and topographical anatomy of the fowl. III. On the nervous supply of the thoracic limb in the fowl. *Japan. J. Vet. Sci.* **22:** 99–101.

Young, J. Z. (1950). "The Life of Vertebrates." Oxford Univ. Press, London and New York.

Zusi, R. L. (1959). The function of the depressor mandibulae muscle in certain passerine birds. *Auk* **76:** 537–539.

Zusi, R. L. (1962). Structural adaptations of the head and neck in the *Black Skimmer, Rynchops nigra* Linnaeus. *Publ. Nuttall Ornithol. Club (Cambridge, Mass.)* No. 3.

CHAPTER X

The Origin of Birds and the Evolution of Sustained Flight

I. The Archaeopteryx

Both birds and dinosaurs are presumed to have evolved from primitive and unspecialized thecodont reptiles belonging to the suborder Pseudosuchia. These were small carnivorous reptiles with numerous thecodont teeth (teeth set in sockets in the jaws). The hind limbs were longer than the front limbs, and the fifth hind toe was reduced in some forms. The actual pseudosuchian ancestor of birds has not been discovered, but Heilmann (1927) reconstructed a hypothetical "proavian" form intermediate between *Archaeopteryx* and specific pseudosuchians (*Ornithosuchus* and *Euparkeria;* see, also, the discussion by Swinton, 1960).

Fossil evidence of the earliest known bird (*Archaeopteryx*) was found in lithographic slate of Upper Jurassic age near Pappenheim, Bavaria. Three specimens (plus an isolated feather) have been found to date (1964): in 1861, 1877, and 1956. The detailed skeletal characters of *Archaeopteryx* have been discussed by Heilmann (1927), de Beer (1954), Van Tyne and Berger (1959), and Swinton (1960).

It was pointed out in Chapter II that the skeleton of *Archaeopteryx* was more reptilian than avian, and Lowe (1944) insisted that *Archaeopteryx* was not a bird at all, but rather was an arboreal, climbing dinosaur which "takes its place not at the bottom of the avian phylum but at the top of the reptilian." Despite Lowe's belief, paleontologists and ornithologists are now generally agreed that *Archaeopteryx* was indeed a bird, although perhaps not the ancestor of later flying birds. The feather impressions found with the skeletons of *Archaeopteryx* suggest that their structure was typical of the feathers of modern birds.

II. The Origin of Flight

Two theories have been offered concerning the origin of flight in birds. Nopcsa (1907) proposed a cursorial origin. He believed that flight developed in long-tailed, bipedal reptiles which flapped their forelimbs as they ran along the ground. He postulated that the scales on the forelimbs elongated and became frayed, eventually evolving into feathers. Nopcsa visualized three stages in the development of flight: (1) parachute or passive flight; (2) flight by force, that is, flapping the wings; (3) soaring or flight by skill. He believed that *Archaeopteryx* was in the "first stage of active flight."

Most authors, however, believe that the first birds were arboreal (e.g., Marsh, 1880; Osborn, 1900; Heilmann, 1927). Their proavian ancestors became tree climbers at a time when there was only a moderate difference in length and configuration of the anterior and posterior limbs. This theory postulates that jumping from branch to branch in trees favored the development of longer metatarsals and a backward-directed hallux, which would enable the animals to secure a better grasp. Now that they were used primarily for climbing, the front limbs "preserved claws on their digits, remained large, and were not reduced as is commonly the case in cursorial animals which adopt the bipedal mode of progression" (de Beer, 1954). Hence, each limb became adapted for specialized functions. Heilmann (1927: p. 198) emphasized the importance of the independence of the front and hind limbs in contrast to the pattern in pterosaurs and bats, in which a patagial skin fold extends between the fore limb and the hind limb. Although Böker (1927: pp. 318–319) thought that the first birds flapped their fore limbs as they jumped from branch to branch de Beer thought it "probable that simple gliding preceded flapping because Archaeopteryx had no carina and its pectoral muscles must have been feeble."

III. Pneumatization

Although many generalizations are stated in books about pneumatized bird bones, much new information is needed, both on the embryological development of pneumatized bones and on their occurrence among the many orders and families of birds. Nearly all birds possess some hollow bones (containing extensions of air sacs from the lungs), but the extent of pneumatization is known for only a very few species. Moreover, most of the "classic" statements on degree and extent of pneumatization need to be verified.

Bellairs and Jenkin (1960) comment that although "it is probable that pneumatization and flight in birds are in some way related, it is clear . . . that the relationship is not a simple one." There is very little pneumatization in swifts, which are among the most aerial of all birds. By contrast, some ratite (nonflying) birds possess a number of pneumatized bones, and the weak-flying hornbills are said to be "among the most richly pneumatized of all birds." At the same time, certain large, strong flying (often soaring) birds are richly pneumatized (e.g., albatrosses, boobies, pelicans, some eagles).

Thus, it seems likely that lightening of the skeleton as a consequence of pneumatization often has been overemphasized in discussing the bird's adaptations for flight. Some evidence suggests that pneumatized bones tend to have a larger diameter in relation to their length than do comparable nonpneumatized bones. Bellairs and Jenkin point out that the greater circumference of such a pneumatic bone will give it "a greater resistance to bending strains, despite the thinness of its wall." Internal bony trabeculae, or struts, also may add greatly to the strength of a bone.

IV. Homoiothermism

The evolution of birds from reptilian ancestors involves a host of changes, among which the acquisition of a physiological equipment to keep the heavier-than-air flying machine afloat in the air is the most important. The major components of such equipment are the powerful flight muscles whose activity is supported by the coordinated action of the circulatory and respiratory systems so as to maintain the energy transformation mechanism at a high level of efficiency. It therefore seems logical to believe that the evolution of the pectoral muscles was largely influenced by the efficiency of the respiratory and circulatory systems. This leads us to the assumption that the proavian, in the adoption of an arboreal mode of life, would have first acquired the ability to maintain a higher metabolic rate than its reptilian ancestor.

There seems to be no doubt that the development of warmbloodedness or homoiothermy would have preceded the attainment of the ability for active flight. It should be pointed out here that active flight should be distinguished from gliding, as is seen in the glider lizard, *Draco*. Swinton (1960) suggested that the pterosaurs probably were warmblooded because they had pneumatic bones. It has been pointed out earlier that pneumaticity is not necessarily an adaptation for flight. In bats, which are flying mammals, there are neither pneumatic bones nor air sacs. The wings of pterosaurs were membranous skin folds supported by greatly elongated phalanges of the fourth digit; the first three digits ended as short clawed fingers and the fifth digit was absent. The whole wing structure, consisting of a single membrane supported by the skeleton of a single digit (and that, too, only along the front edge of the wing, thus making it highly vulnerable for an accidental tear), was indeed a poor substitute for the avian wing. For that matter, the wing of the bat is well fortified by the four digits of the manus.

In addition to pneumaticity of bones, it is probable that the pterosaurs also had air sacs. With the presence of a large sternum and a fairly well developed keel, it is also likely that they had better developed pectoral muscles than other reptilian forms. In recognition of these features we might safely suggest that the pterosaurs had acquired a certain level of homoiothermy. However, this idea cannot be accepted without qualifications. Although bats are warmblooded, they are to a large extent poikilothermous during the daytime when they are inactive. So are they during aestivation or hibernation. This is so because the large surface provided by the patagium is a serious hindrance to the conservation of body heat. Had bats possessed air sacs, also, thus affording the possibility of further evaporation, it is unlikely that they would have attained their present flying ability. On the other hand, the pterosaurs had large membranous patagii as well as air sacs, and it might be suggested that their greatest problem was excessive heat and water loss. One way of solving this problem would have been to become nocturnal in habit like bats. It appears reasonable to speculate that they were nocturnal in activity and rested during the day. The long tail stands as testimony to the fact that they flew very low. The wing attachment shows that they probably were clumsy on the ground, like swifts and bats.

The acquisition of feathers, however, provided an efficient external equipment for thermoregulation and for flight and also marked the beginning of the successful conquest of the air by the lowly reptiles. This step in the evolution of birds is, therefore, to be regarded as one primarily for homoiothermy rather than for providing the mechanical equipment for flight. The *Archaeopteryx* had no keel and consequently no powerful flight muscles, no pneumaticity of bones, but it did possess feathers. So it can be argued that *Archaeopteryx* was at best a glider but that its feathers made possible some temperature control. In that respect, it was more than a mere feathered reptile.

In this context it is pertinent to ask whether *Archaeopteryx* possessed air sacs even though it did not have pneumatic bones? If it did, what was their nature and function? For a solution to this problem reference should be made to the recent work of George and Shah (1965). They have shown from a study of a number of lizards and snakes that the lung in these animals consists of an anterior alveolar portion and a posterior saccular portion (Figs. X.1 and X.2). In some cases the posterior part is only partly saccular and is referred to as semisaccular. In all the snakes studied, the saccular portion of the lung is well developed and extends almost up to the anus. Among lizards, even though this part of the lung

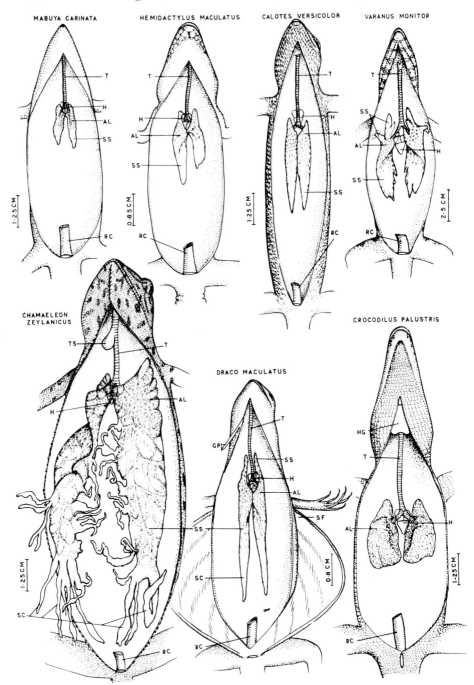

FIG. X.1. (See legend on page 480.)

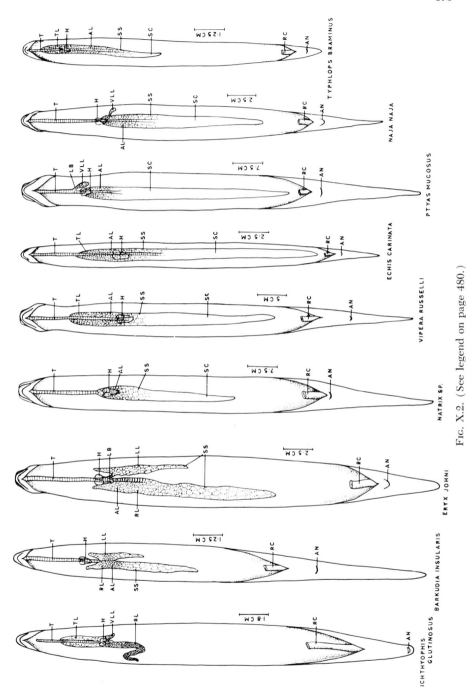

Fig. X.2. (See legend on page 480.)

is not as well developed as in snakes, some lizards show considerably greater saccular lung development than others. The chameleon showed the highest development. The lung in the lizard *Varanus* has a semi-saccular diverticulum extending to the arm and neck. In the gliding lizard, *Draco*, the saccular part is conspicuously long. In the limbless lizard, the posterior semisaccular part is quite prominent. From these observations it seems clear that air sacs are nothing entirely new in birds. Birds have only carried them over from their reptilian ancestors. Possibly *Archaeopteryx* also had air sacs but of the reptilian type.

The fact that some reptiles, as well as birds, have retained these sacs shows that they have a common function to perform in both these groups. Again, the fact that even the ratite birds have air sacs well preserved in their body shows that they are functional. It might be stated that at some stage in the evolution of the Sauropsida the air sacs must have given their possessors survival value. According to George and Shah (1965), the air sacs evolved first in reptiles to effect increased evaporative cooling as an adaptation to leading a terrestrial life and enable these animals to lower body temperature by panting. That lizards pant on hot days is common knowledge. That birds, too, keep panting with their mouths open on hot days is also well known. It has been estimated that the respiratory water loss in the adult chicken is on the average 4.5 gm at 95°F, which is half the total water loss, and 1.4 gm at 85°F (Lee *et al.*, 1945). The survival of an ostrich running on the hot sands of the Sahara Desert has been attributed to its ability to cool and moisten the outside dry air in its air sacs (Bert, 1870). Victorow (1909) obtained a rise in body temperature of 2.6° to 3.2°C in an exercised pigeon after puncturing and plugging its air sacs; in the control the increase in body temperature was only 0.7°C to 0.9°C. The function of air sacs in birds, therefore, could

---

FIGS. X.1. and X.2. The nature of the lung in an amphibian (Ichthyophis), some lizards and snakes, and a crocodile. Note that the saccular or semisaccular portion of the lung seen in lizards and snakes is absent in Ichthyophis and in the crocodile. (By kind permission, George and Shah, 1965).

KEY TO ABBREVIATIONS USED:

AL	= Alveolar lung	RL	= Right lung
AN	= Anus	SC	= Saccular lung
GP	= Gular pouch	SF	= Skin fold
H	= Heart	SS	= Semisaccular lung
HG	= Hypoglossum	T	= Trachea
LB	= Left bronchus	TL	= Tracheal lung
LL	= Left lung	TS	= Tracheal sac
RC	= Rectum	VLL	= Vestigial left lung

well be regarded as a device for temperature regulation by providing greater surface area from which water can be evaporated, as emphasized by George and Shah (1965).

V. Evolution of the Pectoralis Muscle

Birds exhibit great versatility in locomotion. Some are runners, some swimmers, and the rest fliers. Of these, some can perform only one type of locomotion, some two, and others all three, with of course restricted efficiency. Among the fliers, most of them indulge in sustained flapping flight, while some mostly glide, some soar, and some hover. Here again, some have the ability to perform more than one mode of flight, and, within such a spectrum of versatility, varying degrees of maneuverability are also exhibited. Some birds can manipulate a quick and sudden take-off more efficiently than others. Some are particularly gifted with the ability to make quick and sudden turns, as in avoiding an obstacle or negotiating the capture of prey. Undoubtedly these varied abilities are the manifestations of certain intricate structural designs in the avian body. The total body weight in relation to the weight of the pectoral muscles, the shape and area of the wings, and other relationships seem to indicate certain significant adaptations to the mode of flight. Some of these aspects have been discussed by Fisher (1946, 1955), George and Nair (1952), and Hartman (1961). A discussion on the aerodynamics of bird flight is presented by Brown (1961).

The massive pectoral muscles, in their phenomenal attainment as a biochemically powered mechanical system for sustained activity, have no parallel in the realm of skeletal muscles with perhaps the pectoral muscles of bats being the only exception. Of the two pectoral muscles, pectoralis and supracoracoideus, the former is by far the more powerful (Chapter III). The internal organization of this muscle in various birds at the cellular and subcellular levels has revealed the different metabolically adapted patterns as products of evolution (Chapters IV and V). Since it is a soft part and not preserved in fossils, we have no knowledge of its evolution. However, some new information on the functional evolution of the avian pectoralis muscle is now available (George, 1965).

That all the fibers that constitute a muscle are not of the same type is well known. The morphological and biochemical basis for the recognition of heterogeneity in the fibers of the bird pectoralis and other muscles has already been dealt with (Chapters IV, V, VI, and VII). It has been pointed out that the pectoralis and supracoracoideus muscles in different birds are highly specialized and are distinct from the other appendicular muscles. In the generalized pattern of vertebrate appendicular muscles, three types of fibers as mentioned earlier in the case of the fowl pectoralis muscle, can be recognized on the basis of their diameter, color, and mitochondrial density: broad, white, with few small mitochondria (W); narrow, red, with numerous larger mitochondria (R); and the intermediate type (I). These three basic types are represented in the pectoral and other muscles of amphibians (frog), reptiles (lizard), and most mammals. In birds like the pigeon, both W and R types are represented but they are considerably more specialized. The former is specialized for fast and sudden contraction as required in a quick take-off, while the latter is specialized for slower tonic contraction as in sustained flight. In a poor flier, like the domestic fowl, all three types are present.

In soarers, like the Pariah Kite, all fibers are broad but narrower than the broad ones of the pigeon pectoralis and are therefore considered as of the I type. They are also red, circular in cross section, and possess higher mitochondrial density.

Among the passerine birds, two groups have been distinguished on the basis of their pectoralis muscle (Chapter IV): (1) The group of which the Common Myna (starling), is an example, in which the broader type of fiber is considerably narrower but contains more mitochondria than the broad fibers of the pigeon pectoralis. The narrow type of fiber is similar to that in the pigeon. These two types of fibers are regarded as the I and R types respectively, the latter type being more numerous. (2) The group of which the House Sparrow, is an example, in which all the fibers are of the red narrow (R) variety.

In the pectoralis major muscle of bats at least three interesting instances of parallelism are now known. In the giant fruit bat (*Pteropus giganteus*), two types of fibers similar to those in the starling are present but the difference in diameter is less marked. In a bat (*Pipistrellus mimus*) examined by Chandra-Bose and George (unpublished work), the fibers are all of the red variety similar to those of the House Sparrow. On the other hand, the pectoral muscle of a rhinolophid bat *Hipposideros speoris*, however, consists of two types of fibers, resembling the pectoralis muscle of the pigeon. The lines of evolution of the pectoral muscle of birds and bats (Fig. X.3) are discussed by George (1965).

In the evolution of sustained flight the pectoralis muscle of hummingbirds is the ultimate in efficiency. Among the passerines, the pectoralis of birds such as the sparrows, which consists of only the narrow red, fat-utilizing fibers, has reached new heights. However, within the apparent unity in the morphological pattern of these fibers, there exists a biochemical diversity which is exemplified in the regional differentiation described earlier (Chapter IV) in the case of the pectoralis of the House Sparrow. This opens up new avenues for further research.

Biochemical differences in the nerve endings in the red and white muscle fibers of the pectoralis muscles of different birds (Fig. X.4) have been recently reported (Chinoy and George, 1965). They have shown that in spite of the morphological similarity of the nerve endings in the red and white fibers of the pigeon pectoralis, acetylcholinesterase activity is greater in the red fibers and butyrylcholinesterase activity in the white fibers. In the pectoralis muscle as a whole, the former enzyme activity is greater in the pigeon pectoralis, while the activity of the latter is greater in the fowl pectoralis. In the pectoralis of the House Sparrow, which consists of only the red fibers, acetylcholinesterase activity is greater than butyrylcholinesterase activity. These variations also indicate certain definite evolutionary trends at the molecular level (George, 1965).

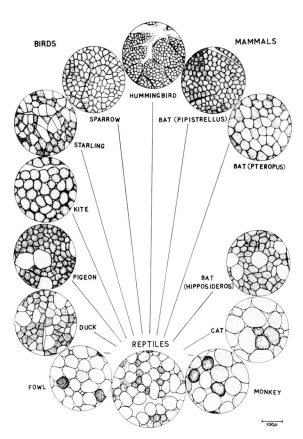

F𝚒𝚐. X.3. Lines of evolution of M. pectoralis in birds and mammals. (By kind permission, George, 1965.)

Evolution is undoubtedly the central theme in biology. It is a multiphased process, acting at all levels in the protoplasmic hierarchy, and it produces at intervals organized systems whose survival is determined on the touchstone of adaptation. Thus envisaged, the evolution of the avian pectoralis muscle from its lowly beginnings in the Mesozoic era, to sustain its possessors through the ages at lofty heights is, indeed, a fascinating story.

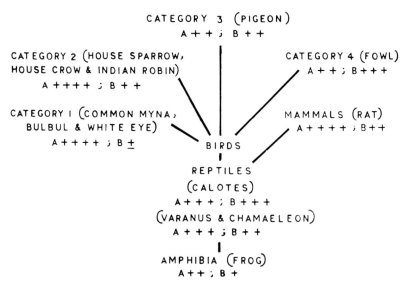

FIG. X.4. Possible trends in the evolution of nerve endings as indicated by the concentrations of acetyl- and butyrylcholinesterases in M. pectoralis of a representative series of vertebrates. (By kind permission, Chinoy and George, 1965.)

KEY TO SYMBOLS:

++++ maximum activity (incubation time 3 hours or less)
+++, ++, medium activity (incubation time 3 to 24 hours)
+, minimum activity (incubation time 24 hours)
±, negligible or nil activity (incubation time more than 24 hours)

REFERENCES

Beebe, C. W. (1915). A tetrapteryx stage in the ancestry of birds. *Zoologica* **2:** 39–52.
Bellairs, A. d'A. (1957). "Reptiles." Hutchinson's Univ. Library, London.
Bellairs, A. d'A., and Jenkin, C. R. (1960). The skeleton of birds. *In* "Biology and Comparative Physiology of Birds" (A. J. Marshall, ed.), Vol. 1, pp. 241–300. Academic Press, New York.
Bert, P. (1870). "Leçon sur la physiologie comparée de la respiration." Baillière, Paris.

Böker, H. (1927). Die biologische Anatomie der Flugarten der Vögel und ihre Phylogenie. *J. Ornithol.* **75:** 304–371.

Brown, R. H. J. (1961). Flight. *In* "Biology and Comparative Physiology of Birds" (A. J. Marshall, ed.), Vol. II, pp. 289–306. Academic Press, New York.

Chinoy, N. J., and George, J. C. (1965). Cholinesterases in the pectoral muscle of some vertebrates. *J. Physiol.* (*London*). **177:** 346–354.

de Beer, G. (1954). *Archaeopteryx lithographica. Bull. Brit. Museum* (*Nat. Hist.*) London.

de Beer, G. (1956). The evolution of ratites. *Bull. Brit. Museum* (*Nat. Hist.*) *Zool.* **4:** 57–70.

Edinger, T. (1926). The brain of Archaeopteryx. *Ann. Mag. Nat. Hist., London* **18:** 151–156.

Edinger, T. (1942). The pituitary body in giant animals fossil and living: a survey and a suggestion. *Quart. Rev. Biol.* **17:** 31–45.

Fisher, H. I. (1946). Adaptations and comparative anatomy of the locomotor apparatus of New World vultures. *Am. Midland Naturalist* **35:** 545–729.

Fisher, H. I. (1955). Avian anatomy, 1925–1950, and some suggested problems. *In* "Recent Studies in Avian Biology" (A. Wolfson, ed.), pp. 57–104. Univ. of Illinois Press, Urbana, Illinois.

George, C. J., and Nair, K. K. (1952). Wing spread and its significance in the flight of some common Indian birds. *J. Univ. Bombay* **20:** 1–5.

George, J. C. (1965). The evolution of the bird and bat pectoral muscles. *Pavo* **3:** (in press).

George, J. C., and Shah, R. V. (1965). Evolution of air sacs in Sauropsida. *J. Animal Morphol. Physiol.* **12:** (in press).

Gregory, W. K. (1946). Some critical phylogenetic stages leading to the flight of birds. *Proc. Linnean Soc. N. Y.* **54–57:** 1–15.

Hartman, F. A. (1961). Locomotor mechanisms of birds. *Smithsonian Inst., Misc. Collection* **143:** 1–91.

Hay, O. P. (1910). On the manner of locomotion of the dinosaurs especially *Diplodocus,* with remarks on the origin of birds. *Proc. Wash. Acad. Sci.* **12:** 1–25.

Heilmann, G. (1927). "The Origin of Birds." Appleton, New York.

Heller, F. (1959). Ein dritter *Archaeopteryx*-Fund aus den Solnhofener Plattenkalken von Langenaltheim/Mft. *Erlanger Geol. Abhandl.* No. 31.

Howard, H. (1950). Fossil evidence of avian evolution. *Ibis* **92:** 1–21.

Lee, D. H. K., Robinson, K. W., Yeates, N. T. M., and Scott, M. I. R. (1945). *Quoted in* Sturkie, P. D. (1954). "Avian Physiology," p. 130. Cornell Univ. Press (Comstock), Ithaca, New York.

Lowe, P. R. (1944). An analysis of the characters of *Archaeopteryx* and Archaeornis. Were they reptiles or birds? *Ibis* **86:** 517–543.

Marsh, O. C. (1880). "Odontornithes: A Monograph on the Extinct Toothed Birds of North America." U. S. Govt. Printing Office, Washington, D. C.

Nopcsa, F. (1907). Ideas on the origin of flight. *Proc. Zool. Soc. London* **1907:** 223–236.

Osborn, H. F. (1900). Reconsideration of the evidence for a common dinosaur-avian stem in the Permian. *Am. Naturalist* **34:** 777–799.

Petronievics, B. (1927). Nouvelles recherches sur l'ostéologie des Archaeornithes. *Ann. Paleontol. Paris* **16:** 39–55.

Piveteau, J. (1955). Oiseaux: Aves Linne. *In* "Traité de paleontologie" (J. Piveteau, ed.), Vol. 5. Masson, Paris.

Steiner, H. (1938). Der *"Archaeopteryx"*-Schwanz der Vogelembryonen. *Vjschr. Naturforsch. Ges. Zürich* **83**: 279–300.

Swinton, W. E. (1958). "Fossil Birds." British Museum (Natural History), London.

Swinton, W. E. (1960). The origin of birds. *In* "Biology and Comparative Physiology of Birds" (A. J. Marshall, ed.), Vol. I, pp. 1–14. Academic Press, New York.

Van Tyne, J., and Berger, A. J. (1959). "Fundamentals of Ornithology." Wiley, New York.

Victorow, C. (1909). *Quoted in* Sturkie, P. D. (1954). "Avian Physiology," p. 105. Cornell Univ. Press (Comstock), Ithaca, New York.

Wetmore, A. (1955). Paleontology. *In* "Recent Studies in Avian Biology" (A. Wolfson, ed.), pp. 44–56. Univ. Illinois Press, Urbana, Illinois.

Wetmore, A. (1956). A check-list of the fossil and prehistoric birds of North America and the West Indies, *Smithsonian Inst., Misc. Collection* **131**: No. 5.

Author Index

Numbers in italics refer to pages on which the complete references are listed.

Subject Index

A

Abdominal muscles, 183–197, 284–286,
  see also individual muscles
  role in respiration, 183–186, 197
Acetyl cholinesterase, 62–64, 179–183,
  483, 484
Acetyl coenzyme A, 208–212, 218
Acid phosphatase, 64
Adenosine diphosphate (ADP), 212, 213
Adenosine triphosphate (ATP), 67, 139,
  140, 210, 212–214
Adenosine triphosphatase (ATPase), 65–
  67, 139, 140
Adipose tissue, 200, 201, 215–217
Air sacs, 476–481
Aldolase, 53
Alkaline phosphatase, 64
Anchor, 293, 334
Aponeurosis(es), 228, 268
Archaeopteryx, 474, 477, 480
Arboreal birds, 474, 475
Automatic extensor, 456
Automatic flexor, 445

B

Biceps loop, 398
Butyryl cholinesterase, 62–64, 180–183,
  483, 484

C

Caloric intake, 215
Caloric value of,
  carbohydrate, 205
  fat, 205
  protein, 205
Capacity for fatty acid oxidation, 240
Carnitine,
  richest source of, 217
  role of, 217, 218
Cholinesterases, *see* individual esterases

Coenzyme Q_{10}, 213
Combustion of fat, 207–210
Cytochrome, 213
Cytochrome oxidase, 58, 59, 126, 128,
  129

D

Dehydrogenases, *see* individual dehydro-
  genases
Development of pectoralis, 68–74
D:aphorase, 55, 56
Diaphragm, mammalian, 25, 183, 197,
  217
Differentiation of fiber types, 69
Diphosphopyridine nucleotide (DPN),
  (NAD), 208, 211–213, 216
Draco, flying lizard, 476, 478, 480
Dystrophy, muscular, 2, 3

E

Electron transport, 212, 213
Electrophoresis of,
  avian muscle proteins, 131
  egg proteins, 131
Endoplasmic reticulum (sarcoplasmic reticulum), 28–31, 51, 52, 57, 64, 65,
  67, 137, 138
Energy,
  for migration, 213–219
  mobilization of, 218
  utilization of, 207–213
Enzymes, *see* individual enzymes
Enzymorphology, *see* individual enzymes
Erythropoiesis, 201
Esterases, *see* individual esterases
Esterification,
  role of lipase, 60, 134, 136, 138, 214,
  216
  of microsomes, 136, 138, 216
Evolution of,
  pectoralis muscle, 481–484